Earth Science

Book 2

interactive SCIENCE

Go to **MyScienceOnline.com** to experience science in a whole new way.

Interactive tools such as **My Planet Diary** connect you to the latest science happenings.

MY PLANET DIARY

- Search **Earth's Journal** for important science news from around the world.

- Use **Earth's Calendar** to find out when cool scientific events occur.

- Explore science **Links** to find even more exciting information about our planet.

- Visit **Jack's Blog** to be the first to know about what is going on in science!

PEARSON

Glenview, Illinois • Boston, Massachusetts • Chandler, Arizona • Upper Saddle River, New Jersey

Teacher's Edition and Resource

Earth Science • Earth Science • Earth Science • Earth Science • Earth Science • Earth Science • Earth Science • Earth Science

Program Authors

You're an author!

As you write in this science book, your answers and personal discoveries will be recorded for you to keep, making this book unique to you. That is why you are one of the primary authors of this book.

✎ **In the space below, print your name, school, town, and state. Then write a short autobiography that includes your interests and accomplishments.**

YOUR NAME

SCHOOL

TOWN, STATE

AUTOBIOGRAPHY

Your Photo

Acknowledgments appear in the Program Guide, which constitutes an extension of this copyright page.

PEARSON

ISBN-13: 978-0-13-320928-0
ISBN-10: 0-13-320928-8
1 2 3 4 5 6 7 8 9 10 V052 15 14 13 12 11

ON THE COVER
Garnet
In general, a mineral has a well-defined chemical composition. Different circumstances and impurities during the mineral's formation can produce a certain amount of variability. In the case of garnets this variability is considerable, because the word *garnet* encompasses several distinct mineral species. While garnets share some chemical characteristics and crystal structure, samples from different sites may differ in color, shape, and other properties.

Program Authors

KATHRYN THORNTON, Ph.D.
Professor and Associate Dean, School of Engineering and Applied Science, University of Virginia, Charlottesville, Virginia
Selected by NASA in May 1984, Dr. Kathryn Thornton is a veteran of four space flights. She has logged more than 975 hours in space, including more than 21 hours of extravehicular activity. As an author on the *Scott Foresman Science* series, Dr. Thornton's enthusiasm for science has inspired teachers around the globe.

DON BUCKLEY, M.Sc.
Information and Communications Technology Director, The School at Columbia University, New York, New York
A founder of New York City Independent School Technologists (NYCIST) and long-time chair of New York Association of Independent Schools' annual IT conference, Mr. Buckley has taught students on two continents and created multimedia and Internet-based instructional systems for schools worldwide.

ZIPPORAH MILLER, M.A.Ed.
Associate Executive Director for Professional Programs and Conferences, National Science Teachers Association, Arlington, Virginia
Ms. Zipporah Miller is a former K–12 science supervisor and STEM coordinator for the Prince George's County Public School District in Maryland. She is a science education consultant who has overseen curriculum development and staff training for more than 150 district science coordinators.

MICHAEL J. PADILLA, Ph.D.
Associate Dean and Director, Eugene P. Moore School of Education, Clemson University, Clemson, South Carolina
A former middle school teacher and a leader in middle school science education, Dr. Michael Padilla has served as president of the National Science Teachers Association and as a writer of the National Science Education Standards. He is professor of science education at Clemson University.

MICHAEL E. WYSESSION, Ph.D.
Associate Professor of Earth and Planetary Science, Washington University, St. Louis, Missouri
An author on more than 50 scientific publications, Dr. Wysession was awarded the prestigious Packard Foundation Fellowship and Presidential Faculty Fellowship for his research in geophysics. Dr. Wysession is an expert on Earth's inner structure and has mapped various regions of Earth using seismic tomography. He is known internationally for his work in geoscience education and outreach.

Instructional Design Author

GRANT WIGGINS, Ed.D.
President, Authentic Education, Hopewell, New Jersey
Dr. Wiggins is a co-author of the "Understanding by Design Handbook". His approach to instructional design provides teachers with a disciplined way of thinking about curriculum design, assessment, and instruction that moves teaching from covering content to ensuring understanding.

The Association for Supervision of Curriculum Development (ASCD), publisher of the "Understanding by Design Handbook" co-authored by Grant Wiggins and registered owner of the trademark "Understanding by Design", has not authorized, approved or sponsored this work and is in no way affiliated with Pearson or its products.

Planet Diary Author

JACK HANKIN
Science/Mathematics Teacher, The Hilldale School, Daly City, California, Founder, Planet Diary Web site
Mr. Hankin is the creator and writer of Planet Diary, a science current events Web site. He is passionate about bringing science news and environmental awareness into classrooms and offers numerous Planet Diary workshops at NSTA and other events to train middle and high school teachers.

ELL Consultant

JIM CUMMINS, Ph.D.
Professor and Canada Research Chair, Curriculum, Teaching and Learning department at the University of Toronto
Dr. Cummins focuses on literacy development in multilingual schools and the role of technology in promoting student learning across the curriculum. *Interactive Science* incorporates essential research-based principles for integrating language with the teaching of academic content based on his instructional framework.

Reading Consultant

HARVEY DANIELS, Ph.D.
Professor of Secondary Education, University of New Mexico, Albuquerque, New Mexico
Dr. Daniels is an international consultant to schools, districts, and educational agencies. He has authored or coauthored 13 books on language, literacy, and education. His most recent works are *Comprehension and Collaboration: Inquiry Circles in Action* and *Subjects Matter: Every Teacher's Guide to Content-Area Reading.*

Reviewers

Contributing Writers

Edward Aguado, Ph.D.
Professor, Department of
   Geography
San Diego State University
San Diego, California

Elizabeth Coolidge-Stolz, M.D.
Medical Writer
North Reading, Massachusetts

Donald L. Cronkite, Ph.D.
Professor of Biology
Hope College
Holland, Michigan

Jan Jenner, Ph.D.
Science Writer
Talladega, Alabama

Linda Cronin Jones, Ph.D.
Associate Professor of Science and
   Environmental Education
University of Florida
Gainesville, Florida

T. Griffith Jones, Ph.D.
Clinical Associate Professor
   of Science Education
College of Education
University of Florida
Gainesville, Florida

Andrew C. Kemp, Ph.D.
Teacher
Jefferson County Public Schools
Louisville, Kentucky

Matthew Stoneking, Ph.D.
Associate Professor of Physics
Lawrence University
Appleton, Wisconsin

R. Bruce Ward, Ed.D.
Senior Research Associate
Science Education Department
Harvard-Smithsonian Center for
   Astrophysics
Cambridge, Massachusetts

Content Reviewers

Paul D. Beale, Ph.D.
Department of Physics
University of Colorado at Boulder
Boulder, Colorado

Jeff R. Bodart, Ph.D.
Professor of Physical Sciences
Chipola College
Marianna, Florida

Joy Branlund, Ph.D.
Department of Earth Science
Southwestern Illinois College
Granite City, Illinois

Marguerite Brickman, Ph.D.
Division of Biological Sciences
University of Georgia
Athens, Georgia

Bonnie J. Brunkhorst, Ph.D.
Science Education and Geological
   Sciences
California State University
San Bernardino, California

Michael Castellani, Ph.D.
Department of Chemistry
Marshall University
Huntington, West Virginia

Charles C. Curtis, Ph.D.
Research Associate Professor
   of Physics
University of Arizona
Tucson, Arizona

Diane I. Doser, Ph.D.
Department of Geological
   Sciences
University of Texas
El Paso, Texas

Rick Duhrkopf, Ph.D.
Department of Biology
Baylor University
Waco, Texas

Alice K. Hankla, Ph.D.
The Galloway School
Atlanta, Georgia

Mark Henriksen, Ph.D.
Physics Department
University of Maryland
Baltimore, Maryland

Chad Hershock, Ph.D.
Center for Research on Learning
   and Teaching
University of Michigan
Ann Arbor, Michigan

Jeremiah N. Jarrett, Ph.D.
Department of Biology
Central Connecticut State
   University
New Britain, Connecticut

Scott L. Kight, Ph.D.
Department of Biology
Montclair State University
Montclair, New Jersey

Jennifer O. Liang, Ph.D.
Department of Biology
University of Minnesota–Duluth
Duluth, Minnesota

Candace Lutzow-Felling, Ph.D.
State Arboretum of Virginia &
   Blanding Experimental Farm
Boyce, Virginia

Joseph F. McCullough, Ph.D.
Physics Program Chair
Cabrillo College
Aptos, California

Heather Mernitz, Ph.D.
Department of Physical Science
Alverno College
Milwaukee, Wisconsin

Sadredin C. Moosavi, Ph.D.
Department of Earth and
   Environmental Sciences
Tulane University
New Orleans, Louisiana

David L. Reid, Ph.D.
Department of Biology
Blackburn College
Carlinville, Illinois

Scott M. Rochette, Ph.D.
Department of the Earth Sciences
SUNY College at Brockport
Brockport, New York

Karyn L. Rogers, Ph.D.
Department of Geological
   Sciences
University of Missouri
Columbia, Missouri

Laurence Rosenhein, Ph.D.
Department of Chemistry
Indiana State University
Terre Haute, Indiana

Sara Seager, Ph.D.
Department of Planetary Sciences
   and Physics
Massachusetts Institute of
   Technology
Cambridge, Massachusetts

Tom Shoberg, Ph.D.
Missouri University of Science
   and Technology
Rolla, Missouri

Patricia Simmons, Ph.D.
North Carolina State University
Raleigh, North Carolina

William H. Steinecker, Ph.D.
Research Scholar
Miami University
Oxford, Ohio

Paul R. Stoddard, Ph.D.
Department of Geology and
   Environmental Geosciences
Northern Illinois University
DeKalb, Illinois

John R. Villarreal, Ph.D.
Department of Chemistry
The University of Texas–Pan
   American
Edinburg, Texas

John R. Wagner, Ph.D.
Department of Geology
Clemson University
Clemson, South Carolina

Jerry Waldvogel, Ph.D.
Department of Biological Sciences
Clemson University
Clemson, South Carolina

Donna L. Witter, Ph.D.
Department of Geology
Kent State University
Kent, Ohio

Edward J. Zalisko, Ph.D.
Department of Biology
Blackburn College
Carlinville, Illinois

Museum of Science.

Special thanks to the Museum of
Science, Boston, Massachusetts,
and Ioannis Miaoulis, the
Museum's president and director,
for serving as content advisors for
the technology and design strand
in this program.

Table of Contents

 Enter the Lab zone for hands-on inquiry.

Chapter Lab Investigation:
• Directed Inquiry: Sand Hills
• Open Inquiry: Sand Hills

Inquiry Warm-Ups: • How Does Gravity Affect Materials on a Slope? • How Does Moving Water Wear Away Rocks? • How Do Glaciers Change the Land? • What Is Sand Made Of? • How Does Moving Air Affect Sediment?

Quick Labs: • Weathering and Erosion • Raindrops Falling • Erosion Cube • Surging Glaciers • Modeling Valleys • Shaping a Coastline • Desert Pavement

my science online .com

Go to MyScienceOnline.com to interact with this chapter's content.
Keyword: Erosion and Deposition

> UNTAMED SCIENCE
• Carving a Canyon

> PLANET DIARY
• Erosion and Deposition

> ART IN MOTION
• Effects of Glaciers

> INTERACTIVE ART
• Mass Movement • Effects of Waves

> REAL-WORLD INQUIRY
• Why Live Where It Floods?

 Enter the Lab zone for hands-on inquiry.

Chapter Lab Investigation:
• Directed Inquiry: Exploring Geologic Time Through Core Samples
• Open Inquiry: Exploring Geologic Time Through Core Samples

Inquiry Warm-Ups: • What's In a Rock?
• Which Layer Is the Oldest? • How Long Till It's Gone? • This Is Your Life! • How Could Planet Earth Form in Space? • Dividing History

Quick Labs: • Sweet Fossils • Modeling Trace Fossils • Modeling the Fossil Record • How Did It Form? • The Dating Game • How Old Is It? • Going Back in Time • Learning From Fossils • Graphing the Fossil Record • Modeling an Asteroid Impact • Cenozoic Timeline

my science online.com

Go to MyScienceOnline.com to interact with this chapter's content. Keyword: A Trip Through Geologic Time

> **UNTAMED SCIENCE**
• Riding the Geo-vator

> **ART IN MOTION**
• Change Over Geologic Time

> **INTERACTIVE ART**
• Fossil Formation • Piecing Together the Past • Index Fossils

> **REAL-WORLD INQUIRY**
• How Do You Find the Age of a Rock?

 Lab zone® Enter the Lab zone for hands-on inquiry.

Chapter Lab Investigation:
  • Directed Inquiry: Design and Build a Solar Cooker
  • Open Inquiry: Design and Build a Solar Cooker

Inquiry Warm-Ups: • What's in a Piece of Coal? • Can You Capture Solar Energy? • Which Bulb Is More Efficient?

Quick Labs: • Observing Oil's Consistency • Fossil Fuels • Producing Electricity • Human Energy Use • Future Energy Use

my science online.com

Go to MyScienceOnline.com to interact with this chapter's content.
Keyword: Energy Resources

> **UNTAMED SCIENCE**
• Farming the Wind

> **PLANET DIARY**
• Energy Resources

> **INTERACTIVE ART**
• Hydroelectric Power Plant • Nuclear Power Plant

> **ART IN MOTION**
• Oil: Long to Form, Quick to Use

> **REAL-WORLD INQUIRY**
• Energy Conservation

 Enter the Lab zone for hands-on inquiry.

Chapter Lab Investigation:
• Directed Inquiry: Water From Trees
• Modeling Ocean Currents
• Open Inquiry: Water From Trees
• Modeling Ocean Currents

Inquiry Warm-Ups: • Where Does the Water Come From? • Mapping Surface Waters • Where Does the Water Go? • What Can You Learn Without Seeing? • How Do Waves Change a Beach? • Bottom to Top

Quick Labs: • Water, Water Everywhere • Water on Earth • What Is a Watershed? • Modeling How a Lake Forms • How Can Algal Growth Affect Pond Life? • Soil Percolation • An Artesian Well • Ocean Conditions • The Shape of the Ocean Floor • Making Waves • Modeling Current • Deep Currents

my science ONLINE.com

Go to MyScienceOnline.com to interact with this chapter's content. Keyword: Water

> **UNTAMED SCIENCE**
• Water Cyclists

> **PLANET DIARY**
• Water

> **INTERACTIVE ART**
• Water Cycle • Water Motion

> **ART IN MOTION**
• How Does Groundwater Collect?

> **REAL-WORLD INQUIRY**
• Water Cycle, Interrupted

> **VIRTUAL LAB**
• How Does the Density of Sea Water Change?

CHAPTER 11

The Atmosphere

The Big Question **372**
How does the sun's energy affect Earth's atmosphere?

 Enter the Lab zone for hands-on inquiry.

Chapter Lab Investigation:
• Directed Inquiry: Heating Earth's Surface
• Open Inquiry: Heating Earth's Surface

Inquiry Warm-Ups: • How Long Will the Candle Burn? • Does Air Have Mass? • Is Air There? • Does a Plastic Bag Trap Heat? • What Happens When Air Is Heated? • Does the Wind Turn?

Quick Labs: • Breathe In, Breathe Out • What Is the Source of Earth's Energy? • Properties of Air • Soda Bottle Barometer • Effects of Altitude on the Atmosphere • Layers of the Atmosphere • Calculating Temperature Changes • How Does the Sun's Energy Reach Earth? • Measuring Temperature • Temperature and Height • Build a Wind Vane • Modeling Global Wind Belts

my science ONLINE.com

Go to MyScienceOnline.com to interact with this chapter's content. Keyword: The Atmosphere

> UNTAMED SCIENCE
• Gliding Through the Atmosphere

> INTERACTIVE ART
• Measuring Air Pressure • Global Winds

> ART IN MOTION
• Greenhouse Effect

> VIRTUAL LAB
• What Do Temperature and Volume Have to Do With Air Pressure?

Video Series: Chapter Adventures

Untamed Science created this captivating video series for interactive SCIENCE **featuring a unique segment for every chapter of the program.**

Featuring videos such as

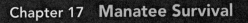

Inquiry

Program Author of
Interactive Science

Associate Dean and Director of
Eugena P. Moore School of Education
Clemson University
Clemson, South Carolina

Michael J. Padilla, Ph.D.

"If students are busy doing lots of hands-on-activities, are they using inquiry skills? What is inquiry, anyway? If you are confused, you're not alone. Inquiry is the heart and soul of science education, with most of us in continuous pursuit of achieving it with our students."

What Is Inquiry?

Simply put, inquiry is thinking like a scientist —being inquisitive, asking why, and searching for answers. It's the process of taking a close examination of something in the quest for information.

Minds-on Inquiry

Students are naturally inquisitive; they want to learn, and they are always asking "Why?" They need practice and support to find answers for themselves. That's why they need experiences that are carefully scaffolded to guide them. We built that scaffolding right into this program.

Scaffolded Learning

The framework below illustrates a series of skill levels developed by educational psychologist Benjamin Bloom in the 1950s, later modified in the 1990s to reflect relevance to 21st century work. Look for the skills questions and tasks throughout the student book, scaffolded just right to provide students with the guidance and intellectual challenge they need.

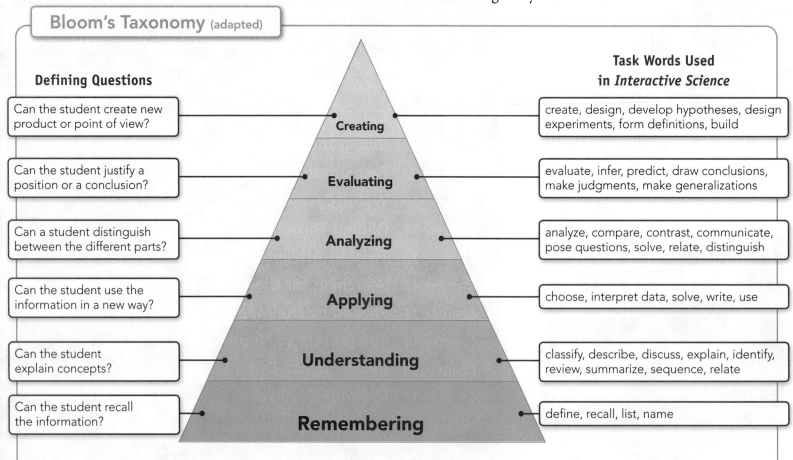

Bloom's Taxonomy (adapted)

Defining Questions

Can the student create new product or point of view? — **Creating**

Can the student justify a position or a conclusion? — **Evaluating**

Can a student distinguish between the different parts? — **Analyzing**

Can the student use the information in a new way? — **Applying**

Can the student explain concepts? — **Understanding**

Can the student recall the information? — **Remembering**

Task Words Used in *Interactive Science*

Creating — create, design, develop hypotheses, design experiments, form definitions, build

Evaluating — evaluate, infer, predict, draw conclusions, make judgments, make generalizations

Analyzing — analyze, compare, contrast, communicate, pose questions, solve, relate, distinguish

Applying — choose, interpret data, solve, write, use

Understanding — classify, describe, discuss, explain, identify, review, summarize, sequence, relate

Remembering — define, recall, list, name

Student Interactivity

We know that students learn better when they are totally engaged in their work. That's why *Interactive Science* gets students involved in their learning every day, on every page. Because the student book is consumable, it provides students with unique opportunities to become totally engaged, whether it's marking the text, completing an illustration or a chart, summarizing relationships using Venn diagrams or other graphic devices, or recording ideas and findings about scientific concepts.

> *Apply It!* Students combine new content understandings with their knowledge of scientific process and experimentation.

> *Students demonstrate critical connections between text and illustration.*

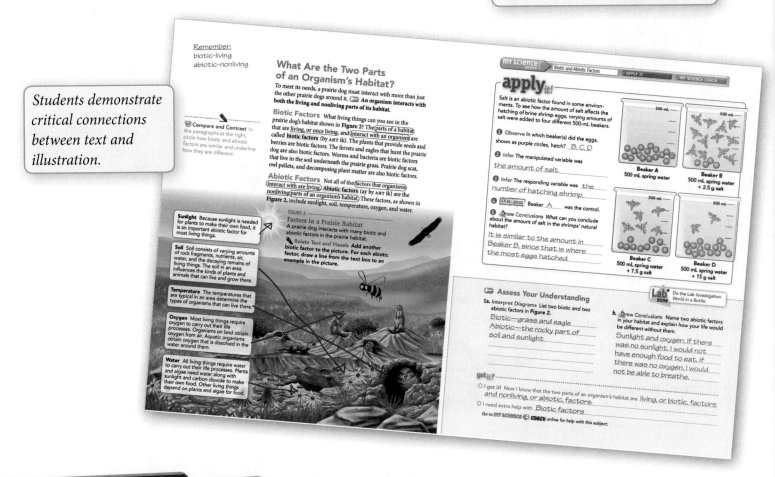

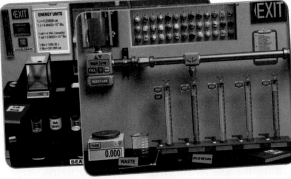

Online Labs and Simulations

For lab experiences without materials, you'll love the Online Virtual Labs. They're realistic, time efficient, and great when meeting in a laboratory is not possible. Have students use them individually, with a partner, or as a class activity to stimulate discussion or shared learning.

Inquiry

Hands-on Inquiry

We know that it is through student engagement and discovery that students really learn to think like scientists. Hands-on inquiry lab activities are built into the program; there are multiple activities per lesson.

Teacher's Lab Resource

Because there are so many labs, you will want to select which ones are best for your students and your class time. That is why the labs are organized in print as blackline masters in the *Teacher's Lab Resource*. Or access them in your teacher center at MyScienceOnline.com. There you can download and even edit the labs to more closely align them to a student's needs.

Using the Labs

The yellow LabZone symbols in the student edition indicate the lab activities that support your instruction. Look for the LabZone symbol. To find your lab, look for its name in the *Teacher's Lab Resource* books or online in the teacher center.

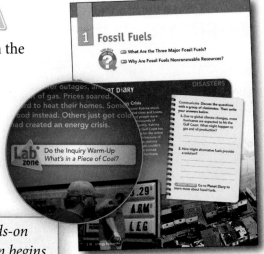

Inquiry Warm-Ups Hands-on experience before the lesson begins

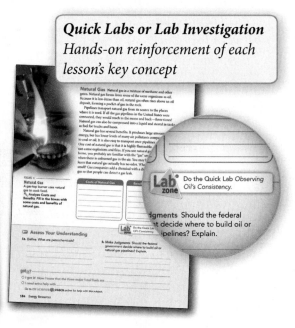

Quick Labs or Lab Investigation *Hands-on reinforcement of each lesson's key concept*

STEM Activity Book

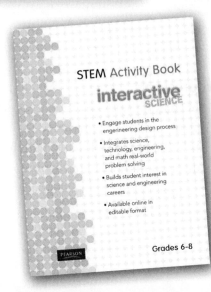

Each day, our lives are filled with more and more products and services that are the result of technology and engineering. The interconnectivity of science, technology, engineering, and mathematics is known as STEM, with each field connected to the others in important ways.

The activities in this book emphasize the interconnectivity of those fields, and use an eight-step design process designed to encourage creativity and imagination in solving design problems.

Inquiry Skill-Building Outside the Student Books

There are many forms of inquiry learning in *Interactive Science*, with lots of options to enrich your students' experiences. All components are in print or online for easy downloading.

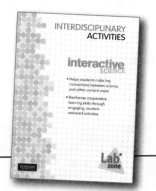

Allow students to demonstrate their understanding of chapter concepts in longer term projects.

Provide students with opportunities to apply the science they have learned to other subject areas.

Stretch students with real-life problem solving—perfect for challenging the advanced students.

Offer students minds-on activities that incorporate the scientific method, each targeting specific science process skills.

Interactive Science—Inquiry Learning at Its Best

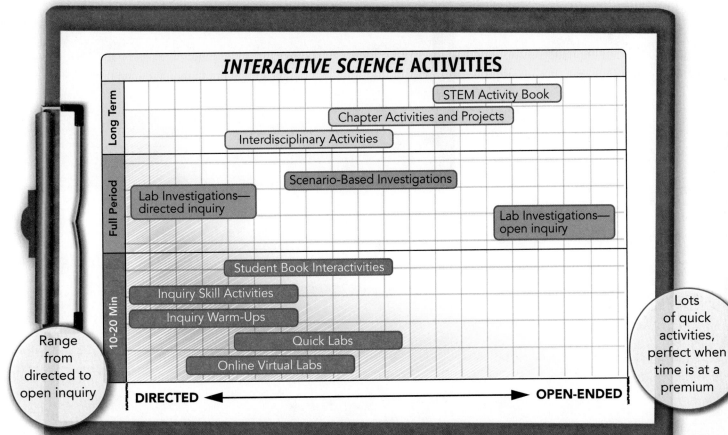

Big Ideas of Science

According to Grant Wiggins' Understanding by Design framework, students reveal their understanding most effectively when provided with complex, authentic opportunities to explain, interpret, apply, shift perspective, empathize, and self-assess. Each chapter in the student edition uses a Big Question to focus students' attention on the content of the chapter. Related Big Questions are organized under one or more Big Ideas. A Big Idea is a concept, theory, principle, or theme that helps learners make sense of a subject.

Students will explore the Big Idea before they read a chapter, writing about what they already know and what they want to know about the topic. After completing the chapter, students will return to these pages in order to record what they have learned and how their thoughts have changed during that learning process.

? BIG IDEAS OF SCIENCE

Have you ever worked on a jigsaw puzzle? Usually a puzzle has a theme that leads you to group the pieces by what they have in common. But until you put all the pieces together you can't solve the puzzle. Studying science is similar to solving a puzzle. The big ideas of science are like puzzle themes. To understand big ideas, scientists ask questions. The answers to those questions are like pieces of a puzzle. Each chapter in this book asks a big question to help you think about a big idea of science. By answering the big questions, you will get closer to understanding the big idea.

✎ **Before you read each chapter, write about what you know and what more you'd like to know.**

Grant Wiggins, coauthor of Understanding by Design

BIGIDEA

Scientists use scientific inquiry to explain the natural world.

Firefighters use science to put out fires. For example, they must know what types of chemicals to use on different types of fires.

What do you already know about how science affects your everyday life? ✎ **What more would you like to know?**

_____
_____
_____
_____
_____
_____
_____
_____
_____

BIGIDEA

Scientists use mathematics in many ways.

The spring scale measures the weight of the oranges, which is a measure of the force of gravity on the oranges.

Which measurement tools have you used in everyday life? ✎ **Which math skills do you need to practice?**

_____
_____
_____
_____
_____
_____
_____
_____
_____

BIGIDEA

Earth is a continually changing planet.

Over millions of years, the Colorado River cut through layers of solid rock to form the Grand Canyon in Arizona.

What do you already know about changes on Earth? ✎ **What more would you like to know?**

_____
_____
_____

Big Questions:

❓ What is the structure of Earth? Chapter 1

❓ How do rocks form? Chapter 2

❓ How do moving plates change Earth's crust? Chapter 3

❓ Why do earthquakes occur more often in some places than in others? Chapter 4

❓ How does a volcano erupt? Chapter 5

❓ What processes break down rock? Chapter 6

❓ What processes shape the surface of the land? Chapter 7

✎ **After reading the chapters, write what you have learned about the Big Idea.**

_____
_____
_____

BIGIDEA

Earth is 4.6 billion years old and the rock record contains its history.

This fossil of a turtle is millions of years old.

What do you already know about Earth's history? ✎ **What more would you like to know?**

_____
_____
_____

Big Question:

❓ How do scientists study Earth's past? Chapter 8

✎ **After reading the chapter, write what you have learned about the Big Idea.**

_____
_____
_____
_____
_____
_____
_____

Connect to the Big Idea ❓ UbD

Have students form a group for each Big Idea and assign a notetaker and speaker for each group. Each group discusses what they already know, and then individuals write in their student editions what else they personally would like to like to know. Individuals share their items with their group as the notetaker compiles the responses and eliminates duplicates. Each group should agree on one key item they want to learn about. Finally, each group's speaker shares the group's key item with the class and the teacher compiles these items on the board. Remember to vary the roles of group notetaker and speaker to give students a variety of experiences.

EXTENSION Select one item about which students want to learn more as an extra credit project.

Connect to the Big Idea

Divide the class into small groups and assign one Big Idea to each group. Each group previews the chapter(s) for the assigned Big Idea and develops an informational poster. Posters should indicate the key ideas that students expect to learn about, as well as any questions that students in the group have about the topic. Groups present their posters to the class and then display them in the classroom. Encourage students to reference the posters as they begin and work through each new chapter.

After students complete the chapter(s) for their Big Idea, they can add information to the poster to reflect on what they have learned.

BIGIDEA
Living things interact with their environment.

People depend on the ocean's living resources, such as codfish, for food.

What do you already know about how you get food, water, and shelter from your surroundings?

✎ **What more would you like to know?**

_____
_____
_____
_____

Big Questions:

❓ What are some of Earth's energy sources? Chapter 9

❓ How do people use Earth's resources? Chapter 17

✎ **After reading the chapters, write what you have learned about the Big Idea.**

_____
_____
_____
_____

BIGIDEA
Earth's land, water, air, and life form a system.

A severe storm, drought, or wildfire could cause changes in Yellowstone National Park that would affect these bison.

What do you already know about how changes in one part of Earth can affect another part?

✎ **What would you like to know?**

_____
_____
_____

Big Questions:

❓ How does fresh water cycle on Earth? Chapter 10

❓ How does the sun's energy affect Earth's atmosphere? Chapter 11

❓ How do meteorologists predict the weather? Chapter 12

❓ What factors affect Earth's climate? Chapter 13

✎ **After reading the chapters, write what you have learned about the Big Idea.**

_____
_____
_____
_____

BIGIDEA

Earth is part of a system of objects that orbit the sun.

Jupiter, its moons, and Earth are all parts of the solar system. Each of them is held in its orbit by gravity.

What do you already know about Earth and the other objects in the solar system? ✎ **What more would you like to know?**

_____
_____
_____

Big Questions:

❓ How do Earth, the moon, and the sun interact? Chapter 14

❓ Why are objects in the solar system different from each other? Chapter 15

✎ **After reading the chapters, write what you have learned about the Big Idea.**

_____
_____
_____
_____

BIGIDEA

The universe is very old, very large, and constantly changing.

This galaxy, visible near the Big Dipper, is so far away that light from it takes 12 million years to reach Earth!

What do you already know about the universe? ✎ **What more would you like to know?**

_____
_____
_____
_____

Big Question:

❓ How do astronomers learn about distant objects in the universe? Chapter 16

✎ **After reading the chapter, write what you have learned about the Big Idea.**

_____
_____
_____
_____

Connect to the Big Idea ❓ UbD

Students can form small groups and choose a Big Idea to study. As each group previews the chapter(s) for the Big Idea, students should discuss and record questions they have about the key ideas in each lesson.

After each group finishes the chapter(s) for its assigned Big Idea, students work together to answer their initial questions based on what they have learned. Each group then holds a press conference. Some members of the group are scientists and the other students are reporters. The reporters should ask the group's questions and the scientists should provide answers by summarizing content from the chapters.

Erosion and Deposition

Introduce the Big Q ? UbD

Have students look at the image and read the Engaging Question and description. Ask students to infer how these rocks could have been carved by nature. Have student volunteers answer the question. Point out that before the canyon formed, there was no gap or break in this column of solid rock layers. Ask: **What process do you know of that breaks up rocks?** *(Weathering)* **What are the agents, or natural forces that weather rocks?** *(Water, living things, oxygen, carbon dioxide, changing temperatures)* **What forces on Earth have you observed picking up or moving rocks, soil, sand, or mud?** *(Accept all reasonable responses. Students may suggest floodwaters, gravity, strong winds, and people.)*

Untamed Science Video

CARVING A CANYON Before viewing, invite students to discuss what they know about erosion. Then play the video. Lead a class discussion and make a list of questions that this video raises. You may wish to have students view the video again after they have completed the chapter to see if their questions have been answered.

To access the online resources for this chapter, search on or navigate to *Erosion and Deposition.*

Untamed Science Video shows river erosion at Canyonlands National park in Utah.

The Big Question allows students to answer the Engaging Question about the processes that reshaped the rocks.

MY SCIENCE online.com > **Erosion and Deposition**

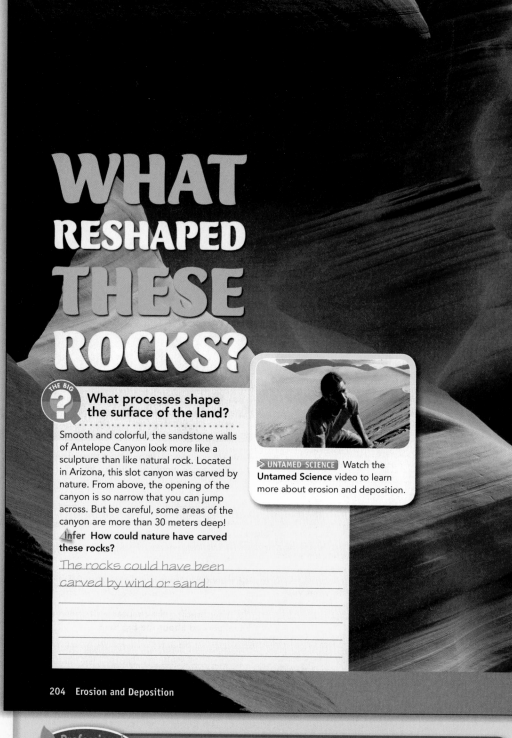

WHAT RESHAPED THESE ROCKS?

THE BIG ?

What processes shape the surface of the land?

Smooth and colorful, the sandstone walls of Antelope Canyon look more like a sculpture than like natural rock. Located in Arizona, this slot canyon was carved by nature. From above, the opening of the canyon is so narrow that you can jump across. But be careful, some areas of the canyon are more than 30 meters deep!

Infer How could nature have carved these rocks?

The rocks could have been
carved by wind or sand.

> UNTAMED SCIENCE Watch the **Untamed Science** video to learn more about erosion and deposition.

Professional Development Note) **From the Author**

Flying over southern Louisiana, I am always fascinated by the Mississippi River delta. The soil that makes up the swampy river delta originated in every state from the Appalachians to the Rocky Mountains. It is easy to see why it is called a "bird's foot delta" with its several claw-like extensions. The Mississippi River delta is a battleground between Mother Nature and humans. The river channel has changed course many times in the past and, if not for the intervention of the U.S. Army Corps of Engineers, the river would again change course, leaving behind the city of New Orleans and all the infrastructure that supports shipping on the present-day channel.

✐ *Kathryn Thornton*

Erosion and Deposition

CHAPTER 7

Chapter at a Glance

CHAPTER PACING: 7–12 periods or $3\frac{1}{2}$–6 blocks

INTRODUCE THE CHAPTER: Use the Engaging Question and the opening image to get students thinking about erosion and deposition. Activate prior knowledge and preteach vocabulary using the Getting Started pages.

Lesson 1: Mass Movement

Lesson 2: Water Erosion

Lesson 3: Glacial Erosion

Lesson 4: Wave Erosion

Lesson 5: Wind Erosion

ASSESSMENT OPTIONS: Chapter Test, **EXAM**VIEW® Assessment Suite, Performance Assessment, Progress Monitoring Assessments, SuccessTracker™

Preference Navigator, in the online Planning tools, allows you to customize *Interactive Science* to your own teaching style. You can also edit lesson plans by selecting the Lesson Planner option.

Digital Teacher's Edition allows you to access your Teacher's Edition and Resource online.

MY SCIENCE online.com

Differentiated Instruction

L1 Brainstorm Processes Help students brainstorm a list of processes that affect the shape of the surface of the land. Ask students questions to prompt the flow of ideas, such as "What things make mountains grow taller or get smaller?" "What things pick up rocks and carry them down a hill?" Allow students to add their responses to the list on the board. Then discuss which things listed on the board may have helped to shape Antelope Canyon.

L3 Write Inferences Have students write two sentences stating two inferences. The first statement should describe how they think Antelope Canyon got its name. The second should state how they think the canyon formed. Challenge students to find out if their inferences are correct, then revise their sentences if necessary.

205

Getting Started

Check Your Understanding

This activity assesses students' understanding of forces. After students have shared their answers, explain that the term mass is not used in the usual scientific sense of "the quantity of matter a body contains." Although an object of high mass will certainly require a lot of force to move it, the word mass in this paragraph refers to a body of matter with no definite shape.

Preteach Vocabulary Skills

Tell students that Latin was the language spoken in ancient Rome and the official language of the Roman Empire dating back several thousand years ago. Many common words as well as science terms are derived from the words of this ancient language. Have students use a dictionary to look up and identify other chapter vocabulary words with Latin origins.

Getting Started

Check Your Understanding

1. **Background** Read the paragraph below and then answer the question.

A giant **mass** of mud blocked the road after a storm. "How did it get there?" asked Gail. "During the storm, the nearby river rose really fast, so the **force** of the water pushed it there," said her dad. "Spring flooding is part of the natural **cycle** of the seasons."

> **Mass** is an amount of matter that has an indefinite size and shape.
>
> **Force** is the push or pull exerted on an object.
>
> A **cycle** is a sequence of events that repeats over and over.

• Why does it take the force of fast-moving water to move a large mass of mud?

A large mass of mud is heavy, so moving it takes a lot of force.

> **MY READING WEB** If you had trouble completing the question above, visit **My Reading Web** and type in **Erosion and Deposition.**

Vocabulary Skill

Word Origins Many science words come to English from other languages. By learning the meaning of a few common Latin roots, you can determine the meaning of new science words.

Latin Word	Meaning of Latin Word	Example
sedere	sit, settle	sediment, n. pieces of rock or soil moved by the process of erosion
flare	blow	deflation, n. the process by which wind removes surface materials

2. **Quick Check** Use the chart to answer the question.
• How does the Latin word *sedere* relate to the word *sediment*?

Pieces of rock or soil settle after they have been moved.

My Reading Web offers leveled readings related to chapter content.

Vocab Flash Cards offer extra practice with the chapter vocabulary words.

Digital Lesson
• Assign the *Check Your Understanding* activity online and have students submit their work to you.
• Assign the *Vocabulary Skill* activity online and have students submit their work to you.

my science ONLINE.com | Erosion and Deposition

mass movement

flood plain

glacier

sand dune

Chapter Preview

LESSON 1
- erosion • sediment • deposition
- gravity • mass movement
- 🔄 Relate Text and Visuals
- 🔺 Infer

LESSON 2
- runoff • rill • gully • stream
- tributary • flood plain • meander
- oxbow lake • delta • alluvial fan
- groundwater • stalactite
- stalagmite • karst topography
- 🔄 Identify Supporting Evidence
- 🔺 Develop Hypotheses

LESSON 3
- glacier • continental glacier
- ice age • valley glacier
- plucking • till • moraine • kettle
- 🔄 Relate Cause and Effect
- 🔺 Draw Conclusions

LESSON 4
- headland • beach
- longshore drift • spit
- 🔄 Summarize
- 🔺 Communicate

LESSON 5
- deflation • sand dune • loess
- 🔄 Ask Questions
- 🔺 Predict

▶ **VOCAB FLASH CARDS** For extra help with vocabulary, visit **Vocab Flash Cards** and type in *Erosion and Deposition.*

Preview Vocabulary Terms

Have students create a personalized science glossary for the vocabulary terms in this chapter, or add to an existing one. In their glossaries, students should define each term and reference the pages in the chapter that define and explain the term. Suggest that students also draw a picture or a diagram to help them understand any of the terms. A list of Academic Vocabulary for each lesson can be found in the Support All Readers box at the start of the lesson.

L1 Have students look at the images on this page as you pronounce the vocabulary word. Have students repeat the word after you. Then read the definition. Use the sample sentence in italics to clarify the meaning of the term.

mass movement *(mas MOOV munt)* any one of several processes that move sediment downhill. *Mass movement occurs when rock and soil become drenched with water and slide downhill.*

flood plain *(fluhd playn)* a flat, wide valley through which a river flows. *A flood happens when a river overflows its banks and covers its flood plain.*

glacier *(GLAY shur)* any large mass of ice that moves over the land. *A glacier changes the land over which it moves through erosion and deposition.*

sand dune *(sand doon)* a deposit of windblown sand. *You are likely to see a sand dune on a beach or in a desert.*

CHAPTER 7

ⓔⓛⓛ Support

Have students complete the **Preview Vocabulary Terms** activity either alone in or pairs. Before students begin creating their science glossaries, write each word and introduce it to students by pointing and saying it aloud.

Beginning
LOW Draw a picture or other visual aid for each vocabulary term in the glossary to associate the term with its definition.

HIGH Write a definition in the native language for support.

Intermediate
LOW/HIGH Include English pronunciations for each term in the glossary.

Advanced
LOW/HIGH For each vocabulary term in the glossary, write a sentence that uses the term correctly.

Mass Movement

What processes shape the surface of the land?

Blended Path
Active learning using Student Edition, Inquiry Path, and Digital Path

Lesson Pacing: 1–2 periods or $\frac{1}{2}$–1 block

🕐 **SHORT ON TIME?** To do this lesson in approximately half the time, do the Activate Prior Knowledge activity followed by a discussion of the Key Concepts to familiarize students with the lesson content. Have students do the Quick Lab. The rest of the lesson can be completed by students independently.

Preference Navigator, in the online Planning tools, allows you to customize *Interactive Science* to your own teaching style. You can also edit lesson plans by selecting the Lesson Planner option.

Digital Teacher's Edition allows you to access your Teacher's Edition and Resource materials online.

my science online.com

Lesson Vocabulary

- erosion
- sediment
- deposition
- gravity
- mass movement

 Content Refresher

Landslides and Mudflows Gravity causes mass movement, but water almost always has a major role. Water reduces friction between rock layers. During a wet season, rocks that were stable can suddenly slide over the other rock layers. In sand or clay, some water might increase stability, but too much water causes flow.

A lahar is a dangerous type of mudflow that occurs on the flanks of volcanoes. Lahars can form when snow and ice melt rapidly during volcanic activity. They also might form after loose volcanic ash is soaked by heavy rain. Lahars generally have a high water content. They flow quickly down steep volcano slopes and are capable of transporting large amounts of debris. Lahars are also referred to as volcanic mudflows or debris flows.

Lahars accompanied the catastrophic eruption of Mount St. Helens on May 18, 1980. Both the eruption of hot volcanic rocks and pyroclastic flows caused the sudden melting of ice and snow, triggering multiple lahars.

LESSON OBJECTIVES

🔑 Describe the processes that wear down and build up Earth's surface.

🔑 Identify the causes of the different types of mass movements.

ENGAGE AND EXPLORE

Teach this lesson using a variety of resources. Begin by reading **My Planet Diary** as a class. Have students discuss the relationship between gravity and landslides and mudslides. Then have students do the **Inquiry Warm-Up activity.** Students will observe and compare the effect of gravity on a marble's movements on a surface with and without sandpaper covering. The **After the Inquiry Warm-Up worksheet** sets up a discussion about the factors that influence the effect gravity has on material on a slope. Have volunteers share their answers to question 4 identifying the factor that clearly influences the effect of gravity on materials on a slope.

EXPLAIN AND ELABORATE

Review the terms *erosion* and *deposition* and then **Teach Key Concepts** by explaining the cycle of processes—weathering, erosion, and deposition—that build up and wear down the surface of Earth.

Continue to **Teach Key Concepts** by explaining the four kinds of mass movement: landslides, mudflows, slump, and creep. **Support the Big Q** by discussing the effects erosion and deposition have on Earth's surface in the instance of a mass movement. Have students practice the inquiry skill in the **Apply It activity.**

Hand out the **Key Concept Summaries** as a review of each part of the lesson. Students can also use the online **Vocab Flash Cards** to review key terms.

EVALUATE

Have students take the **Lesson Quiz.** For an alternate assessment, see the **EXAM**VIEW® Assessment Suite, Progress Monitoring Assessments, or SuccessTracker™.

ⒺⓁⓁ Support

1 Content and Language

Have students create their own drawings to illustrate the terms *landslip, mudflow, slump,* and *creep.* Tell them to use the photographs beside **Figure 1** as models. Ask them to write a sentence using each of the terms explaining what is happening in their drawings.

Lab zone Inquiry Path
Hands-on learning in the Lab zone

Digital Path
Online learning at **my science online**.com

ENGAGE AND EXPLORE

To teach this lesson with an emphasis on inquiry, begin with the **Inquiry Warm-Up activity.** Students will observe and compare the effect of gravity on a marble's movements on a surface with and without sandpaper covering. The **After the Inquiry Warm-Up worksheet** sets up a discussion about the factors that influence the effect gravity has on material on a slope. Have volunteers share their answers to question 4 identifying the factor that clearly influences the effect of gravity on materials on a slope.

EXPLAIN AND ELABORATE

Focus on the **Inquiry Skill** for the lesson. Tell students that when they infer, they interpret an observation or other information. Remind them that an inference is not a fact but one of many possible interpretations. What inferences could be made in the **Inquiry Warm-Up Activity** about the factors that influence the effect of gravity on materials on a slope? *(The degree of smoothness or roughness of a surface of the slope affects the movement of the material.)* Have students do the **Quick Lab** and share their findings about the effects of water and slope angle on the rate of erosion.

Support the Big Q by discussing the effects erosion and deposition have on Earth's surface in the instance of a mass movement. Do the **Teacher Demo** modeling the affects of an earthquake and mudflow. Review the name and affect of each type of mass movement before beginning the **Apply It activity.** Have students share their ideas about what caused the fence to move. Assign the **Lab Investigation** and have students share their results. Students can use the online **Vocab Flash Cards** to review key terms.

EVALUATE

Have students take the **Lesson Quiz.** For an alternate assessment, see the **EXAM**VIEW® Assessment Suite, Progress Monitoring Assessments, or SuccessTracker™.

ENGAGE AND EXPLORE

Teach this lesson using digital resources. Begin by having students learn more about mass movement and explore real-world connections to mass movement at **My Planet Diary** online. Have them access the Chapter Resources to find the **Unlock the Big Question activity.** There they can answer the questions and refine their responses as they continue through the lesson. You can re-assign the activity and have students submit their work so you can track their progress.

EXPLAIN AND ELABORATE

Students reading above, at, or below the lexile measure of this lesson can access basic content readings at their level at **My Reading Web.** Encourage students to use the online **Vocab Flash Cards** to preview key terms. Have students do the **Quick Lab** and share their findings about the effects of water and slope angle on the rate of erosion.

Support the Big Q by discussing the effects erosion and deposition have on Earth's surface in the instance of a mass movement. Assign the **Interactive Art activity** which illustrates the different types of mass movement. Assign the **Apply It activity** online and have students submit their work to you. The **Key Concept Summaries** online allow students to read a summary and see an image associated with each part of the lesson. Online remediation is available at **My Science Coach.**

EVALUATE

Have students take the **Lesson Quiz.** For an alternate assessment, see the **EXAM**VIEW® Assessment Suite, Progress Monitoring Assessments, or SuccessTracker™.

2 Frontload the Lesson

Have students survey the diagrams and captions in this lesson. Then have them write questions they have about the lesson based on their surveys. After students read the lesson, have them answer the questions they wrote at the start of the lesson.

3 Comprehensible Input

To help students understand that a cycle is continuous, direct students to the diagram showing erosion and deposition. Have students trace the cycle as you read, starting with 2. Then have volunteers retell the cycle starting at different steps.

4 Language Production

Pair or group students with varied language abilities to complete labs collaboratively for language practice. Have each student copy the completed written lab for personal reference.

5 Assess Understanding

Ask students to make notes about key concepts from the lesson and use the notes to prepare an oral presentation of the concepts. Encourage students to use the visuals in the lesson to support their presentations.

Mass Movement

Establish Learning Objectives

After this lesson, students will be able to:

🔑 Describe the processes that wear down and build up Earth's surface.

🔑 Identify the causes of the different types of mass movement.

Engage

Activate Prior Knowledge

MY PLANET DIARY Read *Mudflow Hits Town* with the class. Point out the terms *landslide* and *mudflow*. Ask students to speculate about what they think these terms might mean. Ask: **How do you think a mudflow might differ from a flood?** *(Possible answer: A flood is overflowing water, whereas a mudflow is water and mud running downhill.)* **What causes mudflows and other things to move downhill?** *(Gravity)*

BIG IDEAS OF SCIENCE REFERENCE LIBRARY 📖 Have students look up the following topic: Landslides.

Explore

Lab Resource: Inquiry Warm-Up 🔬

🔲 **HOW DOES GRAVITY AFFECT MATERIALS ON A SLOPE?** Students will observe and compare the effect of gravity on a marble's movement on a surface with and without sandpaper on the surface.

LESSON
1 Mass Movement

UNLOCK THE BIG ❓

🔑 What Processes Wear Down and Build Up Earth's Surface?

🔑 What Are the Different Types of Mass Movement?

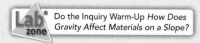

DISASTER

Mudflow Hits Town

In December 2007, severe storms hit the northwestern United States. These storms started landslides in the hills above Woodson, Oregon. When landslide debris dammed a creek in the hills, a deep lake formed. If the debris gave way, a mudflow could run downhill and damage the town.

Fortunately, a landowner called the Oregon Department of Forestry (ODF). People were quickly evacuated and a nearby highway was closed. It wasn't long before the pile of debris collapsed, allowing the water to escape. A large mudflow swept away homes, cars, and trees! But thanks to the ODF, no one was harmed.

Discuss the story with a classmate and answer the question.
What caused the mudflow?
Landslide debris dammed
a creek. The creek bank col-
lapsed. Debris flowed downhill.

▶ **PLANET DIARY** Go to **Planet Diary** to learn more about mass movement.

🔬 **Lab zone** Do the Inquiry Warm-Up *How Does Gravity Affect Materials on a Slope?*

What Processes Wear Down and Build Up Earth's Surface?

On a rainy day, you may have seen water carrying soil and gravel down a driveway. That's an example of **erosion**—the process by which natural forces move weathered rock and soil from one place to another. Gravity, moving water, glaciers, waves, and wind are all agents, or causes, of erosion.

208 Erosion and Deposition

SUPPORT ALL READERS
Lexile Measure = 900L   Lexile Word Count = 720

Prior Exposure to Content: May be the first time students have encountered this topic

Academic Vocabulary: *infer, relate, interpret*

Science Vocabulary: *erosion, sediment, deposition, mass movement*

Concept Level: Generally appropriate for most students in this grade

Preteach With: My Planet Diary "Mudflow Hits Town" and Figure 1 activity

Go to **My Reading Web** to access leveled readings that provide a foundation for the content.

MY SCIENCE online.com

Vocabulary
- erosion • sediment • deposition
- gravity • mass movement

Skills
- ◐ Reading: Relate Text and Visuals
- △ Inquiry: Infer

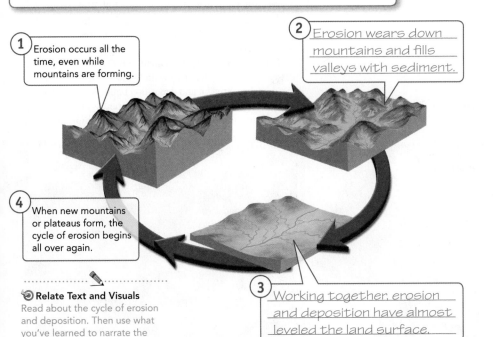

① Erosion occurs all the time, even while mountains are forming.

② Erosion wears down mountains and fills valleys with sediment.

④ When new mountains or plateaus form, the cycle of erosion begins all over again.

③ Working together, erosion and deposition have almost leveled the land surface.

◐ **Relate Text and Visuals**
Read about the cycle of erosion and deposition. Then use what you've learned to narrate the steps in the diagram above.

The process of erosion moves material called **sediment.** Sediment may consist of pieces of rock or soil, or the remains of plants and animals. **Deposition** occurs where the agents of erosion deposit, or lay down, sediment. Deposition changes the shape of the land. You may have watched a playing child who picked up several toys, carried them across a room, and then put them down. This child was acting something like an agent of erosion and deposition.

🔑 **Weathering, erosion, and deposition act together in a cycle that wears down and builds up Earth's surface.** Erosion and deposition are at work everywhere on Earth. As a mountain wears down in one place, new landforms build up in other places. The cycle of erosion and deposition is never-ending.

Lab zone Do the Quick Lab *Weathering and Erosion.*

🔑 **Assess Your Understanding**

got **it**? ....

○ I get it! Now I know the three major processes that shape Earth's surface are <u>weathering, erosion, and</u> <u>deposition.</u>

_____

○ I need extra help with <u>See TE note.</u>
Go to **my science** 🔵 **coach** *online for help with this subject.*

209

Explain

Introduce Vocabulary
Write the terms *erosion* and *deposition* on the board, and underline the suffixes *-sion* and *-tion*. Explain that these word parts, called suffixes, mean "state or quality of." Tell students that learning to recognize suffixes can help them in building vocabulary.

Teach Key Concepts 🔑
Explain to students that different processes—weathering, erosion, and deposition—build up and wear down the surface of Earth. Help students understand the concept of a cycle and this cycle in particular. Ask: **Which parts of this cycle wear down Earth's surface?** *(Weathering and erosion)* **What part builds up Earth's surface?** *(Deposition)* Remind students that this cycle, just like other cycles, has no beginning and no end.

◐ **Relate Text and Visuals** Explain that visuals include photographs, graphs, tables, and diagrams.

21st Century Learning

CRITICAL THINKING Tell students that the cycle of erosion and deposition happens repeatedly, without ending. Ask: **What are some other natural cycles that are never-ending?** *(Cycles of day and night, water cycle, oxygen-carbon dioxide cycle)*

Elaborate

Lab Resource: Quick Lab 🔬
L1 **WEATHERING AND EROSION** Students will explore how weathering affects erosion.

Evaluate

Assess Your Understanding
Have students evaluate their understanding by completing the appropriate sentence.

RTI Response to Intervention
If students have trouble listing the processes that shape Earth's surface, **then** have them reread the Key Concept statement.

my science 🔵 **coach** Have students go online for help in understanding processes that shape Earth's surface.

My Planet Diary provides an opportunity for students to explore real-world connections to mass movement.

my science online .com ▶   Erosion and Deposition

ⒺⓁⓁ Support

1 Content and Language
Write the word *sediment* on the board. Tell students the word comes from the Latin verb *sedere*, meaning "to sit." Sediment is small pieces of matter that are carried away and then are deposited in other places.

2 Frontload the Lesson
Skim the headings, images, and vocabulary terms with students. Have them make predictions about the lesson

content. As you read the text with students, stop after each section and ask them to compare their predictions with the information in the lesson.

3 Comprehensible Input
Display photos and illustrations of examples of mass movement discussed in the lesson. Work with students to describe what is happening in each image and to identify the type of movement shown.

Explain

Teach Key Concepts 🔑

Explain to students there are different kinds of mass movement. List these four examples on the board: landslides, mudflows, slumps, and creep. Ask: **In all four examples, what force causes the movement of material down a slope?** *(Gravity)* **Landslides and mudflows often occur after large storms or earthquakes. What might trigger a landslide or mudflow?** *(Water during a storm reducing friction and the shaking that occurs during an earthquake or road construction)*

Support the Big Q ❓ UbD

EFFECTS OF MASS MOVEMENT Explain that during a mass movement event, both erosion and deposition occur. Erosion occurs as sediment moves downhill and deposition occurs as it comes to rest in a new location. Ask: **In the case of mass movement, how does erosion affect the land surface?** *(The surface gets worn down, sometimes leaving a scar or damage where the mass of rock and soil used to be.)* **How does deposition affect the land surface?** *(The surface gets built up, often with a pile or huge mass of rock or sediment.)*

Teach With Visuals

Tell students to look at **Figure 1,** particularly the photographs that show the results of the mass movements. Ask: **What damage might be caused by a landslide, mudflow, or slump?** *(Homes and property destroyed, roadways covered, people injured or killed)* **What damage might be caused by creep?** *(Roads and fences damaged, trees and poles tilted)* **Which type of mass movement would you classify as the least dangerous and why?** *(Possible answer: Creep, because it happens so slowly it isn't life threatening)*

What Are the Different Types of Mass Movement?

You're sitting on a bicycle at the top of a hill. With a slight push, you can coast down the hill. **Gravity** is the force that pulls you and your bike downward. It also moves rock and other materials downhill.

Gravity causes **mass movement,** any one of several processes that move sediment downhill. Mass movement can be rapid or slow. Erosion and deposition both take place during a mass movement event. 🔑 **The different types of mass movement include landslides, mudflows, slumps, and creep.**

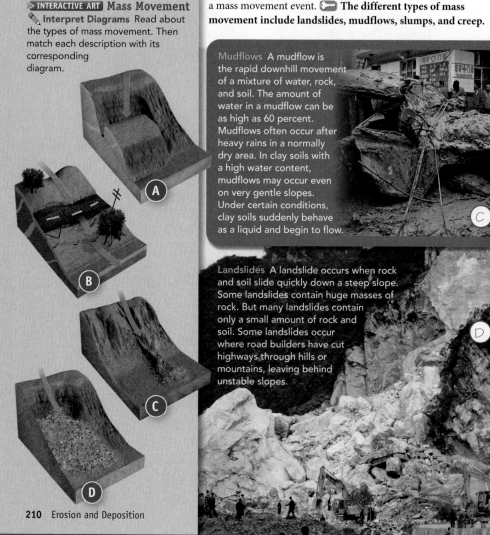

FIGURE 1 ....

▶ **INTERACTIVE ART** Mass Movement
✏️ **Interpret Diagrams** Read about the types of mass movement. Then match each description with its corresponding diagram.

Ⓐ

Ⓑ

Ⓒ

Ⓓ

210 Erosion and Deposition

Mudflows A mudflow is the rapid downhill movement of a mixture of water, rock, and soil. The amount of water in a mudflow can be as high as 60 percent. Mudflows often occur after heavy rains in a normally dry area. In clay soils with a high water content, mudflows may occur even on very gentle slopes. Under certain conditions, clay soils suddenly behave as a liquid and begin to flow.

Ⓒ

Landslides A landslide occurs when rock and soil slide quickly down a steep slope. Some landslides contain huge masses of rock. But many landslides contain only a small amount of rock and soil. Some landslides occur where road builders have cut highways through hills or mountains, leaving behind unstable slopes.

Ⓓ

Interactive Art illustrates the different types of mass movement.

Digital Lesson: Assign the *Apply It* activity online and have students submit their work to you.

my science online .com ▶ | **Mass Movement**

Mass Movement ▸ INTERACTIVE ART ▸ APPLY IT

LESSON 7.1

apply it!

Infer A fence runs across a steep hillside. The fence is tilted downhill and forms a curve rather than a straight line. What do you think happened?

The fence moved as a result of creep.

Slumps If you slump your shoulders, the entire upper part of your body drops down. In the type of mass movement known as **slumps**, a mass of rock and soil suddenly slips down a slope. Unlike a landslide, the material in a slump moves down in one large mass. It looks as if someone pulled the bottom out from under part of the slope. A slump often occurs when water soaks the bottom of soil that is rich in clay.

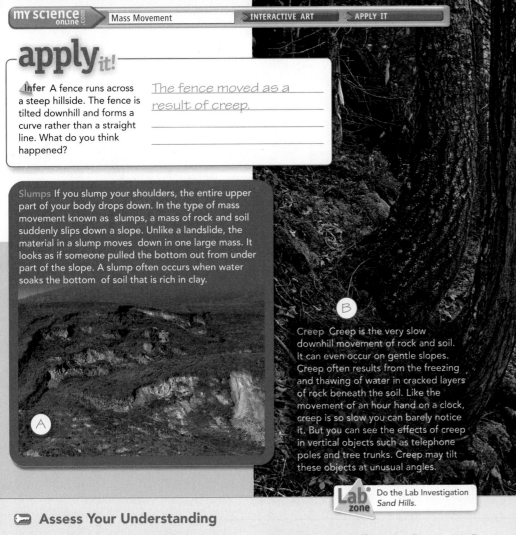

Ⓑ

Creep Creep is the very slow downhill movement of rock and soil. It can even occur on gentle slopes. Creep often results from the freezing and thawing of water in cracked layers of rock beneath the soil. Like the movement of an hour hand on a clock, creep is so slow you can barely notice it. But you can see the effects of creep in vertical objects such as telephone poles and tree trunks. Creep may tilt these objects at unusual angles.

Lab zone Do the Lab Investigation _Sand Hills._

🔑 Assess Your Understanding

1a. Review What is mass movement?

Process that moves sediment downhill; erosion and deposition take place simultaneously.

b. Relate Cause and Effect What force causes all types of mass movement? Explain.

Gravity; it pulls objects downhill.

got it?

O **I get it!** Now I know that mass movement is the _downhill movement of sediment through landslides, mudflows, slump, and creep._

O **I need extra help with** _See TE note._

Go to MY SCIENCE 💬 COACH online for help with this subject.

211

Differentiated Instruction

L1 Clarify Slope Explain that in common speech, a _slope_ means the side of a hill or a mountain or any sloping surface. In this chapter, the term _slope_ means the amount of an incline. Sketch some hills with slopes of different inclines and use the term, for example, "The hill has a steep slope of 60 degrees."

L3 Make Dioramas Have students make three-dimensional models of one or more of the different types of mass movement. Provide a variety of modeling materials such as shoeboxes, clay, sand, gravel, sticks, paint, and brushes. Encourage students to make their models as realistic as possible and display the finished dioramas in the classroom.

Elaborate

Teacher Demo 🔬

MODELING MASS MOVEMENT

L1 Materials soil, large plastic tub, water, watering can

Time 15 minutes

Review with students the different types of mass movement. Tell students that landslides and mudflows often occur after large storms or earthquakes. Using soil, build a model mountain in the plastic tub. Then, as students observe, shake the tub.

Ask: **What does the shaking model?** (An earthquake) **What does the model earthquake cause?** (A landslide) Rebuild the mountain. Use the watering can to "rain" on the model. Continue adding water until some movement of wet sediment occurs. Ask: **What do the watering can and water model?** (A storm with rainfall) **What did the "rainfall" cause?** (A mudflow) **How are earthquakes and storms related to mass movement?** (Movement from an earthquake and water from a storm can trigger mass movement.)

Apply It!

L1 Review the name and affect of each type of mass movement before beginning the activity.

Infer If students have difficulty inferring that creep has occurred, have them look for a tilted and curved fence in the diagrams of **Figure 1** and match that diagram with its corresponding description.

Lab Resource: Lab Investigation 🔬

L2 SAND HILLS Students will use a model to determine the relationship between height and width in a sand hill.

Evaluate

Assess Your Understanding

After students answer the questions, have them evaluate their understanding by completing the appropriate sentence.

RTI Response to Intervention

1a. If students need help defining mass movement, **then** suggest they reread the sentence that contains the boldface term.

b. If students have trouble identifying the force that causes all types of mass movement, **then** remind them why a ball rolls downhill or a pencil drops to the ground when you let go of it.

MY SCIENCE 💬 COACH Have students go online for help in understanding mass movement.

211

Lab zone **After the Inquiry Warm-Up**

Mass Movement

Inquiry Warm-Up, *How Does Gravity Affect Materials on a Slope?*
In the Inquiry Warm-Up, you investigated how the effect gravity has on a material on a slope depends on both the type of material and the slope's condition. Using what you learned from that activity, answer the questions below.

1. **COMPARE AND CONTRAST** Compare the physical qualities of the marble to the physical qualities of the wood block.

   _____

   _____

   _____

2. **INFER** Based on your answer to question 1, which factors may influence the effect of gravity on materials on a slope?

   _____

   _____

3. **CONTROL VARIABLES** What is the only variable that changed between Steps 2 and 3? How did it change?

   _____

   _____

4. **DRAW CONCLUSIONS** Based on your answers to question 3, what factor clearly influences the effect of gravity on materials on a slope?

   _____

Name _____ Date _____ Class _____

Mass Movement

What Processes Wear Down and Build Up Earth's Surface?

got it? ··

○ **I get it!** Now I know the three major processes that shape Earth's surface are _____
_____

○ **I need extra help with** _____
_____

What Are the Different Types of Mass Movement?

1a. REVIEW What is mass movement? _____
_____
_____

b. RELATE CAUSE AND EFFECT What force causes all types of mass

movement? Explain. _____
_____

got it? ··

○ **I get it!** Now I know that mass movement is the _____
_____
_____

○ **I need extra help with** _____
_____

Key Concept Summaries

Mass Movement

What Processes Wear Down and Build Up Earth's Surface?

Erosion is the process by which natural forces move weathered rock and soil from one place to another. Gravity, moving water, glaciers, waves, and wind are all causes, or agents, of erosion.

The process of erosion moves material called **sediment.** Sediment may consist of pieces of rock or soil, or the remains of plants and animals. **Deposition** occurs where the agents of erosion deposit, or lay down, sediment. Deposition changes the shape of the land.

Weathering, erosion, and deposition act together in a cycle that wears down and builds up Earth's surface. Erosion and deposition are at work everywhere on Earth. The cycle of erosion and deposition is never-ending.

What Are the Different Types of Mass Movement?

Gravity is the force that pulls objects downward. It moves rock and other materials downhill.

Gravity causes **mass movement,** any one of several processes that move sediment downhill. Mass movement can be rapid or slow. And erosion and deposition both take place during a mass movement event. **The different types of mass movement include landslides, mudflows, slump, and creep.**

A mudflow is the rapid downhill movement of a mixture of water, rock, and soil. Mudflows often occur after heavy rains in a normally dry area. A landslide occurs when rock and soil slide quickly down a steep slope. In the type of mass movement know as slump, a mass of rock and soil suddenly slips down a slope. Unlike a landslide, the material in a slump moves down in one large mass. Creep is the very slow downhill movement of rock and soil. Creep may tilt vertical objects like telephone poles and tree trunks at unusual angles.

On a separate sheet of paper, explain how gravity causes mass movement and is an agent of erosion and deposition.

Review and Reinforce

Mass Movement

Understanding Main Ideas
Identify each of the examples below by writing *landslide, mudslide, slump,* or *creep* on the line beside it.

---

1. _____ Watery clay soil slides down a mountain.

2. _____ A telephone pole leans downhill.

3. _____ Rock at the top of a steep cliff quickly falls.

4. _____ After a heavy rainfall, rock and soil on a desert hill slide to the bottom.

5. _____ After many years, a gravestone on a hillside falls over.

6. _____ Rock and soil suddenly slip downhill in one large mass.

7. _____ Where a new road was just built, rock and soil move down a slope.

Answer the following questions on a separate sheet of paper.

8. What causes mass movement?

9. Describe how three processes act together to wear down and build up Earth's surface.

Building Vocabulary
Fill in the blank to complete each statement.

---

10. The agents of erosion lay down sediment in new locations in a process called _____.

11. The material moved by erosion is called _____.

12. The process by which natural forces move weathered rock and soil from one place to another is called _____.

13. _____ includes several processes caused by gravity that move sediment downhill.

14. _____ is the force that pulls objects downward.

Mass Movement

Read the passage and study the diagram. Then use a separate sheet of paper to answer the questions that follow.

It's Creepy!

Of all the different types of mass movement, creep changes Earth's surface most. Landslides, mudslides, and slumps sometimes have spectacular—and tragic—results. Yet creep makes the most changes because it is continually occurring almost everywhere. Creep is like the tortoise in the fable of the tortoise and the hare. The slow but steady movement of the tortoise wins the race over the fast but uneven progress of the hare.

How does creep work? The most important process that causes creep involves the freezing and thawing of water in the ground. And, of course, gravity plays a part in creep, as it does in all types of mass movement.

Water from rainfall and runoff seeps into the ground, filling spaces between particles of soil and rock. The water freezes and expands. As the water expands, it lifts up the soil and rock particles. They rise perpendicular to the slope of the hill. When the ground thaws, the force of gravity causes the soil and rock particles to fall back down. But they fall vertically, toward the center of Earth. The result is movement downhill, as you can see in the figure.

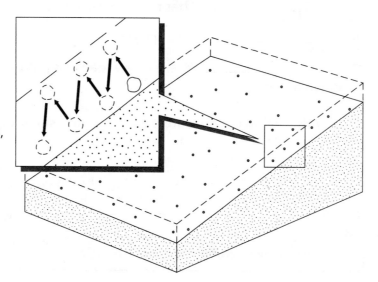

1. What type of mass movement makes the most changes in Earth's surface?
2. What property of water is partly responsible for creep?
3. What causes soil and rock particles to rise?
4. Describe the direction in which soil and rock particles rise.
5. What causes the soil and rock particles to fall?
6. Describe the direction in which soil and rock particles fall.
7. Write a description of the whole process of creep.

Lesson Quiz

Mass Movement

Write the letter of the correct answer on the line at the left.

1. ___ Which type of mass movement happens very slowly?

    A   slump

    B   creep

    C   landslide

    D   mudslide

2. ___ By which process is sediment laid down?

    A   erosion

    B   deposition

    C   weathering

    D   mountain building

3. ___ Which of these is *not* an agent of erosion?

    A   water

    B   gravity

    C   waves

    D   sediment

4. ___ In which type of mass movement can soils behave like a liquid and start flowing?

    A   slump

    B   creep

    C   landslide

    D   mudslide

If the statement is true, write *true*. If the statement is false, change the underlined word or words to make the statement true.

5. _____ The cycle of erosion and deposition is never-ending.

6. _____ Gravity moves rocks and soil uphill.

7. _____ Landslides happen slowly.

8. _____ Slump is an example of mass movement.

9. _____ Weathering is the process by which rock and soil are moved from place to place.

10. _____ Sediment may consist of pieces of rock or soil, or the remains of organisms.

Mass Movement

Answer Key

Mass Movement

After the Inquiry Warm-Up

1. The marble is smaller, lighter, smoother, and rounder than the wood block.

2. size, mass, surface condition, shape

3. The surfaces of both the wood block and board were changed. By adding the sandpaper, both surfaces were made rougher.

4. the smoothness or roughness of the different materials

Key Concept Summaries

Gravity pulls rock and sediment downhill, causing mass movement. By moving weathered rock it causes erosion, and by laying it down in a new place it causes deposition.

Review and Reinforce

1. mudslide

2. creep

3. landslide

4. mudslide

5. creep

6. slump

7. landslide

8. Gravity causes mass movement.

9. Weathering and erosion produce and move sediment, wearing down the land. The agents of erosion also deposit sediment. Deposition changes the shape of the land by building it up.

10. deposition

11. sediment

12. erosion

13. Mass movement

14. Gravity

Enrich

1. creep

2. Water expands when it freezes.

3. The rock and soil particles rise because the water between them freezes and expands.

4. They rise perpendicular to the slope of the hill.

5. the force of gravity

6. They fall vertically, toward the center of Earth.

7. Water seeps into the ground, filling spaces between soil and rock particles. When the water freezes, it lifts up the particles, perpendicular to the hill. When the ground thaws, the particles fall down vertically. The result is movement downhill.

Lesson Quiz

1. B
2. B
3. D
4. D
5. true
6. downhill
7. quickly
8. true
9. erosion
10. true

Place the outside corner, the corner away from the dotted line, in the corner of your copy machine to copy onto letter-size paper.

Teacher Notes

Water Erosion

What processes shape the surface of the land?

Lesson Pacing: 2–3 periods or $\frac{1}{2}$–1 block

🕐 **SHORT ON TIME?** To do this lesson in approximately half the time, do the Activate Prior Knowledge activity followed by a discussion of the Key Concepts to familiarize students with the lesson content. Explore the Big Q by discussing how a river changes from its head to its mouth. Have students do the Quick Labs and have the students do the Real-World Inquiry activity online. The rest of the lesson can be completed by students independently.

> **Preference Navigator,** in the online Planning tools, allows you to customize *Interactive Science* to your own teaching style. You can also edit lesson plans by selecting the Lesson Planner option.
>
> **Digital Teacher's Edition** allows you to access your Teacher's Edition and Resource materials online.

Lesson Vocabulary

- runoff
- rill
- gully
- stream
- tributary
- flood plain
- meander
- oxbow lake
- delta
- alluvial fan
- groundwater
- stalactite
- stalagmite
- karst topography

Content Refresher

Professional Development Note

Two Models of Stream Erosion Many geologists have described the stages of landscape development that have been eroded by rivers and streams using the terms *youth, maturity, old age,* and *rejuvenation. Rejuvenation* occurred when forces uplifted the land, causing the cycle of erosion to begin again. William Morris Davis, a nineteenth-century American geomorphologist, pioneered the use of these terms to describe stream erosion.

Today, geologists view stream erosion as a dynamic process in which stream, its sediment load, and the land surface all tend toward equilibrium. As a stream erodes the land, it gradually reduces the slope of the land until the stream's speed and sediment load are in equilibrium with the slope of the land surface. Any change disturbs the equilibrium and affects other parts of the system. For example, if a stream's volume increases because of heavy rainfall, then erosion along the stream's banks and bed also increases. Uplift of the land surface caused by movement along a fault would increase the stream's slope. This increases the stream's speed and its downcutting into its bed. Stream erosion becomes a process with no specific beginning or idealized end.

LESSON OBJECTIVES

- Explain how moving water causes erosion.
- Describe some of the land features that are formed by water erosion and deposition.

Blended Path
Active learning using Student Edition, Inquiry Path, and Digital Path

ENGAGE AND EXPLORE

Teach this lesson using a variety of resources. Begin by reading **My Planet Diary** as a class. Have students share their experiences with caves and prior knowledge of how they form. Then have students do the **Inquiry Warm-Up activity.** Students will use soap and dripping water to model erosion. The **After the Inquiry Warm-Up worksheet** sets up a discussion about how moving water wears away rocks. Have volunteers share their responses to question 4.

EXPLAIN AND ELABORATE

Teach Key Concepts by explaining that water is an agent of erosion and responsible for shaping much of Earth's surface. **Lead a Discussion** about how water can pick up sediment at one place and deposit it at another, reshaping the surface of Earth.

Lead a Discussion about the sources of water in a major river in your county or state and how the river changes throughout the year. **Teach Key Concepts** by explaining how a flowing river forms valleys, waterfalls, flood plains, meanders, and oxbow lakes. **Lead a Discussion** about how flood plains form as rivers spread out and erode the land. Continue to **Teach Key Concepts** by explaining how alluvial fans and deltas form as the flow of river water slows. **Explore the Big Q** by using **Figure 7** to discuss how a river changes from its head to its mouth. Continue to **Teach Key Concepts** by explaining that groundwater erosion occurs as a result of chemical weathering. **Lead a Discussion** about the sequence of events that results in the formation of a cave. Have students practice the inquiry skill in the **Apply It activity.** To **Answer the Big Q,** lead a class discussion about the processes that shape the surface of the land.

Hand out the **Key Concept Summaries** as a review of each part of the lesson. Students can also use the online **Vocab Flash Cards** to review key terms.

EVALUATE

Have students take the **Lesson Quiz.** For an alternate assessment, see the **EXAM**VIEW® Assessment Suite, Progress Monitoring Assessments, or SuccessTracker™.

ⒺⓁⓁ Support

1 Content and Language

Read the first Key Concept statement aloud to students. Explain that *agent* has two meanings: "a person who acts for some other person or company" and "something that produces a certain effect." Discuss which meaning fits the way *agent* is used in the Key Concept statement. Have students restate the statement using their own words.

Lab zone Inquiry Path
Hands-on learning in the Lab zone

Digital Path
Online learning at my science online.com

ENGAGE AND EXPLORE

To teach this lesson with an emphasis on inquiry, begin with the **Inquiry Warm-Up activity.** Students will use soap and dripping water to model erosion. The **After the Inquiry Warm-Up worksheet** sets up a discussion about how moving water wears away rocks. Have volunteers share their responses to question 4.

EXPLAIN AND ELABORATE

Focus on the **Inquiry Skill** for the lesson. Remind students that a hypothesis is a possible explanation for a set of observations or an answer to a scientific question. What hypothesis could be made in the **Inquiry Warm-Up Activity** about how water wears away rocks? *(Sample: The temperature of the water affects the rate at which it wears away rock.)* **Build Inquiry** by challenging students to identify and trace all the tributaries of a major U.S. river. Have students do the **Quick Lab** and share what they learned about the effect of raindrops on soil.

Build Inquiry by having students compare and contrast the deltas of the major world rivers. **Explore the Big Q** by using **Figure 7** to discuss how a river changes from its head to its mouth. **Build Inquiry** by challenging students to illustrate river environments. Do the **Teacher Demo** to show students how tributaries merge to form larger streams along most of a river's course and then how distributary channels form near its mouth. Do the next **Teacher Demo** to model how carbonic acid forms. Display a United States map showing the state names before having students do the **Apply It activity.** Have students do the **Quick Lab** and share what they learned about groundwater erosion. To **Answer the Big Q** lead a class discussion about the processes that shape the surface of the land. Students can use the online **Vocab Flash Cards** to review key terms.

EVALUATE

Have students take the **Lesson Quiz.** For an alternate assessment, see the **EXAM**VIEW® Assessment Suite, Progress Monitoring Assessments, or SuccessTracker™.

ENGAGE AND EXPLORE

Teach this lesson using digital resources. Begin by having students explore real-world connections to water erosion at **My Planet Diary** online. Have them access the Chapter Resources to find the **Unlock the Big Question activity.** There they can answer the questions and refine their responses as they continue through the lesson. You can re-assign the activity and have students submit their work so you can track their progress.

EXPLAIN AND ELABORATE

Students reading above, at, or below the lexile measure of this lesson can access basic content readings at their level at **My Reading Web.** Encourage students to use the online **Vocab Flash Cards** to preview key terms. Have students do the **Quick Lab** and share what they learned about the effect of raindrops on soil.

Use the **Real-World Inquiry activity** online to allow students to explore the benefits and risks of living in areas that are prone to flooding. **Explore the Big Q** by using **Figure 7** to discuss how a river changes from its head to its mouth. Assign the **Apply It activity** online and have students submit their work to you. Have students do the **Quick Lab** and share what they learned about groundwater erosion. To **Answer the Big Q** lead a class discussion about the processes that shape the surface of the land. The **Key Concept Summaries** online allow students to read a summary and see an image associated with each part of the lesson. Online remediation is available at **My Science Coach.**

EVALUATE

Have students take the **Lesson Quiz.** For an alternate assessment, see the **EXAM**VIEW® Assessment Suite, Progress Monitoring Assessments, or SuccessTracker™.

---

2 Frontload the Lesson
Preview the vocabulary by saying aloud each term. Have students locate a visual of each of the terms in the lesson. Note that there is not a visual for *runoff.*

3 Comprehensible Input
Have students use a graphic organizer to show land features created by water erosion and another to show the land features created by water deposition.

4 Language Production
Pair or group students with varied language abilities to complete labs collaboratively for language practice. Have each student copy the completed written lab for personal reference.

5 Assess Understanding
Divide students into four groups and have each complete a Frayer Model diagram for one key term. It should include the definition, characteristics, an example, and a nonexample of the term. Have each group teach their word to the class.

LESSON 7.2

Water Erosion

Establish Learning Objectives

After this lesson, students will be able to:

🔑 Explain how moving water causes erosion.

🔑 Describe some of the land features that are formed by water erosion and deposition.

Engage

Activate Prior Knowledge

MY PLANET DIARY Read *The Great Blue Hole* with the class. Ask students to share their experiences with caves and prior knowledge of how they form. Then ask students if they have seen or heard news stories about sinkholes forming. Ask: **Why is sinkhole a good name for this cave?** *(Because it is a hole in the ground that formed when its roof sank, or collapsed)*

BIG IDEAS OF SCIENCE REFERENCE LIBRARY 📖 Have students look up the following topics: Caves, Colorado River.

Explore

Lab Resource: Inquiry Warm-Up 🧪

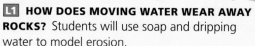 **HOW DOES MOVING WATER WEAR AWAY ROCKS?** Students will use soap and dripping water to model erosion.

LESSON

2 Water Erosion

🔑 **How Does Moving Water Cause Erosion?**

🔑 **What Land Features Are Formed by Water Erosion and Deposition?**

FIELD TRIP

my planet diary

The Great Blue Hole

The boat leaves at 5:30 A.M. But you don't mind the early hour because it's the trip of a lifetime: a visit to the Great Blue Hole of Belize.

The Great Blue Hole is actually the remains of a cave formed by erosion. Several factors, including rising sea levels, caused the roof of the cave to collapse. This resulted in a natural depression called a sinkhole.

The Great Blue Hole is more than 300 meters wide and 125 meters deep. It's possibly the deepest and most massive sinkhole in the world. If you want to explore it, you have to scuba dive through the roof. It's an impressive example of what nature can accomplish over time!

Read the story. Then answer the question.
How was the Great Blue Hole formed?

When the sea level rose, the cave collapsed, forming a sinkhole.

> PLANET DIARY Go to **Planet Diary** to learn more about water erosion.

🧪 Do the Inquiry Warm-Up *How Does Moving Water Wear Away Rocks?*

How Does Moving Water Cause Erosion?

Erosion by water begins with a splash of rain. Some rainfall sinks into the ground. Some evaporates or is taken up by plants. The rest of the water runs off over the land surface. 🔑 **Moving water is the major agent of the erosion that has shaped Earth's land surface.**

212 Erosion and Deposition

SUPPORT ALL READERS

Lexile Measure = 890L   Lexile Word Count = 2055

Prior Exposure to Content: May be the first time students have encountered this topic

Academic Vocabulary: *evidence, factors, hypothesis, processes*

Science Vocabulary: *flood plain, meander, delta, alluvial fan*

Concept Level: Generally appropriate for most students in this grade

Preteach With: My Planet Diary "The Great Blue Hole" and Figure 7 activity

Go to **My Reading Web** to access leveled readings that provide a foundation for the content.

Vocabulary
- runoff • rill • gully • stream • tributary
- flood plain • meander • oxbow lake • delta
- alluvial fan • groundwater • stalactite
- stalagmite • karst topography

Skills
🔁 Reading: Identify Supporting Evidence
△ Inquiry: Develop Hypotheses

Runoff As water moves over the land, it carries particles with it. This moving water is called **runoff.** When runoff flows in a thin layer over the land, it may cause a type of erosion called sheet erosion. The amount of runoff in an area depends on five main factors. The first factor is the amount of rain an area gets. A second factor is vegetation. Grasses, shrubs, and trees reduce runoff by absorbing water and holding soil in place. A third factor is the type of soil. Some types of soils absorb more water than others. A fourth factor is the shape of the land. Steeply sloped land has more runoff than flatter land. Finally, a fifth factor is how people use land. For example, a paved parking lot absorbs no water. All the rain that falls on it becomes runoff. Runoff also increases when farmers cut down crops, since this removes vegetation from the land.

Generally, more runoff means more erosion. In contrast, factors that reduce runoff will reduce erosion. Even though deserts have little rainfall they often have high runoff and erosion because they have few plants and thin soil. In wet areas, runoff and erosion may be low because there are more plants to help protect the soil.

🔁 **Identify Supporting Evidence** As you read the paragraph on the left, number each of the factors that affect runoff.

Factor	Example
1. amount of rain	1. very little
2. vegetation	2. grass
3. soil type	3. loose dirt
4. land shape	4. hilly
5. human use	5. a running trail (Answers will vary based on location.)

FIGURE 1 ....
Factors Affecting Runoff
✏ **Complete the task below.**

1. **List** Record the five main factors affecting runoff.
2. **Identify** Using a specific location, such as a park, identify an example for each factor.
3. **Communicate** Explain to a partner what the runoff would be like at your location.

213

Explain

Introduce Vocabulary
Tell students that *runoff* is a compound word. Explain that a compound word is a single word formed by joining two words, in this case *run* and *off*. Caution students that although the two words may provide clues to the meaning of the single compound word, they may have different definitions when compounded than when used consecutively in a sentence.

Teach Key Concepts 🔑
Explain to students that water is responsible for shaping much of Earth's surface, because water is an agent, or cause, of erosion. Ask: **How can water move soil and sediment?** *(By flowing over Earth's surface)* **In what ways does this water flow?** *(As a sheet, in rills, in gullies, and in streams)* **What factors determine the amount of runoff in an area?** *(Amount of rain, vegetation, type of soil, shape of the land, how the land is used)*

🔁 **Identifying Supporting Evidence** Tell students that a paragraph may contain many statements, but one of those statements will be broader than the others, and will state the main idea. The other statements provide information that backs up, or supports, the main idea. This is supporting evidence.

Lead a Discussion
EFFECTS OF WATER ON EARTH'S SURFACE Remind students that many factors and processes help shape Earth's surface. Ask: **How do people shape Earth's surface?** *(They dig sediment and rocks from one place and dump them at another place.)* Explain that water also picks up sediment at one place and deposits it at another and that water moves much more sediment than people do. Ask: **What evidence have you seen of the effects of water on Earth's surface?** *(Encourage students to consider large features such as canyons and deltas, and small features, such as rills.)*

My Planet Diary provides an opportunity for students to explore real-world connections to water erosion.

E L L Support

1 Content and Language
Help students remember the difference between stalactites and stalagmites by explaining that stalactites grow down from the ceiling while stalagmites grow up from the ground.

2 Frontload the Lesson
Ask students who have visited the Grand Canyon or explored caverns to describe what they saw. Have volunteers explain how the land feature got there.

3 Comprehensible Input
Have students work together to create a display that illustrates the different examples of land features created by water erosion and deposition. Students can find examples in magazines or print out images from online and caption the examples they find.

Elaborate

Make Analogies

L1 **RILLS, GULLIES, STREAMS** Have a volunteer stand in front of the class with arms raised and fingers spread and pointing to the back corners of the ceiling. Make an analogy between the structure of the student's branching fingers and rills, between the student's arms and gullies, and between the trunk of the student's body and a stream. Refer students to **Figure 2** as you make the comparison. Ask: **How are these body parts like the features of stream formation?** *(They both converge, going from more numerous to fewer features and finally a single feature.)*

Build Inquiry

L2 **IDENTIFYING TRIBUTARIES**

Materials map of the United States that shows drainage patterns, tracing paper, pencil

Time 30 minutes

Remind students that major rivers have many tributaries. Review with them the definition of a tributary. Then challenge students to identify and trace all of the tributaries of a major U.S. river. They might choose the Mississippi, Columbia, or Susquehanna.

Ask: **How can you identify tributaries on the map?** *(The tributaries flow into the larger river.)* **What general shape is the river pattern that you traced?** *(Answers will vary. One common pattern resembles a tree trunk with branches.)*

Lab Resource: Quick Lab

L2 **RAINDROPS FALLING** Students will use a plastic dropper, water, a petri dish, and fine soil to model the effect of raindrops on soil.

Evaluate

Assess Your Understanding

After students answer the questions, have them evaluate their understanding by completing the appropriate sentence.

RTI Response to Intervention

1a. If students need help with relating the amount of runoff with the amount of erosion, **then** ask them which will pick up more soil, a few drops of flowing water or a deep sheet of moving water.

b. If students have trouble placing the water features in order of size, **then** suggest they reread the sentences that define each term.

MY SCIENCE COACH Have students go online for help in understanding how water causes erosion.

214 Erosion and Deposition

Stream Formation Because of gravity, runoff and the material it contains flow downhill. As this water moves across the land, it runs together to form rills, gullies, and streams.

Rills and Gullies As runoff travels, it forms tiny grooves in the soil called **rills**. When many rills flow into one another, they grow larger, forming a gully. A **gully** is a large groove, or channel, in the soil that carries runoff after a rainstorm. As water flows through gullies, it moves soil and rocks with it, thus enlarging the gullies through erosion. Gullies only contain water during a rainstorm and for a short time after it rains.

Streams and Rivers Gullies join together to form a larger channel called a stream. A **stream** is a channel along which water is continually flowing down a slope. Unlike gullies, streams rarely dry up. Small streams are also called creeks or brooks. As streams flow together, they form larger and larger bodies of flowing water. A large stream is often called a river.

Tributaries A stream grows into a larger stream or river by receiving water from tributaries. A **tributary** is a stream or river that flows into a larger river. For example, the Missouri and Ohio rivers are tributaries of the Mississippi River. A drainage basin, or watershed, is the area from which a river and its tributaries collect their water.

FIGURE 2 ············
Stream Formation
✎ **Relate Text and Visuals** After you read, do the activity.
1. Shade in the arrows that indicate the direction of sheet erosion.
2. Circle the terms *rills, gully,* and *stream* in the text. Then draw a line from the word to examples of them in the picture.

Do the Quick Lab
Raindrops Falling.

💬 **Assess Your Understanding**

1a. Review How does runoff affect the rate of erosion?

More runoff increases the rate of erosion.

b. Sequence Put these in order of size from smallest to biggest: creek, rill, gully, river.

Rill, gully, creek, river

got it? ············

○ **I get it!** Now I know what runoff does: *It forms rills and then gullies, which join streams, increasing the capacity of water to erode an area.*

○ **I need extra help with** *See TE note.*

Go to **MY SCIENCE COACH** online for help with this subject.

214 Erosion and Deposition

What Land Features Are Formed by Water Erosion and Deposition?

Walking in the woods in summer, you can hear the racing water of a river before you see the river itself. When you reach the river's banks, you see water rushing by. Sand and pebbles tumble along the river bottom. As it swirls downstream, the water also carries twigs, leaves, and bits of soil. In sheltered pools, insects skim the water's calm surface. Beneath the surface, a rainbow trout swims in the clear water. As the seasons change, so does the river. In winter, the surface of the river may freeze. But during spring, it may flood. Throughout the year, the river continues to erode Earth's surface.

FIGURE 3 ··········

River Erosion

✎ **Interpret Photos** How does a river's ability to erode change with the seasons? (*Hint:* Look at how the amount of water changes during each season.)

Spring   Summer   Fall   Winter

Sample: The river would probably erode the landscape the most in spring. During spring, there is a faster, higher flow of water due to snowmelt in the mountains and surrounding areas. It looks like the amount and the flow of the water lessen throughout the seasons. In winter, the water moves slowly because the surface is frozen. But ice chunks can scrape the riverbed and banks.

215

Explain

Lead a Discussion

LOCAL RIVER Ask students to name and describe a major river in your county or state. Ask: **Where does the river get its water?** *(From smaller rivers and streams)* **Where does this water ultimately come from?** *(Precipitation)* **How does this river change throughout the year?** *(Answers will vary, depending on the river chosen. Changes may include amount of water flowing and the physical state of water.)*

Teach With Visuals

Tell students to look at **Figure 3.** Have students compare and contrast the river in each of the four photos. Encourage students to share their experiences and observations of rivers they have observed during different seasons as you lead a discussion about how rivers change throughout the year. Ask: **During which season is the flow of water highest and fastest, and why?** *(Most likely in spring due to snowmelt or during a local wet season due to increased precipitation)* **During which season is the river likely to erode the most sediment?** *(During spring or the season in which the greatest water flow occurs)* Explain that a large amount of fast moving water can erode more than a small amount of slow moving water.

Differentiated Instruction

L1 The Meaning of "Agent" Point out to students that an "agent" of erosion means a "force or substance that causes change," not a representative, such as in "insurance agent," or a spy, such as in "secret agent." Have students write a short paragraph describing how water is an agent of erosion.

L3 Urban Planning Have students use drawing software to make sketches that show how urban areas could be designed to reduce the amount of runoff into streets and local streams. *(Possible solutions on sketches: include open areas for water absorption, include water retention structures, plant appropriate vegetation)*

LESSON 7.2

Explain

Teach Key Concepts 🔑

Explain to students that as a river flows along its course from its mountain source to the ocean, it causes erosion. Through this process, features form. These features include valleys, waterfalls, flood plains, meanders, and oxbow lakes. Ask: **Where along a river's course does a V-shaped valley occur?** *(Near the source where the slopes are steep)* **Where along its course does a wide flood plain occur?** *(Lower down on its course where gently sloping land occurs)* **Which feature is a loop-shaped bend in a river?** *(A meander)*

21st Century Learning

CRITICAL THINKING Tell students that hard rock that erodes slowly is said to be resistant to erosion. Waterfalls occur where resistant rock forms a ledge or cliff over which the water flows and falls. After students have completed **Figure 4,** ask: **Why would the top of a layer of hard rock be higher than the top of a layer of soft rock?** *(The hard rock resists erosion, so while the soft rock below wears away, the hard rock above remains longer.)* **Waterfalls tend to move upstream over time. Why might this happen?** *(Rocks break from the cliff at the waterfall and the cliff moves backward.)* **If a person wanted to visit Niagara Falls in 5,000 years, would it be at the same location? If not, where would it be?** *(No. Niagara Falls would be father upstream.)*

Water Erosion Many rivers begin on steep mountain slopes. Near their source, these rivers can be fast-flowing and generally follow a straight, narrow course. The steep slopes along the river erode rapidly, resulting in a deep, V-shaped valley. As a river flows from the mountains to the sea, it forms many features. 🔑 **Through erosion, a river creates valleys, waterfalls, flood plains, meanders, and oxbow lakes.**

Waterfalls Waterfalls may occur where a river meets an area of rock that is very hard and erodes slowly. The river flows over this rock and then flows over softer rock downstream. Softer rock wears away faster than harder rock. Eventually a waterfall develops where the softer rock was removed. Areas of rough water called rapids also occur where a river tumbles over hard rock.

FIGURE 4 ·······
Waterfalls
✏️ **Apply Concepts**
Where do you think the layers of hard and soft rock are located? Label the areas on the diagram to show your answer.

Hard

Soft

Flood Plain Lower down on its course, a river usually flows over more gently sloping land. The river spreads out and erodes the land, forming a wide river valley. The flat, wide area of land along a river is a flood plain. On a wide flood plain, the valley walls may be kilometers away from the river itself. A river often covers its flood plain when it overflows its banks during a flood. When the flood water finally retreats, it deposits sediment as new soil. This makes a river valley fertile.

216 Erosion and Deposition

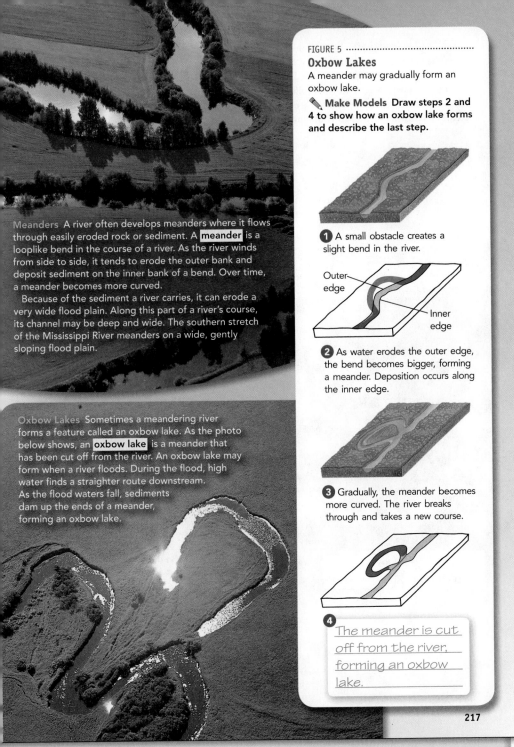

Meanders A river often develops meanders where it flows through easily eroded rock or sediment. A **meander** is a looplike bend in the course of a river. As the river winds from side to side, it tends to erode the outer bank and deposit sediment on the inner bank of a bend. Over time, a meander becomes more curved.

Because of the sediment a river carries, it can erode a very wide flood plain. Along this part of a river's course, its channel may be deep and wide. The southern stretch of the Mississippi River meanders on a wide, gently sloping flood plain.

Oxbow Lakes Sometimes a meandering river forms a feature called an oxbow lake. As the photo below shows, an **oxbow lake** is a meander that has been cut off from the river. An oxbow lake may form when a river floods. During the flood, high water finds a straighter route downstream. As the flood waters fall, sediments dam up the ends of a meander, forming an oxbow lake.

FIGURE 5 ··

Oxbow Lakes
A meander may gradually form an oxbow lake.

✏️ **Make Models** Draw steps 2 and 4 to show how an oxbow lake forms and describe the last step.

1 A small obstacle creates a slight bend in the river.

Outer edge — Inner edge

2 As water erodes the outer edge, the bend becomes bigger, forming a meander. Deposition occurs along the inner edge.

3 Gradually, the meander becomes more curved. The river breaks through and takes a new course.

4 The meander is cut off from the river, forming an oxbow lake.

217

Lead a Discussion

FLOOD PLAINS Discuss with students how flood plains form as rivers spread out and erode the land. Rivers pick up and carry sediment. Sometimes heavy rainstorms and spring snowmelt cause this sediment-carrying water to overflow the river's banks and spread over the flood plain. When flood waters spread out and slow down, they deposit the sediment they carry on the flood plain. This sediment adds nutrients to existing soil on the flood plain, making it a fertile place to grow plants. Direct students' attention to the photo of the flood waters in **Figure 4**. Ask: **In what ways are flood waters on a flood plain both helpful and harmful to people?** (*Flood waters help promote crop growth by adding nutrients to the soil. They are also harmful because they can destroy crops, damage property, and endanger people.*)

Teach With Visuals

Tell students to look at the diagrams and photos in **Figure 5**. Make sure students understand that meanders from because sediment is eroded on the outside bank of a river and deposited on the inside bank. Ask: **Where on a meander does erosion occur?** (*The outside*) **What happens on the inside of a meander?** (*Sediment is deposited there until the river channel is filled.*)

Explain that an oxbow is a U-shaped collar that is placed around an ox's neck. Ask: **Why do you think an oxbow lake is called that?** (*Because it is U-shaped*) **When might a meander become an oxbow lake?** (*When the river floods, and the water finds a more direct route downstream*)

Differentiated Instruction

L3 Locate River Features Provide students with a copy of a map or an aerial photograph of a land area that has several prominent meanders and oxbow lakes. (A good choice would eastern Louisiana, where the lower Mississippi River has formed wide loops and several large oxbow lakes on its flat flood plain.) Have each student locate as many examples of these two features as possible and circle them in different colors.

L1 Write Sentences Review with students the definitions of *flood plain, meander, oxbow lake, erosion,* and *deposition.* Have students write sentences using the words and read them aloud to the class.

Explain

Teach Key Concepts

Explain to students that deposition occurs where the flow of river water slows. Features that form as a result of this deposition include alluvial fans and deltas. Ask: **Where do deltas form?** *(Deltas form where a river enters an ocean or a lake and its water stops flowing downhill.)* Where do alluvial fans form? *(Alluvial fans form where a stream leaves a mountain range and the water slows.)* **Where else is sediment deposited by river water and why?** *(It is deposited on a flood plain. As flood waters expand onto the flood plain, the water flows more slowly.)* **Where in the United states is an example of a delta?** *(The mouth of the Mississippi River, among others)* **Where would you expect to see an alluvial fan?** *(Sample: at the base of the Rocky Mountains)*

Elaborate

Build Inquiry

L2 COMPARE AND CONTRAST DELTAS

Materials atlas or encyclopedia

Time 15 minutes

Review the definition of a delta. Then have pairs of students find maps or aerial photographs in an atlas or encyclopedia that show the deltas or mouths of these major world rivers: Nile River (Egypt), Niger River (Nigeria), Ganges River (Bangladesh), Mekong River (Vietnam), Mississippi River (Louisiana), Columbia River (Oregon/Washington). Have students make drawings and write descriptions of each river. Call on student to compare and contrast the deltas.

Ask: **Why do you think the Columbia River has no delta at its end?** *(The currents of the Pacific Ocean move the sediments away, preventing development of a delta.)*

21st Century Learning

INFORMATION LITERACY Have students work in small groups to research the changes that have occurred to the Mississippi Delta over time. Students should try to find images from different periods that indicate how the land has changed as a result of deposition.

Water Deposition As water moves, it carries sediment with it. Any time moving water slows down, it drops, or deposits, some of the sediment. In this way, soil can be added to a river's flood plain. As the water slows down, large stones quit rolling and sliding. Fine particles fall to the river's bed as the river flows even more slowly. **Deposition creates landforms such as alluvial fans and deltas.**

Deltas A river ends its journey when it flows into a still body of water, such as an ocean or a lake. Because the river water is no longer flowing downhill, the water slows down. At this point, the sediment in the water drops to the bottom. Sediment deposited where a river flows into an ocean or lake builds up a landform called a **delta**. Deltas can be a variety of shapes. Some are arc-shaped, others are triangle-shaped. The delta of the Mississippi River, shown here, is an example of a type of delta called a "bird's foot" delta.

Alluvial Fans Where a stream flows out of a steep, narrow mountain valley, the stream suddenly becomes wider and shallower. The water slows down. Here sediments are deposited in an alluvial fan. An **alluvial fan** is a wide, sloping deposit of sediment formed where a stream leaves a mountain range. As its name suggests, this deposit is shaped like a fan.

FIGURE 6

Deposits by Rivers

✎ **Interpret Photos** Use the pictures above to describe the difference between an alluvial fan and a delta.

An alluvial fan forms when a stream flows out of a narrow mountain valley and sediments are deposited. But a delta forms when a river slows down as it flows into the ocean or a lake.

Key
▨ Mississippi delta

LOUISIANA

MISSISSIPPI

TEXAS

New Orleans

0   50   100 mi
0   50   100 km

Gulf of Mexico

218   Erosion and Deposition

Real-World Inquiry allows students to explore the benefits and risks of living in areas that are prone to flooding.

my science online.com ▸ Water Erosion and Deposition

Rolling Through the Hills

What processes shape the surface of the land?

FIGURE 7 ·············

▶ **REAL-WORLD INQUIRY** You're a tour guide in the area pictured below, and your tour group wants to learn more about some of the features they are seeing.

✎ **Relate Evidence and Explanation** Identify the two missing features on the image below. Then summarize what you would say about them to your tour group.

Sample: As the river flows out of the V-shaped valley, it winds across the land, forming a meander. The land erodes easily, allowing the river to loop and bend. Then, as the river approaches the ocean, it slows down and deposits sediment, forming a delta.

Waterfalls and Rapids Waterfalls and rapids are common where the river passes over harder rock.

V-Shaped Valley Near its source, the river flows through a deep, V-shaped valley. As the river flows, it cuts the valley deeper.

Tributary The river receives water and sediment from a tributary—a smaller river or stream that flows into it.

Oxbow Lake An oxbow lake is a meander cut off from the river by deposition of sediment.

Meander

Valley Widening As the river approaches sea level, it meanders more and develops a wider valley and broader flood plain.

Flood Plain A flood plain forms where the river's power of erosion widens its valley rather than deepening it.

Delta

219

Differentiated Instruction

L1 Match Titles Make a copy of **Figure 7.** On the copy, remove the titles of the annotations, leaving only the definitions and descriptions. Write the annotation titles on small tags, including *Meander* and *Delta*. Have students match the titles to their descriptions.

L3 Travel Journal Provide maps of your state for students to examine. Then challenge students to suppose that they are boating along one of your state's major rivers. Ask them to write a travel journal that summarizes their observations and experiences. Remind them to include descriptions of river features they encounter in their travels.

L1 Describe River Features Call on students to describe river features. Then, reverse the procedure by having students identify a river feature from a description.

Elaborate

Explore the Big Q ❓ UbD

Direct students' attention to **Figure 7.** Help students understand where the river begins and ends. Call on volunteers to read the captions aloud. Have them begin at the river's head. Ask: **Why would a river in the mountains have rapids, waterfalls, and a V-shaped valley?** *(In mountains, the slopes are steep. This causes rivers to have many rapids and to erode narrow valleys. Rivers in mountains commonly flow over cliffs to form waterfalls.)* Have students continue reading the captions. Question them at each step. Then ask them to summarize how the river changes from its head to its mouth.

Build Inquiry

L1 ILLUSTRATE RIVER ENVIRONMENTS

Materials nature magazines, poster board, scissors, tape or glue

Time 90 minutes

Refer students to **Figure 7.** Remind them that rivers have a variety of environments from head to mouth along their course. Have them sketch a river from its head to its mouth on poster board. Then, ask students to find photographs of river environments in magazines or online. Have students tape or glue the photographs to their drawings.

Ask: **Which part of a river might be best for whitewater rafting?** *(Areas near the head)* **Which part would have a wide flood plain?** *(Areas closer to the mouth)* **Where along a river is new land being formed?** *(At the delta)*

Teacher Demo

L1 TRIBUTARIES AND DISTRIBUTARY CHANNELS

Materials chalkboard and chalk or blank overhead transparency and marker

Time 10 minutes

Draw a river with several tributaries on the board or blank transparency. Include arrows to show the direction in which the water flows.

Ask: **What happens when rivers or streams merge?** *(A larger river or stream forms.)* Tell students that rivers merge to form larger streams along most of a river's course. Now draw a main river splitting into several smaller channels at a delta. Include arrows to show the direction of the water's flow. Tells students that river channels often divide at a delta, and here the smaller channels are called distributary channels. Have students compare and contrast the two drawings. Ask: **In which drawing does the river flow into a lake or ocean?** *(In the second drawing of the delta)*

LESSON 7.2

Explain

Teach Key Concepts

Explain to students that water under the ground is called groundwater. This water, like water on the surface, causes erosion. Groundwater erosion occurs as a result of chemical weathering. Ask: **What is chemical weathering?** *(The process that breaks down rocks through chemical changes)* **What agents of chemical weathering are involved in groundwater erosion?** *(Water and carbon dioxide)* Remind students that carbon dioxide gas becomes dissolved in water as the water sinks through air pockets in soil and rocks. The result is a weak acid called carbonic acid, which easily weathers limestone.

Lead a Discussion

CAVES AND CAVERNS Ask students how many of them drink carbonated beverages. Tell students that these beverages contain carbon dioxide and are acidic. Carbon dioxide also makes groundwater acidic and able to break down limestone. As a class, summarize the sequence of events that results in the formation of a cave: a limestone layer that has cracks in it is partially filled with groundwater, the groundwater dissolves limestone below the water table, caves eventually form in the limestone, the water table drops, and the caves are filled with air. Ask: **When do stalactites and stalagmites form in a cave?** *(After the water table has lowered and the cave is filled with air)* **What feature forms if the cave roof collapses, resulting in a depression on the surface?** *(A sinkhole)*

Elaborate

Teacher Demo

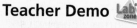

L3 MODEL HOW CARBONIC ACID FORMS

Materials beaker, water, pH paper or pH probe, drinking straw

Time 10 minutes

Fill a beaker halfway with distilled water. Determine the pH of the water. Record this value on the board. Using a drinking straw, exhale into the water in the beaker for several minutes. Determine the pH again, and write this value on the board. The second pH value should be lower, or more acidic, than the first because the exhaled carbon dioxide combined with water to form carbonic acid.

Ask: **What is one source of carbon dioxide in air?** *(The gases organisms breathe out or give off)* **How is this demonstration similar to the way carbonic acid forms in soil?** *(Respiration by plant roots and microorganisms in soil produces carbon dioxide. The carbon dioxide combines with water to form carbonic acid.)*

did you know?

The Schellenberg ice cave in Germany is a limestone cave with ice formations. Cold air is trapped in the lower areas of the cave so the temperature stays near freezing. This keeps the ice formations from melting.

Groundwater Erosion When rain falls and snow melts, not all of the water evaporates or becomes runoff. Some water soaks into the ground. There it fills the openings in the soil and trickles into cracks and spaces in layers of rock. **Groundwater** is the term geologists use for this underground water. Like running water on the surface, groundwater affects the shape of the land.

Groundwater can cause erosion through a process of chemical weathering. Rainwater is naturally acidic. In the atmosphere, water combines with carbon dioxide to form a weak acid called carbonic acid. Carbonic acid can break down limestone. Groundwater containing carbonic acid flows into any cracks in the limestone. Then some of the limestone dissolves and is carried away in a solution of water. This process gradually hollows out pockets in the rock. Over time, these pockets develop into large holes underground, called caves or caverns.

Cave Formations The action of carbonic acid on limestone can also result in deposition. Inside limestone caves, deposits called stalactites and stalagmites often form. Water containing carbonic acid and calcium from limestone drips from a cave's roof. Carbon dioxide escapes from the solution, leaving behind a deposit of calcite. A deposit that hangs like an icicle from the roof of a cave is known as a **stalactite** (stuh LAK tyt). Slow dripping builds up a cone-shaped **stalagmite** (stuh LAG myt) from the cave floor.

FIGURE 8

Groundwater Erosion and Deposition

Explain How do erosion and deposition shape caves? Take notes as you read. Then discuss with a classmate.

Process of Erosion	Process of Deposition
• Some water soaks into ground.	• Water with carbonic acid and
• Water fills cracks in rock layers.	calcium drips from cave roof.
• Erosion by chemical weathering	• Carbon dioxide released
• Water and carbon dioxide form	• Calcite deposits remain, forming
carbonic acid.	stalactites and stalagmites.
• Carbonic acid breaks down	
limestone, forms pockets in rock	

Digital Lesson: Assign the *Apply It* activity online and have students submit their work to you.

MY SCIENCE online.com | **Water Erosion and Deposition**

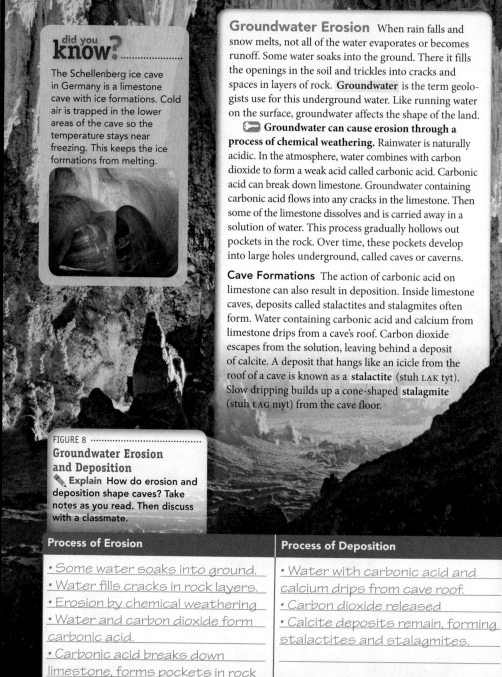

Karst Topography In rainy regions where there is a layer of limestone near the surface, groundwater erosion can significantly change the shape of the land. Streams are rare, because water easily sinks down into the weathered limestone. Deep valleys and caverns are common. If the roof of a cave collapses because of the erosion of the underlying limestone, the result is a depression called a sinkhole. This type of landscape is called **karst topography** after a region in Eastern Europe.

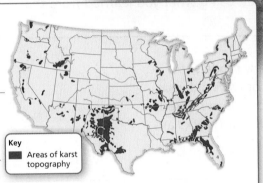
This sinkhole is in Russia's Perm region.

apply it!

Study the map and answer the questions below.

❶ Name three states in which you can find karst topography.

Sample: Texas, Missouri, Florida

❷ ▲ **Develop Hypotheses** Why do you think karst topography occurs in these areas?

Because the bedrock is made of
layers of limestone
_____

Key

■ Areas of karst topography

Do the Quick Lab
Erosion Cube.

🔑 Assess Your Understanding

2a. List Name two features of water erosion.

Sample: oxbow lake, flood plain

b. CHALLENGE What is carbonic acid and how does it affect rock?

Carbonic acid forms when water
combines with carbon dioxide. It
can dissolve limestone.

c. ANSWER THE BIG ? What processes shape the surface of the land?

Erosion and deposition
shape the surface of the land
by removing sediment, trans-
porting it, and depositing it in a
new place.

got it? ....

○ I get it! Now I know that features of erosion and deposition include _meanders, waterfalls,_
valleys, flood plains, oxbow lakes, alluvial fans, and deltas.

○ I need extra help with _See TE note._

Go to **MY SCIENCE 💬 COACH** online for help with this subject.

221

Differentiated Instruction

L1 Compare and Contrast Table As a class or group, help students make a table to compare and contrast the features formed by groundwater erosion with the features formed by groundwater deposition. Encourage each student to contribute at least one concept or term.

L3 Illustrated Flowcharts Have students make two illustrated flowcharts, one for the process that results in the formation of a cave and another for the process that results in the formation of a sinkhole. Students' flowcharts should include both drawings and descriptive captions. Have students present their flowcharts to the class.

Address Misconceptions

L1 UNDERGROUND STREAMS AND LAKES Many students believe that all or most groundwater is held in rivers or lakes beneath Earth's surface. To assess their understanding, ask: **How does groundwater exist beneath Earth's surface?** *(Accept all answers at this time.)* Point out that underground caves do sometimes contain streams and lakes but that this is the exception rather than the rule. Almost all groundwater exists in small pores in rock or in cracks in rock. Have students compare groundwater in rock to the water held in an old, cracked sponge. Ask: **What does such a sponge look like when dry?** *(It is full of holes.)* **When it gets wet, where does water occur in the sponge?** *(In the holes)*

Apply It!

L1 Display a United States map showing the state names before beginning the activity.

▲ **Develop Hypotheses** Remind students that a hypothesis is a possible explanation for a set of observations or an answer to a scientific question. If they have difficulty developing a hypothesis, reread the paragraph about karst topography as a class.

Lab Resource: Quick Lab 🔺

L2 EROSION CUBE Students will use sugar cubes and water to model groundwater erosion.

Evaluate

Assess Your Understanding

After students answer the questions, have them evaluate their understanding by completing the appropriate sentence.

Answer the Big Q ❓ UbD

To help students focus on the Big Question, lead a class discussion about the processes that shape the surface of the land.

R T I Response to Intervention

1a. If students have trouble naming features of water erosion, **then** review **Figure 7** with them.

b. If students need help describing carbonic acid and its effect, **then** suggestion they reread the section on groundwater erosion.

c. If students need help identifying the processes that shape the land surface, **then** have them reread the Key Concept statements.

MY SCIENCE 💬 COACH Have students go online for help in understanding features of water erosion and deposition.

Lab zone ® **After the Inquiry Warm-Up**

Water Erosion

> **Inquiry Warm-Up,** *How Does Moving Water Wear Away Rocks?*
> In the Inquiry Warm-Up, you investigated how moving water wears away rocks by using a model of a bar of soap placed under a dripping faucet. Using what you learned from that activity, answer the questions below.

1. **DEVELOP HYPOTHESES** Assume that the lab accurately models how moving water wears away rocks. Which way or ways did you suggest to speed up the process of wearing the soap away? Based on your response, what variable affects the rate at which rocks are worn down?

    _____

2. **DESIGN EXPERIMENTS** How could you modify or extend the lab to test your hypothesis from question 1?

    _____

    _____

    _____

    _____

3. **USE PRIOR KNOWLEDGE** Besides the speed of water flow, what other variable can you adjust with a faucet?

    _____

4. **POSE QUESTIONS** Think about your answer to question 3. Using your model of a faucet and bars of soap, what other question do you think you might be able to answer about how water wears away rocks?

    _____

    _____

Name _____ Date _____ Class _____

Water Erosion

How Does Moving Water Cause Erosion?

1a. REVIEW How does runoff affect the rate of erosion? _____

_____

b. SEQUENCE Put these in order of size from smallest to biggest: creek,

rill, gully, river. _____

_____

got it? ···

○ **I get it!** Now I know what runoff does: _____

_____

○ **I need extra help with** _____

_____

What Land Features Are Formed by Water Erosion and Deposition?

2a. LIST Name two features of water erosion. _____

_____

b. CHALLENGE What is carbonic acid and how does it affect rock? _____

_____

_____

c. ANSWER What processes shape the surface of the land? _____

_____

_____

got it? ···

○ **I get it!** Now I know that features of erosion and deposition include _____

_____

○ **I need extra help with** _____

_____

Name _____ Date _____ Class _____

Water Erosion

How Does Moving Water Cause Erosion?

Moving water is the major agent of the erosion that has shaped Earth's land surface. As water moves over the land, it carries particles with it. This moving water is called **runoff.** The amount of runoff in an area depends on five main factors: the amount of rain an area gets, the area's vegetation, the type of soil, the shape of the land, and how people use the land.

As runoff travels downhill under gravity, it forms tiny grooves in the soil called **rills.** When many rills flow into one another, they grow large, forming a gully. A **gully** is a large groove, or channel in the soil that carries runoff after a rainstorm. Gullies join together to form a larger channel called a stream. A **stream** is a channel along which water is continually flowing down a slope. A large stream is often called a river. A **tributary** is a stream or river that flows into a larger river.

What Land Features Are Formed by Water Erosion and Deposition?

Through erosion, a river creates valleys, waterfalls, flood plains, meanders, and oxbow lakes. The flat, wide area of land along a river is a **flood plain.** A **meander** is a looplike bend in the course of a river. An **oxbow lake** is a meander that has been cut off from the river.

Deposition creates landforms such as alluvial fans and deltas. Sediment deposited where a river flows into an ocean or lake builds up a landform called a **delta.** An **alluvial fan** is a wide, sloping deposit of sediment formed where a stream leaves a mountain range. It is shaped like a fan.

Groundwater is the term geologists use for underground water. **Groundwater can cause erosion through a process of chemical weathering.** A deposit that hangs like an icicle from the roof of a cave is known as a **stalactite.** Slow dripping builds up a cone-shaped **stalagmite** from the cave floor. **Karst topography** is a type of landscape in rainy regions where there is limestone near the surface and characterized by caverns, sinkholes, and deep valleys.

On a separate sheet of paper, give one example of how moving water on the surface shapes the land and one example of how moving water under the ground shapes the land.

Review and Reinforce

Water Erosion

Understanding Main Ideas
Answer the following questions on a separate sheet of paper.

1. What role has moving water played in shaping Earth's surface?

2. What are five landforms formed by river erosion?

3. What are two landforms formed by river deposition?

4. How does groundwater cause erosion?

Building Vocabulary
Fill in the blank to complete each statement.

5. A bend in a river shaped like a loop is called a(n) _____.

6. Where a stream leaves a mountain range you'll find a(n) _____ _____, a wide, sloping deposit of sediment.

7. A(n) _____ is a channel along which water is continually flowing down a slope.

8. The water that moves over the land and carries particles with it is called _____.

9. A cone-shaped deposit that rises from the floor of a cave is known as a(n) _____.

10. A(n) _____ is a large groove, or channel in the soil that carries runoff after a rainstorm.

11. A type of landscape in rainy regions where caverns, sinkholes, and deep valleys are common is called _____.

12. A(n) _____ is a deposit that hangs from the roof of a cave.

13. When runoff travels downhill, it forms tiny grooves in the soil called _____.

14. The term geologists use for underground water is _____.

15. A river's _____ is the flat, wide area of land along side of it.

Enrich

Water Erosion

Read the passage and study the table. Then use a separate sheet of paper to answer the questions that follow.

Great Rivers of the World

The table lists the top ten rivers in the world. The figures for volume of flow are given in cubic meters per second. If you were to stand on the bank of the river at the widest point, on average that many cubic meters of water would flow by every second. The table also shows how large each river's drainage basin is, given in square kilometers.

The World's Ten Largest Rivers

River	Location	Length (km)	Volume of Flow (m³/s)	Drainage Basin (square km)
Amazon	South America	6,437	140,000	6,133,000
Congo	West Africa	4,667	39,200	4,014,000
Chang Jiang (Yangtze)	China	6,300	21,500	1,942,000
Mississippi	North America	3,766	17,400	3,222,000
Yenisei	Asia	4,506	17,200	2,590,000
Lena	Asia	4,280	15,300	2,424,000
Paraná	South America	2,414	14,700	2,305,000
Ob	Asia	5,150	12,300	2,484,000
Amur	Asia	4,666	9,500	1,844,000
Nile	East Africa	6,671	2,800	2,978,000

1. The table ranks the world's top ten rivers on the basis of what characteristic?
2. Compare the Mississippi's volume of flow with the Amazon's volume of flow.
3. Of the rivers listed, which is the longest?
4. Which of these rivers drains the greatest area?
5. Where does each of these rivers begin and end? What body of water does each river empty into? Use an encyclopedia to find the answers to these questions. Make a table with the information.

Lesson Quiz

Water Erosion

If the statement is true, write *true*. If the statement is false, change the underlined word or words to make the statement true.

1. _____ Vegetation, such as grasses, <u>increases</u> runoff.

2. _____ An <u>oxbow lake</u> is a meander that has been cut off from the river.

3. _____ Groundwater can cause erosion through <u>chemical</u> weathering.

4. _____ A(n) <u>alluvial fan</u> forms when sediment gets laid down where a river flows into an ocean.

5. _____ Waterfalls and rapids occur where rivers meet and flow over <u>hard</u> rock.

6. _____ Deltas and alluvial fans form at the point of river <u>erosion</u>.

Write the letter of the correct answer on the line at the left.

7. ___ What is a channel with continually flowing water that flows into a larger river called?

   A gully

   B flood plain

   C rill

   D tributary

8. ___ Which increases runoff?

   A planting crops

   B cutting down crops

   C flattening land

   D replacing pavement with trees

9. ___ What is a meander?

   A a bend in a river

   B the wide area of land along a river

   C a fan-shaped sediment deposit

   D a large groove in the soil

10. ___ Which features are common in areas of karst topography?

   A streams

   B alluvial fans

   C sinkholes

   D deserts

Water Erosion

Answer Key

After the Inquiry Warm-Up

1. the speed and/or amount of water flowing over them

2. Sample: Add a second faucet and a third bar of soap. Adjust the second faucet so that it is drips faster than the first faucet. Place a bar of soap under each faucet and let them drip for ten minutes. Then compare how much soap was worn away from each bar.

3. water temperature

4. Does the temperature of water affect the rate at which it wears away rock?

Key Concept Summaries

Possible answer: On the surface, where a river flows into an ocean or lake, the river deposits sediment and a delta forms. In a cave under the ground, slow-dripping groundwater builds up a cone-shaped stalagmite from the cave floor.

Review and Reinforce

1. Moving water is the major agent of the erosion that has shaped Earth's land surface. It also builds up the surface through deposition.

2. A river erodes the land to form valleys, waterfalls, flood plains, meanders, and oxbow lakes.

3. River deposition creates alluvial fans and deltas.

4. Groundwater causes erosion through a process of chemical weathering.

5. meander

6. alluvial fan

7. stream

8. runoff

9. stalagmite

10. gully

11. karst topography

12. stalactite

13. rills

14. groundwater

15. flood plain

Enrich

1. They are ranked on the basis of volume of flow.

2. The Mississippi has a volume of flow of 17,400 cubic meters per second, while the Amazon has a volume of flow of 140,000 cubic meters per second, or about eight times as much.

3. The longest is the Nile River.

4. The Amazon has the largest drainage basin.

5. Almost all encyclopedias contain an entry for each of these rivers. As an alternative, students could find these rivers on a world map and then use an atlas. Students' tables should contain an entry for each river and columns for where the river begins, where it ends, and what kind of body of water it empties into.

Lesson Quiz

1. decreases
2. true
3. true
4. delta
5. true
6. deposition
7. D
8. B
9. A
10. C

Place the outside corner, the corner away from the dotted line, in the corner of your copy machine to copy onto letter-size paper.

Glacial Erosion

What processes shape the surface of the land?

Lesson Pacing: 1–2 periods or $\frac{1}{2}$–1 block

🕐 **SHORT ON TIME?** To do this lesson in approximately half the time, do the Activate Prior Knowledge activity followed by a discussion of the Key Concepts to familiarize students with the lesson content. Have students do the Quick Labs. The rest of the lesson can be completed by students independently.

> **Preference Navigator,** in the online Planning tools, allows you to customize *Interactive Science* to your own teaching style. You can also edit lesson plans by selecting the Lesson Planner option.
>
> **Digital Teacher's Edition** allows you to access your Teacher's Edition and Resource materials online.

my science online.com ▶

Lesson Vocabulary

- glacier
- continental glacier
- ice age
- valley glacier
- plucking
- till
- moraine
- kettle

Content Refresher

Glacier Movement Glaciers move by two different processes: ice flow and basal sliding. When the glacial ice becomes thick enough, the force of gravity causes flow to occur. The mechanism by which ice flows is complex. Bonds within the ice crystals break, movement of planes of molecules occurs, and the bonds re-form. Although movement is slow, this process can transport huge amounts of ice. The ice moves from the zone of accumulation, where snowfall exceeds melting, to the zone of ablation, where melting exceeds snowfall.

Basal sliding occurs when a glacier slides over its substrate. Although there may be some exceptions, most basal sliding occurs beneath warm-base glaciers. These glaciers have basal temperatures high enough to allow some melting at their base. Cold-base glaciers often are frozen to the substrate below. Glacier surges are examples of rapid basal sliding.

LESSON OBJECTIVES

- Explain how glaciers form and move.
- Explain how glaciers cause erosion and deposition.

Blended Path
Active learning using Student Edition, Inquiry Path, and Digital Path

ENGAGE AND EXPLORE

Teach this lesson using a variety of resources. Begin by reading **My Planet Diary** as a class. Have students discuss the differences between snow and glacial ice. Then have students do the **Inquiry Warm-Up activity.** Students will model glacial erosion by abrasion. The **After the Inquiry Warm-Up worksheet** sets up a discussion about how glaciers wear land away. Have volunteers share their answers to question 4 about what land under a glacier would look like after the glacier has melted.

EXPLAIN AND ELABORATE

Review the term *glacier* and then **Teach Key Concepts** by explaining the two kinds of glaciers: continental and valley. Continue to **Teach Key Concepts** by explaining that glaciers can only form in places where more snow falls than melts. Have students practice the inquiry skill in the **Apply It activity.**

Teach Key Concepts by explaining the two ways glaciers cause erosion of the land over which they move: plucking and abrasion. Continue to **Teach Key Concepts** by explaining that when a glacier melts, it deposits the sediment it eroded from the land, creating various landforms. **Support the Big Q** by discussing how glaciers are agents of both erosion and deposition and how these two processes shape the surface of the land.

Hand out the **Key Concept Summaries** as a review of each part of the lesson. Students can also use the online **Vocab Flash Cards** to review key terms.

EVALUATE

Have students take the **Lesson Quiz.** For an alternate assessment, see the **EXAM**VIEW® Assessment Suite, Progress Monitoring Assessments, or SuccessTracker™.

ELL Support

1 Content and Language
Write Cloze sentences for students to complete with the vocabulary terms for the lesson.

 **Inquiry Path** Hands-on learning in the Lab zone

ENGAGE AND EXPLORE

To teach this lesson with an emphasis on inquiry, begin with the **Inquiry Warm-Up activity.** Students will model glacial erosion by abrasion. The **After the Inquiry Warm-Up worksheet** sets up a discussion about how glaciers wear land away. Have volunteers share their answers to question 4 about what land under a glacier would look like after the glacier has melted.

EXPLAIN AND ELABORATE

Focus on the **Inquiry Skill** for the lesson. Remind students that when they draw a conclusion, they make a statement that summarizes what they have learned from observations or an experiment. How could the scrape marks the sand-crusted ice made in the soap be described in the **Inquiry Warm-Up Activity?** *(The sand made long scrape marks in the soap.)* Review how rivers erode the land and shape a valley before beginning the **Apply It activity.** Call on students to share their conclusions. Assign the **Quick Lab** and call on students to share their observations about glacier movement.

Support the Big Q by discussing how glaciers are agents of both erosion and deposition and how these two processes shape the surface of the land. **Build Inquiry** by helping students visualize the area of North America that was covered by ice in the last ice age. Have students do the **Quick Lab** and then share their observations of erosion caused by valley glaciers. Students can use the online **Vocab Flash Cards** to review key terms.

EVALUATE

Have students take the **Lesson Quiz.** For an alternate assessment, see the **EXAM**VIEW® Assessment Suite, Progress Monitoring Assessments, or SuccessTracker™.

Digital Path Online learning at my science online.com

ENGAGE AND EXPLORE

Teach this lesson using digital resources. Begin by having students learn more about glacial erosion and deposition and explore real-world connections to glacial erosion at **My Planet Diary** online. Have them access the Chapter Resources to find the **Unlock the Big Question activity.** There they can answer the questions and refine their responses as they continue through the lesson. You can re-assign the activity and have students submit their work so you can track their progress.

EXPLAIN AND ELABORATE

Students reading above, at, or below the lexile measure of this lesson can access basic content readings at their level at **My Reading Web.** Encourage students to use the online **Vocab Flash Cards** to preview key terms. Assign the **Apply It activity** online and have students submit their work to you. Assign the **Quick Lab** and have students share their observations about glacier movement.

Support the Big Q by discussing how glaciers are agents of both erosion and deposition and how these two processes shape the surface of the land. Have students do the **Art in Motion activity** online which shows a model of a glacier forming, growing, and retreating and the effects of these stages. Have students do the **Quick Lab** and then share their observations of erosion caused by valley glaciers. The **Key Concept Summaries** online allow students to read a summary and see an image associated with each part of the lesson. Online remediation is available at **My Science Coach.**

EVALUATE

Have students take the **Lesson Quiz.** For an alternate assessment, see the **EXAM**VIEW® Assessment Suite, Progress Monitoring Assessments, or SuccessTracker™.

2 Frontload the Lesson

Skim the headings, images, and vocabulary terms with students. Have them make predictions about the lesson content. As you read the text with students, stop after each section and ask them to compare their predictions with the information in the lesson.

3 Comprehensible Input

Have students look through the lesson for facts about glaciers. Ask each student to record a fact on an index card and add a visual. Then have students share their cards with each other.

4 Language Production

Pair or group students with varied language abilities to complete labs collaboratively for language practice. Require each student to copy the completed written lab for personal reference.

5 Assess Understanding

Divide the class into small groups. Have each student identify a key concept from the lesson to discuss in his or her group. After the discussions, have students talk about the key concepts as a group.

Glacial Erosion

Establish Learning Objectives

After this lesson, students will be able to:

 Explain how glaciers form and move.

 Explain how glaciers cause erosion and deposition.

Engage

Activate Prior Knowledge

MY PLANET DIARY Read *Why Are Glaciers Blue?* with the class. Encourage students to recall their experiences with snow and ice. Ask: **Is there a difference between snow that has just fallen and snow that has been on the ground for a while?** (*Old snow is less fluffy.*) Tell students that what they observed is similar to how snow starts to become ice in a glacier. Explain that snow that has been on the ground a long time becomes coarsely crystalline and granular.

BIG IDEAS OF SCIENCE REFERENCE LIBRARY 📖 Have students look up the following topic: Glaciers.

Explore

Lab Resource: Inquiry Warm-Up 🧪

L1 **HOW DO GLACIERS CHANGE THE LAND?** Students will use sand frozen into a plastic cup with ice and a bar of soap to model glacial erosion by abrasion.

LESSON
3 Glacial Erosion

 How Do Glaciers Form and Move?

 How Do Glaciers Cause Erosion and Deposition?

MY PLANET DIARY

FUN FACTS

Why Are Glaciers Blue?

If snow is white, why do glaciers look blue? When sunlight hits snow, it bounces right back. Snow is made up of microscopic crystals. It is light and not very dense. As more snow falls, its weight turns some of the crystals underneath into water and vapor. The water and vapor refreeze. This process creates larger, denser ice crystals. Over time, the weight of the snow and the ice on the surface makes these crystals even denser. These are the kind of ice crystals that make up glaciers. When sunlight hits glaciers, these dense ice crystals absorb the red and yellow light. Only the blue light escapes!

After you read, answer the questions below with a classmate.

1. What makes glaciers look blue?

   Glacial ice is denser than snow. It doesn't absorb blue light.

2. In addition to color, what might be some other differences between snow and glacial ice?

   The glacial ice may be heavier and thicker than snow and take longer to melt.

▶ PLANET DIARY Go to **Planet Diary** to learn more about glacial erosion and deposition.

🧪 **Lab zone** Do the Inquiry Warm-Up *How Do Glaciers Change the Land?*

222 Erosion and Deposition

SUPPORT ALL READERS

Lexile Measure = 870L   Lexile Word Count = 1110

Prior Exposure to Content: May be the first time students have encountered this topic

Academic Vocabulary: *cause, conclusion, effect, features*

Science Vocabulary: *glacier, plucking, till, moraine, kettle*

Concept Level: Generally appropriate for most students in this grade

Preteach With: My Planet Diary "Why Are Glaciers Blue?" and Figure 2 activity

Go to **My Reading Web** to access leveled readings that provide a foundation for the content.

my science online.com

Vocabulary
- glacier • continental glacier
- ice age • valley glacier • plucking
- till • moraine • kettle

Skills
- Reading: Relate Cause and Effect
- Inquiry: Draw Conclusions

How Do Glaciers Form and Move?

On a boat trip off the coast of Alaska you sail by evergreen forests and snowcapped mountains. As you round a point of land, you see an amazing sight. A great mass of ice winds like a river between rows of mountains. This river of ice is a glacier. Geologists define a **glacier** as any large mass of ice that moves slowly over land. **Glaciers can form only in an area where more snow falls than melts.** There are two kinds of glaciers—continental glaciers and valley glaciers.

Continental Glaciers A **continental glacier** is a glacier that covers much of a continent or large island. It can spread out over millions of square kilometers. Today, continental glaciers cover about 10 percent of Earth's land. They cover Antarctica and most of Greenland. **Continental glaciers can flow in all directions as they move.** They spread out much as pancake batter spreads out in a frying pan. Many times in the past, continental glaciers have covered larger parts of Earth's surface. These times are known as **ice ages.** About 1 million years ago, continental glaciers covered nearly one third of Earth's land. The glaciers advanced and retreated, or melted back, several times. They most recently retreated about 10,000 years ago.

FIGURE 1 ·····························

Continental Glaciers
You're traveling across Antarctica from Point A to Point H on the route below. The cross section shows changes in the ice sheet along your journey.

Interpret Diagrams What changes in elevation and ice depth will you encounter?

The West ice sheet is thinner and lower in elevation. The land beneath is mostly below sea level. The East ice sheet has spots 3 km thick. It also has the highest elevation. The thinnest ice on my journey is at Point A.

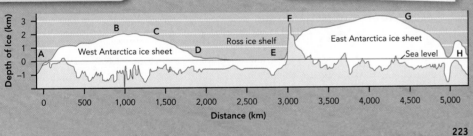

223

Explain

Introduce Vocabulary
Tell students that the word *glacier* comes from French word *glacé* by way of the Vulgar Latin *glacia* and Latin *glacies*, meaning "ice."

Teach Key Concepts
Explain to students that glaciers are large masses of ice that move over the land. The two kinds of glaciers are continental glaciers and valley glaciers. The glacier covering Antarctica is a continental glacier. As it moves, it flows out in all directions. Ask: **In your own words, how would you describe a continental glacier?** (*Possible answer: a mass of moving ice that covers most of a continent or large island*)

Make Analogies
L1 GLACIER MOVEMENT Help students understand how glacier movement is like that of pancake batter in a pan. Have students who have made pancakes describe what happens when they pour a mass of the batter into a pan. Ask: **Why does pancake batter spread out in a pan?** (*Gravity pulls on the batter and makes the pile thinner.*) **Is it possible for solid ice to flow like pancake batter?** (*Accept all answers at this time.*) Convince students that it is possible if the ice becomes thick enough. Also tell them that ice flows much more slowly than pancake batter does. Then ask: **Why do you think glaciers flow?** (*Gravity pulls on the ice and makes the mass thinner.*)

My Planet Diary provides an opportunity for students to explore real-world connections to glacial erosion.

my science online | Glaciers

1 Content and Language
Write the term *moraine* on the board and pronounce it for students. Explain that the term comes from the French word *morre*, meaning "snout."

2 Frontload the Lesson
Skim the headings, images, and vocabulary terms with students. Have them make predictions about the lesson content. As they read, have students stop and either confirm or revise their predictions.

3 Comprehensible Input
Have students prepare an outline of the lesson. The heads should serve as main ideas. Students can add details to the outlines as they read.

Explain

Teach Key Concepts

Explain to students that unlike a continental glacier that spreads out in all directions, a valley glacier is confined to a valley by the mountain on either side of the valley. Ask: **How were such valleys created in the first place?** *(They were eroded by rivers.)* Have students imagine a mountain range with river valleys and capped with snow. Ask: **What would happen if each year more snow fell than melted?** *(Snow would accumulate and become thicker each year.)* **What force might start this thick, heavy snow moving?** *(Gravity)* Tell students that both continental and valley glaciers begin forming and moving in places where more snow falls than melts.

Elaborate

21st Century Learning

CRITICAL THINKING Remind students that glaciers form from snow that builds up in areas where more snow falls than melts. Once formed it moves outward or down a valley under gravity. Ask: **If snow accumulates in some places and glacier ice flows outward, why hasn't ice covered most of the land?** *(The ice eventually melts as it flows into warmer areas.)*

Apply It!

L1 Review how rivers erode the land and shape a valley before beginning the activity.

▲ **Draw Conclusions** Remind students that when they draw a conclusion, they make a statement that summarizes what they have learned from observations or an experiment.

Lab Resource: Quick Lab

L1 SURGING GLACIERS Students will model glacier movement using a plastic lid and wet surface.

Evaluate

Assess Your Understanding

Have students evaluate their understanding by completing the appropriate sentence.

R T I Response to Intervention

If students need help contrasting how glaciers move, **then** have volunteers take turns rereading aloud the Key Concept statements.

MY SCIENCE COACH Have students go online for help in understanding glacier formation and movement.

Valley Glaciers A **valley glacier** is a long, narrow glacier that forms when snow and ice build up high in a mountain valley. The sides of mountains keep these glaciers from spreading out in all directions. Instead, they usually move down valleys that have already been cut by rivers. Valley glaciers are found on many high mountains. Although they are much smaller than continental glaciers, valley glaciers can be tens of kilometers long.

High in mountain valleys, temperatures rarely rise above freezing. Snow builds up year after year. The weight of more and more snow compacts the snow at the bottom into ice. **Gravity constantly pulls a glacier downhill.** Once the layer of snow and ice is more than about 30 to 40 meters deep, the glacier begins to move.

Valley glaciers flow at a rate of a few centimeters to a few meters per day. But a valley glacier that surges, or slides quickly, can move as much as 6 kilometers in a year.

When glaciers recede, they leave behind evidence of their existence.

❶ **Observe** What was the landscape like before glaciers formed?

It had rounded hills and a V-shaped valley.

❷ **Draw Conclusions** What did the glaciers do to the area?

The mountaintop was carved out. The valley became wider.

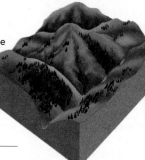

Before glaciers form   **After glaciers have melted**

Do the Quick Lab
Surging Glaciers.

📖 **Assess Your Understanding**

got it?

○ **I get it!** Now I know that glaciers differ in how they move: *Continental glaciers flow in all directions. Valley glaciers move down mountain valleys.*

○ **I need extra help with** *See TE note.*

Go to **MY SCIENCE COACH** online for help with this subject.

Digital Lesson: Assign the *Apply It* activity online and have students submit their work to you.

Glaciers

How Do Glaciers Cause Erosion and Deposition?

The movement of a glacier changes the land beneath it. Although glaciers work slowly, they are a major force of erosion. 🔑 **The two processes by which glaciers erode the land are plucking and abrasion.**

Glacial Erosion As a glacier flows over the land, it picks up rocks in a process called **plucking.** Beneath a glacier, the weight of the ice can break rocks apart. These rock fragments freeze to the bottom of the glacier. When the glacier moves, it carries the rocks with it, as shown in **Figure 2.** Plucking can move huge boulders.

Many rocks remain on the bottom of the glacier, and the glacier drags them across the land. This process, called abrasion, gouges and scratches the bedrock.

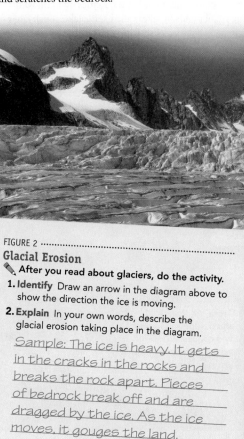

Bedrock

FIGURE 2 ·················

Glacial Erosion

✎ After you read about glaciers, do the activity.

1. **Identify** Draw an arrow in the diagram above to show the direction the ice is moving.

2. **Explain** In your own words, describe the glacial erosion taking place in the diagram.

   Sample: The ice is heavy. It gets in the cracks in the rocks and breaks the rock apart. Pieces of bedrock break off and are dragged by the ice. As the ice moves, it gouges the land.

225

Explain ──────────

Teach Key Concepts 🔑

Explain to students that glaciers cause erosion of the land over which they move. Two ways they do so is by plucking and abrasion. Plucking is the process in which rock gets picked up by a glacier. Abrasion is the scratching or bedrock by rock fragments carried in a glacier Ask: **How can pieces of rock get into the bottom of a glacier?** *(Because a glacier is so heavy, its weight can break rock below it. Once loose, the rock can freeze to the glacier's base.)* **Recall that abrasion is a kind of mechanical weathering. How does abrasion by ice change bedrock?** *(Rock pieces frozen in the glacier breaks up bedrock by carving gouges it in.)*

Make Analogies

L1 Ask students if they have heard the word *plucking* before. Students may have heard of plucking to remove hair or feathers or plucking a stringed instrument. Compare those forms of plucking to a glacier plucking. Ask: **How is plucking a guitar string like plucking a rock?** *(Sample: The string is picked up and moved, just like the rock is picked up and moved by the glacier.)*

Differentiated Instruction

L1 Summarize Glaciers To help students understand the main ideas about glaciers, have them summarize the material in this section. Allow them to choose whether they would like to prepare a verbal, written, or pictorial summary and then present it to the class.

L3 Ice Ages Tell students that during the last one billion years, Earth has had several major ice ages, periods in which continental glaciers covered large part of Earth's surface. Invite students to research Earth's ice ages and create a timeline, noting the length of each ice age and some of the animal life that characterized the time period.

Explain

Teach Key Concepts 🗝

Explain to students that glaciers not only cause erosion but deposition, too. This happens when a glacier's ice melts. The sediment that gets left behind forms landforms. Ask: **What is a landform?** *(A feature of Earth's surface)* **What are some examples of landforms formed by glacial deposition?** *(Samples: moraine, drumlin, kettle lake)*

🔄 **Relate Cause and Effect** Explain to students that relating cause and effect involves looking at two events to determine if one event caused the other. An effect happens as a result of the cause.

Support the Big Q ❓ UbD

GLACIAL EROSION AND DEPOSITION Review with students the meanings of *erosion* and *deposition*. Make sure they understand that in erosion, rock material is picked up and removed, whereas with deposition, it is dropped. Remind students that glaciers are agents of erosion and deposition, and these two processes shape the surface of the land by removing material (erosion) and adding material (deposition). Ask: **When a horn forms, does a glacier remove or add material to the land?** *(Remove)* **Does a horn form through glacial erosion or deposition?** *(Erosion)* **When a moraine forms, does a glacier remove or add material to the land?** *(Add)* **Does a moraine form through glacial erosion or deposition?** *(Deposition)* Suggest that students ask themselves similar questions as they do the activity in **Figure 3.**

Teach With Visuals

Tell students to look at **Figure 3.** Invite volunteers to read the captions for each of the glacial landforms in the figure. Ask: **How is the mountain valley shown here different from a valley made by a river?** *(A river makes a V-shaped valley; a glacier makes a U-shaped valley.)* Explain that through erosion, a glacier widens, deepens, and straightens a river-cut valley. Where there was once a narrow valley, there is now a trough, or U-shaped valley.

Make Analogies

L1 GLACIAL CONVEYOR BELT Discuss with students the way in which rock and sediment get picked up, moved, and deposited by glaciers. Ask: **How is a glacier similar to a conveyer belt?** *(Rock and sediment get added to the glacier, carried to its edge, and then dropped in place like the way materials are moved along by a conveyer belt.)*

✏️ **Relate Cause and Effect** As you read, underline the cause of glacial deposition and circle the effects.

Glacial Deposition A glacier gathers a huge amount of rock and soil as it erodes the land in its path. 🗝 When a glacier melts, it deposits the sediment it eroded from the land, creating various landforms. These landforms remain for thousands of years after the glacier has melted. The mixture of sediments that a glacier deposits directly on the surface is called **till.** Till is made up of particles of many different sizes. Clay, silt, sand, gravel, and boulders can all be found in till.

The till deposited at the edges of a glacier forms a ridge called a **moraine.** A terminal moraine is the ridge of till at the farthest point reached by a glacier. Part of Long Island in New York is a terminal moraine from the continental glaciers of the last ice age.

Retreating glaciers also create features called kettles. A **kettle** is a small depression that forms when a chunk of ice is left in glacial till. When the ice melts, the kettle remains. The continental glacier of the last ice age left behind many kettles. Kettles often fill with water, forming small ponds or lakes called kettle lakes. Such lakes are common in areas such as Wisconsin, that were once covered with ice.

FIGURE 3 ....

> **ART IN MOTION** Glacial Landforms

✏️ **After you read, complete this activity.**

1. **Classify** Identify the features of erosion and deposition in the scene below. Record your answers in the boxes provided on the next page.
2. **CHALLENGE** Identify the feature in the photo on the next page. Describe how it formed.

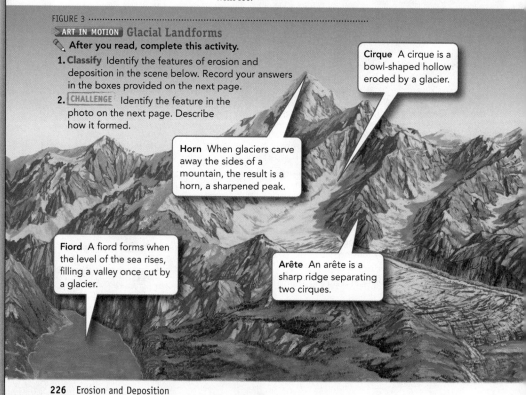

Cirque A cirque is a bowl-shaped hollow eroded by a glacier.

Horn When glaciers carve away the sides of a mountain, the result is a horn, a sharpened peak.

Arête An arête is a sharp ridge separating two cirques.

Fiord A fiord forms when the level of the sea rises, filling a valley once cut by a glacier.

226 Erosion and Deposition

Art in Motion shows a model of a glacier forming, growing, and retreating and the effects of these stages.

MY SCIENCE online.com ▸ | Glacial Landforms

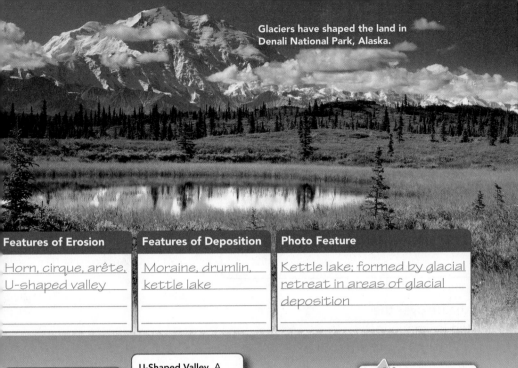

Glaciers have shaped the land in Denali National Park, Alaska.

Features of Erosion	Features of Deposition	Photo Feature
Horn, cirque, arête, U-shaped valley	Moraine, drumlin, kettle lake	Kettle lake; formed by glacial retreat in areas of glacial deposition

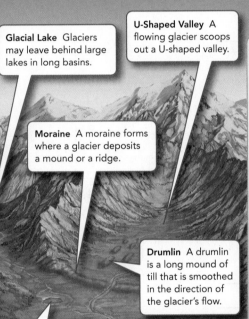

Glacial Lake Glaciers may leave behind large lakes in long basins.

U-Shaped Valley A flowing glacier scoops out a U-shaped valley.

Moraine A moraine forms where a glacier deposits a mound or a ridge.

Drumlin A drumlin is a long mound of till that is smoothed in the direction of the glacier's flow.

Kettle Lake A kettle lake forms when a depression left in till by melting ice fills with water.

 Do the Quick Lab Modeling Valleys.

Assess Your Understanding

1a. Review How do glaciers erode by abrasion?
Glaciers drag rocks as they move, scratching the bedrock.

b. Describe How does a moraine form?
It forms at the edge of a glacier where till is deposited.

got it?

○ I get it! Now I know that glaciers shape the landscape through the processes of plucking, abrasion, and deposition.

○ I need extra help with See TE note.

Go to MY SCIENCE COACH online for help with this subject.

227

Elaborate

Build Inquiry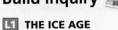

L1 THE ICE AGE

Materials map of North American during the last ice age, current map of North America, marker

Time 15 minutes

Tell students that during the last ice age, a continental glacier covered most of northern North America. Have students use the ice age map provided to redraw the ice margin on a modern map of North America.

Ask: **About how much of North America was covered by ice?** (Samples: all of Canada, about one half of North America) **Was our location covered by ice?** (Answers will vary depending on your location.) **Which present-day country was not covered by the continental glacier?** (Mexico)

21st Century Learning

CRITICAL THINKING Tell students that a valley glacier creates some different features than a continental glacier. Ask: **Why do you think they create different features?** (A continental glacier tends to smooth the landscape, whereas a valley glacier cuts a more rugged topography.)

Lab Resource: Quick Lab

L2 MODELING VALLEYS Students will use a stream table and ice cube to model erosion by valley glaciers.

Evaluate

Assess Your Understanding

After students answer the questions, have them evaluate their understanding by completing the appropriate sentence.

RTI Response to Intervention

1a. If students have trouble describing glacial erosion by abrasion, **then** suggest they think of a glacier as a frozen block of sandpaper.

b. If students need help describing moraine formation, **then** suggest they review the definitions of *till* and *moraine*.

MY SCIENCE COACH Have students go online for help in understanding glacial erosion and deposition.

Differentiated Instruction

L1 Identify Landforms Photocopy **Figure 3,** and replace each boldface term and annotation with lines for students to write on. Give each student a copy of the modified figure. Provide a list of terms, and have students fill in the blanks with the correct names.

L1 Model Glacial Landforms Have students use modeling clay to model a formerly glaciated region. Students might choose to model an alpine region or a continental region.

L3 Glacial Charades Have students write the names of glacial landforms on small strips of paper and place them in a hat or bowl. Have students take turns drawing a paper and using their hands, arms, or bodies to model or act out the landform named.

227

Lab ® **After the Inquiry Warm-Up**
zone

Glacial Erosion

Inquiry Warm-Up, *How Do Glaciers Change the Land?*

In the Inquiry Warm-Up, you investigated how glaciers wear land away by sliding sand-crusted ice over a piece of soap. Using what you learned from that activity, answer the questions below.

---

1. **DESCRIBE** Think about the direction of movement of the ice over the bar of soap. Describe the scrape marks the sand-crusted ice made in the soap.

_____

_____

2. **USE PRIOR KNOWLEDGE** In the lab, you provided the force that slid the ice over the soap. What provides the force that slides a glacier down the side of a mountain?

_____

3. **PREDICT** Suppose that after you slid the ice across the soap, you left it sitting on top of the soap overnight and it melted. Describe how you think the soap would look the next day.

_____

_____

4. **INFER** Based on your answer to question 3, what do you think the land under a glacier would look like after the glacier has melted?

_____

_____

Name _____ Date _____ Class _____

Glacial Erosion

How do Glaciers Form and Move?

got_{it?}···

○ **I get it!** Now I know that glaciers differ in how they move: _____

_____

_____

○ **I need extra help with** _____

_____

How do Glaciers Cause Erosion and Deposition?

1a. REVIEW How do glaciers erode by abrasion? _____

_____

b. DESCRIBE How does a moraine form? _____

_____

got_{it?}···

○ **I get it!** Now I know that glaciers shape the landscape through the processes of _____

_____

○ **I need extra help with** _____

_____

Key Concept Summaries

Glacial Erosion

How Do Glaciers Form and Move?

Geologists define a **glacier** as any large mass of ice that moves slowly over land. **There are two kinds of glaciers—continental glaciers and valley glaciers. A continental glacier** is a glacier that covers much of a continent or large island. **Continental glaciers can flow in all directions as they move.** Many times in the past, continental glaciers have covered large parts of Earth's surface. These times are known as **ice ages.**

A **valley glacier** is a long, narrow glacier that forms when snow and ice build up high in a mountain valley. **The sides of mountains keep these glaciers from spreading out in all directions. Instead, they usually move down valleys that have already been cut by rivers.**

Glaciers can form only in an area where more snow falls than melts. Gravity constantly pulls a glacier downhill.

How Do Glaciers Cause Erosion and Deposition?

The movement of a glacier changes the land beneath it. **The two processes by which glaciers erode the land are plucking and abrasion.** As a glacier flows over the land, it picks up rocks in a process called **plucking.** Many rocks remain on the bottom of the glacier, and the glacier drags them across the land. This process, called abrasion, gouges and scratches the bedrock.

When a glacier melts, it deposits the sediment it eroded from the land, creating landforms. The mixture of sediments that a glacier deposits directly on the surface is called **till.** Till is made up of clay, silt, sand, gravel, and boulders. The till deposited at the edges of a glacier forms a ridge called a **moraine.** A terminal moraine is the ridge of till at the farthest point reached by a glacier. A **kettle** is a small depression that forms when a chunk of ice is left in glacial till and later melts. If the kettle gets filled with water, a kettle lake forms. Other features of glacial erosion or deposition include horns, arêtes, cirques, U-shaped valleys, and drumlins.

On a separate sheet of paper, summarize how glaciers change Earth's surface.

Review and Reinforce

Glacial Erosion

Understanding Main Ideas
Answer the following questions on a separate sheet of paper.

1. What are the two kinds of glaciers, and how are they different?

2. How do glaciers form?

3. How do glaciers move?

4. By what processes do glaciers erode the land?

5. When do glaciers deposit sediment?

Complete the table by writing *erosion* or *deposition* for each landform.

	Glacial Landform	Result of Erosion or Deposition?
6.	Moraine	
7.	Horn	
8.	Cirque	
9.	Kettle	
10.	U-shaped valley	
11.	Arête	
12.	Drumlin	

Building Vocabulary
Fill in the blank to complete each statement.

13. A glacier picks up rocks through a process called _____.

14. Times when continental glaciers cover large parts of Earth's surface are called _____.

15. A(n) _____ is any large mass of ice that moves slowly over land.

16. The sediments deposited by a glacier are called _____.

Enrich

Glacial Erosion

The authors of your textbook sent out forms to glaciers around the world, asking the glaciers for basic information about themselves. Read the form sent back by Ms. Mendenhall Glacier. Then use a separate sheet of paper to answer the questions that follow.

Profile of a Glacier

Name Mendenhall Glacier   **Date** April 1, 2010

Place of Birth In the mountains of Juneau, Alaska

Current Residence Generally the same as place of birth, though I am retreating a little each year. My precise location is 59° N 134° W.

Date of Birth I really can't remember my date of birth, but it's likely that I was born thousands or even millions of years ago.

Type of Glacier I am definitely a valley glacier, and I'm proud of it.

Size I'm only about 100 square kilometers. That's not particularly large for a glacier, but I'm good looking. I take a great picture, especially from above.

Neighbors I have many glacier neighbors in the area. There are several right around me. But the neighbors I really love are to the west, over in Glacier Bay National Park. There, 12 glaciers have their terminuses, or ends, in Glacier Bay. In fact, those glaciers often "calve" into the bay. Calving occurs when part of the glacier breaks off and falls into a bay or any body of water. I do some calving myself into Mendenhall Lake. By the way, the largest glacier in North America is not too far away, though I'm not sure he's really a neighbor. That's Malaspina Glacier, which covers about 5,000 square kilometers to the north of Glacier Bay National Park.

Friends Thousands of human friends visit me each year. Most come from Juneau, the capital of Alaska. It's only 21 kilometers up the road from Juneau to my visitor center. If you don't have a car, you can always take a bus.

1. Where is Mendenhall Glacier?
2. What type of glacier is it, and how big is it?
3. If you visit Glacier Bay National Park, what glaciers would you see?
4. What is the largest glacier in North America, and how large is it?
5. What does it mean when a glacier calves?

Name _____ Date _____ Class _____

Glacial Erosion

Write the letter of the correct answer on the line at the left.

1. ___ What makes up till?

   A clay only

   B sand only

   C silt and sand only

   D clay, silt, sand, gravel, and boulders

2. ___ Which landform is formed by glacial deposition?

   A moraine

   B cirque

   C horn

   D arête

3. ___ A glacier begins to move when the snow and ice build to which thickness?

   A 10 to 20 meters

   B 20 to 30 meters

   C 30 to 40 meters

   D 100 to 200 meters

4. ___ By which process does a glacier pick up rocks?

   A abrasion

   B plucking

   C melting

   D deposition

If the statement is true, write *true*. If the statement is false, change the underlined word or words to make the statement true.

5. _____ A <u>continental</u> glacier flows in all directions.

6. _____ Glaciers gouge and scratch bedrock through the process of <u>abrasion</u>.

7. _____ A small depression called a <u>kettle</u> forms when a chunk of ice is left in glacial till.

8. _____ During the ice ages, <u>valley</u> glaciers covered large parts of Earth's surface.

9. _____ A glacier is any large mass of ice that moves <u>quickly</u> over land.

10. _____ A glacier deposits sediment when it <u>freezes</u>.

Glacial Erosion

Answer Key

After the Inquiry Warm-Up

1. The sand made long scrape marks in the soap, parallel to the motion of the ice.

2. gravity

3. The scraped and gouged soap would be covered with the sand left behind by the ice.

4. The scraped and gouged land would be covered with sand, dust, rocks, and boulders left behind when the glacier melted.

Key Concept Summaries

Glaciers erode the land by plucking, or picking up rocks, and abrasion, or scratching bedrock. When they melt, glaciers deposit the sediment they eroded, creating landforms.

Review and Reinforce

1. A valley glacier is a long, narrow glacier that forms when snow and ice build up high in a mountain valley. A continental glacier is a glacier that covers much of a continent or large island.

2. Glaciers form only in areas where more snow falls than melts. Snow builds up, and a glacier's weight compacts the snow, forming ice that then begins to move downhill.

3. When the depth of a glacier reaches about 30 to 40 meters, the glacier begins to move downhill because of gravity. Continental glaciers flow in all directions.

4. Glaciers erode the land by plucking and abrasion.

5. When glaciers melt, they deposit sediment.

6. Deposition

7. Erosion

8. Erosion

9. Deposition

10. Erosion

11. Erosion

12. Deposition

13. plucking

14. ice ages

15. glacier

16. till

Enrich

1. in the mountains north of Juneau, Alaska, at 59° N 134° W

2. It is a valley glacier of 100 square kilometers.

3. You can see 12 glaciers with their terminuses in Glacier Bay. You might also see those glaciers calve into the bay.

4. Malaspina Glacier; about 5,000 square kilometers

5. part of the glacier breaks off and falls into a body of water

Lesson Quiz

1. D
2. A
3. C
4. B
5. true
6. true
7. true
8. continental
9. slowly
10. melts

Place the outside corner, the corner away from the dotted line, in the corner of your copy machine to copy onto letter-size paper.

Wave Erosion

 What processes shape the surface of the land?

Lesson Pacing: 1–2 periods or $\frac{1}{2}$–1 block

🕐 **SHORT ON TIME?** To do this lesson in approximately half the time, do the Activate Prior Knowledge activity followed by a discussion of the Key Concepts to familiarize students with the lesson content. Have students do the Quick Lab. The rest of the lesson can be completed by students independently.

Preference Navigator, in the online Planning tools, allows you to customize *Interactive Science* to your own teaching style. You can also edit lesson plans by selecting the Lesson Planner option.

Digital Teacher's Edition allows you to access your Teacher's Edition and Resource materials online.

my science online .com

Lesson Vocabulary

- headland
- beach
- longshore drift
- spit

 ## Content Refresher

Coastlines One difference between rocky coastlines and sandy coastlines is the amount of sediment available. A beach forms where sediment is abundant. The sand often originates far from the beach. Much of the sand on North Carolina's Cape Hatteras, for example, originally came from the Hudson River, Long Island, and southern New England.

Many coastlines around the world include headlands, some of which are very famous. Examples of well-known headlands include the Cape of Good Hope, Gibraltar, Land's End, Cape Henry, Cape Cod, Cabo San Lucas, and Cape Horn. As waves approach an irregular shore, they become refracted, concentrating their energy on either side of headlands. As they crash into both sides of a headland, they erode the land. At the same time waves spread out in neighboring bays. As their energy becomes dispersed, they deposit sediment along the bay shoreline. The net effect of this simultaneous headland erosion and bay deposition is the straightening of irregular coastlines.

LESSON OBJECTIVE

🔖 Describe how ocean waves cause erosion and deposition.

Blended Path
Active learning using Student Edition, Inquiry Path, and Digital Path

ENGAGE AND EXPLORE

Teach this lesson using a variety of resources. Begin by reading **My Planet Diary** as a class. Have students share their experiences with rough water and waves. Then have students do the **Inquiry Warm-Up activity.** Students will use a hand lens to observe beach sand and see what it is made up of. The **After the Inquiry Warm-Up worksheet** sets up a discussion about the origins of beach sand. Have volunteers share their answers to question 4 as to whether sand is a cause or an effect of erosion.

EXPLAIN AND ELABORATE

Teach Key Concepts by explaining how ocean waves cause erosion by breaking down rock and picking up and moving sediment. Continue to **Teach Key Concepts** by explaining that ocean waves change coastlines through deposition, forming beaches, sandbars, barrier beaches, and spits. **Lead a Discussion** about the process of longshore drift. Have students practice the inquiry skill in the **Apply It activity.**

Hand out the **Key Concept Summaries** as a review of each part of the lesson. Students can also use the online **Vocab Flash Cards** to review key terms.

EVALUATE

Have students take the **Lesson Quiz.** For an alternate assessment, see the **EXAM**VIEW® Assessment Suite, Progress Monitoring Assessments, or SuccessTracker™.

E L L Support

1 Content and Language

Pronounce and define aloud vocabulary terms for students. Suggest that they create a personal glossary or add to one, with each term and its definition on one side of an index card and in the student's primary language on the other side.

DIFFERENTIATED INSTRUCTION KEY
L1 Struggling Students or Special Needs
L2 On-Level Students **L3** Advanced Students

LESSON PLANNER 7.4

Lab zone Inquiry Path
Hands-on learning in the Lab zone

ENGAGE AND EXPLORE

To teach this lesson with an emphasis on inquiry, begin with the **Inquiry Warm-Up activity.** Students will use a hand lens to observe beach sand and see what it is made up of. The **After the Inquiry Warm-Up worksheet** sets up a discussion about the origins of beach sand. Have volunteers share their answers to question 4 as to whether sand is a cause or an effect of erosion.

EXPLAIN AND ELABORATE

Focus on the **Inquiry Skill** for the lesson. Remind students that when they communicate with a partner, they should take turns expressing their ideas and listening to their partner's ideas. How well could partners communicate in the **Inquiry Warm-Up Activity?** *(Sample: I listened to my partner's ideas about sand being a cause of erosion and then explained why I thought sand was both a cause and an effect of erosion.)* Do the **Teacher Demo** to model wave refraction. Help students identify the sea cave and sea arch in **Figure 2** before assigning the **Apply It activity.** Have students share their conclusions. Have students do the **Quick Lab** exploring the relationship between wave impact and erosion along a shoreline. Students can use the online **Vocab Flash Cards** to review key terms.

EVALUATE

Have students take the **Lesson Quiz.** For an alternate assessment, see the **EXAM**VIEW® Assessment Suite, Progress Monitoring Assessments, or SuccessTracker™.

Digital Path
Online learning at **my science online.com**

ENGAGE AND EXPLORE

Teach this lesson using digital resources. Begin by having students learn more about wave erosion and deposition at **My Planet Diary** online. Have them access the Chapter Resources to find the **Unlock the Big Question activity.** There they can answer the questions and refine their responses as they continue through the lesson. You can re-assign the activity and have students submit their work so you can track their progress.

EXPLAIN AND ELABORATE

Students reading above, at, or below the lexile measure of this lesson can access basic content readings at their level at **My Reading Web.** Encourage students to use the online **Vocab Flash Cards** to preview key terms. Use the **Interactive Art activity** online to allow students to see models of moving water and the effects on landforms via erosion and deposition. Assign the **Apply It activity** online and have students submit their work to you. Have students do the **Quick Lab** exploring the relationship between wave impact and erosion along a shoreline. The **Key Concept Summaries** online allow students to read a summary and see an image associated with each part of the lesson. Online remediation is available at **My Science Coach.**

EVALUATE

Have students take the **Lesson Quiz.** For an alternate assessment, see the **EXAM**VIEW® Assessment Suite, Progress Monitoring Assessments, or SuccessTracker™.

2 Frontload the Lesson
Preview the lesson title and heads with students. Ask them to use this information to predict what they will learn about in the lesson.

3 Comprehensible Input
Have students use a graphic organizer to list the land features formed by wave erosion.

4 Language Production
Pair or group students with varied language abilities to complete labs collaboratively for language practice. Have each student copy the completed written lab for personal reference.

5 Assess Understanding
Have students keep a content area log. Use a two-column format with the headings "What I Understand" and "What I Don't Understand." Follow up so that students can move items from the "Don't Understand" to the "Understand" column.

Lexile Measure = 920L

Wave Erosion

Establish Learning Objective

After this lesson, students will be able to:

 Describe how ocean waves cause erosion and deposition.

Engage

Activate Prior Knowledge

MY PLANET DIARY Read *Lila's Blog* with the class. Have students share their experiences with rough water and waves. Ask: **How do you think waves affect beaches?** *(Accept all reasonable responses. Students who have visited the same beach over a number of years may be aware of erosion due to wave action.)*

BIG IDEAS OF SCIENCE REFERENCE LIBRARY Have students look up the following topic: Sea Stacks.

Explore

Lab Resource: Inquiry Warm-Up

L1 **WHAT IS SAND MADE OF?** Students will use a hand lens to observe beach sand and see what it's made up of.

LESSON

4 Wave Erosion

UNLOCK THE BIG **?**

🔑 **How Do Waves Cause Erosion and Deposition?**

MY PLANET DIARY

BLOG

Posted by: Lila
Location: Camden, Maine

I was returning home from an island picnic on our 24-foot motor boat, when the wind whipped up. The water in the bay became rough. The waves were splashing up the sides of the boat. Even though my dad slowed down, our boat slammed into wave after wave. My head hit the ceiling of the cabin, as I got bounced each time the boat hit a wave. Anything not strapped down slipped toward the back of the boat. It was scary!

After you read about Lila's trip, answer the question.

How did the waves affect Lila's boat ride?

The boat bounced.
Things slipped to the
back of the boat.

▷ **PLANET DIARY** Go to **Planet Diary** to learn more about wave erosion and deposition.

Lab zone Do the Inquiry Warm-Up *What Is Sand Made Of?*

How Do Waves Cause Erosion and Deposition?

The energy in waves comes from the wind. When the wind makes contact with the water some of its energy transfers to the water, forming waves. As a wave approaches land the water becomes shallower. The friction between the wave and the bottom causes the wave to slow down, and the water moves forward as the wave breaks. This forward-moving water provides the force that shapes the land along the shoreline.

228 Erosion and Deposition

SUPPORT ALL READERS

Lexile Measure = 920L   Lexile Word Count = 853

Prior Exposure to Content: May be the first time students have encountered this topic

Academic Vocabulary: *communicate, summarize*

Science Vocabulary: *headland, beach, longshore drift, spit*

Concept Level: Generally appropriate for most students in this grade

Preteach With: My Planet Diary "Lila's Blog" and Figure 2 activity

Go to **My Reading Web** to access leveled readings that provide a foundation for the content.

my science online.com

Vocabulary
- headland
- longshore drift
- beach
- spit

Skills
- Reading: Summarize
- Inquiry: Communicate

Erosion by Waves 🔊 **Waves shape the coast through erosion by breaking down rock and moving sand and other sediment.** One way waves erode the land is by impact. Large waves can hit rocks along the shore with great force. This energy in waves can break apart rocks. Over time, waves can make small cracks larger. Eventually, the waves cause pieces of rock to break off. Waves also erode by abrasion. As a wave approaches shallow water, it picks up sediment, including sand and gravel. This sediment is carried forward by the wave. When the wave hits land, the sediment wears away rock like sandpaper wearing away wood.

Waves coming to shore gradually change direction. The change in direction occurs as different parts of a wave begin to drag on the bottom. The waves in **Figure 1** change direction as they approach the shore. The energy of these waves is concentrated on headlands. A **headland** is a part of the shore that sticks out into the ocean. It is made of harder rock that resists erosion by the waves. But, over time, waves erode the headlands and even out the shoreline.

✏️ **Summarize** Read the text about wave erosion and explain how a wave erodes by abrasion.

<u>The wave picks up</u>
<u>and moves sediment</u>
<u>toward shore. When</u>
<u>the wave breaks, the</u>
<u>sediment scrapes</u>
<u>the shore.</u>

FIGURE 1 ....
Wave Erosion
✏️ **Identify** Shade in the arrows that indicate where the greatest energy of the waves is concentrated.

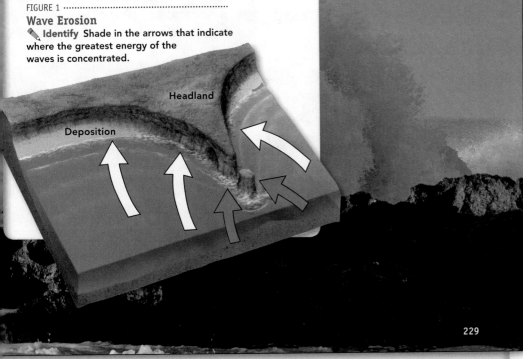

Headland

Deposition

229

Explain

Introduce Vocabulary
Explain to students that scientific terms often have multiple meanings. Students are aware of the word spit used as a *verb*. In science, a spit is a small beach that extends out into the water.

Teach Key Concepts 🔑
Explain to students that like the water in rivers and the ice in glaciers, ocean water causes erosion. Waves break down rock. They also pick up and move sediment. The effect of this erosion is the shaping of coasts. Ask: **What is the name of the process that breaks down rocks?** *(Weathering)* **What are two ways in which waves cause rocks to break down?** *(By impact and abrasion)* **How are these two processes different?** *(Weathering by impact occurs due to the great force of the ocean water itself, whereas weathering by abrasion happens due to the grinding of sediment carried by ocean water.)* Remind students that wind has a great deal of energy and waves are caused by wind. Relate the energy passed on to waves by wind to the ability of waves to cause erosion.

🔊 **Summarize** Tell students that when they summarize material, they restate the main ideas, but do not include all details or supporting evidence.

Make Analogies
L1 **WAVE ABRASION** Remind students that abrasion is a kind of weathering by wind, water, or ice. Ask: **How are waves like sandpaper?** *(Waves, like sandpaper, carry bits of rocks. When these rock particles rub against a surface, they wear down that surface.)*

My Planet Diary provides an opportunity for students to explore real-world connections to wave erosion and deposition.

my science online.com ▸ Wave Erosion

LESSON 7.4

(E)(L)(L) Support

1 Content and Language
Write the term headland on the board and underline each word that makes up this compound word. Have students explain how the two words combine to describe this physical feature.

2 Frontload the Lesson
Ask volunteers who have visited sea cliffs or other structures caused by wave erosion to describe what they saw. Have volunteers try to explain how the water is able to create these features.

3 Comprehensible Input
Have students look through magazines or go online to find examples of the land features created by wave erosion. Students can create a poster that displays the different examples along with captions that explain how each feature forms.

Explain

Teach Key Concepts 🔑

Explain to students that erosion is not the only process by which waves change coastlines. They also do so through deposition. Landforms that form through wave deposition include beaches, sandbars, barrier beaches, and spits. Ask: **What happens to a wave to cause it to drop the sediment it carries?** *(The wave slows down.)* **How is this similar to deposition that occurs on a river delta?** *(In both cases, deposition results from moving water slowing down and dropping its sediment.)* **What kind of sediment is usually deposited on beaches?** *(Sand, and in some cases coral and shell fragments)* **What landform forms when a beach sand builds up and projects out into the water like a finger?** *(A spit)*

Lead a Discussion

WAVE DEPOSITION AND LONGSHORE DRIFT Ask: **What might cause waves to approach a beach at an angle?** Explain that wind causes waves to come from a particular direction and waves drag on the bottom as they approach the shore. Then have students describe the way waves lap up on a beach. Encourage students to mention the thin wash of water that moves up and then back down the beach. Ask: **After waves lap up onto the beach, what causes the water to move back into the ocean?** *(Gravity)* **In which direction does gravity pull the water?** *(Straight down the slope of the beach)* **If a sand grain were moving along with this water, what path would it have?** *(A zigzag path along the beach)* Tell students that they have just explained longshore drift.

21st Century Learning

COMMUNICATION Have students read *Sea Stacks* in the **Big Ideas of Science Reference Library** and create a poster or multimedia presentation showing what they learned. Students should use at least six images, each labeled with the name the sea stack is known by and its location, plus a map showing the locations of all the sea stacks they included. Do they see a pattern in where these landforms occur?

Landforms Created by Wave Erosion Think of an ax striking the trunk of a tree. The cut gets bigger and deeper with each strike of the blade. Finally the tree falls. In a similar way, ocean waves that hit a steep, rocky coast erode the base of the land there. Where the rock is softer, the waves erode the land faster. Over time the waves may erode a hollow area in the rock called a sea cave. Eventually, waves may erode the base of a cliff so much that the rock above collapses. The result is a wave-cut cliff. A sea arch is another feature of wave erosion that forms when waves erode a layer of softer rock that underlies a layer of harder rock. If an arch collapses, a pillar of rock called a sea stack may result.

Deposits by Waves Deposition occurs when waves slow down, causing the water to drop its sediment. 🔑 **Waves shape a coast when they deposit sediment, forming coastal features such as beaches, sandbars, barrier beaches, and spits.**

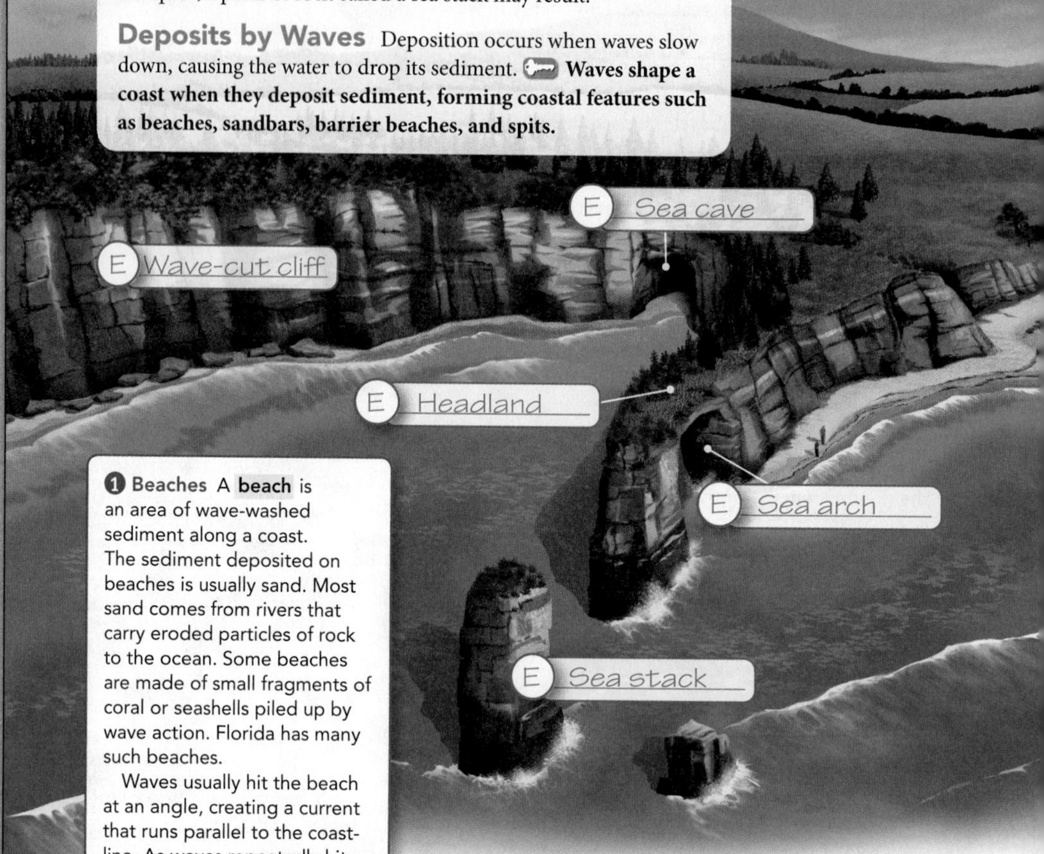

E Sea cave

E Wave-cut cliff

E Headland

E Sea arch

❶ Beaches A **beach** is an area of wave-washed sediment along a coast. The sediment deposited on beaches is usually sand. Most sand comes from rivers that carry eroded particles of rock to the ocean. Some beaches are made of small fragments of coral or seashells piled up by wave action. Florida has many such beaches.

Waves usually hit the beach at an angle, creating a current that runs parallel to the coastline. As waves repeatedly hit the beach, some of the beach sediment moves down the beach with the current, in a process called **longshore drift**.

E Sea stack

FIGURE 2 ·······

 INTERACTIVE ART **The Changing Coast**

✏ **Apply Concepts** Use what you've learned about features of wave erosion and deposition to complete the activity.

1. Identify the landforms above. Label them in the spaces on the art.
2. Write an *E* or a *D* in each circle to indicate whether the landform was shaped by erosion or deposition.

230 Erosion and Deposition

Interactive Art models moving waves and the effects of erosion and deposition on landforms.

Digital Lesson: Assign the *Apply It* activity online and have students submit their work to you.

my science online.com | **Wave Erosion**

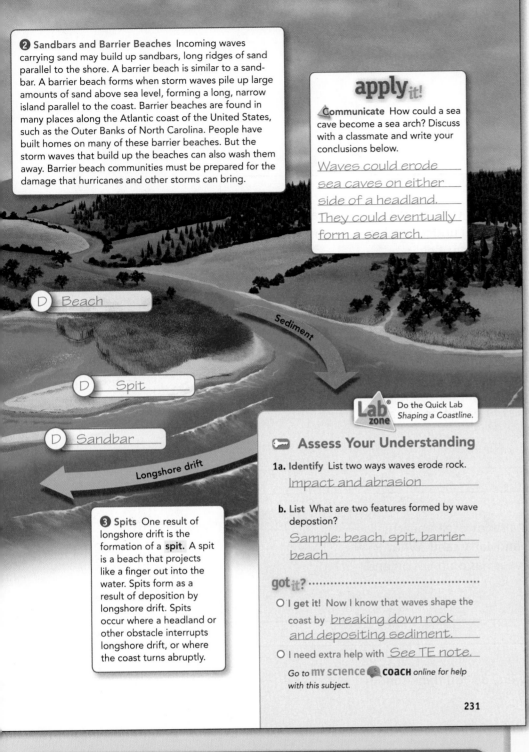

②Sandbars and Barrier Beaches Incoming waves carrying sand may build up sandbars, long ridges of sand parallel to the shore. A barrier beach is similar to a sandbar. A barrier beach forms when storm waves pile up large amounts of sand above sea level, forming a long, narrow island parallel to the coast. Barrier beaches are found in many places along the Atlantic coast of the United States, such as the Outer Banks of North Carolina. People have built homes on many of these barrier beaches. But the storm waves that build up the beaches can also wash them away. Barrier beach communities must be prepared for the damage that hurricanes and other storms can bring.

apply it!

Communicate How could a sea cave become a sea arch? Discuss with a classmate and write your conclusions below.

Waves could erode sea caves on either side of a headland. They could eventually form a sea arch.

D Beach

Sediment

D Spit

D Sandbar

Longshore drift

③Spits One result of longshore drift is the formation of a **spit.** A spit is a beach that projects like a finger out into the water. Spits form as a result of deposition by longshore drift. Spits occur where a headland or other obstacle interrupts longshore drift, or where the coast turns abruptly.

Lab zone® Do the Quick Lab *Shaping a Coastline.*

🔑 Assess Your Understanding

1a. Identify List two ways waves erode rock.

Impact and abrasion

b. List What are two features formed by wave deposition?

Sample: beach, spit, barrier beach

got it?

O **I get it!** Now I know that waves shape the coast by breaking down rock and depositing sediment.

O **I need extra help with** See TE note.

Go to **MY SCIENCE ⑤ COACH** online for help with this subject.

231

Differentiated Instruction

L3 Investigate Beach Erosion Many coastal communities that experience severe beach erosion during storms are using modern technology to rebuild and protect their beaches from continued erosion. Invite students to find out about this technology and report their findings to the class.

L1 Classify Landforms Have students divide a piece of posterboard into several sections and title each section with the name of one coastline feature. Students can collect photographs of each landform and display them in the appropriate sections. Have students include labels and a short caption with each photograph.

Elaborate

Teacher Demo

L2 MODEL WAVE REFRACTION

Materials chain of students, gymnasium

Time 15 minutes

Remind students that wave energy is concentrated along rocky headlands. Then have a group of at least 15 students join hands and stand side-by-side. Instruct them to start walking forward at the same rate. Now tell students in the middle of the chain that they are approaching a headland and will have to walk more slowly. Tell the students on the ends to continue walking at the faster rate. Make sure that students continue to hold hands.

Ask: **What happened to the ends of the chain when the middle slowed down?** *(The ends curved toward the headland)* **Why is more wave energy concentrated on headlands?** *(Just as more people walked into the headlands, more wave energy is directed onto headlands.)*

Apply It!

L1 Help students identify the sea cave and sea arch in **Figure 2** before beginning the activity.

Communicate Remind students that when they communicate with a partner, they should take turns expressing their ideas and listening to their partner's idea.

Lab Resource: Quick Lab

L1 SHAPING A COASTLINE Students will explore the relationship between wave impact and erosion along a shoreline.

Evaluate

Assess Your Understanding

After students answer the questions, have them evaluate their understanding by completing the appropriate sentence.

RTI Response to Intervention

1a. If students need help identifying two ways waves erode rock, **then** lead a class discussion about what happens when waves hit land.

b. If students have trouble identifying features formed by wave deposition, **then** help them review the Key Concept statement about deposition.

MY SCIENCE ⑤ COACH Have students go online for help in understanding wave erosion and deposition.

Lab **zone** **After the Inquiry Warm-Up**

Wave Erosion

Inquiry Warm-Up, *What Is Sand Made Of?*

In the Inquiry Warm-Up, you investigated the different characteristics of two samples of beach sand and posed questions that might help you understand their origins. Using what you learned from that activity, answer the questions below.

1. **INFER** If the sand is the result of erosion, what should both sand samples be made of?

   _____

   _____

2. **INFER** If sand accumulates on beaches because of deposition, what do you think carries it there?

   _____

   _____

3. **USE PRIOR KNOWLEDGE** If you've ever been to a sandy ocean beach, you know that waves near the shore pick up and carry sand. What effect do you think the sand carried in the waves has on rocks on and near the beach?

   _____

   _____

4. **RELATE CAUSE AND EFFECT** Based on your answers, do you think sand is a cause or an effect of erosion? Explain.

   _____

   _____

Assess Your Understanding

Wave Erosion

How Do Waves Cause Erosion and Deposition?

1a. IDENTIFY List two ways waves erode rock. _____
_____

b. LIST What are two features formed by wave deposition? _____
_____

got it? ···

○ **I get it!** Now I know that waves shape the coast by _____
_____

○ **I need extra help with** _____
_____

Name _____ Date _____ Class _____

Wave Erosion

How Do Waves Cause Erosion and Deposition?

Waves contain energy and are formed by winds. **Waves shape the coast through erosion by breaking down rock and moving sand and other sediment.** One way waves erode is by impact. Waves also erode by abrasion. Waves coming to shore gradually change direction. The change occurs as different parts of a wave begin to drag on the bottom. The energy of these waves is concentrated on headlands. A **headland** is a part of the shore that sticks out into the ocean. It is made of harder rock that resists erosion by waves. But over time, waves erode the headlands and even-out the shoreline.

Ocean waves that hit a steep, rocky coast erode the base of the land there. Where the rock is softer, the waves erode the land faster. Over time the waves may erode a hollow area in the rock called a sea cave. Eventually, waves may erode the base of a cliff so much that the rock above collapses. The result is a wave-cut cliff. A sea arch is another feature of wave erosion that forms when waves erode a layer of soft rock that underlies a layer of harder rock. If an arch collapses, a pillar of rock called a sea stack may remain.

Waves shape a coast when they deposit sediment, forming coastal features such as beaches, sandbars, barrier beaches, and spits. A **beach** is an area of wave-washed sediment along a coast. The sediment deposited on beaches is usually sand. Most sand comes from rivers that carry eroded particles of rock to the ocean.

As waves repeatedly hit the beach at an angle, some of the beach sediment moves down the beach with the current, in a process called **longshore drift.** One result of longshore drift is a **spit,** a beach that projects like a finger out into the water. Incoming waves carrying sand may build up sandbars, long ridges of sand parallel to the shore. A barrier beach is similar to a sandbar, but forms when storm waves pile sand up above sea level forming a long, narrow island parallel to the coast.

On a separate sheet of paper, summarize how waves shape the coast.

Name _____ Date _____ Class _____

Review and Reinforce

Wave Erosion

Understanding Main Ideas
On a separate sheet of paper, identify each numbered landform in the diagram below and describe how it formed.

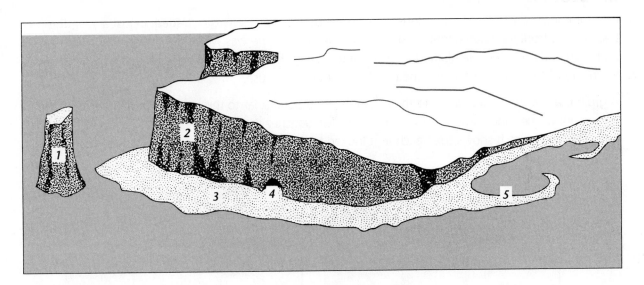

Answer the following questions on a separate sheet of paper.

6. What are two ways in which waves erode the land?

7. Explain how waves eventually even out a shoreline.

8. What are four features formed by wave erosion?

Building Vocabulary
Fill in the blank to complete each statement.

9. The process by which beach sediment moves down the beach with the current is called _____.

10. An area of wave-washed sediment along a coast is a(n) _____.

11. A(n) _____ is a beach that projects like a finger out into the water.

12. A(n) _____ is a part of the shore that sticks out into the ocean.

Enrich

Wave Erosion

> Read the passage and study the two sketches below. Then use a separate sheet of paper to answer the questions that follow.

My Beach Is Shrinking!

Last summer, Juan Sanchez sent a letter to his local city council. He was outraged. In just a year, the beach in his front yard had begun to shrink. Mr. Sanchez said he was worried that soon he would have no beach and no home. He blamed the council for giving the go-ahead to construction of a groin at the boundary of the public beach and the beach in front of his house.

A groin is a low wall extending into the ocean, built perpendicular to the shore. A groin interrupts the movement of the sand carried by longshore drift. Mr. Sanchez included the sketches below to prove his point. The first sketch shows the beach as it looked two summers ago. The second shows what it looked like last summer.

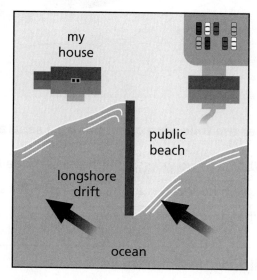

1. How has the groin changed the public beach?
2. How has the groin changed the beach in front of Mr. Sanchez's house?
3. Why did those changes occur?
4. Does Mr. Sanchez have good reason to fear loss of his beach and home?
5. What would happen if the groin were removed?
6. In your opinion, should the groin be removed? Give reasons for your answer.

Lesson Quiz

Wave Erosion

If the statement is true, write *true*. If the statement is false, change the underlined word or words to make the statement true.

1. _____ Sometimes, when a sea arch collapses, a sea <u>cave</u> remains.

2. _____ Where coastal rock is softer, waves erode the land <u>faster</u>.

3. _____ When waves <u>speed up</u>, wave deposition occurs.

4. _____ Waves erode the land by abrasion and <u>deposition</u>.

5. _____ In the process called <u>longshore drift</u>, beach sediment gets moved down a beach with the current.

6. _____ Waves change direction as they approach shore because they begin to <u>drag</u>.

Write the letter of the correct answer on the line at the left.

7. ___ As waves approach the shore and change direction, on which landform is most of their energy concentrated?

   A headlands

   B beaches

   C sandbars

   D sea caves

8. ___ Which process occurs when waves carrying sediment wear away rocks along a coast?

   A deposition

   B abrasion

   C impact

   D chemical weathering

9. ___ Which landform is a long, narrow island parallel to the coast?

   A sandbar

   B headland

   C barrier beach

   D spit

10. ___ Which is a coastal feature formed by wave erosion?

   A sandbar

   B spit

   C beach

   D sea arch

Wave Erosion

Answer Key

After the Inquiry Warm-Up

1. Both sand samples should be made of tiny particles of rock.

2. Sand is carried to the beach by ocean currents and waves.

3. When waves hit the shore, the sand in the water erodes rocks on or near the beach

4. Sand is both an effect of erosion and a cause of it. Sand is created when rock erodes. But sand in ocean waves (as well as in wind) also causes erosion of rocks.

Key Concept Summary

Waves shape the coast through erosion by breaking down rock through impact and abrasion and moving sand and other sediment. They also deposit sediment, forming coastal features such as beaches, sandbars, barrier beaches, and spits.

Review and Reinforce

1. A sea stack forms when a sea arch collapses.

2. A wave-cut cliff forms when waves erode the base of a cliff so much that the rock above collapses.

3. A beach forms when waves deposit sediment along a coast.

4. A sea cave forms when waves erode a hollow area in the rock along a coast.

5. A spit forms as a result of deposition at points where a headland or another obstacle interrupts the longshore drift.

6. Waves erode land by impact and by abrasion.

7. Waves eventually even out a shoreline as their energy becomes concentrated on headlands.

8. beaches, sandbars, barrier beaches, and spits

9. longshore drift   10. beach

11. spit   12. headland

Enrich

1. The groin has increased the area of the public beach as sediment has been deposited along the side of the groin facing the longshore current.

2. The groin has prevented sediment from being deposited on Mr. Sanchez's beach, so the beach there has shrunk.

3. The groin prevented longshore drift from moving sediment down the beach toward Mr. Sanchez's section.

4. He does have a good reason for his fears because if the process continues, both the beach in front of his house and the house itself may be in the ocean.

5. The beach would return to its original shape because of longshore drift.

6. Answers may vary. Some students may assert Mr. Sanchez's right to retain his beach. Other students may suggest that the public beach should take priority over Mr. Sanchez's rights.

Lesson Quiz

1. stack   2. true

3. slow down   4. impact

5. true   6. true

7. A   8. B

9. C   10. D

Place the outside corner, the corner away from the dotted line, in the corner of your copy machine to copy onto letter-size paper.

Wind Erosion

 What processes shape the surface of the land?

Lesson Pacing: 1–2 periods or $\frac{1}{2}$–1 block

🕐 **SHORT ON TIME?** To do this lesson in approximately half the time, do the Activate Prior Knowledge activity followed by a discussion of the Key Concepts to familiarize students with the lesson content. Have students do the **Quick Lab.** The rest of the lesson can be completed by students independently.

Preference Navigator, in the online Planning tools, allows you to customize *Interactive Science* to your own teaching style. You can also edit lesson plans by selecting the Lesson Planner option.

Digital Teacher's Edition allows you to access your Teacher's Edition and Resource materials online.

Lesson Vocabulary
- deflation
- sand dune
- loess

Content Refresher

Loess Loess is made up mostly of silt-sized particles and has the texture of flour or talcum powder. It often forms a thick blanket of sediment, in some places tens of meters thick, spread over hundreds of square kilometers. Loess forms the surface deposit in the Midwest, Great Plains and northwestern United States, central and northern China, Europe, Argentina, and New Zealand.

There are two major sources of the wind-deposited silt and clay that form loess: deserts and the flood plains of glacial streams. The loess of the U.S. Midwest formed as a result of deflation at the end of the last ice age. Many meltwater streams flowed away from the glaciers. High winds blew silt and clay from the flood plains of these streams and deposited it on higher ground.

Loess blown great distances from desert regions blankets large regions of China. The vast Loess Plateau is a highland area in north central China. Its loess deposits are the thickest in the world. Here the sequence of alternating loess deposits and soil represent a span of 2.6 million years.

LESSON OBJECTIVE

🔑 Explain how wind cause erosion and deposition.

Blended Path
Active learning using Student Edition, Inquiry Path, and Digital Path

ENGAGE AND EXPLORE

Teach this lesson using a variety of resources. Begin by reading **My Planet Diary** as a class. Have students to tell what they already know about sand dunes. Then have students do the **Inquiry Warm-Up activity.** Students will simulate wind erosion. The **After the Inquiry Warm-Up worksheet** sets up a discussion about how moving air effects sediment. Have volunteers share their answers to question 4 about the factors that determine how moving air affects sediments.

EXPLAIN AND ELABORATE

Support the Big Q by leading a discussion about how wind erosion affects Earth's surface, explaining that deflation is the main process by which wind erosion occurs. **Teach Key Concepts** by explaining that the results of wind erosion and deposition include landforms called dunes and deposits called loess. Have students practice the inquiry skill in the **Apply It activity.**

Hand out the **Key Concept Summaries** as a review of each part of the lesson. Students can also use the online **Vocab Flash Cards** to review key terms.

EVALUATE

Have students take the **Lesson Quiz.** For an alternate assessment, see the **EXAM**VIEW® Assessment Suite, Progress Monitoring Assessments, or SuccessTracker™.

ELL Support

1 Content and Language
Write simple sentences using the terms *deflation, sand dune,* and *loess.* Read the sentences aloud, prompting students to repeat after you. Then have students write their own sentences using each term.

Lab zone Inquiry Path
Hands-on learning in the Lab zone

Digital Path
Online learning at MY SCIENCE ONLINE.com

ENGAGE AND EXPLORE

To teach this lesson with an emphasis on inquiry, begin with the **Inquiry Warm-Up activity.** Students will simulate wind erosion. The **After the Inquiry Warm-Up worksheet** sets up a discussion about how moving air effects sediment. Have volunteers share their answers to question 4 about the factors that determine how moving air affects sediments.

EXPLAIN AND ELABORATE

Focus on the **Inquiry Skill** for the lesson. Remind students that when they predict, they use what they already know to make an inference about what might happen. How could prior knowledge about kernels of corn be used to make a prediction in the **Inquiry Warm-Up Activity?** *(Sample: I knew that kernels of corn were heavier than cornmeal, so I didn't think they could be moved very far by the air from the straw.)* **Support the Big Q** by leading a discussion about how wind erosion affects Earth's surface, explaining that deflation is the main process by which wind erosion occurs. Review the effect plant roots can have on dune erosion before assigning the **Apply It activity.** Have students share their ideas about how to hold sand dunes in place. Have students do the **Quick Lab** and share their models of the formation of desert pavement. Students can use the online **Vocab Flash Cards** to review key terms.

EVALUATE

Have students take the **Lesson Quiz.** For an alternate assessment, see the **EXAM**VIEW® Assessment Suite, Progress Monitoring Assessments, or SuccessTracker™.

ENGAGE AND EXPLORE

Teach this lesson using digital resources. Begin by having students learn more about wind erosion and explore real-world connections to wind erosion and deposition at **My Planet Diary** online. Have them access the Chapter Resources to find the **Unlock the Big Question activity.** There they can answer the questions and refine their responses as they continue through the lesson. You can re-assign the activity and have students submit their work so you can track their progress.

EXPLAIN AND ELABORATE

Students reading above, at, or below the lexile measure of this lesson can access basic content readings at their level at **My Reading Web.** Encourage students to use the online **Vocab Flash Cards** to preview key terms. **Support the Big Q** by leading a discussion about how wind erosion affects Earth's surface, explaining that deflation is the main process by which wind erosion occurs. Assign the **Apply It activity** online and have students submit their work to you. Have students do the **Quick Lab** and share their models of the formation of desert pavement. The **Key Concept Summaries** online allow students to read a summary and see an image associated with each part of the lesson. Online remediation is available at **My Science Coach.**

EVALUATE

Have students take the **Lesson Quiz.** For an alternate assessment, see the **EXAM**VIEW® Assessment Suite, Progress Monitoring Assessments, or SuccessTracker™.

2 Frontload the Lesson
Have the students restate the objective in their own words. As they read through the lesson, ask students add information to support their restated objective.

3 Comprehensible Input
Have students outline the lesson by using the headings and subheadings. As they read, students can list the main point under each heading. Pair students with more proficient readers if needed.

4 Language Production
Pair or group students with varied language abilities to complete labs collaboratively for language practice. Have each student copy the completed written lab for personal reference.

5 Assess Understanding
Ask students to use their outlines to prepare an oral presentation of the concepts in this lesson. Encourage students to use the visuals in the lesson to support their presentations.

LESSON 7.5

Wind Erosion

Establish Learning Objective

After this lesson, students will be able to:

🔑 Explain how wind causes erosion and deposition.

Engage

Activate Prior Knowledge

MY PLANET DIARY Read *Saving the Navajo Rangelands* with the class. Encourage students who have visited a desert or have seen deserts in films to describe sand dunes they observed. Ask: **How do you think erosion of sand dunes can be reduced?** *(Accept all reasonable responses. Students might suggest blocking wind or planting drought-tolerant plants on dunes.)*

BIG IDEAS OF SCIENCE REFERENCE LIBRARY 📖
Have students look up the following topic: Dunes.

Explore

Lab Resource: Inquiry Warm-Up

L1 **HOW DOES MOVING AIR AFFECT SEDIMENT?** Students will use cornmeal in a pan and a straw to simulate wind erosion.

LESSON

5 Wind Erosion

 🔑 How Does Wind Cause Erosion and Deposition?

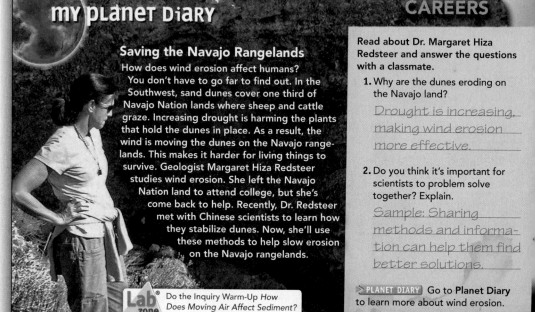

my planet diary

Saving the Navajo Rangelands

How does wind erosion affect humans? You don't have to go far to find out. In the Southwest, sand dunes cover one third of Navajo Nation lands where sheep and cattle graze. Increasing drought is harming the plants that hold the dunes in place. As a result, the wind is moving the dunes on the Navajo range-lands. This makes it harder for living things to survive. Geologist Margaret Hiza Redsteer studies wind erosion. She left the Navajo Nation land to attend college, but she's come back to help. Recently, Dr. Redsteer met with Chinese scientists to learn how they stabilize dunes. Now, she'll use these methods to help slow erosion on the Navajo rangelands.

Lab zone Do the Inquiry Warm-Up *How Does Moving Air Affect Sediment?*

CAREERS

Read about Dr. Margaret Hiza Redsteer and answer the questions with a classmate.

1. Why are the dunes eroding on the Navajo land?

   Drought is increasing, making wind erosion more effective.

2. Do you think it's important for scientists to problem solve together? Explain.

   Sample: Sharing methods and information can help them find better solutions.

▶ **PLANET DIARY** Go to **Planet Diary** to learn more about wind erosion.

How Does Wind Cause Erosion and Deposition?

Wind can be a powerful force in shaping the land in areas where there are few plants to hold the soil in place. In the east African nation of Eritrea, sandstorms like the one in the photo are common. Strong winds blowing over loose soil can reduce visibility.

232 Erosion and Deposition

SUPPORT ALL READERS

Lexile Measure = 900L   Lexile Word Count = 675

Prior Exposure to Content: May be the first time students have encountered this topic

Academic Vocabulary: *conclusion, predict, question*

Science Vocabulary: *deflation, sand dune, loess*

Concept Level: Generally appropriate for most students in this grade

Preteach With: My Planet Diary "Saving the Navajo Rangelands" and Figure 1 activity

Go to **My Reading Web** to access leveled readings that provide a foundation for the content.

my science online.com

Vocabulary
- deflation • sand dune
- loess

Skills
- Reading: Ask Questions
- Inquiry: Predict

Deflation Wind causes erosion mainly by deflation. Geologists define **deflation** as the process by which wind removes surface materials. You can see the process of deflation in **Figure 1.** When wind blows over the land, it picks up the smallest particles of sediment, such as clay and silt. The stronger the wind, the larger the particles it can pick up. Slightly heavier particles, such as sand, might skip or bounce for a short distance. But sand soon falls back to the ground. Strong winds can roll heavier sediment particles over the ground. In deserts, deflation can sometimes create an area of rock fragments called *desert pavement.* There, wind has blown away the smaller sediment, leaving behind rocky materials.

Abrasion Abrasion by wind-carried sand can polish rock, but it causes relatively little erosion. Geologists think that most desert landforms are the result of weathering and water erosion.

> ✎ **Vocabulary Word Origins**
> The Latin word *flare* means "to blow." How does *flare* relate to the word *deflation?*
>
> *It helps describe how the wind removes surface materials.*

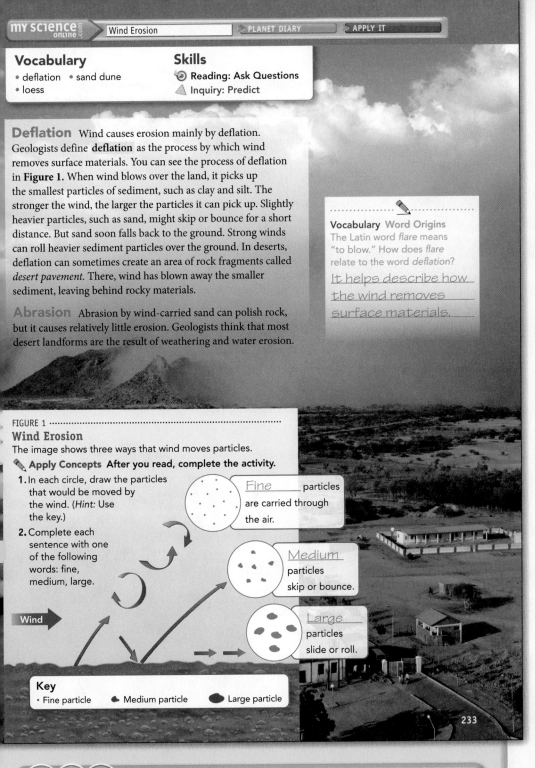

FIGURE 1 ·····················
Wind Erosion
The image shows three ways that wind moves particles.

✎ **Apply Concepts** After you read, complete the activity.

1. In each circle, draw the particles that would be moved by the wind. (*Hint:* Use the key.)
2. Complete each sentence with one of the following words: fine, medium, large.

Fine particles are carried through the air.

Medium particles skip or bounce.

Large particles slide or roll.

Wind

Key
- Fine particle ● Medium particle ⬬ Large particle

233

Explain

Introduce Vocabulary
Write the word *deflation* on the board and circle the prefix. Explain to students that the prefix *de-* means "down." Through the process of deflation, wind wears down Earth's surface.

Support the Big Q ？ UbD

WIND EROSION Lead a discussion about how wind erosion affects Earth's surface. Explain that although wind causes abrasion, just as water and ice do, deflation is the main process by which wind erosion occurs. Ask students to describe being in a sandstorm or being hit by blowing sediment. Ask: **How does sediment that is blown by the wind get into the air?** (*It is picked up from the ground at some locations.*) **Which sizes of sediment would be picked up?** (*Mostly the finer grains, such as clay and silt*) **Which size gets bounced along?** (*Mostly sand*) **Which sizes would remain on the ground?** (*Mostly the larger grains, such as gravel or pebbles*) Show students a photograph of desert pavement in Arizona or another desert region. Explain that wind has blown away the smaller sediment, leaving behind this pavement of larger rock particles too heavy to be moved. Ask: **What effect might abrasion have on the individual rock surfaces of the desert pavement?** (*Wind may polish and shape individual rocks.*)

Address Misconceptions

L1 WIND EROSION AND DESERTS Students may think that erosion by the wind only occurs in desert regions. Explain that wind erosion occurs anywhere that sediment and soil are exposed to the wind. Ask: **Why might sediment in deserts be more vulnerable to wind erosion?** (*There are few plants and little moisture to help anchor the sediment.*)

> **My Planet Diary** provides an opportunity for students to explore real-world connections to wind erosion and deposition.

my science online.com | Wind Erosion

ⓔⓛⓛ Support

1 Content and Language
Explain that the word *loess* comes from the German word *Löss,* which means "loose."

2 Frontload the Lesson
Ask students if they have ever seen a sandblaster at work. Have volunteers describe what a sandblaster is used for and how it works.

3 Comprehensible Input
Show students video of the effects of wind on the shape and size of sand dunes. After viewing, encourage students to summarize what they saw.

Explain

Teach Key Concepts 🔑

Explain to students that wind picks up and erodes sediment, and when it slows down, wind deposits sediments. The result of wind erosion and deposition includes landforms called dunes and deposits called loess. Ask: **Which size sediment makes up dunes?** *(Sand)* **How high does sand blow?** *(Not very high, since it skips and bounces)* **How does sand move around a dune?** *(It moves from one side of the dune to the other.)* **What size sediment makes up loess?** *(clay and silt)*

🔄 **Ask Questions** Tell students that asking questions before and during reading will help them focus on and remember the main ideas of the passage.

Elaborate

21st Century Learning

CRITICAL THINKING Remind students that although both are deposited by wind, loess and the sediment in dunes are made up primarily of different size particles. Ask: **Which do you think would be better soil in which to grow crops—old sand dunes or old loess deposits?** *(Loess deposits)* **Why do you think farms are abundant in the Midwestern United States?** *(Loess deposits are common there.)*

21st Century Learning

INTERPERSONAL SKILLS Have students read *Dunes* in the **Big Ideas of Science Reference Library.** Pairs should work together to write ten multiple choice quiz questions about sand dunes. Key terms to include: dune, saltation, windward side, leeward side, slip face, tail dune, climbing dune, barchan dune, seif dune, and star-shaped dune. Students should use images when appropriate.

🔄 **Ask Questions** Read the headings on this page, then write down one question you have. After you read, try to answer your question.

Sample: What is a loess deposit?

Answer: a fine, wind-deposited sediment

FIGURE 2

Dune Formation
✏️ **Draw Conclusions** Why do these dunes have different shapes?

The wind direction is different in these two areas. This affects the shape of the dune.

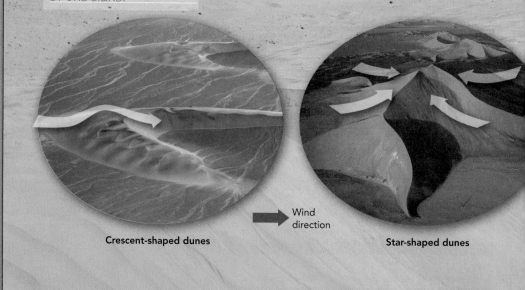

Crescent-shaped dunes

Wind direction

Star-shaped dunes

Deposits by Wind All the sediment picked up by wind eventually falls to the ground. This happens when the wind slows down or an obstacle, such as a boulder or a clump of grass, traps the windblown sand sediment. 🔑 **Wind erosion and deposition may form sand dunes and loess deposits.** When the wind meets an obstacle, the result is usually a deposit of windblown sand called a **sand dune.** The shape of sand dunes is determined by the direction of the wind, the amount of sand, and the presence of plants.

Sand Dunes You can see sand dunes on beaches and in deserts where wind-blown sediment has built up. Sand dunes come in many shapes and sizes. Some are long, with parallel ridges, while others are U-shaped. They can also be very small or very large. Some sand dunes in China are 500 meters high. Sand dunes move over time. Little by little, the sand shifts with the wind from one side of the dune to the other. Sometimes plants begin growing on a dune. Plant roots can help to anchor the dune in one place.

Loess Deposits Sediment that is smaller than sand, such as particles of clay and silt, is dropped far from its source in large deposits. This fine, wind-deposited sediment is **loess** (LOH es). There are large loess deposits in central China and in states such as Nebraska, South Dakota, Iowa, Missouri, and Illinois. Loess helps to form fertile soil. Many areas with thick loess deposits are valuable farmlands.

234 Erosion and Deposition

Digital Lesson: Assign the *Apply It* activity online and have students submit their work to you.

my science ʊɴʟɪɴᴇ.ᴄᴏᴍ ▶ | **Wind Erosion**

apply it!

Look at the photos and answer the questions with a classmate.

1 *Predict* Which dune do you think is likely to erode faster? Why?

I think Dune A would erode faster.
There is no vegetation holding the
sand in place. When it's windy, the
sand is more likely to be carried
away.

2 Why do you think plants grew on Dune B?

There might have been less wind
and more precipitation.

3 How could sand dunes be held in place to prevent them from drifting onto a parking lot?

A sand fence could be built,
or native vegetation could be
planted.

Dune A

Dune B

Do the Quick Lab
Desert Pavement.

Assess Your Understanding

1a. Review What is deflation?

The process of wind removing
surface materials.

b. Relate Cause and Effect What causes wind to deposit sand or other sediment?

Wind deposits sediment when
it slows or meets an obstacle.

c. [CHALLENGE] In a desert, a soil mixture of sand and small rocks is exposed to wind erosion. How would the land surface change over time?

Wind would carry away more
sand than rock. Larger sedi-
ments would remain, creating
an area of desert pavement.

got it? ....

○ I get it! Now I know that wind causes erosion through *deflation and abrasion.*

○ I need extra help with *See TE note.*

Go to **my science COACH** *online for help with this subject.*

235

Apply It!

L1 Review with the class the effect plant roots can have on dune erosion before beginning the activity.

△ **Predict** Remind students that when they predict, they use what they already know to make an inference about what might happen. Then ask students to observe and describe the two dunes pictured, in order to help them identify what they already know.

Lab Resource: Quick Lab

L1 **DESERT PAVEMENT** Students will use coins and flour in a pan to model the formation of desert pavement.

Evaluate

Assess Your Understanding

After students answer the questions, have them evaluate their understanding by completing the appropriate sentence.

RTI Response to Intervention

1a. If students have trouble describing deflation, **then** have them look for and reread the sentence that contains that boldface term.

b. If students need help with the cause of wind deposition, **then** help them review how deposition by wind or even water takes place.

c. If students need help making a prediction about wind erosion, **then** suggest they review how desert pavement forms.

my science COACH Have students go online for help in understanding wind erosion and deposition.

Differentiated Instruction

L1 **Sediment Sizes** Explain that geologists describe sediment primarily as clay, silt, sand, and gravel. These categories represent sediment particles, called grains, of different sizes, from smallest (clay) to largest (gravel). The smaller the particle, the lighter it is and the easier it is for the wind to pick up and carry. Large and heavy particles like gravel only get pushed along the ground surface, whereas small and light particles like clay and silt get picked up and carried long distances.

L3 **Wind Erosion Skit** Have students form a group to write and act out a short skit about wind erosion and deposition. Different students can play sediments grains of different sizes.

Lab zone **After the Inquiry Warm-Up**

Wind Erosion

Inquiry Warm-Up, *How Does Moving Air Affect Sediment?*

In the Inquiry Warm-Up, you investigated how moving air affects sediment by observing the effect of air blown over cornmeal. Using what you learned from that activity, answer the questions below.

1. **PREDICT** Suppose you replaced the cornmeal with kernels of corn and then repeated the lab, blowing through the straw just as gently. How do you think the results would compare?

   _____

   _____

2. **DEVELOP HYPOTHESES** Based on your answer to question 1, what is one factor that determines how moving air affects sediment? Explain your response.

   _____

   _____

   _____

   _____

3. **PREDICT** Suppose you thoroughly sprayed the cornmeal with water and then repeated the lab, blowing through the straw just as gently. How do you think the results would compare?

   _____

   _____

4. **DEVELOP HYPOTHESES** Based on your answer to question 3, what is another factor that determines how moving air affects sediment? Explain your response.

   _____

   _____

   _____

   _____

Name _____ Date _____ Class _____

Wind Erosion

How Does Wind Cause Erosion and Deposition?

1a. REVIEW What is deflation? _____

_____

b. RELATE CAUSE AND EFFECT What causes wind to deposit sand or other

sediment? _____

_____

c. CHALLENGE In a desert, a soil mixture of sand and small rocks

is exposed to wind erosion. How would the land surface change

over time? _____

_____

_____

gotit?··

○ **I get it!** Now I know that wind causes erosion through _____

_____

○ **I need extra help with** _____

_____

Name _____ Date _____ Class _____

Key Concept Summary

Wind Erosion

How Does Wind Cause Erosion and Deposition?

Wind can be a powerful force in shaping the land in areas where there are few plants to hold the soil in place. Wind causes erosion mainly by deflation. Geologists define **deflation** as the process by which wind removes surface materials. When wind blows over the land, it picks up the smallest particles of sediment, such as clay and silt. The stronger the wind, the larger the particles that it can pick up. Slightly heavier particles, such as sand, might skip or bounce for a short distance. But sand soon falls back to the ground. Strong winds can roll heavier sediment particles over the ground. In deserts, deflation can sometimes create an area of rock fragments called *desert pavement*. There, wind has blown away the smaller sediment, leaving behind rocky material.

Abrasion by wind-carried sand can polish rock, but it causes relatively little erosion. Geologists think that most desert landforms are the result of weathering and water erosion.

Wind deposition happens when the wind slows down or meets an obstacle, such as a boulder or clump of grass, that traps the windblown sediment. **Wind erosion and deposition may form sand dunes and loess deposits.**

When the wind meets an obstacle, the result is usually a deposit of windblown sand called a **sand dune.** Sand dunes occur on beaches and in deserts where wind-blown sediment has built up. Sand dunes come in many shapes and sizes. Sometimes plants begin growing on a dune. Plant roots can help to anchor the dune in one place.

Sediment that is smaller than sand, such as particles of clay and silt, is dropped far from its source in large deposits. This fine, wind-deposited sediment is **loess.** Loess helps to form fertile soil. Many areas with thick loess deposits are valuable farmlands.

On a separate sheet of paper, summarize how wind changes Earth's surface.

Place the outside corner, the corner away from the dotted line, in the corner of your copy machine to copy onto letter-size paper.

COPYRIGHT © BY PEARSON EDUCATION INC., OR ITS AFFILIATES. ALL RIGHTS RESERVED.

235C

Review and Reinforce

Wind Erosion

Understanding Main Ideas
Answer the following questions in the spaces provided.

1. Describe the process by which wind causes erosion.

   _____

   _____

2. Describe how wind moves different sizes of sediment.

   _____

   _____

   _____

   _____

3. How does a sand dune form?

   _____

   _____

4. How are the sediments in loess deposits different from the sediments in a sand dune?

   _____

   _____

Building Vocabulary
Fill in the blank to complete each statement.

5. The process by which wind removes surface materials is _____.

6. Fine sediment deposited by wind is _____.

7. A deposit of windblown sand is called a(n) _____

   _____.

Wind Erosion

There are five main kinds of sand dunes. Read the passage and study the diagrams below. Then use a separate sheet of paper to answer the questions that follow.

Kinds of Sand Dunes

A sand dune is a sand dune is a sand dune. Right? Not really. The type of dune that forms depends mainly on the wind direction and the amount of sand available.

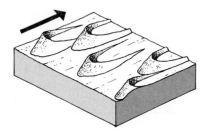 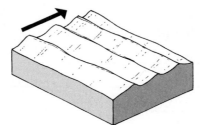 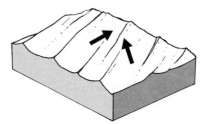

Barchan dunes form when the wind direction stays the same and the supply of sand is limited. They are often found as a single dune.

Transverse dunes form when the wind direction stays the same and the supply of sand is large.

Longitudinal dunes form when the wind blows in two slightly different directions and the supply of sand is limited.

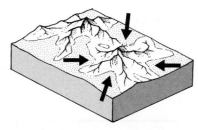 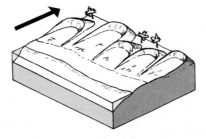

Star dunes form when the wind blows in three or more different directions. Star dunes are often found as a single dune.

Parabolic dunes form along coasts and point away from the wind blowing in off the water. Vegetation often covers parts of a parabolic dune.

1. If the wind is constant and there is a great amount of sand, what kind of sand dune forms?
2. If the amount of sand is limited and the wind generally blows from the same direction, what kind of sand dunes can be formed?
3. Describe the conditions in which star dunes form.
4. In a desert area where the wind shifts to a slightly different direction, what kind of sand dunes would result?
5. Which kinds of sand dunes are you most likely to see as single dunes?
6. Which kinds of sand dunes would you expect to see at the sea shore?

Lesson Quiz

Wind Erosion

Write the letter of the correct answer on the line at the left.

1. ___ What is desert pavement?

   A   wind-blown clay

   B   wind-blown clay and silt

   C   an area of rock fragments exposed by wind

   D   an area of sand deposits exposed by wind

2. ___ What happens when wind slows down or meets an obstacle?

   A   erosion

   B   chemical weathering

   C   deposition

   D   mechanical weathering

3. ___ What makes up loess?

   A   clay only

   B   clay and silt

   C   sand only

   D   clay, silt, sand, and gravel

4. ___ Which size particles does the wind usually skip and bounce for short distances?

   A   sand

   B   boulders

   C   clay and silt

   D   clay

If the statement is true, write *true*. If the statement is false, change the underlined word or words to make the statement true.

5. _____ When wind blows over the land, it picks up the smallest particles of sediment.

6. _____ Loess helps to form fertile soil.

7. _____ Abrasion by wind-carried sand causes much erosion.

8. _____ Plant roots do help to anchor sand dunes in one place.

9. _____ The shape of a sand dune is determined by the speed of the wind.

10. _____ The weaker the wind, the larger the particles that it can pick up.

Wind Erosion

Answer Key

After the Inquiry Warm-Up

1. The kernels of corn would shift very little, if at all.

2. The size or mass of the sediment particles; A gentle breeze moved a lot of cornmeal but had no effect on kernels of corn, so it appears to be harder for moving air to move larger or more massive sediment particles.

3. The cornmeal would stay in place.

4. Whether the sediment is dry or wet; A gentle breeze moved a lot of dry cornmeal but had no effect on wet cornmeal, so it appears to be harder for moving air to move sediment when it is wet.

Key Concept Summaries

Wind causes erosion mainly by deflation. Wind also causes deposition when it slows down or meets an obstacle, forming sand dunes and loess deposits.

Review and Reinforce

1. Wind causes erosion mainly by deflation, the process by which wind removes surface materials.

2. Wind picks up and moves through the air the smallest particles of sediment, such as clay and silt. Slightly heavier particles, such as sand, get skipped or bounced for a short distance. Larger particles slide or roll along the ground.

3. When the wind meets an obstacle, it deposits the sand it has been carrying. The result is a sand dune.

4. The sediments in loess deposits are clay and silt, which are finer than the sand grains in a sand dune.

5. deflation
6. loess
7. sand dune

Enrich

1. transverse dunes
2. barchan dunes
3. Star dunes form when the wind blows in three or more directions.
4. longitudinal dunes
5. barchan dunes and star dunes
6. parabolic dunes

Lesson Quiz

1. C
2. C
3. B
4. A
5. true
6. true
7. little
8. true
9. direction
10. stronger

Place the outside corner, the corner away from the dotted line, in the corner of your copy machine to copy onto letter-size paper.

Study Guide

Review the Big Q UbD

Have students complete the statement at the top of the page. This Key Concept supports their understanding of the chapter's Big Question. Have students return to the chapter opener question. What is different about how students view the image of Antelope Canyon now that they have completed the chapter? Thinking about this will help them prepare for the *Apply the Big Q* activity in the Review and Assessment.

Partner Review

Have partners review definitions of vocabulary terms by using the Study Guide to quiz each other. Students could read the Key Concept statements and leave out words for their partner to fill in, or change a statement so that it is false and then ask their partner to correct it.

Pair Activity: Concept Map

Help pairs of students develop one way to show how the information in this chapter is related. Remind them that agents of erosion and deposition wear down and build up landforms on Earth's surface. Provide each group with poster paper, markers, and index cards. Have students brainstorm to identify the key concepts, key terms, details, and examples, and write each one on an index card. Use the questions below to help students add to and organize the information on the cards into a concept map they draw on the poster board. Prompt students to use connecting word or phrases, such as "causes," "erodes by," and "forms features that include," to indicate the basis for the organization of the map. Explain that the phrases should form a sentence between or among a set of concepts.

- What processes wear down and build up Earth's surface?
- What are the different types of mass movement?
- How does moving water cause erosion?
- What land features are formed by water erosion and deposition?

My Science Coach allows students to complete the *Practice Test* online.

The Big Question allows students to complete the *Apply the Big Q* activity about the processes that break down rock.

Vocab Flash Cards offer a way to review the chapter vocabulary words.

my science
online.com ▸ Erosion and Deposition

CHAPTER
7 Study Guide

REVIEW THE BIG ?

The surface of the land is shaped by the processes of erosion and deposition caused by gravity, <u>water</u>, <u>wind</u>, glaciers, and <u>waves</u>.

LESSON 1 Mass Movement

🔑 Weathering, erosion, and deposition act together in a cycle that wears down and builds up Earth's surface.

🔑 The different types of mass movement include landslides, mudflows, slumps, and creep.

Vocabulary
- erosion • sediment • deposition
- gravity • mass movement

LESSON 2 Water Erosion

🔑 Moving water is the major agent of erosion that has shaped Earth's land surface. Ground-water erodes through chemical weathering.

🔑 Through erosion, a river forms valleys, waterfalls, flood plains, meanders, and oxbow lakes. Deposition forms alluvial fans and deltas.

Vocabulary
- runoff • rill • gully • stream • tributary
- flood plain • meander • oxbow lake
- delta • alluvial fan • groundwater
- stalactite • stalagmite • karst topography

LESSON 3 Glacial Erosion

🔑 Glaciers can form only in an area where more snow falls than melts.

🔑 Continental glaciers can flow in all directions as they move.

🔑 Gravity constantly pulls a glacier downhill.

🔑 Glaciers erode the land through plucking and abrasion. When a glacier melts, it deposits the sediment it eroded from the land.

Vocabulary
- glacier • continental glacier • ice age
- valley glacier • plucking • till • moraine • kettle

LESSON 4 Wave Erosion

🔑 Waves shape the coast through erosion by breaking down rock and moving sand and other sediment.

🔑 Waves shape a coast when they deposit sediment, forming coastal features such as beaches, sandbars, barrier beaches, and spits.

Vocabulary
- headland • beach
- longshore drift • spit

LESSON 5 Wind Erosion

🔑 Wind erosion and deposition may form sand dunes and loess deposits.

Vocabulary
- deflation
- sand dune
- loess

E L L Support

4 Language Production

Have students play a game "20 Questions" using the vocabulary terms and other important concepts from the chapter. Tell students they can ask you 20 questions in order to identify the vocabulary term you are thinking of. Encourage students to incorporate information from the chapter in their questions.

Beginning
LOW/HIGH Allow students to use words and short phrases as questions.

Intermediate
LOW/HIGH Allow students extra time to formulate their questions.

Advanced
LOW/HIGH Allow students to act as coaches for students with less advanced language proficiency.

Review and Assessment

LESSON 1 Mass Movement

1. What is the process by which weathered rock, sediment, and soil are moved from place to place?

a. runoff   b. delta formation
c. erosion   d. longshore drift

2. Freezing and thawing of water can cause creep, which is _a very slow downhill movement of rock and soil._

3. Compare and Contrast How are landslides and mudflows similar? How are they different?
Both are types of mass movement that occur rapidly. Landslides are mostly dry; mudflows include water.

4. Sequence Identify the steps in the erosion cycle. Explain why it has no beginning or end.
Erosion wears down land. Deposition fills up hollows. New mountains or plateaus form, which are eroded. It's continuous because the forces of erosion and deposition don't stop.

5. Relate Cause and Effect What type of mass movement is shown below? Explain.

A slump; the bottom soil was water soaked, causing it to slip.

LESSON 2 Water Erosion

6. Which feature typically contains water only during a rainstorm and right after it rains?

a. a river   b. a rill
c. a gully   d. a stream

7. Sediments are deposited in an alluvial fan because _the water carrying them has slowed down._

8. Sequence Complete the flowchart about stream formation.

Stream Formation

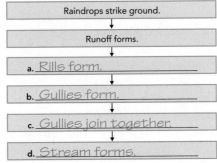

Raindrops strike ground.
↓
Runoff forms.
↓
a. _Rills form._
↓
b. _Gullies form._
↓
c. _Gullies join together._
↓
d. _Stream forms._

9. Make Judgments Your family looks at a new house right on a riverbank. Why might they hesitate to buy this house?
The house might be in the river's flood plain and could be damaged by a future flood.

10. Write About It Explain to visitors to your valley how the lake called *Oxbow Lake* formed. Use words and a drawing.
See TE rubric.

237

Review and Assessment

Assess Understanding
Have students complete the answers to the Review and Assessment questions. Have a class discussion about what students find confusing. Write Key Concepts on the board to reinforce knowledge.

RTI Response to Intervention
3. If students cannot compare and contrast mass movements, **then** have them review the paragraphs describing the different kinds of mass movement.

8. If students need help with sequencing stream formation, **then** have them reread the sentences that contain the boldface terms and review how stream formation takes place.

Alternate Assessment
L1 DESIGN A GAME Challenge student groups or pairs to design a card or board game about landforms and deposits formed by erosion and deposition. For example, they might have players draw cards and answer trivia questions. Another idea is to design a board illustrating landforms that players must identify to move forward. Remind students to make rules, spinners, game pieces, and so on for their games. Students can exchange games with or play their own game against other groups or pairs.

CHAPTER 7

Write About It Assess student's writing using this rubric.

SCORING RUBRIC	SCORE 4	SCORE 3	SCORE 2	SCORE 1
Explain how an oxbow lake forms	Describes all the processes involved.	Describes some of the processes involved.	Incorrectly describes the processes involved.	Does not describe the processes involved.
Use words and a drawing	Uses both words and a drawing correctly.	Partially uses both words and a drawing.	Uses both words and a drawing, but they are not complete.	Does not include either words or a drawing.

R T I Response to Intervention

12. If students have trouble describing glacial features, **then** have them look back at **Figure 3** to review the various features formed by glacial erosion and deposition.

16. If students cannot apply concepts about wave erosion, **then** have them review the processes by which wave erosion occurs and features that form as a result.

19. If students need help with comparing and contrasting abrasion and deflation, **then** have them locate the highlighted terms and review the definitions.

Apply the Big Q ? UbD

TRANSFER Students should be able to demonstrate understanding of erosion and deposition by answering this question. See the scoring rubric below.

Connect to the Big Idea ? UbD

BIG IDEA Earth is a continually changing planet.

Send students back to the Big Ideas of Science at the beginning of their student edition. Have them read what they wrote about changes on Earth before they started the chapter. Lead a class discussion about how their thoughts have changed. If all chapters have been completed, have students fill in the bottom section for the Big Idea.

L3 WRITING IN SCIENCE Ask students to write a news item that explains to readers how the processes of erosion and deposition reveal that Earth is a continually changing planet.

CHAPTER 7 Review and Assessment

LESSON 3 Glacial Erosion

11. What do you call a mass of rock and soil deposited directly by a glacier?

a. kettle   (b.) till

c. slump   d. loess

12. When glaciers drag attached rocks across the land, they *carve the land surface, forming valleys.*

13. Solve Problems You're in the mountains studying a valley glacier. What methods would you use to tell if it is advancing or retreating?

You could observe the land-forms in front of the glacier. If the glacier is retreating, terminal moraines and other till deposits should exist far in front of the glacier.

LESSON 4 Wave Erosion

14. What is a rocky part of the shore that sticks out in the ocean?

a. spit   b. barrier beach

c. rill   (d.) headland

15. Waves change direction as they near shore because *different parts of the waves drag on the bottom.*

16. Apply Concepts Under what conditions would you expect abrasion to cause the most erosion on a beach?

In a storm when the waves are stronger and more frequent.

17. **Write About It** You're walking on a beach and see a spit. Explain how a spit could have formed from a rocky headland.
See TE rubric.

LESSON 5 Wind Erosion

18. What do you call the erosion of sediment by wind?

a. drifting   b. deposition

c. plucking   (d.) deflation

19. Compare and Contrast How is wind deflation different from wind abrasion?

Deflation causes most wind erosion by removing surface materials. Abrasion polishes surface materials but doesn't remove much.

20. Relate Cause and Effect How does a loess deposit form?

Very fine particles are carried long distances by wind, fall to the ground, and accumulate.

APPLY THE BIG ? What processes shape the surface of the land?

21. Suppose you are a geologist traveling in a region that has limestone bedrock and plenty of rainfall. What features would you expect to find in this landscape? How do they form?

I would expect to find caves and sinkholes and other fea-tures of a region with karst topography. Caves form when groundwater containing car-bonic acid dissolves limestone, carrying it away. A sinkhole forms when the roof of a cave collapses.
See TE rubric.

Write About It Assess student's writing using this rubric.

SCORING RUBRIC	SCORE 4	SCORE 3	SCORE 2	SCORE 1
Explain how a spit forms from a rocky headland	Correctly describes all the processes involved in the formation.	Correctly describes some of the processes involved in the formation.	Incorrectly describes the processes involved in the formation.	Does not describe the processes involved in the formation.

? What processes shape the surface of the land? Assess student's response using this rubric.

SCORING RUBRIC	SCORE 4	SCORE 3	SCORE 2	SCORE 1
Identify landforms	Correctly identifies both landforms.	Correctly identifies only one landform.	Incorrectly identifies landforms.	Does not identify any landforms.
Describe how they form	Correctly describes the processes that form both landforms.	Correctly describes the processes that form only one landform.	Incorrectly describes the processes that form both landforms.	Does not describe the processes that form either landform.

Standardized Test Prep

Multiple Choice

Circle the letter of the best answer.

1. The diagram shows a meander. Where would sediment likely be eroded to help form an oxbow?

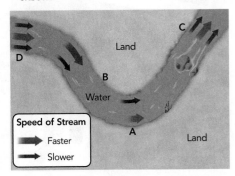

Speed of Stream
➡ Faster
→ Slower

Ⓐ at A   **B** at B
C at C   **D** at D

2. What is the slow, downhill mass movement of rock and soil caused by gravity?

Ⓐ creep   **B** a glacier
C a landslide   **D** runoff

3. What is an alluvial fan?

   A a landform created by wind deposition
   B a landform created by water erosion
   C a landform created by glacial erosion
   Ⓓ a landform created by water deposition

4. What is the name for a small depression created by the melting of a chunk of ice in glacial sediment?

   A till   Ⓑ kettle
   C moraine   **D** spit

5. What "drifts" in longshore drift?

   A a chunk of glacier   **B** a river's course
   Ⓒ beach sediment   **D** groundwater

Constructed Response

Use the diagram below and your knowledge of science to help you answer Question 6. Write your answer on a separate piece of paper.

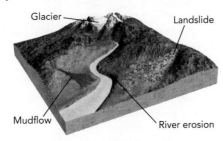

Glacier   Landslide
Mudflow   River erosion

6. Describe how gravity affects the erosion of Earth's surface in mass movement, running water, and glaciers.
See TE note.

239

Standardized Test Prep

Test-Taking Skills

INTERPRETING ILLUSTRATIONS Remind students that when they answer a question about a diagram, they must first look carefully at the picture to sort through information provided. Not all the information in the diagram may help them answer the question. They should use what they already know from the chapter or from their own lives to understand what the picture shows and rule out unnecessary information. For example, the positions of the letters in the diagram will help them identify the outer edge of the bend where erosion occurs. The key and arrows showing the speed of the stream and the position of rocks in the stream are unnecessary information and will not help them answer the question.

Constructed Response

6. During mass movement, gravity pulls rocks or sediment downhill. Running water moves downhill because of the force of gravity. As the water flows, it erodes Earth's surface. Gravity also causes glacial ice to flow. The flowing ice erodes rock and sediment from some places and deposits it in other places. This can create valleys in which rivers flow.

Additional Assessment Resources

Chapter Test
EXAMVIEW® Assessment Suite
Performance Assessment
Progress Monitoring Assessments
SuccessTracker™

Ⓔ Ⓛ Ⓛ Support

5 Assess Understanding

Have ELLs complete the Alternate Assessment. Provide guidelines on the information it must cover, and a rubric for assessment. You may wish to have them complete the activity in small groups of varying language proficiencies.

Beginning

LOW/HIGH Allow students to work on designing the game board and game pieces.

Intermediate

LOW/HIGH Allow students to write the questions and answers.

Advanced

LOW/HIGH Allow students to write the instructions for playing and scoring the game.

Remediate If students have trouble with...

QUESTION	SEE LESSON	STANDARDS
1	2	
2	1	
3	2	
4	3	
5	4	
6	1, 2, 3	

Science Matters

Science and Society

Have students read *Floodwater Fallout*. Explain that the flooding in this area was so great because many rivers flow into the Mississippi River at this point—including the Missouri River, which is the longest river in the United States. Display a map that shows the Mississippi River watershed, and point out that the states closest to the center of the watershed were affected the most by the flooding. Have students identify other rivers on the map that could have contributed to the flooding.

Explain that levees are manmade embankments, usually composed of soil, that are built up at the edges of rivers to keep the bank of the river higher than its natural banks. This allows the river to have a much larger capacity during times of extremely heavy rain. Tell students that the drawback to levees is that if the water gets past them, the damage can often be intensified. This happened in New Orleans, Louisiana in 2005 when Hurricane Katrina made landfall. Floodwaters covered 80% of the city. Other flood prevention methods include building up riverbanks with rocks that help prevent the natural banks from becoming eroded. People can also place sandbags on riverbanks as temporary levees in cases of unusually heavy rainfall or snowmelt.

As students research flood prevention on flood plains, have them note the advantages living on a flood plain provides that make people choose to live there.

Ask: **How does flooding occur?** *(Extended periods of heavy rain or unusually large amounts of melting snow create more water than a river can contain.)* **Why do governments encourage flood prevention?** *(Recovery from flood damage can be very costly.)*

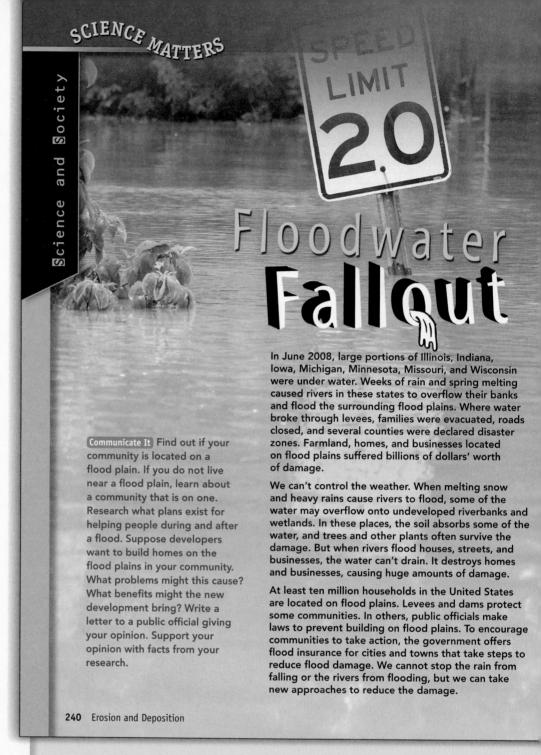

SPEED LIMIT 20

Floodwater Fallout

Communicate It Find out if your community is located on a flood plain. If you do not live near a flood plain, learn about a community that is on one. Research what plans exist for helping people during and after a flood. Suppose developers want to build homes on the flood plains in your community. What problems might this cause? What benefits might the new development bring? Write a letter to a public official giving your opinion. Support your opinion with facts from your research.

In June 2008, large portions of Illinois, Indiana, Iowa, Michigan, Minnesota, Missouri, and Wisconsin were under water. Weeks of rain and spring melting caused rivers in these states to overflow their banks and flood the surrounding flood plains. Where water broke through levees, families were evacuated, roads closed, and several counties were declared disaster zones. Farmland, homes, and businesses located on flood plains suffered billions of dollars' worth of damage.

We can't control the weather. When melting snow and heavy rains cause rivers to flood, some of the water may overflow onto undeveloped riverbanks and wetlands. In these places, the soil absorbs some of the water, and trees and other plants often survive the damage. But when rivers flood houses, streets, and businesses, the water can't drain. It destroys homes and businesses, causing huge amounts of damage.

At least ten million households in the United States are located on flood plains. Levees and dams protect some communities. In others, public officials make laws to prevent building on flood plains. To encourage communities to take action, the government offers flood insurance for cities and towns that take steps to reduce flood damage. We cannot stop the rain from falling or the rivers from flooding, but we can take new approaches to reduce the damage.

Quick Facts

Many people wonder whether there is or ever was organic life on Mars. One factor that may be able to tell us more is the presence or absence of water. In 2008, tests done in a laboratory aboard NASA's Phoenix Mars Lander identified water in a soil sample. The water was collected from frozen soil in the form of ice. A promising indicator that liquid water once flowed on Mars is the presence of calcium carbonate in Martian soil. Common on Earth, calcium carbonate is formed when carbon dioxide in the atmosphere reacts with water in soil. Calcium carbonate helps prevent the soil from becoming too acidic, which could be harmful to organic life. Have students research to find out other evidence that there was liquid water on Mars and how that may indicate whether there could have been life on Mars.

Any Way the Wind Blows

Mars is a pretty cool place. Gusts of wind blow frosty sand dunes around and cause strange streaks of sand and frost. When the Mars Rovers arrived on Mars in 2004, scientists at the National Aeronautics and Space Administration got their first chance to learn about wind and erosion on another planet. The rovers captured pictures of grains of Martian sand (called "blueberries" by the scientists) and of the patterns of dust and rock on the surface of Mars. From these pictures, scientists learned a lot about wind erosion.

By measuring these Martian blueberries and recording where they landed on the surface, scientists could estimate how strong Martian winds must be. Looking at the patterns of sand and bare rock, they could tell which directions the winds on Mars blow. Data showed that they blow from either the northwest or the southeast.

Scientists used all their measuring, counting, and other observations to design a computer model. The model can describe what happens to a planet's sandy surface when the wind starts blowing. By counting millions of blueberries on Mars, scientists are learning how to track wind erosion anywhere in the solar system!

Research It Dr. Douglas Jerolmack is a geophysicist who helped prove there is wind on Mars. Research Dr. Jerolmack's observations. Write a paragraph giving reasons why Dr. Jerolmack's scientific claims are considered to be valid (true).

▲ Scientists measured "blueberries"—grains of Martian sand and dust.

Frontiers of Technology

Have students read *Any Way the Wind Blows.* Tell students that these "blueberries" were found both on the surface and embedded in the ground. They were analyzed and found to be made of hematite, a mineral form of iron oxide. Explain that the blueberries are not actually blue, but are named for their color in images NASA released in which they had altered the color and the spherules appeared to be blue.

Tell students that similar spherules were found on the moon during the Apollo 12 and Apollo 14 missions. Those spherules were thought to have been created by a meteor impact. At first, this is how scientists thought the Martian spherules might have been created. However, spherules were found deep in the soil. This disproved the impact theory because the spherules were not consistent with debris from a meteor impact. Tell students the spherules found deeper in the soil had a shiny surface, different from the dusty appearance of the surface spherules. If possible, show students pictures of both kinds of spherules and have them compare.

As students research Dr. Jerolmack's work, have them note what kind of evidence and what kind of experiments he relied on to prove his theory.

Ask: **How did scientists learn about wind erosion on Mars?** *(They measured the blueberries and studied the sand and bare rock on the surface, from which they could tell the strength and direction of the wind on Mars.)* **How could a computer be useful in this process?** *(Scientists cannot study the surface of Mars directly but a computer can create a model of the Martian surface and use it to test theories about wind.)*

241

A Trip Through Geologic Time

Introduce the Big Q ? UbD

Have students look at the image and read the Engaging Question and description. Ask students to develop a hypothesis that explains what scientists can learn from fossils. Have student volunteers answer the question. Point out that details of many body parts of this insect are clearly visible in the photograph. Remind students that studying insects can deepen our understanding of many aspects of life on Earth. Ask: **What kinds of insects are common where you live?** *(Answers will vary. Students will likely mention common flies, ants, mosquitoes, or bees.)* **Have you ever looked carefully at an insect, either dead or alive? If so, what did you notice?** *(Students may indicate that they took special note of body parts such as wings or legs, or that they noticed the way the insect moved.)*

Untamed Science Video

RIDING THE GEO-VATER Before viewing, invite students to discuss what they know about fossils. Then play the video. Lead a class discussion and make a list of questions that this video raises. You may wish to have students view the video again after they have completed the chapter to see if their questions have been answered.

To access the online resources for this chapter, search on or navigate to *A Trip Through Geologic Time.*

Untamed Science Video shows what scientists can learn form a bug trapped in amber.

The Big Question allows students to answer the Engaging Question about what can be learned from a bug.

my science online.com ▶ A Trip Through Geologic Time

WHAT CAN YOU LEARN FROM A BUG?

? THE BIG Q

How do scientists study Earth's past?

Long ago, a fly got stuck in resin from a tree. Today, that fly is a fossil that scientists can study. It's a clue to what Earth was like on the day the fly got stuck.

Develop Hypotheses **What do you think scientists can learn from fossils like this?**

Sample: Scientists can learn what living things in the past looked like.

▶ **UNTAMED SCIENCE** Watch the **Untamed Science** video to learn more about fossils.

242 A Trip Through Geologic Time

Professional Development Note

From the Author

President Kennedy's 1962 speech at Rice University is most remembered for his bold challenge to send a man to the moon and bring him safely home to Earth, but in this remarkable speech he also painted a model of 50,000 years of human history compressed into just half a century. In this model, humans learned to construct shelters 10 years ago, learned to write and use wheels 5 years ago, and invented penicillin, television, and nuclear power only last week. It is quite humbling to think that our entire life span, and that of everyone we know—our children, parents, and grandparents—is only a heartbeat in human history.

✍ *Kathryn Thornton*

A Trip Through Geologic Time

CHAPTER 8

Chapter at a Glance

CHAPTER PACING: 11–17 periods or $5\frac{1}{2}$–$8\frac{1}{2}$ blocks

INTRODUCE THE CHAPTER: Use the Engaging Question and the opening image to get students thinking about Earth's past. Activate prior knowledge and preteach vocabulary using the Getting Started pages.

Lesson 1: Fossils

Lesson 2: The Relative Age of Rocks

Lesson 3: Radioactive Dating

Lesson 4: The Geologic Time Scale

Lesson 5: Early Earth

Lesson 6: Eras of Earth's History

ASSESSMENT OPTIONS: **EXAM**VIEW® Assessment Suite, SuccessTracker™ Online, Progress Monitoring Assessments

Preference Navigator, in the online Planning tools, allows you to customize *Interactive Science* to your own teaching style. You can also edit lesson plans by selecting the Lesson Planner option.

Digital Teacher's Edition allows you to access your Teacher's Edition and Resource online.

my science online .com | A Trip Through Geologic Time

CHAPTER 8

Differentiated Instruction

L1 **Use Visuals** Help students understand that the photograph is an extreme close-up shot of a fly suspended in amber. Explain that tree sap turns into amber as it ages. Point out that this dramatic photograph shows an insect that seems nearly perfectly preserved. Ask students how they know that the gold in the photograph is not merely a background color. *(The bubbles help the viewer understand that the gold is a colored substance rather than a color background.)*

L3 **Insect Parts** Ask students to identify any parts of the fly's body by name that they know. *(Responses might include head, thorax, abdomen, wings, legs, antenna, and so on.)*

243

CHAPTER 8 Getting Started

Getting Started

Check Your Understanding

This activity assesses students' understanding of the processes that shape Earth's surface, including the rock cycle. After students have shared their answers, explain that the theory of plate tectonics states that Earth's plates are in slow, constant motion, driven by convection currents in the mantle. Volcanoes can form at convergent boundaries along these plates, producing igneous rocks during eruptions. Over time, weathering can break rocks down into smaller pieces, or sediment, which are carried away to new locations.

Preteach Vocabulary Skills

Remind students that a prefix is a word part added to the beginning of a root word that changes the root word's meaning. Write the words *intrusion* and *extrusion* on the board. Explain that the root comes from the Latin verb *trudere*, meaning "to push or thrust." Underline the prefixes in both words and work with students to combine the meaning of each prefix with the root word to determine each term's definition.

Check Your Understanding

1. **Background** Read the paragraph below and then answer the question.

> Forces inside Earth move large pieces, or plates, of Earth's crust very slowly over long periods of time. These forces are explained by **plate tectonics.** Where these plates meet, volcanic eruptions can produce **igneous rocks.** Over time, rivers, wind, and ice can break down the rocks and carry **sediment** to new places.

The theory of **plate tectonics** states that pieces of Earth's upper layers move slowly, carried by convection currents inside Earth.

An **igneous rock** forms when melted material hardens inside Earth or on the surface.

Sediment is made up of small pieces of rock and other material.

- How do volcanic eruptions produce rocks?
  <u>Melted material flows out of the volcano and then hardens into rock.</u>

> **MY READING WEB** If you had trouble answering the question above, visit **My Reading Web** and type in *A Trip Through Geologic Time.*

Vocabulary Skill

Prefixes The root of a word is the part of the word that carries the basic meaning. A prefix is a word part placed in front of the root to change the meaning of the root or to form a new word. Look at the examples in the table below.

Prefix	Meaning	Example
in-	inside, inward	intrusion, *n.*
ex-	outside, outward	extrusion, *n.*
super-	over, above	superposition, *n.*

2. **Quick Check** The root *–trusion* means "pushing." What might *extrusion* mean? <u>Pushing out</u>

244 A Trip Through Geologic Time

My Reading Web offers leveled readings related to chapter content.

Vocab Flash Cards offer extra practice with the chapter vocabulary words.

Digital Lesson

- Assign the *Check Your Understanding* activity online and have students submit their work to you.
- Assign the *Vocabulary Skill* activity online and have students submit their work to you.

my science online.com | A Trip Through Geologic Time

fossil

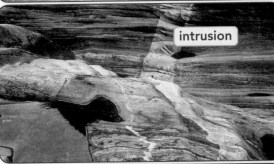
intrusion

law of superposition

vertebrate

CHAPTER 8

Chapter Preview

LESSON 1
- fossil • mold • cast
- petrified fossil • carbon film
- trace fossil • paleontologist
- evolution • extinct
- ⟳ Compare and Contrast
- △ Pose Questions

LESSON 2
- relative age • absolute age
- law of superposition • extrusion
- intrusion • fault • index fossil
- unconformity
- ⟳ Relate Text and Visuals
- △ Infer

LESSON 3
- radioactive decay • half-life
- ⟳ Identify the Main Idea
- △ Calculate

LESSON 4
- geologic time scale • era
- period
- ⟳ Summarize
- △ Make Models

LESSON 5
- comet
- ⟳ Sequence
- △ Communicate

LESSON 6
- invertebrate • vertebrate
- amphibian • reptile
- mass extinction • mammal
- ⟳ Identify Supporting Evidence
- △ Classify

> **VOCAB FLASH CARDS** For extra help with vocabulary, visit **Vocab Flash Cards** and type in *A Trip Through Geologic Time.*

245

Preview Vocabulary Terms

Have students create a three-column chart to rate their knowledge of the vocabulary terms before they read the chapter. In the first column of the chart, students should list the terms for the chapter. In the second column, students should identify whether they can define and use the word, whether they have heard or seen the word before, or whether they do not know the word. As the class progresses through the chapter, have students write definitions for each term in the last column of the chart. A list of Academic Vocabulary for each lesson can be found in the Support All Readers box at the start of the lesson.

L1 Have students look at the images on this page as you pronounce the vocabulary word. Have students repeat the word after you. Then read the definition. Use the sample sentence in italics to clarify the meaning of the term.

fossil *(FAH sul)* The preserved remains or traces of living things. *A fossil is often found embedded in rock.*

intrusion *(in TROO zhun)* A mass of igneous rock below Earth's surface. *An intrusion is always found in rock that is older than the intrusion itself.*

law of superposition *(law uv soo pur puh ZISH un)* A scientific law stating that in horizontal sedimentary rock layers, the oldest layer is at the bottom. *The law of superposition helps scientists date multiple layers of rock.*

vertebrate *(VUR tuh brit)* An animal with a backbone. *A reptile is one example of a vertebrate.*

ⒺⓁⓁ Support

Have students work in small groups to complete their charts cooperatively for the Preview Vocabulary Terms activity. Read aloud and review the vocabulary terms before students begin their charts.

Beginning
LOW Complete the chart using the vocabulary terms in the native language.

HIGH Write a definition for each known vocabulary term in the native language.

Intermediate
LOW/HIGH Discuss the definitions for known vocabulary terms in cooperative groups.

Advanced
LOW Write a sentence using each of the vocabulary terms that is already known.

Fossils

How do scientists study Earth's past?

Lesson Pacing: 2–3 periods or 1–1$\frac{1}{2}$ blocks

🕐 **SHORT ON TIME?** To do this lesson in approximately half the time, do the Activate Prior Knowledge activity followed by a discussion of the Key Concepts to familiarize students with the lesson content. Have students do the Quick Labs. The rest of the lesson can be completed by students independently.

Preference Navigator, in the online Planning tools, allows you to customize *Interactive Science* to your own teaching style. You can also edit lesson plans by selecting the Lesson Planner option.

Digital Teacher's Edition allows you to access your Teacher's Edition and Resource materials online.

my science online.com

Lesson Vocabulary

- fossil
- mold
- cast
- petrified fossil
- carbon film
- trace fossil
- paleontologist
- evolution
- extinct

Content Refresher

Burgess Shale One of the best sources of fossils from the Cambrian Explosion is the Burgess shale, an outcropping of rock in the Canadian Rockies of British Columbia. The Burgess shale contains fossils of some 120 different types of marine invertebrates. It remains the most important window on the explosion of life that marks the Cambrian Period. The fossils were discovered in 1909 by Charles Walcott, a well-respected paleontologist who at that time headed the Smithsonian Institution in Washington, D.C. Since the discovery of the Burgess shale, over 70,000 fossils have been collected from the site.

Development of the Theory of Evolution The English scientist Charles Darwin (1809–1882) explained his theory of evolution in his book *On the Origin of Species,* published in 1859. The theory has been revised since then, but it remains much as Darwin explained it. The variety and regular sequence of life forms found in the fossil record has made the theory of evolution central to an understanding of life on Earth, how it has changed over time, and how living things are related today.

LESSON OBJECTIVES

🔑 Explain how fossils form.
🔑 Identify the different kinds of fossils.
🔑 Describe what fossils tell about organisms and environments of the past.

Blended Path
Active learning using Student Edition, Inquiry Path, and Digital Path

ENGAGE AND EXPLORE

Teach this lesson using a variety of resources. Begin by reading **My Planet Diary** as a class. Have students tell what they already know about fossils. Then have students do the **Inquiry Warm-Up activity.** Students will examine, draw, and describe a rock sample. The **After the Inquiry Warm-Up worksheet** sets up a discussion about the students' investigation of a rock sample and their ideas about how its parts got into the rock. Have volunteers share their labeled drawings of rocks.

EXPLAIN AND ELABORATE

Teach Key Concepts by using **Figure 1** to explain the three basic steps in the formation of a fossil.

Continue to **Teach Key Concepts** by explaining the different kinds of fossils: molds and casts, petrified fossils, carbon films, and trace fossils. **Support the Big Q** by discussing that fossils are the remains of plants or animals and also physical evidence of the presence of organisms, such as tracks or burrows. Have students practice the inquiry skill in the **Apply It activity.**

Continue to **Teach Key Concepts** by explaining how scientists use fossils to understand organisms from the past and the environments in which they lived. **Lead a Discussion** about extinct species.

Hand out the **Key Concept Summaries** as a review of each part of the lesson. Students can also use the online **Vocab Flash Cards** to review key terms.

EVALUATE

Have students take the **Lesson Quiz.** For an alternate assessment, see the **EXAM**VIEW® Assessment Suite, Progress Monitoring Assessments, or SuccessTracker™.

ELL Support

1 Content and Language

Explain that *mold* and *cast* are words that have several meanings. Have student find the words in a dictionary and choose the definition that is most likely to fit in this lesson. As they read, have them check to see if they chose the correct definition.

DIFFERENTIATED INSTRUCTION KEY
L1 Struggling Students or Special Needs
L2 On-Level Students **L3** Advanced Students

LESSON PLANNER 8.1

Inquiry Path
Hands-on learning in the Lab zone

ENGAGE AND EXPLORE

To teach this lesson with an emphasis on inquiry, begin with the **Inquiry Warm-Up activity.** Students will examine, draw, and describe a rock sample. The **After the Inquiry Warm-Up worksheet** sets up a discussion about the students' investigation of a rock sample and their ideas about how its parts got into the rock. Have volunteers share their labeled drawings of rocks.

EXPLAIN AND ELABORATE

Focus on the **Inquiry Skill** for the lesson. Point out to students that posing questions as they read or do an activity can help them focus on important details. What questions could be asked as someone labeled their detailed drawing of a rock sample in the **Inquiry Warm-Up Activity?** *(Sample: Questions about shape, size, texture, color, and other details.)* Have students do the **Quick Lab** to explore how fossils of soft parts form.

Support the Big Q by discussing that fossils are the remains of plants or animals and also physical evidence of the presence of organisms, such as tracks or burrows. Do the **Teacher Demo** to model how petrified fossils are formed. **Build Inquiry** to allow students to model mold and cast fossils. Review the characteristics of molds and casts and look again at the images of the raised fern and the hollow fern in **Figure 2** before assigning the **Apply It activity.** Have students share their questions about the organism in the cast fossil. Have students do the **Quick Lab** to explore modeling trace fossils.

Have students do the **Quick Lab** to model fossil records and infer what they can tell about Earth's past. Students can use the online **Vocab Flash Cards** to review key terms.

EVALUATE

Have students take the **Lesson Quiz.** For an alternate assessment, see the **EXAM**VIEW® Assessment Suite, Progress Monitoring Assessments, or SuccessTracker™.

Digital Path
Online learning at **my science online**.com

ENGAGE AND EXPLORE

Teach this lesson using digital resources. Begin by having students learn more about fossils at **My Planet Diary** online. Have them access the Chapter Resources to find the **Unlock the Big Question activity.** There they can answer the questions and refine their responses as they continue through the lesson. You can re-assign the activity and have students submit their work so you can track their progress.

EXPLAIN AND ELABORATE

Students reading above, at, or below the lexile measure of this lesson can access basic content readings at their level at **My Reading Web.** Encourage students to use the online **Vocab Flash Cards** to preview key terms. Have students do the **Quick Lab** to explore to explore how fossils of soft parts form. Use the **Interactive Art activity** online to show students the process of fossil formation.

Support the Big Q by discussing that fossils are the remains of plants or animals and also physical evidence of the presence of organisms, such as tracks or burrows. Assign the **Apply It activity** online and have students submit their work to you. Have students do the **Quick Lab** to explore modeling trace fossils.

Have students do the **Quick Lab** to model fossil records and infer what they can tell about Earth's past. Use the **Interactive Art activity** online to show students how fossils and rock types found in a present-day environment provide scientists with clues and information about the environment and climate of the past. The **Key Concept Summaries** online allow students to read a summary and see an image associated with each part of the lesson. Online remediation is available at **My Science Coach.**

EVALUATE

Have students take the **Lesson Quiz.** For an alternate assessment, see the **EXAM**VIEW® Assessment Suite, Progress Monitoring Assessments, or SuccessTracker™.

2 Frontload the Lesson

Have students restate the objectives in their own words and then revise their stated objectives as the read through the lesson.

3 Comprehensible Input

Have students create drawings of how a fossil might form, using **Figure 1** as a model. Have them write captions for the drawings to explain the process in their own words.

4 Language Production

Pair or group students with varied language abilities to complete labs collaboratively for language practice. Have each student copy the completed written lab for personal reference.

5 Assess Understanding

Make true or false statements using lesson content and have students indicate if they agree or disagree with a thumbs up or thumbs down gesture to check whole-class comprehension.

LESSON 8.1

Fossils

Establish Learning Objectives

After this lesson, students will be able to:

- Explain how fossils form.
- Identify the different kinds of fossils.
- Describe what fossils tell about organisms and environments of the past.

Engage

Activate Prior Knowledge

MY PLANET DIARY Read *A Dinosaur Named Sue* with the class. Point out that the cliff made visible layers of rock that were formed over millions of years. Ask: **How do scientists know that dinosaurs lived in Earth's past?** *(Many students will mention evidence from fossils.)* **What is a fossil?** *(Sample: A fossil is an organism that has turned to rock.)* Tell students that in this lesson they will learn about different kinds of fossils and what they reveal.

BIG IDEAS OF SCIENCE REFERENCE LIBRARY Have students look up the following topics: Family Tree, Fossils.

Explore

Lab Resource: Inquiry Warm-Up

L1 **WHAT'S IN A ROCK?** Students will examine a rock sample and make detailed drawings and descriptions of any shapes they see within the rock.

LESSON

1 Fossils

- What Are Fossils?
- What Are the Kinds of Fossils?
- What Do Fossils Show?

MY PLANET DIARY

DISCOVERY

A Dinosaur Named Sue

On a hot day in August 1990, Sue Hendrickson was hunting for fossils near the town of Faith, South Dakota. She found some little pieces of bone below a cliff. When she looked up at the cliff, she saw more bones. These bones weren't little. They were enormous! She and other scientists determined that they were the bones of a *Tyrannosaurus rex*. In fact, she'd found the largest and most complete skeleton of a *Tyrannosaurus* ever discovered. Today, the skeleton, nicknamed "Sue," is on display at the Field Museum in Chicago.

Communicate Write your answer to each question below. Then discuss your answers with a partner.

1. What science skills did Sue Hendrickson use when she discovered Sue?

   Sample: Observing, inferring

2. What do you think scientists can learn by studying dinosaur skeletons?

   Sample: How the dinosaurs' bodies worked; how dinosaurs moved

   > **PLANET DIARY** Go to **Planet Diary** to learn more about fossils.

Lab zone Do the Inquiry Warm-Up *What's in a Rock?*

246 A Trip Through Geologic Time

SUPPORT ALL READERS

Lexile Measure = 900L   **Lexile Word Count = 1073**

Prior Exposure to Content: Most students have encountered this topic in earlier grades

Academic Vocabulary: *compare, contrast, question*

Science Vocabulary: *fossil, evolution, extinct*

Concept Level: Generally appropriate for most students in this grade

Preteach With: My Planet Diary "A Dinosaur Named Sue" and Figure 1 activity

Go to **My Reading Web** to access leveled readings that provide a foundation for the content.

MY SCIENCE online.com

Vocabulary
- fossil • mold • cast • petrified fossil • carbon film
- trace fossil • paleontologist • evolution • extinct

Skills
- Reading: Compare and Contrast
- Inquiry: Pose Questions

What Are Fossils?

Sue is one of the most nearly complete dinosaur fossils ever found. Fossils are the preserved remains or traces of living things. **Most fossils form when living things die and are buried by sediment. The sediment slowly hardens into rock and preserves the shapes of the organisms.** Sediment is made up of rock particles or the remains of living things. Most fossils form from animals or plants that once lived in or near quiet water such as swamps, lakes, or shallow seas where sediment builds up. In **Figure 1,** you can see how a fossil might form.

When an organism dies, its soft parts often decay quickly or are eaten by animals. That is why only hard parts of an organism generally leave fossils. These hard parts include bones, shells, teeth, seeds, and woody stems. It is rare for the soft parts of an organism to become a fossil.

FIGURE 1 ....
> INTERACTIVE ART How a Fossil Forms
A fossil may form when sediment quickly covers an organism's body.

An organism dies and sinks to the bottom of a lake.

The organism is covered by sediment.

✏ **Sequence** What happens next?
<u>The sediment becomes rock,</u>
<u>preserving the remains.</u>

 Do the Quick Lab
Sweet Fossils.

👄 Assess Your Understanding

got **it?** ....

O **I get it!** Now I know that fossils are <u>preserved remains of living things</u>
<u>that are buried by sediments.</u>

O **I need extra help with** <u>See TE note.</u>

Go to my science 🄢 COACH *online for help with this subject.*

247

ⒺⓁⓁ Support

1 Content and Language
Explain to students that word *fossil* comes from the Latin verb *fodere,* meaning "to dig." Discuss with students how the original Latin meaning relates to the English term.

2 Frontload the Lesson
Skim the headings, images, and vocabulary with students. Have them make predictions about the lesson content.

3 Comprehensible Input
To sharpen students' understanding of fossils, help them distinguish the soft and hard parts of an organism. Have students choose a common mammal that might die naturally near quiet water, such as a squirrel or bird. Then have them use a two-column chart to list the hard parts of the animal and the soft parts that would decay or be eaten.

Explain

Introduce Vocabulary
Tell students that there are various kinds of fossils. The term *fossil* refers to the preserved remains or evidence of a once-living thing.

Teach Key Concepts 🔑
Explain to students that fossils form as the result of a long process. Encourage them to think of this process as a series of basic steps. Ask: **What three actions must occur for a fossil to form?** *(An organism dies; the organism is covered by sediment; the sediment hardens into rock.)* **Why do so few dead organisms become fossils?** *(Soft body parts may decay quickly. Often, dead organisms are eaten by animals, so nothing is left to form a fossil.)*

Elaborate

Lab Resource: Quick Lab 🔬
L1 SWEET FOSSILS Students will explore how fossils of soft parts form.

Evaluate

Assess Your Understanding
Have students evaluate their understanding by completing the appropriate sentence.

ⓇⓉⒾ Response to Intervention
If students cannot define *fossils,* **then** have them look at **Figure 1** and reread the Key Concept statement aloud.

my science 🄢 COACH Have students go online for help in understanding the formation of fossils.

My Planet Diary provides an opportunity for students to explore real-world connections to fossils.

Interactive Art shows the process of fossil formation.

my science online.com | Fossils

Explain

Teach Key Concepts 🔑

Explain to students that there are several kinds of fossils found in different substances. Ask: **What is the name of the kind of fossil that turns the remains of an organism into stone?** *(Petrified fossil)* **In addition to rock, what other substances can preserve the remains of organisms?** *(Ice, tar, amber)* **What kind of fossil is a footprint?** *(A trace fossil)* **How are a mold and a cast related?** *(A mold forms around an organism buried in sediment. After the organism decays, the space left inside the mold becomes filled in and solidifies, forming a cast.)*

🔄 **Compare and Contrast** Tell students that when they compare two things, they tell how the things are alike. When they contrast two things, they tell how the things are different.

Support the Big Q ❓ UbD

DIFFERENCES AMONG FOSSILS Point out that fossils also include physical evidence, such as tracks or burrows that the organism left behind. Remind students that the formation of a fossil is the exception rather than the rule when an organism dies. Ask: **Which organisms or parts of organisms would be most likely to become fossils?** *(Organisms with hard parts such as shells and bones)* **Suppose you found a fossil of a clamshell. What can you conclude about the organism that once lived and how it became a fossil?** *(The organism may once have lived under water or near an ocean. The clamshell must have been covered with sediments, which eventually hardened.)*

Elaborate

Teacher Demo

L1 **MODEL PETRIFIED FOSSILS**

Materials pan, paper towel, white glue, paper plate, water

Time 5 minutes twice a day for 2 days

Review how a petrified fossil forms. Then mix two parts water to one part white glue. Roll a paper towel in the mixture, making sure the whole towel is moistened. Then stand the towel on end on a paper plate, and allow it to dry. The result will be a rock-hard "petrified fossil" that retains the original towel's shape.

Ask: **How did this activity model the formation of a petrified fossil?** *(The glue dissolved in water seeped into spaces in the paper towel and hardened when the water evaporated, just as minerals dissolved in water seep into cells of an organism and harden.)*

What Are the Kinds of Fossils?

🔑 **Fossils found in rock include molds and casts, petrified fossils, carbon films, and trace fossils. Other fossils form when the remains of organisms are preserved in substances such as tar, amber, or ice.** Look at examples of the kinds of fossils in **Figure 2**.

Molds and Casts The most common fossils are molds and casts. A **mold** is a hollow area in sediment in the shape of an organism or part of an organism. A mold forms when the organism is buried in sediment. Later, water may deposit minerals and sediment into a mold, forming a cast. A **cast** is a solid copy of the shape of an organism. Molds and casts can preserve fine details.

Petrified Fossils A fossil may form when the remains of an organism become petrified. The term *petrified* means "turned into stone." **Petrified fossils** are fossils in which minerals replace all of an organism, or a part, such as a dinosaur bone. This can also happen to wood, such as tree trunks. Water carrying minerals seeps into spaces in the plant's cells. Over time, the water evaporates, leaving the minerals behind.

Carbon Films Another type of fossil is a **carbon film**, an extremely thin coating of carbon on rock. When sediment buries an organism, some gases escape from the sediment, leaving carbon behind. Eventually, only a thin film of carbon remains. This process can preserve the delicate parts of plant leaves and insects.

🔄 **Compare and Contrast** How are carbon films and preserved remains different?

Sample: Carbon films preserve only a thin film of carbon. Preserved remains preserve the entire organism.

FIGURE 2 ·······

Types of Fossils
In addition to petrified fossils, fossils may be molds and casts, carbon films, trace fossils, or preserved remains.

✏️ **Classify** Identify each fossil shown here by its type.

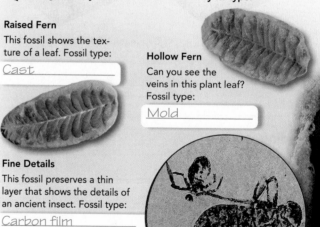

Raised Fern
This fossil shows the texture of a leaf. Fossil type:

Cast

Hollow Fern
Can you see the veins in this plant leaf? Fossil type:

Mold

Fine Details
This fossil preserves a thin layer that shows the details of an ancient insect. Fossil type:

Carbon film

Where They Walked
This footprint shows how a dinosaur walked. Fossil type:

Trace fossil

Digital Lesson: Assign the *Apply It* activity online and have students submit their work to you.

my science online.com | **Fossil Types**

apply it!

This fossil is of an ancient organism called *Archaeopteryx*. Study the photograph and then answer the questions.

1 What type of fossil is this?

Cast

2 **Pose Questions** List two questions about the organism that studying this fossil could help you answer.

Sample: How did the organism move?
Did the organism have feathers?

Trace Fossils

Trace fossils provide evidence of the activities of ancient organisms. A fossilized footprint is one example. In such a fossil, a print is buried by sediment, which slowly becomes solid rock. Trails and burrows can also become trace fossils.

Preserved Remains

Some processes can preserve entire organisms. For example, some organisms become trapped in sticky tar or tree resin. When the resin hardens, it becomes a substance called amber. Freezing can also preserve remains.

Frozen in Time
Ice preserved even the fur and skin of this woolly mammoth for thousands of years. Fossil type:

Preserved remains

From Wood to Stone
Minerals replaced other materials inside this tree, producing the colors shown here. Fossil type:

Petrified fossil

Lab zone Do the Quick Lab *Modeling Trace Fossils.*

🔑 Assess Your Understanding

1a. **Identify** A (mold/trace fossil) can form when sediment buries the hard part of an organism.

b. **Explain** A petrified fossil forms when _____ minerals _____ replace parts of a(n) _____ organism _____.

c. **Make Generalizations** What might you learn from a carbon film that you could not learn from a cast?

Sample: Fine details of the
organism's body structure

got it? ....

○ **I get it!** Now I know that the kinds of fossils are molds, casts, petrified fossils, trace fossils, carbon films, and preserved remains.

○ **I need extra help with** See TE note.

Go to **my science** **⑤ coach** *online for help with this subject.*

249

Differentiated Instruction

L1 **Compare and Contrast Types of Fossils** Help students make up a chart consisting of five columns labeled *Petrified Fossils, Molds and Casts, Carbon Films, Trace Fossils,* and *Preserved Remains.* As students read through the section, help them add details and drawings to their charts.

L3 **The La Brea Tar Pits** Encourage students to research the preserved remains discovered in the La Brea tar pits of Los Angeles. Students can prepare a brief presentation that includes visual aids.

Build Inquiry **Lab**

L1 **MODEL MOLD AND CAST FOSSILS**

Materials shell, petroleum jelly, modeling compound, plaster of Paris, water, paper cup, plastic spoon

Time 20 minutes

Review how a mold fossil and a cast fossil form. Then have students coat a shell with petroleum jelly and press the shell into modeling compound. From that impression, students can make a cast by pouring plaster of Paris into the modeling compound. (Mix 2 parts plaster of Paris with 1 part water.) Allow the plaster of Paris to harden overnight. Then students can separate the plaster from the modeling compound. Have students write a description comparing and contrasting the mold and the cast.

Ask: **Which object is the cast?** *(Plaster of Paris object)* **The mold?** *(Modeling compound)* **Which object looks more like the original shell?** *(Cast)*

Apply It!

L1 Review the characteristics of molds and casts. Look again at the images of the raised and hollow fern in **Figure 2** before beginning the activity.

🔺 **Pose Questions** Point out to students that posing questions as they read can help them focus on important details.

Lab Resource: Quick Lab **Lab**

L2 **MODELING TRACE FOSSILS** Students will explore modeling trace fossils.

Evaluate

Assess Your Understanding

After students answer the questions, have them evaluate their understanding by completing the appropriate sentence.

RTI Response to Intervention

1a. If students need help with identifying kinds of fossils, **then** have them reread the paragraphs under the red heads *Molds and Casts* and *Trace Fossils.*

1b. If students cannot explain the formation of a petrified fossil, **then** have them locate the highlighted term and reread the paragraph.

1c. If students have trouble comparing kinds of fossils, **then** have them reread the paragraph under the red head *Carbon Films.*

my science **⑤ coach** Have students go online for help in understanding kinds of fossils.

Explain

Teach Key Concepts 🔑

Explain to students that scientists use fossils to understand organisms from the past and the environments in which they lived. Ask: **What is the fossil record?** *(All of the information about past life gathered by paleontologists)* **How do scientists use the fossil record?** *(They analyze evidence in the fossil record to learn more about past environments and organisms.)*

Lead a Discussion

Students are probably familiar with the idea of extinct species, especially dinosaurs. Ask **What species can you name that have become extinct?** *(Samples: various species of dinosaur, wooly mammoths, dodo)*

Teach With Visuals

Tell students to look at **Figure 3.** Ask: **Which of the organisms shown might have turned into a petrified fossil?** *(Sequoia)* Remind students that plant parts such as tree trunks can become petrified when minerals replace some or all parts of the organism. Ask: **Which part of the crocodilian would likely form a petrified fossil?** *(Teeth or bones)* **Which of the three fossils shown do you think is a petrified fossil?** *(The bat)* **Which of these fossils looks like a carbon film?** *(The palm)*

21st Century Learning

CRITICAL THINKING Ask students to name two categories into which all of the organisms in **Figure 3** could be divided. *(Living organisms and extinct organisms)* Have students classify the organisms they can see in the illustration. Point out that some of these organisms are no longer found in Wyoming but there are living relatives of these organisms in other places. *(Living: palms, crocodilian, bat, gar, Sequoia; Extinct: Coryphodon, Hyracotherium, Uintatherium)*

What Do Fossils Show?

Would you like to hunt for fossils all over the world? And what could you learn from them? Scientists who study fossils are called **paleontologists** (pay lee un TAHL uh jists). Together, all the information that paleontologists have gathered about past life is called the fossil record. 🔑 **The fossil record provides evidence about the history of life and past environments on Earth. The fossil record also shows how different groups of organisms have changed over time.**

Fossils and Past Environments Paleontologists use fossils to build up a picture of Earth's past environments. The fossils found in an area tell whether the area was a shallow bay, an ocean bottom, or a freshwater swamp.

Fossils also provide evidence about the past climate of a region. For example, coal has been found in Antarctica. But coal forms only from the remains of plants that grow in warm, swampy regions. The presence of coal shows that the climate of Antarctica was once much warmer than it is today. **Figure 3** shows another example of how fossils show change in an environment.

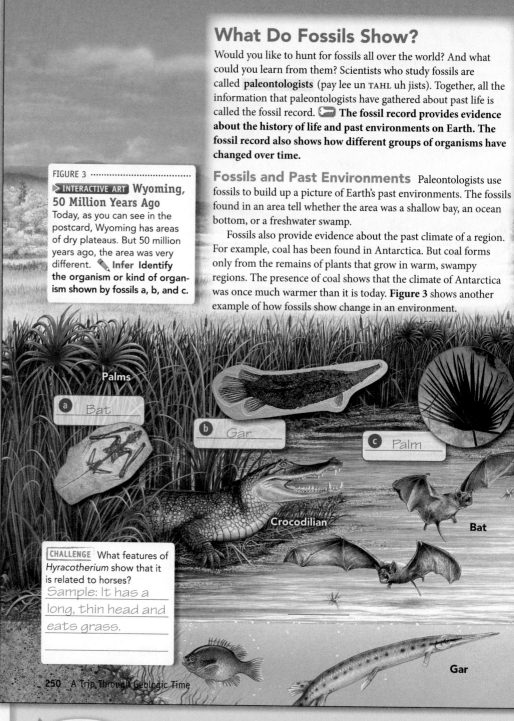

FIGURE 3 ············
▶ **INTERACTIVE ART** **Wyoming, 50 Million Years Ago**
Today, as you can see in the postcard, Wyoming has areas of dry plateaus. But 50 million years ago, the area was very different. ✎ **Infer** Identify the organism or kind of organism shown by fossils a, b, and c.

Palms

ⓐ Bat

ⓑ Gar

ⓒ Palm

Crocodilian

Bat

CHALLENGE What features of *Hyracotherium* show that it is related to horses?
Sample: It has a long, thin head and eats grass.

Gar

250 A Trip Through Geologic Time

Teacher to Teacher
Professional Development Note

Activity Using rotating stations, students can take on the role of paleontologists as they discover first-hand how scientists reconstruct what happened in the past using fossils. Interpreting a geologic timeline begins by creating a travel brochure in which students must compare and contrast events in each era. Analyzing pictures of rock layers, students begin learning how to apply the principle of superposition and how it's used in relative dating. A mock fossil dig accompanied with a fossil identification key illustrates the process scientists must go through when identifying the different types of fossils.

✉ *Emily Compton*
Park Forest Middle School
Baton Rouge, LA

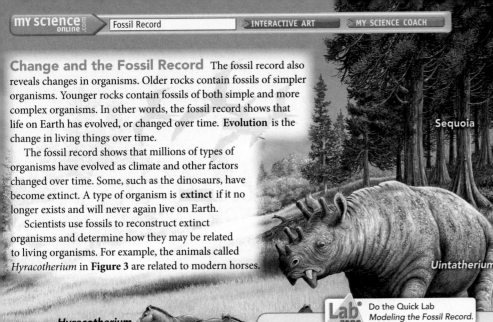
Sequoia

Uintatherium

Change and the Fossil Record
The fossil record also reveals changes in organisms. Older rocks contain fossils of simpler organisms. Younger rocks contain fossils of both simple and more complex organisms. In other words, the fossil record shows that life on Earth has evolved, or changed over time. **Evolution** is the change in living things over time.

The fossil record shows that millions of types of organisms have evolved as climate and other factors changed over time. Some, such as the dinosaurs, have become extinct. A type of organism is **extinct** if it no longer exists and will never again live on Earth.

Scientists use fossils to reconstruct extinct organisms and determine how they may be related to living organisms. For example, the animals called *Hyracotherium* in **Figure 3** are related to modern horses.

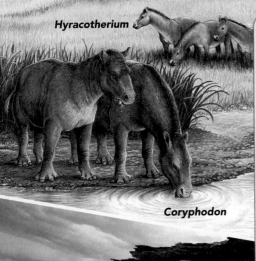
Hyracotherium

Coryphodon

Greetings FROM
WYOMING

Lab zone
Do the Quick Lab
Modeling the Fossil Record.

🔑 Assess Your Understanding

2a. Explain What does the fossil record show about how life has changed over time?
<u>Sample: Many kinds of organisms have evolved, but many have become extinct.</u>

b. Apply Concepts Give an example of a question you could ask about a fossil of an extinct organism.
<u>Sample: To what modern organisms is the extinct organism related?</u>

got it? ....

○ **I get it!** Now I know that the fossil record shows <u>how environments and organisms have changed over time.</u>

○ **I need extra help with** <u>See TE note.</u>

Go to my science **COACH** *online for help with this subject.*

251

Make Analogies
L1 GRADUAL CHANGES To help students understand the concept of evolution, compare gradual change over long periods (millions of years) with gradual change over short periods (70 or 80 years). Ask: **How do people's bodies change gradually during the course of their lifetimes?** *(People's bodies grow for about 20 years. After people reach adulthood, their bodies stop growing. However, bodies undergo other gradual changes including gaining and losing weight, gaining and losing strength and agility, and so on.)*

Elaborate

Lab Resource: Quick Lab 🔬
L2 MODELING THE FOSSIL RECORD Students will model the fossil record and make inferences about Earth's past.

Evaluate

Assess Your Understanding
After students answer the questions, have them evaluate their understanding by completing the appropriate sentence.

RTI Response to Intervention
2a. If students have trouble interpreting the fossil record, **then** have them reread the Key Concept statement.

b. If students have trouble asking a question, **then** have them review the paragraph about extinct organisms under the red head *Change and the Fossil Record.*

my science ⑤ **COACH** Have students go online for help in understanding how the fossil record shows changes in organisms and environments.

Interactive Art shows how fossils and rock types found in a present-day environment provide scientists with clues and information about the environment and climate of the past.

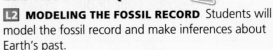
my science online | Fossil Record

Differentiated Instruction

L1 Summarize What The Fossil Record Shows Help students clarify their understanding of three kinds of information the fossil record shows. On the board, write *The fossil record provides evidence…* three times. Then ask pairs of students to reread the text to identify key phrases that complete each statement to show how the fossil record provides evidence "about the history of life on Earth," "about past environments," and "that different groups of organisms have changed over time."

Name _____ Date _____ Class _____

Lab zone After the Inquiry Warm-Up

Fossils

Inquiry Warm-Up, *What's in a Rock?*

In the Inquiry Warm-Up, you investigated a rock sample and inferred how its parts got into the rock. Using what you learned from that activity, answer the questions below.

1. **OBSERVE** What colors and shades of colors did you observe in the rock sample? Describe your findings in detail.

   _____

   _____

2. **INFER** Where do you think the rock sample came from? Describe the type of land formation.

   _____

   _____

3. **COMPARE AND CONTRAST** Look at the rock sample without a hand lens. How does viewing the rock sample under the hand lens differ?

   _____

   _____

4. **COMMUNICATE** Use the space below to draw two more sides of your rock in detail. Add labels to identify fossils, shapes, lines, and other notable characteristics of the rock.

Assess Your Understanding

Fossils

What Are Fossils?

got it? ···

○ **I get it!** Now I know that fossils are _____

_____

○ **I need extra help with** _____

_____

What Are the Kinds of Fossils?

1a. **IDENTIFY** A (mold/trace fossil) can form when sediment buries the hard part of an organism.

b. **EXPLAIN** A petrified fossil forms when _____ replace parts of a(n) _____.

c. **MAKE GENERALIZATIONS** What might you learn from a carbon film that you could not learn from a cast?

_____

_____

got it? ···

○ **I get it!** Now I know that the kinds of fossils are _____

_____

○ **I need extra help with** _____

_____

Name _____ Date _____ Class _____

Fossils

What Do Fossils Show?

2a. EXPLAIN What does the fossil record show about how life has changed over time?

_____

_____

b. APPLY CONCEPTS Give an example of a question you could ask about a fossil of an extinct organism.

_____

_____

got it? ···

○ **I get it!** Now I know that the fossil record shows _____

_____

_____

○ **I need extra help with** _____

_____

Key Concept Summaries

Fossils

What Are Fossils?

Fossils are reserved remains or traces of living things. **Most fossils form when living things die and are buried by sediment. The sediment slowly** **hardens into rock and preserves the shapes of the organisms.** Sediment is made up of rock particles or the remains of living things.

What Are the Kinds of Fossils?

Fossils found in rock include molds and casts, petrified fossils, carbon films, and trace fossils. Other fossils form when the remains of organisms are preserved in substances such as tar, amber, or ice. A **mold** is a hollow area in sediment in the shape of an organism or part of an organism. A **cast** is a solid copy of the shape of an organism. In a **petrified fossil,** minerals have replaced part or all of an organism. A **carbon film** is an extremely thin coating of carbon on a fossil that preserves the delicate parts of plant leaves and insects. **Trace fossils** such as footprints provide evidence of the activities of ancient organisms.

What Do Fossils Show?

A **paleontologist** is a scientist who studies fossils. The combined information about fossils collected by scientists throughout history is called the fossil record. **The fossil record provides evidence about the history of life and past environments on Earth. The fossil record also shows how different** **groups of organisms have changed over time.** The term **evolution** is used to identify the process of gradual change in living things over long periods. A type of organism is **extinct** if it no longer exists and will never again live on Earth.

On a separate sheet of paper, explain how fossils help scientists make discoveries about the lives of organisms and about how environments have changed over time.

Review and Reinforce

Fossils

Understanding Main Ideas
Fill in the blanks in the table below. Answer the questions that follow on a separate sheet of paper.

	Type of Fossil	Description
1.	Petrified fossil	Fossils in which _____ replace all or part of an organism
2.	_____	A hollow area in sediment in the shape of an organism
3.	_____	A solid copy of the shape of the organism
4.	Carbon film	An extremely thin coating of _____ on rock
5.	Trace fossils	Evidence of the _____ of ancient organisms
6.	_____	Remains of organisms in tar, amber, or ice

7. Describe how a mold is related to a cast.

8. What can a paleontologist tell from fossil footprints of a dinosaur?

9. What does the fossil record reveal about the evolution of life on Earth?

Building Vocabulary
Match each term with its definition by writing the letter of the correct term in the right column on the line beside the definition in the left column.

10. ___ no longer and never again existing as an organism on Earth

11. ___ the preserved remains or traces of living things

12. ___ the process by which all the different kinds of living things have changed over long periods of time

13. ___ the type of rock that is made of hardened sediment

14. ___ an extremely thin coating of carbon on rock

15. ___ a scientist who studies fossils

a. evolution

b. sedimentary rock

c. extinct

d. paleontologist

e. fossils

f. carbon film

Name _____ Date _____ Class _____

Fossils

Read the passage and look at the diagram below it. Then answer the questions that follow on a separate sheet of paper.

Traces of Tracks

Paleontologists can learn a lot from trace fossils. The figure below shows fossil footprints. The larger prints were made by a dinosaur. The smaller prints were made at the same time by a small mammal. Can you infer what happened?

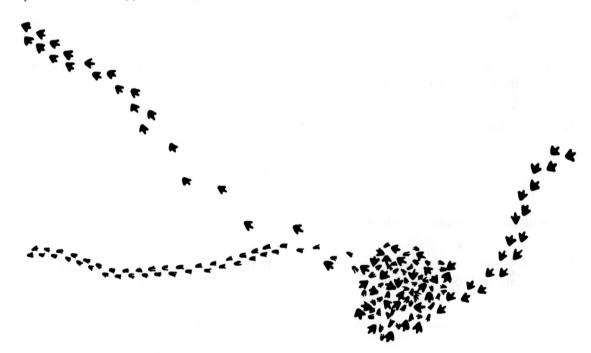

1. What are trace fossils?
2. When these animals made the prints, was the soil moist or dry? Explain.
3. How did the prints become trace fossils?
4. From which direction did the dinosaur come? From which direction did the mammal come?
5. Did either animal change its speed? How can you tell?
6. What prints lead away from the meeting of these animals?
7. How do you interpret these trace fossils? Tell what happened.

Name _____ Date _____ Class _____

Fossils

Write the letter of the correct answer on the line at the left.

1. ___ A hollow area in sediment in the shape of an organism or part of an organism is

   A   a cast

   B   a mold

   C   a trace fossil

   D   a petrified fossil

2. ___ A solid copy of the shape of an organism is

   A   a mold

   B   a carbon film

   C   a cast

   D   a fossil record

3. ___ What type of fossils provide evidence of the activities of ancient organisms?

   A   molds and casts

   B   petrified fossils

   C   trace fossils

   D   carbon films

4. ___ Which of the following substances is *not* able to preserve entire organisms?

   A   sticky tar

   B   water

   C   amber

   D   ice

Fill in the blank to complete each statement.

5. Most fossils form when living things die and are buried by _____ that hardens into rock over time.

6. A(n) _____ is an extremely thin coating of carbon on rock.

7. The term _____ is used to identify a scientist who studies fossils.

8. Scientists study the _____ to learn about the history of life, past environments on Earth, and how different groups of organisms have changed over time.

9. _____ is the gradual change in living things over long periods.

10. An organism is _____ if it no longer exists and will never live again on Earth.

Fossils

Answer Key

After the Inquiry Warm-Up

1. Accept all reasonable observations and descriptions for the colors of the rock sample. Students should indicate the variety of colors and shades of the colors. Sample: white, brown, and black particles mixed in with light gray particles.

2. Answers may vary. Sample: The rock sample has green moss, which may indicate that it was in a wet or very moist area. So the sample may have come from a forested area.

3. Answers may vary. Sample: Without the lens, the colors blend together. Under a hand lens, I can see more of the details of the shapes and colors of the rock sample.

4. Students' drawings should include details that indicate the shapes, sizes and textures of their rocks.

Key Concept Summaries

Fossils give scientists valuable evidence about the sizes, shapes, activities, and environments of living organisms. By analyzing the fossil record, scientists are able to draw conclusions about how organisms lived and died, and how they and their environments changed over time.

Review and Reinforce

1. minerals
2. Mold
3. Cast
4. carbon
5. activities
6. Preserved remains

7. A mold is an empty space in rock in the shape of an organism or part of an organism. If water carrying dissolved minerals and sediment seeps and deposits those minerals and sediments into the mold, the result is a cast in the shape of the organism.

8. Fossil footprints can provide clues about the dinosaur's size and behavior.

9. The fossil record provides evidence that many different organisms have existed at different times. The fossil record also shows that groups of organisms have changed over time.

10. c
11. e
12. a
13. b
14. f
15. d

Enrich

1. Trace fossils are fossils that provide evidence of activities of ancient organisms.

2. The soil must have been moist to hold the shape of the print.

3. The prints became trace fossils when the sediment hardened into rock.

4. The dinosaur came from the upper left; the mammal came from the left.

5. The dinosaur began at a walk and then started to run, as evidenced by the sudden difference in stride length.

6. The dinosaur's prints lead away from the meeting.

7. Answers may vary. A typical answer might describe how the dinosaur saw the mammal; attacked, killed, and devoured the mammal; and then walked away.

Lesson Quiz

1. B
2. C
3. C
4. B
5. sediment
6. carbon film
7. paleontologist
8. fossil record
9. Evolution
10. extinct

The Relative Age of Rocks

 How do scientists study Earth's past?

Lesson Pacing: 2–3 periods or 1–1½ blocks

🕐 **SHORT ON TIME?** To do this lesson in approximately half the time, do the Activate Prior Knowledge activity followed by a discussion of the Key Concepts to familiarize students with the lesson content. Have students do the Quick Lab. The rest of the lesson can be completed by students independently.

> **Preference Navigator,** in the online Planning tools, allows you to customize *Interactive Science* to your own teaching style. You can also edit lesson plans by selecting the Lesson Planner option.
>
> **Digital Teacher's Edition** allows you to access your Teacher's Edition and Resource materials online.

Lesson Vocabulary

- relative age
- absolute age
- law of superposition
- extrusion
- intrusion
- fault
- index fossil
- unconformity

Content Refresher
Professional Development Note

Nicolaus Steno Danish geologist Nicolaus Steno (1638–1686) developed the law of superposition in the 1660s. On a visit to the Mediterranean island of Malta, Steno noticed that the "tongue stones" sold there as good-luck charms were actually fossilized shark teeth from the island's rock layers. Steno hypothesized that the island had once been under water and that the rock layers had been laid down in succession and that the deepest rocks were the oldest.

Trilobites Scientists use certain types of trilobites as index fossils. Trilobites ("three-lobed" organisms) were a type of arthropod that was widespread in the Paleozoic Era. Trilobites scavenged the muddy sea bottom for food, walking on slender, jointed legs. They became extinct in the Permian mass extinction.

LESSON OBJECTIVES

🗝 Describe how geologists determine the relative age of rocks.

🗝 Explain how unconformities and folding can alter the order of rock layers.

Blended Path
Active learning using Student Edition, Inquiry Path, and Digital Path

ENGAGE AND EXPLORE

Teach this lesson using a variety of resources. Begin by reading **My Planet Diary** as a class. Have students discuss how water carries away rock and soil particles. Then have students do the **Inquiry Warm-Up activity.** Students will use clay to create a model of rock layers. The **After the Inquiry Warm-Up worksheet** sets up a discussion about the positions of sediment layers. Have volunteers share their answers to question 4.

EXPLAIN AND ELABORATE

Teach Key Concepts by explaining that geologists use the law of superposition to determine the relative ages of sedimentary rock layers. Continue to **Teach Key Concepts** by explaining that geologists can infer relative age by comparing two or more layers in which a certain index fossil occurs. **Support the Big Q** by using **Figures 2 and 3** to discuss how intrusions and faults convey information about relative age. Have students practice the inquiry skill in the **Apply It activity.**

Continue to **Teach Key Concepts** by explaining how erosion, folding, and motion along faults can affect Earth's geologic record. Have students practice the inquiry skill in the **Apply It activity.**

Hand out the **Key Concept Summaries** as a review of each part of the lesson. Students can also use the online **Vocab Flash Cards** to review key terms.

EVALUATE

Have students take the **Lesson Quiz.** For an alternate assessment, see the **EXAM**VIEW® Assessment Suite, Progress Monitoring Assessments, or SuccessTracker™.

ⒺⓁⓁ Support

1 Content and Language
Read the following sentences aloud to students. *Alicia is five years old. Alicia is younger than her sister and older than her brother.* Ask students which sentence tells Alicia's absolute age and which sentence tells her relative age. Have students write sentences telling their own absolute age and relative age.

Lab zone Inquiry Path
Hands-on learning in the Lab zone

Digital Path
Online learning at my science online.com

ENGAGE AND EXPLORE

To teach this lesson with an emphasis on inquiry, begin with the **Inquiry Warm-Up activity.** Students will use clay to create a model of rock layers. The **After the Inquiry Warm-Up worksheet** sets up a discussion about the positions of sediment layers. Have volunteers share their answers to question 4.

EXPLAIN AND ELABORATE

Focus on the **Inquiry Skill** for the lesson. Remind students that when they make an inference they combine the evidence with their experience or knowledge. What inference could be made in the **Inquiry Warm-Up Activity** about the affect the shape of an object has upon the stacked layers? *(The results remain the same regardless of the shape of the object.)* **Support the Big Q** by using **Figures 2 and 3** by discussing how intrusions and faults convey information about relative age. Review the information relating to intrusions and the law of superposition before beginning the **Apply It activity.** Have students share their inferences about the relative ages of areas B and E. **Build Inquiry** by inviting students to compare and label rock samples. Do the **Lab Investigation** having students explore what rocks and fossils tell about Earth's past.

Review the descriptions of unconformities and folding and study the diagrams in **Figure 5** before beginning the **Apply It activity.** Have students share their inferences about the history of the area in the photograph. Have students do the **Quick Lab** to explore modeling and deforming rock samples. Students can use the online **Vocab Flash Cards** to review key terms.

EVALUATE

Have students take the **Lesson Quiz.** For an alternate assessment, see the **EXAM**VIEW® Assessment Suite, Progress Monitoring Assessments, or SuccessTracker™.

ENGAGE AND EXPLORE

Teach this lesson using digital resources. Begin by having students learn more about the age of rock layers and explore real-world connections to the age of rock layers at **My Planet Diary** online. Have them access the Chapter Resources to find the **Unlock the Big Question activity.** There they can answer the questions and refine their responses as they continue through the lesson. You can re-assign the activity and have students submit their work so you can track their progress.

EXPLAIN AND ELABORATE

Students reading above, at, or below the lexile measure of this lesson can access basic content readings at their level at **My Reading Web.** Encourage students to use the online **Vocab Flash Cards** to preview key terms.

Support the Big Q by using **Figures 2 and 3** by discussing how intrusions and faults convey information about relative age. Assign the **Apply It activity** online and have students submit their results to you. Use the **Interactive Art activity** online to show students how scientists use index fossils to match rock layers.

Assign the **Apply It activity** online and have students submit their results to you. Have students do the **Quick Lab** to explore modeling and deforming rock samples. The **Key Concept Summaries** online allow students to read a summary and see an image associated with each part of the lesson. Online remediation is available at **My Science Coach.**

EVALUATE

Have students take the **Lesson Quiz.** For an alternate assessment, see the **EXAM**VIEW® Assessment Suite, Progress Monitoring Assessments, or SuccessTracker™.

2 Frontload the Lesson
Preview the lesson title and heads with students. Ask them to use this information to predict what they will learn about in this lesson.

3 Comprehensible Input
Have students work in pairs to create tables to organize the information in the first section of the lesson. Students should record details in their tables about the clues geologists use to determine the age of sedimentary rock layers.

4 Language Production
Pair or group students with varied language abilities to complete labs collaboratively for language practice. Have each student copy the completed written lab for personal reference.

5 Assess Understanding
Divide the students into teams of four. Give each member a number of 1, 2, 3, or 4. Ask the essential questions from the lesson. Have groups work together to answer the question so all can agree on the answer. Call out a number and the corresponding members in each group answers.

LESSON 8.2

The Relative Age of Rocks

Establish Learning Objectives

After this lesson, students will be able to:

🔑 Describe how geologists determine the relative age of rocks.

🔑 Explain how unconformities and folding can alter the order of rock layers.

Engage

Activate Prior Knowledge

MY PLANET DIARY Read *Owen's Blog* with the class. Tell students that coulee refers to a valley or drainage zone. Many coulees in the northwestern United States were cut by water from rapidly melting glaciers, which is what Owen means by "Ice Age floods." Ask: **What is the process by which water carries away rock and soil particles?** *(Erosion)*

BIG IDEAS OF SCIENCE REFERENCE LIBRARY 📖
Have students look up the following topic: Dating Rocks.

Explore

Lab Resource: Inquiry Warm-Up 🧪

L2 **WHICH LAYER IS THE OLDEST?** Students will use clay to create a model of the sequence of rock layers.

LESSON 2

The Relative Age of Rocks

UNLOCK THE BIG ?

🔑 How Old Are Rock Layers?

🔑 How Can Rock Layers Change?

MY PLANET DIARY

BLOG

Posted by **Owen**

Location **Tacoma, WA**

A couple of summers ago, my dad took me rock climbing for the first time. I went to a place called Frenchman Coulee in central Washington. It was really cool because the rock was basalt, which forms in giant pillars. It starts as lava, and then cools and you can see the different lava flows in the rock. Another cool thing is that Frenchman Coulee, which is a canyon, was gouged out by huge Ice Age floods.

✏ **Communicate** Discuss the question below with a partner. Then answer it on your own.

How do you think scientists figure out the age of the basalt layers at Frenchman Coulee?

Sample: Scientists assume that the lower layers are older.

▶ **PLANET DIARY** Go to **Planet Diary** to learn more about the age of rock layers.

🧪 **Lab zone** Do the Inquiry Warm-Up *Which Layer Is the Oldest?*

How Old Are Rock Layers?

If you found a fossil in a rock, you might start by asking, "What is it?" Your next question would probably be, "How old is it?" The first step is to find the age of the rock.

Relative and Absolute Age Geologists have two ways to express the age of a rock. The **relative age** of a rock is its age compared to the ages of other rocks. You have probably used the idea of relative age when comparing your age with someone else's. For example, if you say that you are older than your brother but younger than your sister, you are describing your relative age.

SUPPORT ALL READERS

Lexile Measure = 860L   **Lexile Word Count = 1084**

Prior Exposure to Content: May be the first time students have encountered this topic

Academic Vocabulary: *infer, interpret, relate*

Science Vocabulary: *relative age, absolute age, extrusion, intrusion*

Concept Level: Generally appropriate for most students in this grade

Preteach With: My Planet Diary "Owen's Blog" and Figure 4 activity

Go to **My Reading Web** to access leveled readings that provide a foundation for the content.

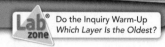

Vocabulary
- relative age • absolute age • law of superposition
- extrusion • intrusion • fault • index fossil
- unconformity

Skills
- Reading: Relate Text and Visuals
- Inquiry: Infer

The relative age of a rock does not provide its absolute age. The **absolute age** of a rock is the number of years that have passed since the rock formed. It may be impossible to know a rock's absolute age exactly, so geologists often use both absolute and relative ages.

Rock Layers Fossils are most often found in layers of sedimentary rock. Geologists use the law of superposition to determine the relative ages of sedimentary rock layers. **According to the law of superposition, in undisturbed horizontal sedimentary rock layers the oldest layer is at the bottom. Each higher layer is younger than the layers below it.** The deeper you go, the older the rocks are.

Figure 1 shows rock layers in the Grand Canyon. Rock layers like these form a record of Earth's history. Scientists can study this record to understand how Earth and life on Earth have changed.

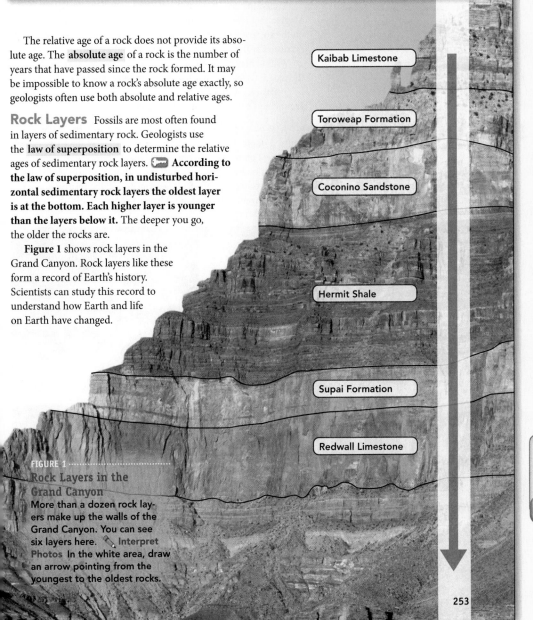

Kaibab Limestone

Toroweap Formation

Coconino Sandstone

Hermit Shale

Supai Formation

Redwall Limestone

FIGURE 1
Rock Layers in the Grand Canyon
More than a dozen rock layers make up the walls of the Grand Canyon. You can see six layers here. ✎ **Interpret Photos** In the white area, draw an arrow pointing from the youngest to the oldest rocks.

253

Explain

Introduce Vocabulary

It's not all relative. It's sometimes absolute. Tell students that geologists express the age of rocks in two different ways, just as people express age in everyday life. The term *absolute age* gives the actual, specific age of something. The term *relative age* gives the age of something compared to, or in relation to, the age of something else.

Teach Key Concepts 🔑

Explain to students that the relative ages of horizontal layers of rock can be understood according to the law of superposition. Ask: **Where is the oldest layer of rock located?** (At the bottom) **What is the relative age of the highest layer of rock?** (It is younger than the rock layers below it.) **Why is it important that the rock layers be undisturbed?** (If the rock layers are undisturbed, you know that the oldest are on the bottom, and the youngest are at the top. If the rock has been disturbed, layers might be missing or relocated.)

Teach With Visuals

Tell students to look at **Figure 1**. Ask: **What type of age does this photograph help you identify?** (Relative age) **Which layer or layers are younger than Hermit Shale?** (Coconino Sandstone, Toroweap Formation, Kaibab Limestone)

My Planet Diary provides an opportunity for students to explore real-world connections to the age of rock layers.

LESSON 8.2

1 Content and Language
Write the word *fault* on the board. Explain that the term's scientific meaning is different than its everyday meaning. In geology, a *fault* refers to an extended break in a body of rock.

2 Frontload the Lesson
Ask students who have visited the Grand Canyon to describe what they saw.

Encourage students to explain what the sides of the canyon look like.

3 Comprehensible Input
Have students draw several rock sedimentary rock layers. Then have them add and label an intrusion, an extrusion, and a fault. Finally, have students label the layers from oldest to youngest.

Explain

Teach Key Concepts 🔑

Explain to students that scientists compare rock layers to infer the relative ages of the layers. In a similar way, scientists can infer relative age by comparing two or more layers in which a certain index fossil occurs. Ask: **What are characteristics of a fossil that can be used as an index fossil?** (*A fossil that existed for a short period of time and that was distributed widely*)

Support the Big Q ❓ UbD

Direct students' attention to **Figure 2** and **Figure 3**. Encourage them to think about how each of these geologic features conveys information about relative age to scientists. Ask: **How do geologists use extrusions and intrusions to determine relative age?** (*Extrusions and intrusions are always younger than the rocks beneath and surrounding them.*) **Are faults younger or older than the rock they cut through?** (*Younger*) **What might cause a gap in the geologic record?** (*Erosion might wear away a layer of rock. When a new layer forms, the layer that was originally there would be lost.*)

Elaborate

Apply It!

L1 Review the information relating to intrusions and the law of superposition before beginning the activity.

🔺 **Infer** Remind students that when they make an inference they combine the evidence with their experience or knowledge. Ask: **What can you infer about the relative ages of areas C and E?** (*Layer C must be older, because the intrusion at E cuts through layer C.*) **What can you infer about the relative ages of areas B and C?** (*Layer C must be younger, because it is higher than Layer B.*)

Vocabulary Prefixes How does knowing the prefixes *in-* and *ex-* help you remember the difference between an intrusion and an extrusion?

Sample: In- means "inside" and ex- means "outside," so I know that an intrusion forms inside Earth and an extrusion forms outside Earth.

apply it!

The diagram below shows rock layers found at a site.

❶ Circle the area on the diagram that shows an intrusion.

❷ Shade the oldest layer on the diagram.

❸ **Infer** What can you infer about the relative ages of areas B and E?

Layer B must be older, because the intrusion at E cuts through layer B.

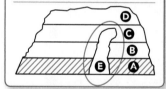

Clues From Igneous Rock There are other clues to the relative ages of rocks besides the position of rock layers. To determine relative age, geologists also study extrusions and intrusions of igneous rock, faults, and index fossils.

Molten material beneath Earth's surface is called magma. Magma that reaches the surface is called lava. Lava that hardens on the surface and forms igneous rock is called an **extrusion.** An extrusion is always younger than the rocks below it.

Magma may push into bodies of rock below the surface. There, the magma cools and hardens into a mass of igneous rock called an **intrusion.** An intrusion is always younger than the rock layers around and beneath it. **Figure 2** shows an intrusion.

Clues From Faults More clues come from the study of faults. A **fault** is a break in Earth's crust. Forces inside Earth cause movement of the rock on opposite sides of a fault.

A fault is always younger than the rock it cuts through. To determine the relative age of a fault, geologists find the relative age of the youngest layer cut by the fault. **Figure 3** shows a fault.

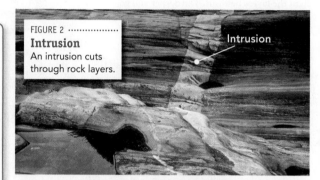
FIGURE 2
Intrusion
An intrusion cuts through rock layers.
Intrusion

FIGURE 3
Fault
Rock layers break and shift along a fault.
Fault line
Fault line

Digital Lesson: Assign the *Apply It* activity online and have students submit their work to you.

Interactive Art shows how scientists use index fossils to match rock layers.

MY SCIENCE online.com | Age of Rocks

How Do Fossils Show Age?
To date rock layers, geologists first find the relative age of a layer of rock at one location. Then they can match layers in other locations to that layer.

Certain fossils, called index fossils, help geologists match rock layers. To be useful as an **index fossil,** a fossil must be widely distributed and represent an organism that existed for a geologically short period of time. 🗝 **Index fossils are useful because they tell the relative ages of the rock layers in which they occur.** Scientists infer that layers with matching index fossils are the same age.

You can use index fossils to match rock layers. Look at **Figure 4,** which shows rock layers from four different locations. Notice that two of the fossils are found in only one of these rock layers. These are the index fossils.

FIGURE 4 ....
> INTERACTIVE ART **Index Fossils**
Scientists use index fossils to match rock layers.
✏ **Interpret Diagrams** Label the layers to match the first area shown. Circle the fossil or fossils that you can use as index fossils. What can you infer about the history of Location 4?

<u>Sample: Layer B must</u>
<u>have eroded over time.</u>

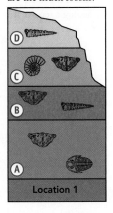
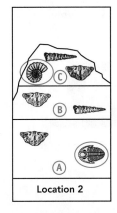
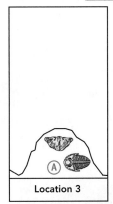
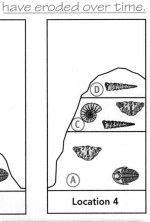

| Location 1 | Location 2 | Location 3 | Location 4 |

Lab zone — Do the Lab Investigation *Exploring Geologic Time Through Core Samples.*

🗝 Assess Your Understanding

1a. Explain In an area with several different rock layers, which is oldest? Explain.

<u>The lowest layer is most likely</u>
<u>the oldest, because it was</u>
<u>deposited first.</u>

b. Infer How could a geologist match the rock layers in one area to rock layers found in another area?

<u>Sample: The scientist could look</u>
<u>for index fossils in the rock lay-</u>
<u>ers and match them to index</u>
<u>fossils found in another area.</u>

got it? ....

○ **I get it!** Now I know that you can find the relative age of rocks by <u>using the law of super-</u>
<u>position, intrusions and extrusions, faults, and index fossils.</u>

○ **I need extra help with** <u>See TE note.</u>

Go to **my science** 🖥 **coach** *online for help with this subject.*

255

Differentiated Instruction

L1 Relative and Absolute Ages
Write the following statements about children in a family on the board: *Anthony is the youngest. Melony is 4 years old. Ashley is older than Melony but younger than Shatiqua.* Help students identify these statements as providing absolute or relative ages. Place the children in order from oldest to youngest. *(Shatiqua, Ashley, Melony, Anthony)*

L3 Indexes Explain that an index is an organizational tool that tells where something can be found. Ask students why we might use the term *index finger* for the finger next to the thumb. *(It is the finger we use for pointing.)* Explain that like these other forms of indexes, an index fossil "points" to other occurrences of a particular fossil in a particular era.

Elaborate ————————

Build Inquiry 🧪

L2 COMPARE ROCK SAMPLES

Materials hand lens, samples of granite, basalt, sandstone, and shale

Time 15 minutes

Invite students to recall the origins of sedimentary rocks and igneous rocks. Then label the samples as follows:

Granite—forms intrusions

Basalt—forms extrusions

Sandstone—formed mainly of sandy sediment

Shale—formed mainly of muddy sediment

Ask: **Which of the rocks would occur as a layer?** *(Basalt, sandstone, shale)* **Which rock would cut across other rock layers?** *(Granite)*

21st Century Learning

INTERPERSONAL SKILLS Have pairs of students share their shaded diagrams for **Figure 4.** Invite one student to explain orally to his or her partner why only two fossils can be used as index fossils. *(The two index fossils appear in only one time period but in several different locations.)* Then the other student should explain orally the way in which Location 4 differs from the other three locations, and why. *(Location 4 lacks a layer B, probably because of erosion before layer C was deposited.)*

Lab Resource: Lab Investigation 🧪

L2 EXPLORING GEOLOGIC TIME THROUGH CORE SAMPLES Students will explore what rocks and fossils tell about Earth's past.

Evaluate ————————

Assess Your Understanding

After students answer the questions, have them evaluate their understanding by completing the appropriate sentence.

🇷🇹🇮 Response to Intervention

1a. If students need help with identifying relative ages of rock layers, **then** have them locate reread the section on rock layers and the law of superposition.

b. If students need help with inferring scientific methods, **then** have them review the definition and uses of index fossils.

my science **coach** Have students go online for help in understanding the relative ages of rock layers.

Explain

Teach Key Concepts 🔑

Explain to students that rock layers can appear in different positions from what is expected. Ask: **How has erosion affected Earth's geologic record?** *(Erosion has caused parts of the geologic record to disappear.)* **What other events or forces make it challenging for scientists to reconstruct Earth's history?** *(Folding as well as motion along faults can change the position of rock layers.)*

Teach With Visuals

Draw students' attention to **Figure 5.** Ask students if they have ever heard someone use the word *erosion,* and in what context. Invite students to describe any first-hand experiences they may have had in which they saw the process or the result of erosion in soil, sand, or rock. Ask: **What kinds of forces can cause erosion in rock?** *(Water, wind)* **After rock is eroded, what additional event must occur to create an unconformity?** *(New deposits of sediment must build up on the eroded area.)*

🔄 **Relate Text and Visuals** Tell students that relating text and visuals can help them clarify information and deepen their understanding of a topic. Whenever they see a reference to a visual in the text, they should look at the visual before they continue reading, and refer back to it as they continue to read.

How Can Rock Layers Change?

The geologic record of sedimentary rock layers is not complete. In fact, most of Earth's geologic record has been lost to erosion. 🔑 **Gaps in the geologic record and folding can change the position in which rock layers appear.** Motion along faults can also change how rock layers line up. These changes make it harder for scientists to reconstruct Earth's history. **Figure 5** shows how the order of rock layers may change.

Gaps in the Geologic Record When rock layers erode away, an older rock surface may be exposed. Then deposition begins again, building new rock layers. The surface where new rock layers meet a much older rock surface beneath them is called an unconformity. An **unconformity** is a gap in the geologic record. It shows where rock layers have been lost due to erosion.

✏️ **Relate Text and Visuals**
Underline the sentences that explain how the rock layers in **Figure 5** changed.

FIGURE 5

Unconformities and Folding

✏️ **Draw Conclusions** Shade the oldest and youngest layers in the last two diagrams. Label the unconformity. Circle the part of the fold that is overturned.

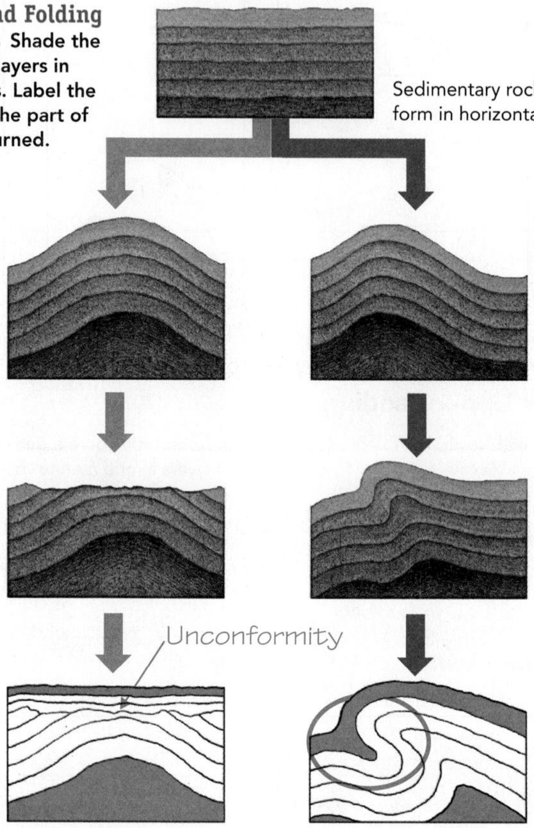

Sedimentary rocks form in horizontal layers.

Unconformity

Folding bends the rock layer.

The surface is eroded.

Unconformity

New sediment is deposited, forming rock layers above the unconformity.

Overturned Fold

Folding bends the rock layer.

Folding continues, further bending the rock layer.

Over time, the layers may fold completely over. This is called an overturned fold.

Digital Lesson: Assign the *Apply It* activity online and have students submit their work to you.

my science ᴼⁿˡⁱⁿᵉ | **Changing Layers**

Folding Sometimes, forces inside Earth fold rock layers so much that the layers are turned over completely. In this case, the youngest rock layers may be on the bottom!

No one place holds a complete geologic record. Geologists compare rock layers in many places to piece together as complete a sequence as possible.

apply it!

Study the photo. Then answer the questions.

❶ What does the photo show? (an unconformity/folding)

❷ What evidence do you see for your answer to Question 1?
The layers are bent at an angle.

❸ **CHALLENGE** What can you infer about the history of this area?
After the rock layers formed, forces inside Earth raised and folded them.

 Do the Quick Lab
How Did It Form?

🔑 Assess Your Understanding

2a. List Name two ways rock layers can change.
Unconformity, folding

b. Explain How does folding change rock layers?
Folded rock layers are no longer flat. Sometimes older layers end up on top.

c. Draw Conclusions Two locations include a layer of rock with a particular index fossil. In one location, the layer occurs in a higher position than in the other. What can you conclude about the history of the two areas?
Sample: One area has experienced folding, or some rock layers have worn away.

got it?

○ I get it! Now I know that rock layers can change due to erosion that causes unconformities and folding of rock layers.

○ I need extra help with See TE note.

Go to my science COACH online for help with this subject.

257

Differentiated Instruction

L1 Understanding Causes of Unconformities Pair less proficient readers with more proficient readers. Refer them to **Figure 5,** and write the questions that follow on the board. Ask students to draw on previous knowledge to give detailed answers. Encourage them to use the table of contents and index to locate information in other parts of the textbook.

What process could have made the sedimentary layers? *(Deposition from water, wind, waves, or glaciers)* **What could have caused the folding of the layers?** *(Forces from inside Earth can cause movement.)* **What could have caused the wearing away of the surface?** *(Chemical or mechanical weathering, and then erosion by water, wind, waves, or glaciers)*

Make Analogies
L1 FOLDING LAYERS UNDER To help students understand the concept of geologic folding, compare this process with that of layers of blankets being folded over on a bed. Ask: **If several layers of blankets were folded over so that they were turned completely over, the top layer—the bedspread—could lie next to the bottom sheet. What misconception could be made as a result of this folding?** *(It might be thought that the bedspread was the next lowest layer to the bottom sheet.)*

Elaborate

Apply It!
L1 Review the descriptions of unconformities and folding and study the diagrams in **Figure 5** before beginning the activity. Ask: **Do the shapes of the rock layers in the photograph more closely resemble the shapes of the unconformity or the shapes of the overturned fold in Figure 5?** *(Overturned fold)*

Lab Resource: Quick Lab
L2 HOW DID IT FORM? Students will explore modeling and deforming rock samples.

Evaluate

Assess Your Understanding
After students answer the questions, have them evaluate their understanding by completing the appropriate sentence.

RTI Response to Intervention
2a. If students cannot name two ways rock layers can change, **then** have them review the information under the head *How Rocks Can Change.*

b. If students cannot explain how folding changes rock layers, **then** have them review the diagrams in **Figure 5.**

c. If students need help with explaining unconformities and index fossils, **then** have them review how geologists use index fossils to date rock layers.

my science COACH Have students go online for help in understanding causes of change in rock layers.

Lab zone **After the Inquiry Warm-Up**

The Relative Age of Rocks

Inquiry Warm-Up, *Which Layer Is the Oldest?*
In the Inquiry Warm-Up, you investigated positions of sediment layers. Using what you learned from that activity, answer the questions below.

1. **SEQUENCE** Draw the layers as they appear over the bowl. Name the colors and label the sequence of the layers from oldest to youngest as if these layers were sediment.

2. **COMMUNICATE** How would you describe the layers of your model from oldest to youngest as if these layers were sediment?

   _____

   _____

   _____

3. **DRAW CONCLUSIONS** Why do you think that the order of layers remained the same after the stack was pressed over the rounded object?

   _____

   _____

   _____

4. **INFER** Would objects that were rounded, but differently shaped, change the results you saw after cutting off the top of the dome? Explain.

   _____

   _____

Assess Your Understanding

The Relative Age of Rocks

How Old Are Rock Layers?

1a. EXPLAIN In an area with several different rock layers, which is oldest? Explain.

_____

_____

b. INFER How could a geologist match the rock layers in one area to rock layers found in another area?

_____

_____

got it? ....

O **I get it!** Now I know that you can find the age of rocks by _____

_____

O **I need extra help with** _____

_____

How Can Rock Layers Change?

2a. LIST Name two ways rock layers can change.

_____

b. EXPLAIN How does folding change rock layers?

_____

_____

c. DRAW CONCLUSIONS Two locations include a layer of rock with a particular index fossil. In one location, the layer occurs in a higher position than in the other. What can you conclude about the history of the two areas?

_____

_____

got it? ....

O **I get it!** Now I know that rock layers can change due to _____

_____

O **I need extra help with** _____

_____

Name _____ Date _____ Class _____

The Relative Age of Rocks

How Old Are Rock Layers?

The **relative age** of a rock is its age compared to the ages of other rocks. The **absolute age** of a rock is the number of years that have passed since the rock formed. Geologists use the **law of superposition** to determine the relative ages of sedimentary rock layers. **According to the law of superposition, in horizontal sedimentary rock layers the oldest layer is at the bottom. Each higher layer is younger than the layers below it.**

Geologists study extrusions, intrusions, faults, and index fossils to determine the relative ages of rocks.

An **extrusion** is formed by lava that hardened on the Earth's surface and formed igneous rock. An **intrusion** is magma, which cools and hardens into a mass of igneous rock below the Earth's surface. A **fault** is a break in Earth's crust.

Fossils that are widely distributed and that represent organisms that existed for a geologically short period of time could be used as **index fossils. Index fossils are useful because they tell the relative ages of the rock layers in which they occur.**

How Can Rock Layers Change?

The geologic record of sedimentary rock layers is not complete. Most of our planet's geologic record has disappeared through erosion. **Gaps in the geologic record and folding can change the position in which rock layers appear.** These changes make it

more challenging for scientists to identify accurately the ages of some rocks. An **unconformity** is a gap in the geologic record. An unconformity shows where rock layers have disappeared due to erosion.

On a separate sheet of paper, explain the methods geologists use to determine the relative ages of rock, as well as some of the challenges they face.

Name _____ Date _____ Class _____

The Relative Age of Rocks

Understanding Main Ideas
Look at the diagram below. Then answer the questions that follow on a separate sheet of paper.

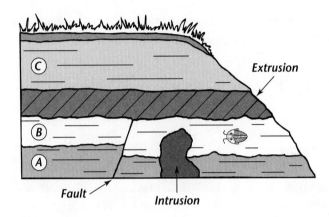

1. What is the youngest rock layer? Explain.
2. Is the extrusion older or younger than rock layer B? Explain.
3. Is the fault older or younger than rock layer A? Explain.
4. How could a geologist use the fossil in rock layer B to date a rock layer in another location?

Building Vocabulary
Match each term with its definition by writing the letter of the correct definition in the right column on the line beside the term in the left column.

5. ___ fault

6. ___ extrusion

7. ___ unconformity

8. ___ relative age

9. ___ law of superposition

10. ___ intrusion

11. ___ absolute age

12. ___ index fossils

a. the number of years since a rock has formed

b. a break in Earth's crust

c. the way to determine relative ages of rocks

d. a hardened layer of magma beneath Earth's surface

e. the age of a rock compared with the age of other rocks

f. fossils used to help geologists match rock layers

g. the surface where new rock layers meet a much older rock surface beneath them

h. a hardened layer of lava on Earth's surface

The Relative Age of Rocks

Read and look at the diagrams below. Then answer the questions that follow on a separate sheet of paper.

The Grandest Canyon of All

How did the Grand Canyon form? It formed through the processes that build up and wear down the surface of the Earth. The figures below show how this majestic landscape came to be.

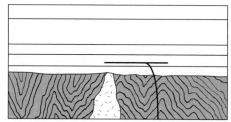

A Several sedimentary rock layers form over ancient rock.

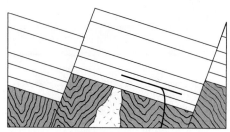

B Forces within Earth cause large faults, and layers of the sedimentary rock shift.

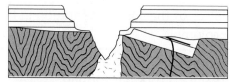

C Weathering and erosion wear down the whole area.

D More sedimentary rock layers form over the old, eroded surface.

E Finally, the Colorado River flows over the surface and cuts down through the layers of rock, forming the Grand Canyon.

1. How do sedimentary rock layers form?
2. What happened to the sedimentary rock layers that first formed over the ancient rock?
3. Where in this sequence of events is the formation of an unconformity?
4. How did the Grand Canyon itself form?
5. Which is older, the Grand Canyon or the rock layers now exposed on the canyon walls? Explain your reasoning.

Lesson Quiz

The Relative Age of Rocks

Write the letter of the correct answer on the line at the left.

1. ___ The number of years that have passed since he rock formed is the rock's

   A relative age

   B law of superposition

   C absolute age

   D index fossil

2. ___ The age of a rock compared to the ages of other rocks is the rock's

   A absolute age

   B geologic age

   C sedimentary age

   D relative age

3. ___ A formation of igneous rock on Earth's surface is known as

   A a gap

   B an intrusion

   C a fault

   D an extrusion

4. ___ A break in Earth's crust is called

   A an intrusion

   B a fault

   C a layer

   D an index fossil

Fill in the blank to complete each statement.

5. Geologists use the law of _____ to determine the relative ages of sedimentary rock layers.

6. A mass of igneous rock below the Earth's surface is called a(n) _____.

7. Because of _____, most of the geologic record of sedimentary rock layers has been lost.

8. A gap in the geologic record is known as a(n) _____.

9. The position in which rock layers appear can be changed by gaps in the geologic record and by _____.

10. According to the law of _____, in horizontal sedimentary rock layers the oldest layer is at the bottom and the youngest layer is at the top.

The Relative Age of Rocks

Answer Key

After the Inquiry Warm-Up

1. Drawings and labeling will vary according to the colors students used. In all cases, the first stacked layer is the oldest and the last stacked layer is the youngest.

2. Answers will vary. Students may describe the order by color of the oldest layers to the younger layers. Sample: The red layer is the oldest and indicated the first layer. The next layer is blue and it is not as old as the red layer. The yellow layer is the youngest layer and is the last layer.

3. Answers will vary. Students may indicate that though the shape of the stack is changed by pressing it over the rounded object, the composition of the stack does not change.

4. Answers will vary. Students will likely explain that the results will remain the same regardless of the shape of the object.

Key Concept Summaries

Geologists analyze extrusions, intrusions, faults, and index fossils to determine the relative ages of rocks. Their judgments are based on the law of superposition but are made more complicated by gaps in the geologic record and folding.

Review and Reinforce

1. Layer C is the youngest because the law of superposition says that a layer is younger than the layers below it.

2. The extrusion is younger because extrusions are always younger than the rock layers below them.

3. The fault is younger than layer A because rock layers are always older than the faults they contain.

4. The fossil might be an index fossil. Geologists can use index fossils to match rock layers at locations that are far apart.

5. b
6. h
7. g
8. e
9. c
10. d
11. a
12. f

Enrich

1. Sedimentary rock layers form when sediment is deposited in flat layers, one on top of the other. Over years, the sediment hardens and changes into sedimentary rock.

2. They weathered and eroded away.

3. When the first sedimentary layers eroded away, new layers formed on top of the eroded surface. The boundary where the eroded and new layers make contact is an unconformity.

4. The Grand Canyon formed when the flow of the Colorado River caused the water to erode and cut through the rock layers.

5. The rock layers are older because they formed before the river cut the canyon.

Lesson Quiz

1. C
2. D
3. D
4. B
5. superposition
6. intrusion
7. erosion
8. unconformity
9. folding
10. superposition

Place the outside corner, the corner away from the dotted line, in the corner of your copy machine to copy onto letter-size paper.

Radioactive Dating

Lesson Pacing: 1–2 periods or $\frac{1}{2}$–1 block

🕐 **SHORT ON TIME?** To do this lesson in approximately half the time, do the Activate Prior Knowledge activity followed by a discussion of the Key Concepts to familiarize students with the lesson content. Have students do the Quick Labs. The rest of the lesson can be completed by students independently.

Preference Navigator, in the online Planning tools, allows you to customize *Interactive Science* to your own teaching style. You can also edit lesson plans by selecting the Lesson Planner option.

Digital Teacher's Edition allows you to access your Teacher's Edition and Resource materials online.

Lesson Vocabulary

- radioactive decay
- half-life

Content Refresher

Isotopes An element has a specific number of protons in its atoms, and this number never varies. Atoms of the same element, however, can have different numbers of neutrons. Atoms of an element with different numbers of neutrons are called isotopes. In some isotopes—radioactive isotopes—forces that bind protons and neutrons together are weak. The result is that these nuclei spontaneously decay.

All carbon atoms have six protons. Carbon-14, which has eight neutrons, is absorbed by living things while they are alive. After an organism dies, the carbon-14 in its body begins to decay to form nitrogen-14, which escapes into the air. Carbon-12, which has six neutrons and is the most common isotope of carbon, is not radioactive and does not decay. By comparing the amounts of carbon-14 and carbon-12 in a fossil, researchers can determine when the organism lived.

Unstable radioactive isotopes occur naturally in Earth's crust. For example, granite forms when molten material hardens underground, forming an intrusion. Within that granite may be some potassium-40, which decays into argon-40. Scientists can determine the age of the rock by comparing the amounts of these two isotopes.

LESSON OBJECTIVES

🔑 Explain what happens during radioactive decay.

🔑 Describe what can be learned from radioactive dating.

Blended Path
Active learning using Student Edition, Inquiry Path, and Digital Path

ENGAGE AND EXPLORE

Teach this lesson using a variety of resources. Begin by reading **My Planet Diary** as a class. Have students discuss the discovery of radioactivity. Then have students do the **Inquiry Warm-Up activity.** Students will measure and cut pieces of clay to explore the concept of half-life. The **After the Inquiry Warm-Up worksheet** sets up a discussion about radioactive dating. Have volunteers share their answers to question 4 saying if it is possible to perform the action on a cube of any size.

EXPLAIN AND ELABORATE

Explain the term *radioactive* and then **Teach Key Concepts** by explaining that during the decay process atoms of the decaying element break down to form atoms of a different element and particles and energy are released.

Continue to **Teach Key Concepts** by explaining how radioactive elements are used in the absolute dating of rocks and fossils. **Lead a Discussion** about atoms to be certain students have the background they need to understand the concept of radioactive dating. **Support the Big Q** by explaining that while carbon-14 is a radioactive isotope of carbon, not all isotopes of carbon are radioactive, reviewing the concept of isotopes, if necessary.

Hand out the **Key Concept Summaries** as a review of each part of the lesson. Students can also use the online **Vocab Flash Cards** to review key terms.

EVALUATE

Have students take the **Lesson Quiz.** For an alternate assessment, see the **EXAM**VIEW® Assessment Suite, Progress Monitoring Assessments, or SuccessTracker™.

ELL Support

1 Content and Language

Have students write sentences describing the relationships shown in the table in the **Do the Math activity.** For example, *Uranium-235 has a half-life of 713 million years and is used to date rocks in the range of 10 million to 4.6 billion years.*

 **Inquiry Path** Hands-on learning in the Lab zone

ENGAGE AND EXPLORE

To teach this lesson with an emphasis on inquiry, begin with the **Inquiry Warm-Up activity.** Students will measure and cut pieces of clay to explore the concept of half-life. The **After the Inquiry Warm-Up worksheet** sets up a discussion about radioactive dating. Have volunteers share their answers to question 4 saying if it is possible to perform the action on a cube of any size.

EXPLAIN AND ELABORATE

Focus on the **Inquiry Skill** for the lesson. Remind students that when they calculate, they use addition, subtraction, multiplication, or division to find an answer. What calculations were performed in the **Inquiry Warm-Up Activity?** *(Reducing the size of the initial cube by one fourth, one eighth, and one sixteenth)* Have students do the **Quick Lab** to model the half-lives of radioactive elements.

Support the Big Q by explaining that while carbon-14 is a radioactive isotope of carbon, not all isotopes of carbon are radioactive, reviewing the concept of isotopes, if necessary. **Build Inquiry** to model radioactive dating. Have students do the **Quick Lab** using half-lives to determine approximate ages. Students can use the online **Vocab Flash Cards** to review key terms.

EVALUATE

Have students take the **Lesson Quiz.** For an alternate assessment, see the **EXAM**VIEW® Assessment Suite, Progress Monitoring Assessments, or SuccessTracker™.

Digital Path Online learning at my science online.com

ENGAGE AND EXPLORE

Teach this lesson using digital resources. Begin by having students learn more about the uses of radioactivity at **My Planet Diary** online. Have them access the Chapter Resources to find the **Unlock the Big Question activity.** There they can answer the questions and refine their responses as they continue through the lesson. You can re-assign the activity and have students submit their work so you can track their progress.

EXPLAIN AND ELABORATE

Students reading above, at, or below the lexile measure of this lesson can access basic content readings at their level at **My Reading Web.** Encourage students to use the online **Vocab Flash Cards** to preview key terms. Have students do the **Quick Lab** to model the half-lives of radioactive elements.

Assign the **Do the Math activity** online and have students submit their work to you. The **Real-World Inquiry activity** online allows students to perform radioactive dating on different fossils. **Support the Big Q** by explaining that while carbon-14 is a radioactive isotope of carbon, not all isotopes of carbon are radioactive, reviewing the concept of isotopes, if necessary. Have students do the **Quick Lab** using half-lives to determine approximate ages. The **Key Concept Summaries** online allow students to read a summary and see an image associated with each part of the lesson. Online remediation is available at **My Science Coach.**

EVALUATE

Have students take the **Lesson Quiz.** For an alternate assessment, see the **EXAM**VIEW® Assessment Suite, Progress Monitoring Assessments, or SuccessTracker™.

2 Frontload the Lesson

Preview the lesson with students by calling attention to the titles, visuals, captions, and vocabulary.

3 Comprehensible Input

Explain that using a outline format can help students understand the information in this lesson by identifying the main ideas and details. Have students prepare an outline of the lesson. The heads should serve as main ideas. Students can add details to the outlines as they read.

4 Language Production

Pair or group students with varied language abilities to complete labs collaboratively for language practice. Have each student copy the completed written lab for personal reference.

5 Assess Understanding

Make true or false statements using lesson content and have students indicate if they agree or disagree with a thumbs up or thumbs down gesture to check whole-class comprehension.

LESSON 8.3

Radioactive Dating

Establish Learning Objectives

After this lesson, students will be able to:

🔑 Explain what happens during radioactive decay.

🔑 Describe what can be learned from radioactive dating.

Engage

Activate Prior Knowledge

MY PLANET DIARY Read *Marie Curie* with the class. Make sure students understand that covering the plate with black paper kept light away from the plate, so that Becquerel could be sure that light did not cause the change in the plate. Ask: **Have you ever seen an object glow in the dark? What do you think was causing the object to emit light?** (*Students may say that it is radioactivity, but radioactive materials are no longer used to make objects glow in the dark.*)

BIG IDEAS OF SCIENCE REFERENCE LIBRARY 📖
Have students look up the following topic: Dating Rocks.

Explore

Lab Resource: Inquiry Warm-Up

L1 HOW LONG TILL IT'S GONE? Students will measure and cut pieces of clay to explore the concept of half-life.

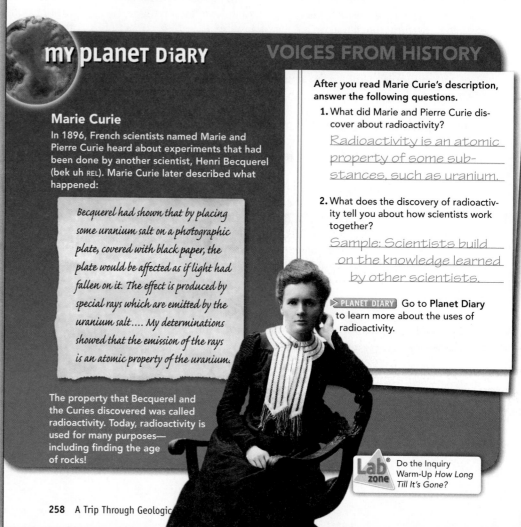

LESSON 3

Radioactive Dating

🔑 **What Is Radioactive Decay?**

🔑 **What Is Radioactive Dating?**

MY PLANET DIARY — VOICES FROM HISTORY

Marie Curie

In 1896, French scientists named Marie and Pierre Curie heard about experiments that had been done by another scientist, Henri Becquerel (bek uh REL). Marie Curie later described what happened:

> Becquerel had shown that by placing some uranium salt on a photographic plate, covered with black paper, the plate would be affected as if light had fallen on it. The effect is produced by special rays which are emitted by the uranium salt.... My determinations showed that the emission of the rays is an atomic property of the uranium.

The property that Becquerel and the Curies discovered was called radioactivity. Today, radioactivity is used for many purposes— including finding the age of rocks!

After you read Marie Curie's description, answer the following questions.

1. What did Marie and Pierre Curie discover about radioactivity?

   Radioactivity is an atomic property of some substances, such as uranium.

2. What does the discovery of radioactivity tell you about how scientists work together?

   Sample: Scientists build on the knowledge learned by other scientists.

▶ **PLANET DIARY** Go to **Planet Diary** to learn more about the uses of radioactivity.

Lab zone Do the Inquiry Warm-Up *How Long Till It's Gone?*

258 A Trip Through Geologic

SUPPORT ALL READERS

Lexile Measure = 840L   Lexile Word Count = 691

Prior Exposure to Content: May be the first time students have encountered this topic

Academic Vocabulary: *calculate, generalizations, identify*

Science Vocabulary: *half-life, radioactive decay*

Concept Level: May be difficult for students who struggle with math

Preteach With: My Planet Diary "Marie Curie" and Figure 1 activity

Go to **My Reading Web** to access leveled readings that provide a foundation for the content.

my science online.com

LESSON 8.3

Vocabulary
• radioactive decay
• half-life

Skills
○ Reading: Identify the Main Idea
△ Inquiry: Calculate

What Is Radioactive Decay?

Most elements usually do not change. But some elements can break down, or decay, over time. These elements release particles and energy in a process called **radioactive decay**. These elements are said to be radioactive. 🗝 **During radioactive decay, the atoms of one element break down to form atoms of another element.**

Half-Life The rate of decay of each radioactive element never changes. The **half-life** of a radioactive element is the time it takes for half of the radioactive atoms to decay. You can see in **Figure 1** how a radioactive element decays over time.

FIGURE 1 ······························
Half-Life
The half-life of a radioactive element is the amount of time it takes for half of the radioactive atoms to decay.

✏ **Graph** What pattern do you see in the graph? Use the pattern to complete the last bar.

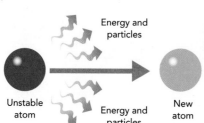

Energy and particles

Unstable atom

Energy and particles

New atom

Decay of Radioactive Element

100% 50% 75% 87.5% 93.75%

50% 25% 12.5% 6.25%

Start 1 2 3 4
Number of Half-Lives

■ Amount of radioactive element remaining
■ Amount of new element formed

Lab zone® Do the Quick Lab *The Dating Game.*

🗝 **Assess Your Understanding**

got it? ·······························

○ I get it! Now I know that radioactive decay occurs when _atoms break down and change into other atoms._

○ I need extra help with _See TE note._

Go to **my science COACH** online for help with this subject.

259

Explain

Introduce Vocabulary

Tell students that any element that breaks down into another element over time is decaying. The term *radioactive decay* is the name for this process, during which the element is radioactive.

Teach Key Concepts 🗝

Explain to students that an element is said to be *radioactive* as it goes through the process of decay. Ask: **What happens to the atoms of the decaying element?** (*The atoms break down to form atoms of a different element.*) **What else is produced during the decay process?** (*Particles and energy are released.*)

Teach With Visuals

Have students look at **Figure 1**. Ask: **After two half-lives, how much of the radioactive element remains?** (*25 percent*) **After three half-lives, how much of the radioactive element remains?** (*12.5 percent*)

Elaborate

Lab Resource: Quick Lab 🔬

L3 THE DATING GAME Students will model half-lives of radioactive elements.

Evaluate

Assess Your Understanding

Have students evaluate their understanding by completing the appropriate sentence.

RTI Response to Intervention

If students need help with explaining the cause of radioactive decay, **then** have them reread the first paragraph under *What is Radioactive Decay?*

my science COACH Have students go online for help in understanding the process of radioactive decay.

My Planet Diary provides an opportunity for students to explore real-world connections to radioactive dating.

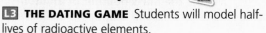
my science online | Radioactive Decay

Explain

Teach Key Concepts 🔑

Explain to students that it is natural for radioactive elements to occur in igneous rocks. Scientists analyze this natural process to determine the absolute ages of rocks. Remind students that the absolute age of a rock is the number of years since it formed. Explain that different radioactive elements are used in the absolute dating of rocks and fossils. Ask: **What is the first step scientists take in radioactive dating?** (*Measuring the amount of radioactive element in a rock*) **What do they do next?** (*Compare that amount with the amount of the new, stable element being formed from the first element's decay*)

Lead a Discussion

Invite students to think about what they know about atoms. Use students' responses to judge how much review individual students need to understand the concept of radioactive dating. Ask: **What is an atom?** (*Students may know that an atom is the smallest part of an element that has all the properties of that element.*) **What does an atom contain?** (*Protons, neutrons, energy*) **What is the atomic number of an atom?** (*The number of protons in the nucleus.*) **What is the mass number of an atom?** (*The number of protons and neutrons in the nucleus*)

Elaborate

Do the Math!

L1 Point out to students that all of the elements in the table except carbon-14 could be used to date objects more than 4.6 billion years old. Explain that an element is generally useful for dating objects with ages up to several times its half-life.

🔺 **Calculate** If students have trouble calculating the number of half-lives that have passed, have them write this series of fractions $\frac{1}{2}$, $\frac{1}{4}$, $\frac{1}{8}$, $\frac{1}{16}$. They can count the number of half lives by following the progression until they reach the fraction mentioned in the problem. Ask: **A rock contains 25 percent of the uranium-238 it started with. What fraction of the original amount is that?** ($\frac{1}{4}$) **How many half-lives have passed?** (*2*)

See *Math Skill* and *Problem-Solving Activities* for support.

What Is Radioactive Dating?

Radioactive elements occur naturally in igneous rocks. Scientists use the rate at which these elements decay to calculate the rock's age. As a radioactive element within the igneous rock decays, it changes into another element. So the composition of the rock changes slowly over time. The amount of the radioactive element decreases. But the amount of the new element increases.

Determining Absolute Ages Geologists use radioactive dating to determine the absolute ages of rocks. 🔑 In radioactive dating, scientists first determine the amount of a radioactive element in a rock. Then they compare that amount with the amount of the stable element into which the radioactive element decays. They use this information and the half-life of the element to calculate the age of the rock.

Potassium-Argon Dating Scientists often date rocks using potassium-40. This form of potassium decays to stable argon-40 and has a half-life of 1.3 billion years. Potassium-40 is useful in dating the most ancient rocks because of its long half-life.

do the math!

Radioactive Dating

A rock contains 25% of the potassium-40 it started with. How old is the rock?

STEP 1 Determine how many half-lives have passed.
After one half-life, 50% of the potassium would remain. After two half-lives, 25% of the potassium would remain. So two half-lives have passed.

STEP 2 Find the half-life of potassium-40.
The half-life of potassium-40 is 1.3 billion years.

STEP 3 Multiply the half-life by the number of half-lives that have passed.
1.3 billion years/half-life × 2 half-lives = 2.6 billion years, so the rock is about 2.6 billion years old.

Elements Used in Radioactive Dating

Radioactive Element	Half-life (years)	Dating Range (years)
Carbon-14	5,730	500–50,000
Potassium-40	1.3 billion	50,000–4.6 billion
Rubidium-87	48.8 billion	10 million–4.6 billion
Thorium-232	14 billion	10 million–4.6 billion
Uranium-235	713 million	10 million–4.6 billion
Uranium-238	4.5 billion	10 million–4.6 billion

❶ **Calculate** A rock from the moon contains 12.5% of the potassium-40 it began with. How old is the rock? (*Hint:* $12.5\% = \frac{1}{8}$)

3.9 billion years

❷ **Calculate** A fossil contains $\frac{1}{16}$ of the carbon-14 it began with. How old is the fossil?

22,920 years

Digital Lesson: Assign the *Do the Math* activity online and have students submit their work to you.

Real-World Inquiry allows students to perform radioactive dating on different fossils.

my science online.com | **Radioactive Dating**

Carbon-14 Dating

Carbon-14 is a radioactive form of carbon. All plants and animals contain carbon, including some carbon-14. After an organism dies, the carbon-14 in the organism's body decays. It changes to stable nitrogen-14. <u>To determine the age of a sample, scientists measure the amount of carbon-14 that is left in the organism's remains.</u> Carbon-14 has been used to date fossils such as frozen mammoths and the skeletons of prehistoric humans.

Carbon-14 has a half-life of only 5,730 years. For this reason, it generally can't be used to date fossils or rocks older than about 50,000 years. The amount of carbon-14 left would be too small to measure accurately. Also, most rocks do not contain much carbon.

✎ **Identify the Main Idea**
Underline the main idea in the first paragraph to the left.

FIGURE 2 ·······················
▶ REAL-WORLD INQUIRY **Using Carbon-14 Dating**
Scientists have dated these skeletons to 5,000–6,000 years ago. But they do not use radioactive dating to find the age of stone artifacts made by people.
✎ **Make Generalizations** Why not?

<u>The stones existed before</u>
<u>they were made into tools.</u>
<u>Radioactive dating cannot</u>
<u>show when the stones were</u>
<u>made into tools.</u>

Lab zone Do the Quick Lab How Old Is It?

🔑 Assess Your Understanding

1a. Identify Scientists use the method of (radioactive dating/relative dating) to find the absolute age of a rock.

b. Apply Concepts The half-life of thorium-232 is 14 billion years. A rock with 25% of its thorium-232 remaining is _28 billion_ years old.

c. CHALLENGE A scientist finds stone tools in the ruins of an ancient house. The house also has ashes in a fireplace. How could the scientist estimate the age of the stone tools?
Sample: The scientist could use radioactive dating to find the age of the ashes. The tools are probably about the same age.

got it? ·······················

○ I get it! Now I know that radioactive dating is done by _using radioactive elements to_
find the absolute age of objects.

○ I need extra help with _See TE note._

Go to **my science COACH** online for help with this subject.

261

Differentiated Instruction

L1 Dating the Moon Rocks Tell students that scientists have estimated that the moon is about 4.5 billion years old. Their estimates were based on analysis of the rocks brought back to Earth by the Apollo astronauts. Have students use the table in the *Do the Math* activity to determine which elements could be used to date the moon rocks *(Any except carbon-14).*

Explain

Support the Big Q ❓ UbD

CARBON-14 All carbon atoms are not radioactive. Review the concept of isotopes, and tell students that carbon-14 is a radioactive isotope of carbon with 6 protons and 8 neutrons in the nucleus. Other carbon isotopes, such as carbon-12, which has 6 protons and 6 neutrons in the nucleus, are not radioactive. Ask: **What is the half-life of carbon-14?** *(5,730 years)* **Is this shorter or longer than most isotopes used for radioactive dating?** *(Shorter)*

✎ **Identify the Main Idea** Tell students that the main idea is the most important idea in a paragraph or section of text. Other facts support the main idea.

Build Inquiry Lab zone

L2 MODEL RADIOACTIVE DATING

Materials 100 pennies, paper cup

Time 20 minutes

Review the definition of *half-life.* Have students place the pennies in a cup, shake it, dump the pennies out, and remove the pennies that come up heads. Then have students take the remaining pennies and repeat the procedure three more times.

Ask: **How does this activity model half-life?** *(Coins have a 50% chance of turning up heads or tails. Half-life is the time it takes for 50% of radioactive atoms to decay.)*

Have students graph their results and compare their graphs to the bar graph in **Figure 1.**

Lab Resource: Quick Lab Lab zone

L3 HOW OLD IS IT? Students will use half-lives to determine approximate ages.

Evaluate

Assess Your Understanding

After students answer the questions, have them evaluate their understanding by completing the appropriate sentence.

RTI Response to Intervention

1a. If students cannot identify dating methods, **then** have them review the paragraph under the red head *Determining Absolute Ages.*

b. If students need help with determining the age of the rock, **then** have them review *Do the Math.*

c. If students need help, **then** have them think about the ashes.

my science COACH Have students go online for help in understanding radioactive dating.

261

Lab® zone **After the Inquiry Warm-Up**

Radioactive Dating

> **Inquiry Warm-Up,** *How Long Till It's Gone?*
> In the Inquiry Warm-Up, you investigated a process that is similar to that used in radioactive dating. Using what you learned from that activity, answer the questions below.

1. **COMMUNICATE** Write an imaginary email to a friend that describes the actions you took during this activity. Be sure to include a summary of what you learned.

   _____

   _____

2. **CALCULATE** Use fractions to explain how big each piece would be, compared to the original size, if you cut the piece of clay three times.

   _____

3. **DRAW CONCLUSIONS** Repeating this process as many or as few times as necessary, is it possible to make a piece of clay that is one-tenth of its original size? Why or why not?

   _____

   _____

4. **INFER** How many cuts would it take to end up with NO clay remaining? [HINT: Suppose you could use a powerful microscope when the piece of clay became too small to see with the naked eye.]

   _____

   _____

Name _____ Date _____ Class _____

Radioactive Dating

What Is Radioactive Decay?

got_it? ....

○ **I get it!** Now I know that radioactivity decay occurs when _____

_____

○ **I need extra help with** _____

_____

What Is Radioactive Dating?

1a. **IDENTIFY** Scientists use the method of (radioactive dating/relative dating) to find the absolute age of a rock.

b. **APPLY CONCEPTS** The half-life of potassium-40 is 1.3 billion years. A rock with 25% of its potassium-40 remaining is _____ years old.

c. CHALLENGE A scientist finds stone tools in the ruins of an ancient house. The house also has ashes in a fireplace. How could the scientist estimate the age of the stone tools?

_____

_____

_____

got_it? ....

○ **I get it!** Now I know that radioactive dating is done by _____

_____

○ **I need extra help with** _____

_____

Key Concept Summaries

Radioactive Dating

What Is Radioactive Decay?

Some elements decay, or break down, over time, releasing particles and energy. This process is called **radioactive decay,** and the elements are considered to be radioactive. **During radioactive decay, the atoms of one element break down to form** **atoms of another element.** The **half-life** of a radioactive element is the time it takes for half of the radioactive atoms to decay. The rate of decay of each radioactive element never changes.

What Is Radioactive Dating?

Radioactive elements in igneous rocks decay over time into other elements. This slowly changes the composition of the rock. Geologists use radioactive dating to determine the absolute ages of rocks. **In radioactive dating, scientists first determine the amount of a radioactive element in a rock. Then they compare that amount with the amount of the stable element into which the radioactive element decays.** They calculate the age of the rock using this information and the half-life of the element.

Some elements used by scientists in radioactive dating include potassium-40 and carbon-14. Potassium-40 has a long half-life, which is useful in dating the most ancient rocks. All plants and animals contain some carbon-14, which decays after the organism dies. Scientists measure the amounts of carbon-14 to determine the age of a rock sample.

On a separate sheet of paper, explain how scientists are able to determine the absolute ages of rocks.

Name _____ Date _____ Class _____

Radioactive Dating

Understanding Main Ideas
Look at the diagram below. Then answer the questions that follow on a separate sheet of paper.

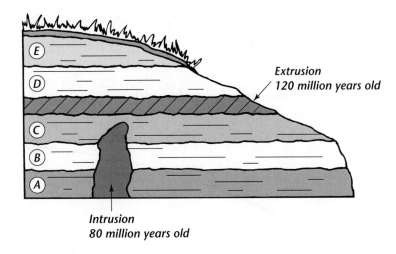

Extrusion
120 million years old

Intrusion
80 million years old

1. Can geologists use radioactive dating to find the absolute ages of sedimentary layers A, B, C, D, and E? Explain why or why not.
2. Can geologists use radioactive dating to find the absolute ages of the extrusion or the intrusion? Explain why or why not.
3. What is the relative age of rock layer C? Explain how you determined its age.
4. Explain the natural process on which radioactive dating is based.

Building Vocabulary
Fill in the blank to complete each statement below.

5. During a natural process called _____, the atoms of one element break down to form atoms of another element.

6. The elements formed after atoms have broken down and reformed are said to be

   _____.

7. The time it takes for half of the atoms in a sample of a radioactive element to decay

   is called the element's _____.

Radioactive Dating

> The graph below shows radioactive decay over time. Look at the graph and then answer the questions that follow on a separate sheet of paper.

A Continuous Process

In potassium-argon dating, geologists measure the amount of radioactive potassium-40 in igneous rock and compare that amount with the amount of stable argon-40. From this comparison, geologists can tell the absolute age of the rock.

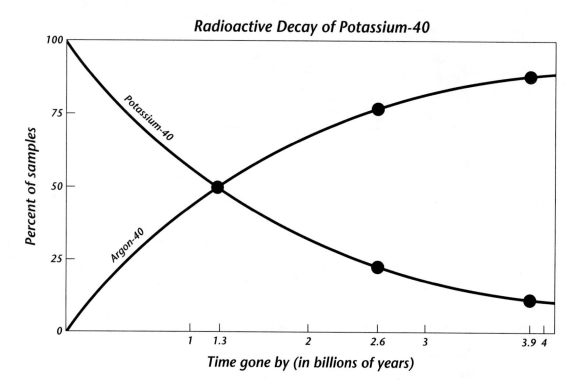

Radioactive Decay of Potassium-40

1. When the rock first forms, what is the percent of potassium-40 compared with the percent of argon-40?
2. What is the half-life of potassium-40?
3. What are the percentages of the two elements at 1.3 billion years?
4. After the first 1.3 billion years, does the rock contain more potassium-40 or argon-40?
5. What are the percentages of the two elements after three half-lives of potassium-40?
6. Do 1.3 billion years have to pass before a difference in the amounts of these two elements occurs? Explain.

Lesson Quiz

Radioactive Dating

If the statement is true, write *true*. If the statement is false, change the underlined word or words to make the statement true.

1. _____ Most elements <u>do not</u> change.

2. _____ Some <u>elements</u> can decay over time.

3. _____ The rate of decay of any radioactive element <u>changes frequently</u>.

4. _____ Radioactive elements occur naturally in <u>sedimentary</u> rocks.

5. _____ Geologists use radioactive dating to determine <u>the absolute ages of rocks</u>.

6. _____ All plants and <u>animals</u> contain carbon.

Fill in the blank to complete each statement.

7. An element that has broken down and released particles and energy is said to be _____.

8. _____ is a method of determining the absolute ages of rocks.

9. _____ is the time it takes for half of the radioactive atoms in an element to decay.

10. During _____, the atoms of one element break down to form atoms of another element.

Radioactive Dating

Answer Key

After the Inquiry Warm-Up

1. Sample: Hi Raif: Today in class we used clay cubes to investigate a process that is similar to the process scientists use in radioactive dating. We learned that the clay kept getting smaller and smaller each time we cut it in half.

2. one half, one fourth, one eighth

3. It is not possible, because the successive cuts reduce the size to one half, one fourth, one eighth, and one sixteenth of the original size. The denominations of the fractional parts are all powers of 2.

4. Since you are cutting the piece of clay in half each time, no matter how many cuts you made, there would always be some clay remaining.

Key Concept Summaries

Scientists use radioactive dating to determine the absolute ages of rocks. Radioactive dating is a method of analyzing the natural process of radioactive decay in elements, in which the atoms of one element break down to form atoms of another element.

Review and Reinforce

1. Since radioactive dating is used only on igneous rock, this process would not work on sedimentary layers A, B, C, D, and E. Sedimentary rock layers are made of particles from other rocks. Dating would provide the ages of those particles, not of the rock itself.

2. They can use radioactive dating because extrusions and intrusions are made of igneous rock.

3. Rock layer C is at least 80 million years old. It is possible to identify its relative age because we know the age of the intrusion that cuts partway across it. An intrusion is always younger than the rock it cuts through.

4. Radioactive dating is based on the concept of radioactive decay. During radioactive decay, the atoms of one element break down to form the elements of another element.

5. radioactive decay

6. radioactive

7. half-life

Enrich

1. potassium-40, 100%; argon-40, 0%

2. 1.3 billion years

3. Each amounts to 50%.

4. more argon-40

5. potassium-40, 12.5%; argon-40, 87.5%

6. No. The potassium-40 immediately begins to decay into argon-40 when the rock is formed.

Lesson Quiz

1. true
2. true
3. never changes
4. igneous
5. true
6. true
7. radioactive
8. Radioactive dating
9. Half-life
10. radioactive decay

Place the outside corner, the corner away from the dotted line, in the corner of your copy machine to copy onto letter-size paper.

The Geologic Time Scale

How do scientists study Earth's past?

Lesson Pacing: 1–2 periods or ½–1 block

🕐 **SHORT ON TIME?** To do this lesson in approximately half the time, do the Activate Prior Knowledge activity followed by a discussion of the Key Concepts to familiarize students with the lesson content. Have students do the Quick Lab. The rest of the lesson can be completed by students independently.

> **Preference Navigator,** in the online Planning tools, allows you to customize *Interactive Science* to your own teaching style. You can also edit lesson plans by selecting the Lesson Planner option.
>
> **Digital Teacher's Edition** Edition allows you to access your Teacher's Edition and Resource materials online.

my science ONLINE.com

Lesson Vocabulary

- geologic time scale   • era   • period

 Content Refresher

Professional Development Note

Development of the Time Scale The concept of geologic time was first developed in the late 1700s and early 1800s. Geologists in England and other parts of Europe devised the geologic time scale during the 1800s. They established these eras, periods, and epochs through relative dating methods, carefully correlating rock layers throughout the world using index fossils—a monumental achievement.

The Paleogene Period includes these five epochs (with starting date in millions of years ago): Paleocene (65.5), Eocene (55.8), and Oligocene (33.9). The Neogene Period includes these epochs: Miocene (23.03) and Pliocene (5.33). The Quaternary Period includes these two epochs: Pleistocene (1.8) and Holocene (0.01). Today, we are in the Holocene Epoch of the Quaternary Period of the Cenozoic Era.

LESSON OBJECTIVE

🔑 Establish how and why the geologic time scale is used to show Earth's history.

Blended Path
Active learning using Student Edition, Inquiry Path, and Digital Path

ENGAGE AND EXPLORE

Teach this lesson using a variety of resources. Begin by reading **My Planet Diary** as a class. Have students discuss the table showing Earth's history in a day. Then have students do the **Inquiry Warm-Up activity.** Students will create a timeline of their own lives. The **After the Inquiry Warm-Up worksheet** sets up a discussion of how to make a model of a geologic time scale. Have volunteers share the timelines they created in response to question 4.

EXPLAIN AND ELABORATE

Teach Key Concepts by explaining that scientists use the geologic time scale as an organizational tool to make it easier to communicate information about Earth's history. **Support the Big Q** by identifying the major changes in the fossil record that mark the beginning and end of each time unit on the geologic time scale. Have students practice the inquiry skill in the **Apply It activity.**

Hand out the **Key Concept Summaries** as a review of each part of the lesson. Students can also use the online **Vocab Flash Cards** to review key terms.

EVALUATE

Have students take the **Lesson Quiz.** For an alternate assessment, see the **EXAM**VIEW® Assessment Suite, Progress Monitoring Assessments, or SuccessTracker™.

E L L Support

1 Content and Language

Have students complete this Cloze sentence using vocabulary terms for the lesson: There are three major _____ on the Geologic Time Scale, each of which is divided into _____.

Lab zone Inquiry Path
Hands-on learning in the Lab zone

ENGAGE AND EXPLORE

To teach this lesson with an emphasis on inquiry, begin with the **Inquiry Warm-Up activity.** Students will create a timeline of their own lives. The **After the Inquiry Warm-Up worksheet** sets up a discussion of how to make a model of a geologic time scale. Have volunteers share the timelines they created in response to question 4.

EXPLAIN AND ELABORATE

Focus on the **Inquiry Skill** for the lesson. Point out that making models is necessary when dealing with things or processes that cannot be observed because they are too small, too large, or take place too slowly. What type of model could be created in the **Inquiry Warm-Up Activity?** *(A timeline)* **Support the Big Q** by identifying the major changes in the fossil record that mark the beginning and end of each time unit on the geologic time scale. Do the **Build Inquiry** having students create a bar graph to show the actual proportions of the divisions in the geologic time scale. Review the geologic time scale in **Figure 2** before beginning the **Apply It activity.** Have students share the ideas about the advantages and disadvantages of using a 1 m = 1 million years scale. Have students do the **Quick Lab** comparing the major units of geologic time to distances in a long hallway. Students can use the online **Vocab Flash Cards** to review key terms.

EVALUATE

Have students take the **Lesson Quiz.** For an alternate assessment, see the **EXAM**VIEW® Assessment Suite, Progress Monitoring Assessments, or SuccessTracker™.

Digital Path
Online learning at MY SCIENCE ONLINE.com

ENGAGE AND EXPLORE

Teach this lesson using digital resources. Begin by having students learn more about Earth's history and explore real-world connections to Earth's history at **My Planet Diary** online. Have them access the Chapter Resources to find the **Unlock the Big Question activity.** There they can answer the questions and refine their responses as they continue through the lesson. You can re-assign the activity and have students submit their work so you can track their progress.

EXPLAIN AND ELABORATE

Students reading above, at, or below the lexile measure of this lesson can access basic content readings at their level at **My Reading Web.** Encourage students to use the online **Vocab Flash Cards** to preview key terms. Assign the **Apply It activity** online and have students submit their results to you. Have students do the **Quick Lab** comparing the major units of geologic time to distances in a long hallway. The **Key Concept Summaries** online allow students to read a summary and see an image associated with each part of the lesson. Online remediation is available at **My Science Coach.**

EVALUATE

Have students take the **Lesson Quiz.** For an alternate assessment, see the **EXAM**VIEW® Assessment Suite, Progress Monitoring Assessments, or SuccessTracker™.

2 Frontload the Lesson

Skim the headings, images, and vocabulary terms with students. Have them make predictions about the lesson content. As you read the text with students, stop after each section and ask them to compare their predictions with the information in the lesson.

3 Comprehensible Input

Have students study the scale in **Figure 2.** Discuss the labels on the visual. Ask students to complete these sentences. The first segment of time on the Geologic Time Scale is named ____. The ____ Era follows Precambrian Time. The ____ Era is sandwiched between the Paleozoic Era and the ____ Era.

4 Language Production

Pair or group students with varied language abilities to complete labs collaboratively for language practice. Have each student copy the completed written lab for personal reference.

5 Assess Understanding

Divide the class into small groups. Have each student identify a key concept from the lesson to discuss in his or her group. After the discussions, have students talk about the key concepts as a group.

LESSON 8.4

The Geologic Time Scale

Establish Learning Objective

After this lesson, students will be able to:

🔑 Explain how and why the geologic time scale is used to show Earth's history.

Engage

Activate Prior Knowledge

MY PLANET DIARY Read *Earth's History in a Day* with the class. Point out that the intervals shown for Earth's 4.6-billion-year history and a single 24-hour day are in proportion. Ask: **What is the longest span between events in the table?** *(10 hours between events C and D)* **What is the shortest span?** *(Less than 20 minutes between events H and I)* Tell students that they will learn about a scale developed by scientists to help them organize information about Earth's history.

BIG IDEAS OF SCIENCE REFERENCE LIBRARY 📖 Have students look up the following topic: Geologic Time.

Explore

Lab Resource: Inquiry Warm-Up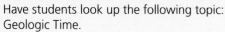

[L1] **THIS IS YOUR LIFE!** Students will create a timeline of their own lives.

The Geologic Time Scale

 🔑 **What Is the Geologic Time Scale?**

MY PLANET DIARY

SCIENCE STATS

Earth's History in a Day

Suppose you could squeeze all of Earth's 4.6-billion-year history into one 24-hour day. The table shows the times at which some major events would take place.

	Time	First Appearance
A	Midnight	Earth
B	3:00 A.M.	Rocks
C	4:00 A.M.	Bacteria
D	2:00 P.M.	Algae
E	8:30–9:00 P.M.	Seaweeds and jellyfish
F	10:00 P.M.	Land plants
G	10:50 P.M.	Dinosaurs
H	11:39 P.M.	Mammals
I	11:58:43 P.M.	Humans

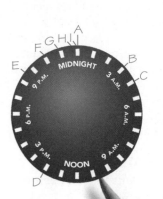

Use the data in the table to answer these questions.

1. ✎ **Sequence** Write the letter for each event on the clock diagram.

2. Did anything surprise you about the data? If so, what?

   <u>Sample: I was surprised that dinosaurs</u>
   <u>arose so late.</u>

▶ **PLANET DIARY** Go to **Planet Diary** to learn more about Earth's history.

Lab zone Do the Inquiry Warm-Up *This Is Your Life!*

SUPPORT ALL READERS

Lexile Measure = 920L   Lexile Word Count = 567

Prior Exposure to Content: Many students may have misconceptions on this topic

Academic Vocabulary: *model, summarize*

Science Vocabulary: *era, geologic time scale, period*

Concept Level: Generally appropriate for most students in this grade

Preteach With: My Planet Diary "Earth's History in a Day" and Figure 2 activity

Go to **My Reading Web** to access leveled readings that provide a foundation for the content.

my science online.com

LESSON 8.4

Vocabulary
- geologic time scale
- era • period

Skills
- Reading: Summarize
- Inquiry: Make Models

What Is the Geologic Time Scale?

When you speak of the past, what names do you use for different spans of time? You probably use names such as century, decade, year, month, week, and day. But these units aren't very helpful for thinking about much longer periods of time. Scientists needed to develop a way to talk about Earth's history.

🔑 **Because the time span of Earth's past is so great, geologists use the geologic time scale to show Earth's history.** The **geologic time scale** is a record of the geologic events and the evolution of life forms as shown in the fossil record.

Scientists first developed the geologic time scale by studying rock layers and index fossils worldwide. With this information, scientists placed Earth's rocks in order by relative age. Later, radioactive dating helped determine the absolute age of the divisions in the geologic time scale. **Figure 1** shows some of the earliest known rocks.

🔄 **Summarize** Write two or three sentences to summarize the information on this page.

Sample: The geologic time scale records events over Earth's history. Scientists developed it by studying rock layers and fossils.

FIGURE 1 ·······························

Ancient Rocks
The Isua rocks in Greenland are among the oldest rocks on Earth. They formed after heat and pressure changed sedimentary rocks that formed under early oceans.

263

Explain

Introduce Vocabulary

Explain to students that scientists realized it would be helpful to devise new terms to identify long periods of time in Earth's geologic history. The words *era* and *period* were not new to the English language, but as they came to be used by geologists, these words took on new, scientific definitions. An era is the longest span of time and a period is the next longest span.

Teach Key Concepts 🔑

Explain to students that the geologic time scale was developed by scientists as an organizational tool to make it easier to communicate information about Earth's history. Ask: **Why was it was necessary or desirable to devise the geologic time scale?** *(There were no terms to identify the extremely long periods of time in Earth's history.)* **What did scientist study as they were developing the geologic time scale?** *(Rock layers and index fossils)* Point out that, unlike days and years, the length of an era or a period is not standard. The lengths of a day and a year are based on the movements of Earth relative to the sun. These movements form a repeating pattern. The dividing points between eras and periods are based on events in Earth's history, and do not form a repeating pattern.

🔄 **Summarize** Tell students that summarizing is creating a short statement that presents the most important points about a subject and does not include every detail.

My Planet Diary provides an opportunity for students to explore real-world connections to Earth's history.

my science online | Geologic Time Scale

1 Content and Language
Write the terms *Cenozoic, Mesozoic, and Paleozoic* on the board. Explain that *-zoic* means "life." It is a word part derived from the Greek word for "animal" with the suffix *-ic* added. *Ceno-* means "recent," *meso-* means "middle," and *paleo-* means "ancient or early."

2 Frontload the Lesson
Ask volunteers to describe the fossils of animals they have seen in museums and to try to explain how long ago some of these animals lived.

3 Comprehensible Input
Have students create a table like the one shown in this lesson. Students can illustrate the table with additional examples of life forms from the different periods shown.

Explain

Teach With Visuals

Tell students to look at **Figure 2**. Ask: **Why is a time scale used instead of a calendar to represent Earth's history?** *(A calendar would be hard to use because Earth's history is so long.)* **Why does this figure make the most sense arranged vertically in the order it appears here?** *(The vertical arrangement from most recent years on top to most distant years on bottom is the same as what would be found in the ground itself, not counting unconformities.)* **When did geologic time begin?** *(About 4,600 years ago.)* **When does geologic time end?** *(It doesn't; we are now in the Quaternary Period of he Cenozoic Era.)* Encourage students to think about scale and scale models. Ask them to identify which era would take up the most space if the chart were drawn to scale *(Precambrian Time)*.

Support the Big Q ? UbD

ERAS AND PERIODS Remind students that the geologic time scale is a tool that scientists use to keep track of Earth's history. Major changes in the fossil record mark the beginning and end of each time unit. Ask: **How long is a geologic period?** *(A period doesn't have an exact length. Periods vary from the 30 million years of the Silurian to the 78 million years of the Cretaceous.)* **Which is the largest division of geologic time?** *(Era)*

Address Misconceptions

L1 ROOM FOR ERA Thanks to cartoons and comic strips, many children think that dinosaurs and people lived at the same time. Some students may still believe this. Tell them that dinosaurs lived in the Mesozoic Era, and people didn't exist until the Quaternary Period. Ask: **What are the periods of the Mesozoic Era?** *(Triassic, Jurassic, Cretaceous)* **Is the Quaternary Period part of the Mesozoic Era?** *(No)* **So could people and dinosaurs have existed at the same time?** *(No)*

FIGURE 2

The Geologic Time Scale
The divisions of the geologic time scale are used to date events in Earth's history.

✎ **Calculate** After you read the next page, calculate and fill in the duration of each period. Then use the time scale to identify the period in which each organism below lived.

Organism: *Wiwaxia*
Age: about 500 million years
Period: Cambrian

Organism: *Velociraptor*
Age: about 80 million years
Period: Cretaceous

Organism: *Smilodon*
Age: about 12,000 years
Period: Quaternary

264 A Trip Through Geologic Time

	PERIOD	MILLIONS OF YEARS AGO	DURATION (MILLIONS OF YEARS)
Cenozoic Era	QUATERNARY	1.8	1.8
	NEOGENE	23	21.2
	PALEOGENE	66	43
Mesozoic Era	CRETACEOUS	146	80
	JURASSIC	200	54
	TRIASSIC	251	51
Paleozoic Era	PERMIAN	299	48
	CARBONIFEROUS	359	60
	DEVONIAN	416	57
	SILURIAN	444	28
	ORDOVICIAN	488	44
	CAMBRIAN	542	54
Precambrian Time		4,600	4,058

Digital Lesson: Assign the *Apply It* activity online and have students submit their work to you.

my science online.com — Geologic Time Scale

Dividing Geologic Time As geologists studied the fossil record, they found major changes in life forms at certain times. They used these changes to mark where one unit of geologic time ends and the next begins. Therefore, the divisions of the geologic time scale depend on events in the history of life on Earth. **Figure 2** shows the major divisions of the geologic time scale.

Precambrian Time Geologic time begins with a long span of time called Precambrian Time (pree KAM bree un). Precambrian Time, which covers about 88 percent of Earth's history, ended 542 million years ago. Few fossils survive from this time period.

Eras Geologists divide the time between Precambrian Time and the present into three long units of time called **eras.** They are the Paleozoic Era, the Mesozoic Era, and the Cenozoic Era.

Periods Eras are subdivided into units of geologic time called **periods.** You can see in **Figure 2** that the Mesozoic Era includes three periods: the Triassic Period, the Jurassic Period, and the Cretaceous Period.

The names of many of the geologic periods come from places around the world where geologists first described the rocks and fossils of that period. For example, the name *Cambrian* refers to Cambria, a Latin name for Wales. The rocks shown below are in Wales. The dark bottom layer dates from the Cambrian period.

apply it!

Refer to the geologic time scale shown in **Figure 2** to answer the questions below.

Suppose you want to make a model of the geologic time scale. You decide to use a scale of 1 cm = 1 million years.

❶ Not counting Precambrian time, which era would take up the most space? _Paleozoic_

❷ Make Models How long would the Mesozoic Era be in your model? _185 cm_

❸ **CHALLENGE** Suppose you used a different scale: 1 m = 1 million years. What would be one advantage and one disadvantage of this scale?

Advantage: It could
show smaller divisions
of time. Disadvan-
tage: It would take
lots of space to show
all of Earth's history.

Lab Do the Quick Lab
zone *Going Back in Time.*

🔑 Assess Your Understanding

1a. Define The geologic time scale is a record of _life forms_ and _geologic events_ .

b. Sequence Number the following periods in order from earliest to latest.

Neogene __4__   Jurassic __2__
Quaternary __5__   Triassic __1__
Cretaceous __3__

c. Draw Conclusions Refer to My Planet Diary and **Figure 2.** During which period did modern humans arise?

Quaternary

got it?

○ I get it! Now I know that geologic time _is divided into eras and periods to_ _show the long span of Earth's history._

○ I need extra help with _See TE note._

Go to **my science ⬤ COACH** *online for help with this subject.*

265

Differentiated Instruction

L1 **Understanding Tables** Make sure that students understand the table in **Figure 2** by having them answer questions such as these: *What is the name of the earliest era in geologic time? What are the Periods of the Paleozoic Era, from oldest to most recent? How long did the Jurassic Period last?* You may wish to redraw the table horizontally for students who have difficulty interpreting a vertical timeline.

L3 **Create a Timeline** Invite students to research Earth's ice ages and create a timeline, noting the length of each ice age and some of the animal life that characterized each ice age.

Elaborate

Build Inquiry **Lab zone**

L3 **COMPARE AND CONTRAST VISUALS**

Materials paper, colored pencils or markers

Time 20 minutes

Review the geologic time scale. Remind students that **Figure 2** is not drawn to scale. Explain that the Cenozoic Era represents $1\frac{1}{2}$% of the total time of 4,600 millions of years. The Mesozoic Era represents 4%; the Paleozoic Era represents $6\frac{1}{2}$%; and Precambrian Time represents 88%. Have students show these proportions in a single bar graph.

Ask: **How does your visual compare and contrast with Figure 2?** *(Both represent time in four successive divisions. My visual shows the proportion of total time represented by each span. The time scale conveys the relationship numerically.)*

Apply It!

L1 Review the geologic time scale in **Figure 2** before beginning the activity.

△ **Make Models** Point out that making models is necessary when dealing with things or processes that cannot be observed (too small, too large, take place too slowly). The geologic time scale is such a model. Ask: **If one particular period represents 75 percent of a timeline, how much of a scale model will that particular period represent?** *(75 percent)*

Lab Resource: Quick Lab **Lab zone**

L2 **GOING BACK IN TIME** Students will compare the major units of geologic time to distances in a long hallway.

Evaluate

Assess Your Understanding

After students answers the questions, have them evaluate their understanding by completing the appropriate sentence.

R T I Response to Intervention

1a. If students cannot define *geologic time scale,* **then** have them locate the highlighted term and reread the definition.

b. If If students need help with sequencing periods, **then** have them review **Figure 2.**

c. If students have trouble identifying events in geologic history, **then** have them review **Figure 2.**

my science ⬤ COACH Have students go online for help in understanding how geologic time is divided.

265

Name ______________________ Date ____________ Class ____________

Lab zone After the Inquiry Warm-Up

The Geologic Time Scale

Inquiry Warm-Up, *This Is Your Life!*

In the Inquiry Warm-Up, you investigated how to make a model of a geologic time scale. Using what you learned from that activity, answer the questions below.

1. **OBSERVE** How many periods make up your timeline? Which is the longest period, and which is the shortest period? Explain.

____

____

____

2. **INTERPRET DATA** Which period contains most of the important events in your life?

____

____

3. **DRAW CONCLUSIONS** What can you conclude about the relationship between the length of a period and the importance of the events in that period?

____

____

4. **GRAPH** In the space below, sketch a timeline for a person you know who is much older than you are. How would you construct a timeline representing this person's life? How would you choose to divide this timeline into parts? Note the ways in which this timeline is both similar to and different from your own timeline.

Place the outside corner, the corner away from the dotted line, in the corner of your copy machine to copy onto letter-size paper.

Assess Your Understanding

The Geologic Time Scale

What Is the Geologic Time Scale?

1a. DEFINE The geologic time scale is a record of _____
and _____.

b. SEQUENCE Number the following periods in order from earliest to
latest.

Neogene ____

Quaternary ____

Cretaceous ____

Jurassic ____

Triassic ____

c. DRAW CONCLUSIONS Refer to My Planet Diary and **Figure 2.** During
which period did modern humans arise?

_____

got it? ....

○ **I get it!** Now I know that geologic time _____

_____

○ **I need extra help with** _____

_____

Name _____ Date _____ Class _____

The Geologic Time Scale

What Is the Geologic Time Scale?

The history of the Earth covers an enormous length of time. Scientists have developed new terms to identify long periods. **Because the time span of Earth's past is so great, geologists use the geologic time scale to show Earth's history.** The **geologic time scale** is a record of the geologic events and the evolution of life forms as shown in the fossil record.

In the geologic time scale, scientists have placed Earth's rocks in order by relative age. Then they divided geologic time into parts, based on times in Earth's history when there were major changes in life forms. The earliest part of the geologic time scale was named Precambrian Time. This part, which is by far the longest of the geologic time scale, ended 542 million years ago.

Scientists divided the time between Precambrian Time and the present into three long units of time called **eras.** These are the Paleozoic Era, the Mesozoic Era, and the Cenozoic Era. Moreover, scientists subdivided eras into units of geologic time called **periods.** The Paleozoic Era is made up of six periods; the Mesozoic Era is made up of three periods; and the Cenozoic Era is made up three periods. The last of these, the Quaternary Period, continues to the present time.

On a separate sheet of paper, summarize how scientists classify geologic time.

Place the outside corner, the corner away from the dotted line, in the corner of your copy machine to copy onto letter-size paper.

Review and Reinforce

The Geologic Time Scale

Understanding Main Ideas

Put the following items in order from oldest (D) to most recent (A) by writing a letter in the blank beside each one.

1. ___ Mesozoic Era

2. ___ Precambrian Time

3. ___ Cenozoic Era

4. ___ Paleozoic Era

Answer the following questions on a separate sheet of paper.

5. Why is the geologic time scale used to show Earth's history?

6. How would you rewrite the following sentence to make it true? *Geologists subdivide periods into eras.*

7. What methods did geologists use when they first developed the geologic time scale?

8. How did geologists decide where one division of the geologic time scale ends and the next begins?

Building Vocabulary

Match each term with its definition by writing the letter of the correct term in the right column on the line beside the definition in the left column.

9. ___ a unit of geologic time that subdivides eras   **A.** period

10. ___ a long unit of time used to divide the time between Precambrian Time and the present   **B.** geologic time scale

11. ___ a record of the geologic events and the evolution of life forms as shown in the fossil record   **C.** era

The Geologic Time Scale

The figure below shows how old the layers of the Grand Canyon are. Answer the questions that follow on a separate sheet of paper.

A Young Canyon Made of Old Layers

As the Colorado River cut down through Earth's crust to form the Grand Canyon, it exposed layer after layer of sedimentary rock.

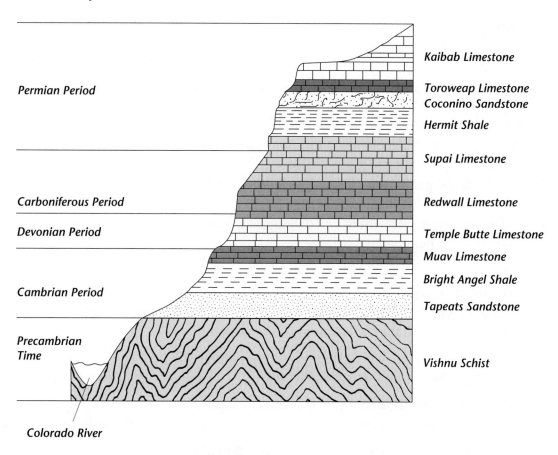

1. Did any of the rock in this part of the Grand Canyon form before the Paleozoic Era began? Explain.
2. During which period did the Redwall limestone form?
3. During which period did the Bright Angel shale form?
4. During which period did the Coconino sandstone form?
5. Did any of the rock that forms the Grand Canyon form during the Mesozoic Era? Explain.
6. What periods of the Paleozoic Era are not represented by rock of the Grand Canyon? How might you account for such gaps?

Name _____ Date _____ Class _____

The Geologic Time Scale

If the statement is true, write *true.* **If the statement is false, change the underlined word or words to make the statement true.**

1. _____ The geologic time scale is a record of <u>the geologic events and the evolution of life forms</u> as shown in the fossil record.

2. _____ The first step in developing <u>the geologic time scale</u> was studying rock layers and index fossils worldwide.

3. _____ Scientists divided the time between Precambrian Time and the present into <u>four</u> units of time, or eras.

4. _____ <u>Periods</u> are subdivided into units of geologic time called <u>eras</u>.

Fill in the blank to complete each statement.

5. Because the time span of Earth's past is so great, geologists use the _____ time scale to show Earth's history.

6. Scientists chose where units of geologic time began and ended based on major changes in _____ at certain times.

7. The long span of time that begins geologic time is called

   _____.

8. Geologists divided the time between Precambrian Time and the present into three long units of time called _____.

9. The Triassic Period, the Jurassic Period, and the Cretaceous Period occurred in the _____ Era.

10. _____ for many of the geologic periods come from places around the world where geologists first described the rocks and fossils of that period.

The Geologic Time Scale

Answer Key

After the Inquiry Warm-Up

1. Answers will vary. Students may choose to use the three periods suggested in the activity. Periods will vary according to students' choices about how to divide their timelines into parts.

2. Answers will vary.

3. Answers will vary. Students may indicate that the most important events do not necessarily appear in the longest period of the timeline.

4. Students' timelines will vary. Some students may construct this timeline with the same number of periods, each period spanning a greater number of years than the periods in their own timelines. Other students may divide the older person's timeline into a greater number of periods.

Key Concept Summary

Scientists divided geologic time into parts, based on times in Earth's history when there were major changes in life forms. The geologic time scale is divided into Precambrian time and three eras. These three eras contain between three and six periods of time.

Review and Reinforce

1. C

2. A

3. D

4. B

5. Geologists use the geologic time scale to show Earth's history because the time span of Earth's past is so great.

6. Geologists subdivide eras into periods.

7. They studied rock layers and index fossils worldwide. With that information, they placed Earth's rock layers in order by relative age.

8. The divisions of the geologic time scale depend on events in the history of life on Earth.

9. A

10. C

11. B

Enrich

1. Yes. The bottom slanted rock layers formed in Precambrian Time, which was before the Paleozoic Era.

2. Carboniferous Period

3. Cambrian Period

4. Permian Period

5. No. The rock layers end with the Permian Period, which is before the Mesozoic Era began.

6. Neither the Ordovician nor the Silurian periods are represented by rock layers. It could be that no sediment was deposited during those periods or that layers formed but were later eroded away.

Lesson Quiz

1. true
2. true
3. false; three
4. false; Eras, periods
5. geologic
6. life forms
7. Precambrian Time
8. eras
9. Mesozoic
10. Names

Place the outside corner, the corner away from the dotted line, in the corner of your copy machine to copy onto letter-size paper.

Early Earth

 How do scientists study Earth's past?

Lesson Pacing: 1–2 periods or $\frac{1}{2}$–1 block

SHORT ON TIME? To do this lesson in approximately half the time, do the Activate Prior Knowledge activity followed by a discussion of the Key Concepts to familiarize students with the lesson content. Have students do the Quick Lab. The rest of the lesson can be completed by students independently.

Preference Navigator, in the online Planning tools, allows you to customize *Interactive Science* to your own teaching style. You can also edit lesson plans by selecting the Lesson Planner option.

Digital Teacher's Edition allows you to access your Teacher's Edition and Resource materials online.

my science online.com

Lesson Vocabulary

• comet

 ## Content Refresher

Origin of Life on Earth There is more than one scientific hypothesis of how life began on Earth. Perhaps comets striking Earth brought organic molecules necessary for life, or perhaps conditions on Earth were right for complex chemicals to come together as a primitive organism. Some scientists believe Earth's first organisms may have originated in what seems at first to be an unlikely location: in or around hydrothermal vents—fissures in Earth's surface from which heated water flows—on the ocean floor.

Undersea hydrothermal vents spew seawater that has seeped down into Earth's crust and been superheated by molten rock. Its temperature can exceed 375°C. When scientists first explored some of these vents in 1979, they were surprised to find that, despite being located far deeper than sunlight can reach, the area around the vents was teeming with life, including varieties of worms, fishes, and crabs. Hyperthermophiles, microorganisms that can live at temperatures above 90°C, are the base of these ecosystems. Having passed through volcanic areas of the crust, the water flowing from the vents is rich in minerals and sulfur compounds. Though toxic to most known organisms, the single-celled bacteria around the vents are able to use these sulfur compounds to produce food through chemosynthesis. Scientists are now trying to determine if the unique mix of chemicals and energy in or near these hydrothermal vents could have fueled chemical processes that led to the creation of the first living organisms on Earth.

LESSON OBJECTIVE

Explain how Earth developed during Precambrian time.

Blended Path
Active learning using Student Edition, Inquiry Path, and Digital Path

ENGAGE AND EXPLORE

Teach this lesson using a variety of resources. Begin by reading **My Planet Diary** as a class. Have students discuss the challenges faced by scientists who study life under water. Then have students do the **Inquiry Warm-Up activity.** Students will make a model that demonstrates the formation of Earth. The **After the Inquiry Warm-Up worksheet** sets up a discussion about early Earth. Have volunteers share their answers to question 4 about how other planets may have formed.

EXPLAIN AND ELABORATE

Teach Key Concepts by explaining that scientists believe that dust, rock, and ice made up Earth in its earliest state until the force of gravity pulled the matter together. **Lead a Discussion** about the gases in the early atmosphere and the second atmosphere and how the formation of this atmosphere lead to the formation of the oceans. **Support the Big Q** by using **Figure 3** to discuss early Precambrian organisms, helping students understand that scientists use these fossils to learn more about Earth's early life forms. Have students practice the inquiry skill in the **Apply It activity.**

Hand out the **Key Concept Summaries** as a review of each part of the lesson. Students can also use the online **Vocab Flash Cards** to review key terms.

EVALUATE

Have students take the **Lesson Quiz.** For an alternate assessment, see the **EXAM**VIEW® Assessment Suite, Progress Monitoring Assessments, or SuccessTracker™.

ELL Support

1 Content and Language

Have students identify the comets in the artist's illustration in **Figure 1.** Discuss what a comet might look like in the night sky.

Lab zone Inquiry Path
Hands-on learning in the Lab zone

Digital Path
Online learning at my science online.com

ENGAGE AND EXPLORE

To teach this lesson with an emphasis on inquiry, begin with the **Inquiry Warm-Up activity.** Students will make a model that demonstrates the formation of Earth. The **After the Inquiry Warm-Up worksheet** sets up a discussion about early Earth. Have volunteers share their answers to question 4 about how other planets may have formed.

EXPLAIN AND ELABORATE

Focus on the **Inquiry Skill** for the lesson. Remind students that human begins communicate in many ways, including words, images, and gestures. What details could be communicated about the force of the magnet in the **Inquiry Warm-Up Activity?** *(The force of the magnet was strong enough to attract the filings.)* **Support the Big Q** by using **Figure 3** to discuss early Precambrian organisms, helping students understand that scientists use these fossils to learn more about Earth's early life forms. Review the paragraphs under the red head *Earth Takes Shape* before beginning the **Apply It activity.** Have students share their ideas about how Earth's atmosphere would be different without organisms capable of photosynthesis. **Build Inquiry** by allowing students to compare and contrast atmospheric gases. Have students do the **Quick Lab** explore how stromatolites formed. Students can use the online **Vocab Flash Cards** to review key terms.

EVALUATE

Have students take the **Lesson Quiz.** For an alternate assessment, see the **EXAM**VIEW® Assessment Suite, Progress Monitoring Assessments, or SuccessTracker™.

ENGAGE AND EXPLORE

Teach this lesson using digital resources. Begin by having students learn more about deep ocean vents and explore real-world connections to early life on Earth at **My Planet Diary** online. Have them access the Chapter Resources to find the **Unlock the Big Question activity.** There they can answer the questions and refine their responses as they continue through the lesson. You can re-assign the activity and have students submit their work so you can track their progress.

EXPLAIN AND ELABORATE

Students reading above, at, or below the lexile measure of this lesson can access basic content readings at their level at **My Reading Web.** Encourage students to use the online **Vocab Flash Cards** to preview key terms. **Support the Big Q** by using **Figure 3** to discuss early Precambrian organisms, helping students understand that scientists use these follies to learn more about Earth's early life forms. Assign the **Apply It activity** online and have students submit their work to you. Have students do the **Quick Lab** explore how stromatolites formed. The **Key Concept Summaries** online allow students to read a summary and see an image associated with each part of the lesson. Online remediation is available at **My Science Coach.**

EVALUATE

Have students take the **Lesson Quiz.** For an alternate assessment, see the **EXAM**VIEW® Assessment Suite, Progress Monitoring Assessments, or SuccessTracker™.

2 Frontload the Lesson
Use the section headings to help set the purpose for reading. Have students compose sentences that tell what they think they will learn about in each of the sections, beginning with *The Age of Earth.* For instance, *I think this section will tell me how old Earth is.*

3 Comprehensible Input
Have students use a Venn Diagram to record how Earth's first and second atmospheres were alike and how they were different.

4 Language Production
Pair or group students with varied language abilities to complete labs collaboratively for language practice. Have each student copy the completed written lab for personal reference.

5 Assess Understanding
Have students keep a content area log. Use a two-column format with the headings "What I Understand" and "What I Don't Understand." Follow up so that students can move items from the "Don't Understand" to the "Understand" column.

Early Earth

Establish Learning Objective

After this lesson, students will be able to:

🔑 Explain how Earth developed during Precambrian time.

Engage

Activate Prior Knowledge

MY PLANET DIARY Read *Exploring Life Under Water* with the class. Point out that 71% of Earth's surface is covered by ocean water. Yet only a small part of this underwater world has been explored by scientists. Ask: **How are scientists able to reach the ocean floor to do their work?** *(They use submersibles.)* **Why are scientists so interested in the bacteria that live there?** *(Scientists believe that these bacteria may resemble some of the earliest life forms on our planet.)*

BIG IDEAS OF SCIENCE REFERENCE LIBRARY 📖
Have students look up the following topics: Atmosphere, Deep Sea Vents.

Explore

Lab Resource: Inquiry Warm-Up 🧪

L1 **HOW COULD PLANET EARTH FORM IN SPACE?**
Students will make a model that demonstrates the formation of Earth.

LESSON 5 Early Earth

🔑 **How Did Earth Form?**

MY PLANET DIARY

Exploring Life Under Water

Dr. Anna-Louise Reysenbach always loved water sports. She was also interested in organisms that live in strange, extreme environments. Now, as a biology professor at Portland State University in Oregon, she gets to combine her two loves—and learn about early life on Earth!

Dr. Reysenbach uses submersibles, or submarines, to study bacteria that live deep under the ocean. No sunlight reaches these depths. There, hot water carrying dissolved minerals from inside Earth flows out through vents. Some kinds of bacteria use chemical energy from this material to make food, much as plants use the energy from sunlight. Scientists think that these bacteria are very similar to some of the earliest forms of life on Earth.

CAREERS

✏️ **Communicate** Discuss the work of Dr. Reysenbach with a partner. Then answer these questions on your own.

1. How are the bacteria near ocean vents different from many other organisms on Earth?
   They use chemical energy instead of energy from sunlight to produce food.

2. Would you like to work under water in a submersible? Why, or why not?
   Sample: Yes, because I would like to see what underwater creatures look like up close.

▶ **PLANET DIARY** Go to **Planet Diary** to learn more about deep ocean vents.

🧪 Do the Inquiry Warm-Up How Could Planet Earth Form in Space?

266 A Trip Through Geologic Time

SUPPORT ALL READERS
Lexile Measure = 910L   Lexile Word Count = 819

Prior Exposure to Content: May be the first time students have encountered this topic

Academic Vocabulary: *communicate, sequence*

Science Vocabulary: *comet*

Concept Level: Generally appropriate for most students in this grade

Preteach With: My Planet Diary "Exploring Life Underwater" and Figure 1 activity

Go to **My Reading Web** to access leveled readings that provide a foundation for the content.

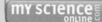

Vocabulary
• comet

Skills
📖 Reading: Sequence
△ Inquiry: Communicate

How Did Earth Form?

Using radioactive dating, scientists have determined that the oldest rocks ever found on Earth are about 4 billion years old. But scientists think Earth formed even earlier than that.

The Age of Earth According to these scientists' hypothesis, the moon formed from material knocked loose when a very young Earth collided with another object. This means Earth and the moon are about the same age. Scientists have used radioactive dating to find the age of moon rocks that astronauts brought back to Earth. The oldest moon rocks are about 4.6 billion years old. Scientists infer that Earth is also roughly 4.6 billion years old—only a little older than those moon rocks.

Earth Takes Shape 🗝 **Scientists think that Earth began as a ball of dust, rock, and ice in space. Gravity pulled this mass together.** As Earth grew larger, its gravity increased, pulling in more dust, rock, and ice nearby.

The energy from collisions with these materials raised Earth's temperature until the planet was very hot. Scientists think that Earth may have become so hot that it melted. Denser materials sank toward the center, forming Earth's dense, iron core. Less dense, molten material hardened over time to form Earth's outer layers—the solid crust and mantle.

FIGURE 1 ··································
Early Earth
This artist's illustration shows Earth shortly after the moon formed. Earth was hot and volcanic, and contained no liquid water. The moon was much closer to Earth than it is today. Over time, Earth's surface began to cool, forming solid land.

✎ **Make Generalizations**
Could life have existed on Earth at the time shown in the illustration? Why, or why not?

Sample: No; life needs liquid water to survive, and it did not then exist on Earth.

267

Explain

Introduce Vocabulary

Students will likely know that a comet is a kind of celestial body, but they may not know much about its makeup. Tell them that a comet is a ball of dust, gas, and ice that orbits the sun.

Teach Key Concepts 🗝

Explain to students that scientists believe that Earth did not begin as a dense, solid planet. Ask: **What substances do scientists believe made up Earth in its earliest state?** *(Dust, rock, ice)* **What caused these substances to come together in a ball in space?** *(The force of gravity)*

21st Century Learning

CRITICAL THINKING Ask students to take note of the series of causes and effects in the paragraphs under the red head *Earth Takes Shape*. Point out that cue words such as *because* or *due to* are not always present in sentences containing causes and effects. Use the third sentence to help students see that Earth's growth *caused* the force of gravity to increase, which in turn, *caused* Earth to grow. Ask students to say what the increase in gravity caused. *(An increase in the amount of dust, rock, and ice pulled into the ball)*

My Planet Diary provides an opportunity for students to explore real-world connections to early life on Earth.

my science online | Early Earth

(E L L) Support

1 Content and Language
Distribute a simplified cloze paragraph about the age of Earth and how it was formed. Provide students with a list of correct answers to fill in the blanks.

2 Frontload the Lesson
Show students a photo of Earth taken from space. Have students identify features they see in the photo.

Then have students discuss whether they think Earth had these features when it first formed.

3 Comprehensible Input
Invite students to study **Figure 1** in order to label the illustration with specific terms such as *comet, moon, volcano, land, lava,* and *sky.*

Explain

Lead a Discussion

Tell students that Earth's early atmosphere was very different from the atmosphere we know now. Ask: **What gases do scientists think may have been in the early atmosphere?** *(Hydrogen and helium)* **What gases were in the second atmosphere?** *(Carbon dioxide, water vapor, nitrogen, and other gases)* **How did the formation of this atmosphere lead to the formation of oceans?** *(As Earth cooled, water vapor in the atmosphere condensed and formed rain, which fell to Earth and collected in the oceans.)*

↻ **Sequence** Explain that a sequence is the order in which a series of events occurs.

21st Century Learning ▣K

COMMUNICATION Have students read *Atmosphere* in the **Big Ideas of Science Reference Library** and write an essay from the point of view of an alien being. This being is entering Earth's atmosphere and travelling from the exosphere through the upper thermosphere, lower thermosphere, mesosphere, and stratosphere to get to the troposphere. Students should describe the changes that happen as the alien passes through each layer.

Teach With Visuals

Tell students to look at **Figure 2**. Ask: **What important contrast between Earth's first and second atmospheres is identified by the purple arrows and the labels *Ultraviolet light* and *Ozone layer*?** *(The presence of an ozone layer in the second atmosphere is an important contrast.)* **What do the contrasting colors and forms on the two images of Earth's surface tell you about the effect of the ozone layer?** *(The presence of the ozone layer created dramatically different conditions on Earth's surface.)*

Support the Big Q ❓ UbD

EARLY PRECAMBRIAN ORGANISMS Ask students to look at the photograph of stromatolite fossils in **Figure 3**. Scientists study these fossils to learn more about Earth's early life forms. Remind students that oxygen is a product of photosynthesis. Ask: **What did the first life forms look like?** *(They were single-celled and resembled present-day bacteria.)* **How did they get energy?** *(They used energy from the sun to make their own food.)* **What was the effect of the release of oxygen in the atmosphere?** *(The amount of oxygen in the atmosphere slowly increased.)*

FIGURE 2 ·····························

Development of the Atmosphere
The illustration shows the difference between Earth's first and second atmospheres.

✎ **Relate Text and Visuals**
Fill in the missing information for each atmosphere.

> **First atmosphere**
> Gases included:
> <u>hydrogen and helium</u>
>
> Blown away by:
> <u>particles from the sun</u>

Ultraviolet light

↻ **Sequence** How did Earth's oceans develop over time?
1. <u>Volcanoes and comets released water vapor.</u>
2. <u>Water vapor condensed to form rain.</u>
3. <u>Rainwater accumulated to form oceans.</u>

The Atmosphere Early Earth may have included light gases such as hydrogen and helium. Then the sun released strong bursts of particles called the solar wind. Earth's gravity could not hold the light gases, and the solar wind blew away Earth's first atmosphere.

After Earth lost its first atmosphere, a second atmosphere formed. Volcanic eruptions and collisions with comets added carbon dioxide, water vapor, nitrogen, and other gases to the atmosphere. A **comet** is a ball of dust, gas, and ice that orbits the sun. **Figure 2** shows the first and second atmospheres.

The Oceans At first, Earth's surface was too hot for water to remain a liquid. All water remained as water vapor. As Earth's surface cooled, the water vapor began to condense to form rain. The rainwater gradually accumulated and formed oceans. The oceans absorbed much of the carbon dioxide from the atmosphere.

The Continents During early Precambrian Time, much of Earth's rock cooled and hardened. Less than 500 million years after Earth formed, the rock at the surface formed continents.

Scientists have found that the continents move very slowly over Earth's surface because of forces inside Earth. Over billions of years, Earth's landmasses have repeatedly formed, broken apart, and then crashed together again.

apply it!

❶ Draw a diagram showing Earth's structure after oceans began to form.

❷ ✎ **Communicate** Write a caption for your diagram explaining how Earth changed over time.
<u>Sample: As Earth cooled, dense material sank toward the center, forming the core.</u>

> Students should show Earth with layers, including a core, oceans of liquid water, and an atmosphere.

Digital Lesson: Assign the *Apply It* activity online and have students submit their work to you.

my science online.com | **Early Earth**

Second atmosphere
Gases from volcanoes and comets:
<u>Carbon dioxide, water vapor, nitrogen</u>
Gases from organisms:
<u>Oxygen</u>

Ozone layer

Ultraviolet light

Early Organisms Scientists cannot pinpoint when or where life began on Earth. But scientists have found fossils of single-celled organisms in rocks that formed about 3.5 billion years ago. Scientists think that all other forms of life on Earth arose from these simple organisms. **Figure 3** shows remains of organisms similar to these early life forms. The bacteria Dr. Reysenbach studies are probably similar to these early organisms.

About 2.5 billion years ago, many organisms began using energy from the sun to make food. This process is called photosynthesis. One waste product of photosynthesis is oxygen. As organisms released oxygen, the amount of oxygen in the atmosphere slowly grew. Some oxygen changed into a form called ozone. The atmosphere developed an ozone layer that blocked the ultraviolet rays of the sun. Shielded from these rays, organisms could live on land.

FIGURE 3 ·····························
Stromatolites
These stromatolite fossils (stroh MAT uh lyt) from Australia are the remains of reefs built by early organisms. Some similar fossils are more than three billion years old.

 Do the Quick Lab
Learning From Fossils.

🔑 Assess Your Understanding

1a. Identify Earth formed <u>4.6 billion</u> years ago.

b. 🔄 **Sequence** Write the numbers 1, 2, and 3 to show the correct order of the events below.

<u>3</u>   Ozone layer forms.

<u>1</u>   Earth loses its first atmosphere.

<u>2</u>   Volcanoes and collisions with comets add water vapor to the atmosphere.

c. CHALLENGE How would Earth's atmosphere be different if organisms capable of photosynthesis had not evolved?
<u>There would be no oxygen in the atmosphere.</u>

got it? ·····························

O **I get it!** Now I know that key features of early Earth were <u>a hot volcanic period followed by changes in the atmosphere, oceans, continents, and the development of single-celled life forms.</u>

O **I need extra help with** <u>See TE note.</u>

Go to MY SCIENCE COACH online for help with this subject.

269

Differentiated Instruction

L1 Relate Cause and Effect Help students recognize the causes and effects that led to the formation of Earth's atmosphere, oceans, and continents. As they answer the following questions, you might wish to have them fill in a cause-and-effect organizer. *What factors contributed to Earth's second atmosphere? How did oceans form? How were the continents formed?*

Elaborate

Apply It!

L1 Review the paragraphs under the red head *Earth Takes Shape* before beginning the activity.

🔺 **Communicate** Remind students that human beings communicate in many ways, including words, images, and gestures. Ask: **What details about Earth's structure will be communicated by your drawing?** (*The drawing communicates the presence of Earth's layers, core, oceans, and atmosphere.*) **What additional information about the subject will be communicated by the words in your caption?** (*Sample: Information about the process that led to the formation of the core*)

Build Inquiry

L2 COMPARING AND CONTRASTING ATMOSPHERIC GASES

Materials paper, colored pencils

Time 15 minutes

Review early Earth's atmosphere. Tell students that Earth's early atmosphere was about 92% carbon dioxide, 5% nitrogen, 0% oxygen, and 3% other gases. Today's atmosphere is about 78% nitrogen, 21% oxygen, and 1% other gases, including carbon dioxide. Have students make circle graphs of each atmosphere and discuss the differences. Ask: **Why did the percentage of oxygen change?** (*Early life forms gave off oxygen as a waste product.*)

Lab Resource: Quick Lab

L2 LEARNING FROM FOSSILS Students will explore how stromatolites formed.

Evaluate

Assess Your Understanding

After students answer the questions, have them evaluate their understanding by completing the appropriate sentence.

RTI Response to Intervention

1a. If students cannot identify Earth's age, **then** have them reread the paragraph under the red head *The Age of Earth.*

b. If students need help with sequencing events in Earth's early history, **then** have them review the material under the red heads *The Atmosphere* and *Early Organisms.*

c. If students have trouble applying knowledge of photosynthesis, **then** have them study the last paragraph under the red head *Early Organisms.*

MY SCIENCE COACH Have students go online for help in understanding early Earth.

269

Lab **zone** **After the Inquiry Warm-Up**

Early Earth

Inquiry Warm-Up, *How Could Planet Earth Form in Space?*
In the Inquiry Warm-Up, you investigated how to make a model of early Earth. Using what you learned from that activity, answer the questions below.

1. **OBSERVE** What happened to the iron filings after blowing through the straw in Step 4?

   _____

   _____

2. **DRAW CONCLUSIONS** Why did you get this result from blowing through the straw?

   _____

   _____

3. **APPLY CONCEPTS** How does the magnet in the activity work like Earth's gravity?

   _____

   _____

4. **MAKE GENERALIZATIONS** Do you think other planets may have formed as Earth did? Explain.

   _____

   _____

Assess Your Understanding

Early Earth

How Did Earth Form?

1a. **IDENTIFY** Earth formed _____ years ago.

b. **SEQUENCE** Write the numbers 1, 2, and 3 to show the correct order of the events below.

___ Ozone layer forms.

___ Earth loses its first atmosphere.

___ Volcanoes and collisions with comets add water vapor to the atmosphere.

c. CHALLENGE How would Earth's atmosphere be different if organisms capable of photosynthesis had not evolved?

_____

_____

got it?···

○ **I get it!** Now I know that key features of early Earth were _____

_____

_____

○ **I need extra help with** _____

_____

Early Earth

How Did Earth Form?

Based on radioactive dating of the oldest rocks found on Earth, scientists have determined that Earth is about 4.6 billion years old. Scientists have also used radioactive dating on moon rocks brought back to Earth by astronauts. They hypothesize that the moon is about the same age and that it was formed soon after Earth collided with another object. **Scientists think that Earth began as a ball of dust, rock, and ice in space. Gravity pulled this mass together.** Gravity increased as Earth grew larger.

The collision of the dust, ice, and rock created energy that raised Earth's temperature, making it hot enough to melt, sinking the densest materials to Earth's core and leaving the less dense material to harden as crust and mantle on Earth's surface.

Earth's first atmosphere consisted of light gases such as hydrogen and helium. The gases were blown away by solar wind. Earth's second—and present—atmosphere was formed after collisions with comets added carbon dioxide, water vapor, nitrogen, and oxygen to the atmosphere. A **comet** is a ball of dust, gas, and ice that orbits the sun. As Earth's surface cooled, scientists believe that oceans were formed when water vapor condensed to form rain, which gradually accumulated. Scientists have found that Earth's large landmasses, or continents, move over the Earth's surface. For billions of years, they have repeatedly formed, broken apart, and crashed together again.

Scientists have found fossils of the earliest known form of life on Earth. These single-celled organisms formed about 3.5 billion years ago.

Photosynthesis played a crucial role in the spreading of life on Earth. During photosynthesis, organisms created oxygen. The amount of oxygen in the atmosphere grew and allowed a layer of ozone to protect Earth from the sun's ultraviolet rays. The ozone layer allowed organisms to live and grow on land.

On a separate sheet of paper, explain what scientists have theorized about important events involving early Earth.

Early Earth

Understanding Main Ideas
Put the six events or processes in the correct sequence by writing their letters in the correct order in the numbered blanks below.

A. Volcanic eruptions release carbon dioxide into the atmosphere.

B. Early organisms release oxygen into the air.

C. Oceans form on Earth's surface.

D. Hydrogen and helium are captured by gravity to form an atmosphere.

E. A dense, iron core forms at Earth's center.

F. Earth is a ball of dust, rock, and ice in space.

1. ___

2. ___

3. ___

4. ___

5. ___

6. ___

Answer the following questions on a separate sheet of paper.

7. What were the earliest life forms on Earth like?

8. What hypothesis explains why Earth and the moon are about the same age?

9. How did photosynthesis lead to the development of animals living on land?

10. How have scientists used radioactive dating to show that Earth is about 4.6 billion years old?

Building Vocabulary
Fill in the blank to complete each statement.

11. A(n) _____ is a ball of dust and ice that orbits the sun.

12. The process of _____ involves organisms using energy from the sun to make food.

Enrich

Early Earth

> Read the passage below and then answer the questions that follow in the spaces provided.

Life and Earth's Atmosphere

More than 3 billion years ago, an amazing thing happened on Earth. Certain types of bacteria developed the ability to make their own food. These bacteria made food by using a process called photosynthesis. Using energy from the sun, the bacteria combined carbon dioxide and water to make food and oxygen. The oxygen that was given off had a big effect on Earth's atmosphere.

At first, the oxygen was taken up by iron that was in the ocean water. This caused the iron and oxygen, or iron oxides, to fall to the ocean bottom and form deposits of iron-rich sedimentary rock. Most of the iron that is used today to make cars and buildings comes from these deposits. Eventually most of the iron in the oceans had combined with oxygen and fallen to the ocean floor. Now, oxygen that was produced by microbes was free to enter the atmosphere. As a result, the oxygen level in Earth's atmosphere began to increase significantly about 2.5 billion years ago. Slowly, over hundreds of millions of years, the oxygen level increased to the present-day level of about 20 percent.

The buildup of oxygen in Earth's atmosphere allowed the emergence of organisms that cannot exist without oxygen. Animals, for example, take in oxygen, combine it with the food they eat, and produce a waste product: carbon dioxide.

1. What advantage does an organism have because of photosynthesis?

   _____

2. What gas is given off during photosynthesis?

   _____

3. After certain types of bacteria first started producing oxygen, where did most of the oxygen go?

   _____

   _____

   _____

4. Why was the buildup of oxygen in Earth's atmosphere important for animals and other types of organisms?

   _____

   _____

Lesson Quiz

Early Earth

Write the letter of the correct answer on the line at the left.

1. ___ According to scientists, both Earth and the moon are

   A about 1.6 billion years old

   B about 4.6 billion years old

   C about 9.6 billion years old

   D about 14 billion years old

2. ___ After water vapor condensed to form rain and then gradually accumulated, which of the following was formed?

   A Earth's first atmosphere

   B Earth's second atmosphere

   C Earth's oceans

   D Earth's continents

3. ___ Which of the following is *not* an important part of Earth's second atmosphere?

   A helium

   B oxygen

   C water vapor

   D carbon dioxide

4. ___ The earliest form of life known on Earth was

   A leafy plants

   B bacteria

   C fossils

   D single-celled organisms

Fill in the blank to complete each statement.

5. Scientists believe that _____ and the moon are about the same age.

6. According to scientists, Earth began as a ball of dust, rock, and _____ in space.

7. _____ pulled this mass together.

8. A(n) _____ is a ball of dust, gas, and ice that orbits the sun.

9. According to scientists, over billions of years, Earth's _____ have formed, broken apart, and crashed together again.

10. Scientists believe that Earth's core and crust formed after the materials pulled by Earth's gravity became very hot and _____.

Early Earth

Answer Key

After the Inquiry Warm-Up

1. Answers should indicate that the iron filings gathered on the surface of the paper around the poles of the magnet.

2. Answers will vary. Sample: The force of the magnet was strong enough to attract the filings from that distance across the paper.

3. Answers will vary. Students may indicate that like the gravity, which pulled materials in space into a ball, the magnet pulled the iron filings into a clump.

4. Answers will vary. Students may indicate that other planets formed the same way as Earth. Gravity pulled particles in space into a sphere.

Key Concept Summary

Scientists have theorized that Earth began as a ball of dust, rock, and ice in space; that gravity gathered these materials, which melted and formed Earth's core, crust, and mantle; that many of the elements of Earth's atmosphere were added after it collided with comets; that oceans and continents later formed; and that 2.5 billion years ago, photosynthesis finally allowed many organisms to grow.

Review and Reinforce

1. F
2. E
3. D
4. A
5. C
6. B
7. They were single-celled organisms that were probably similar to present-day bacteria.

8. When Earth was very young, it collided with a large object. The collision threw a large amount of material from both bodies into orbit around Earth. This material combined to form the moon.

9. In photosynthesis, oxygen is released as a waste product. Oxygen released into the air was changed into ozone, which blocks out ultraviolet rays of the sun.

10. Scientists used radioactive dating to show that the oldest moon rocks are about 4.6 billion years old. Because Earth is slightly older than the moon, Earth must be roughly 4.6 billion years old.

11. comet

12. photosynthesis

Enrich

1. It can make its own food.

2. oxygen

3. Most oxygen was taken up by iron in the oceans and settled to the ocean floor along with the iron.

4. Animals and other types of organisms use oxygen to get energy from food.

Lesson Quiz

1. B	2. C
3. A	4. D
5. Earth	6. ice
7. Gravity	8. comet
9. landmasses	10. melted

Place the outside corner, the corner away from the dotted line, in the corner of your copy machine to copy onto letter-size paper.

Eras of Earth's History

6 How do scientists study Earth's past?

Blended Path
Active learning using Student Edition, Inquiry Path, and Digital Path

Lesson Pacing: 3–4 periods or $1\frac{1}{2}$ –2 blocks

🕐 **SHORT ON TIME?** To do this lesson in approximately half the time, do the Activate Prior Knowledge activity followed by a discussion of the Key Concepts to familiarize students with the lesson content. Explore the Big Q using Figure 6 to discuss the landmark events and life forms in each era. Have students do the Quick Labs. The rest of the lesson can be completed by students independently.

Preference Navigator, in the online Planning tools, allows you to customize *Interactive Science* to your own teaching style. You can also edit lesson plans by selecting the Lesson Planner option.

Digital Teacher's Edition allows you to access your Teacher's Edition and Resource materials online.

my science online.com

Lesson Vocabulary

• invertebrate • vertebrate • amphibian • reptile
• mass extinction • mammal

Content Refresher
Professional Development Note

Movement of Earth's Plates Toward the end of the Paleozoic Era, the continents came together to form Pangaea ("all lands"). One result was the formation of the Appalachian Mountains, which dominate eastern North America. These mountains probably rose as Africa collided with North America. The mountains have since weathered and eroded from a once greater height.

Both the formation and breakup of Pangaea were the result of movements of Earth's lithospheric plates. These plates fit closely together along cracks in the lithosphere. As they move, they collide, pull apart, or slide past one another. Near Hawaii, the Pacific plate is moving at a rate of about 8.3 cm per year.

LESSON OBJECTIVES

🗝 Discuss the major events in the Paleozoic Era.
🗝 Discuss the major events in the Mesozoic Era.
🗝 Discuss the major events in the Cenozoic Era.

ENGAGE AND EXPLORE

Teach this lesson using a variety of resources. Begin by reading **My Planet Diary** as a class. Have students discuss the questions they have about the history of life on Earth. Then have students do the **Inquiry Warm-Up activity.** Students will determine criteria for constructing and dividing a time scale. The **After the Inquiry Warm-Up worksheet** sets up a discussion about timelines. Have volunteers share their answers to question 4 about which is the better tool for presenting a person's history: a timeline or a list of key events.

EXPLAIN AND ELABORATE

Teach Key Concepts by explaining the dramatic changes in life forms that occurred at the beginning of the Paleozoic Era. Continue to **Teach Key Concepts** by discussing the dramatic change in life forms that occurred during the Devonian Period. **Lead a Discussion** about the major events during the Paleozoic Era. Continue to **Teach Key Concepts** by telling students about two major events during the Permian Period: the mass extinction and the formation of the supercontinent.

Teach Key Concepts by explaining why the Triassic Period of the Mesozoic Era is also known as the Age of Reptiles. Have students practice the inquiry skill in the **Apply It activity.** Continue to **Teach Key Concepts** by explaining that Earth's geologic history is divided into eras and periods according to large, dramatic events or changes in life forms that occurred.

Teach Key Concepts by discussing the three periods of the Cenozoic Era. **Explore the Big Q** using **Figure 6** to discuss the landmark events and life forms in each era.

Hand out the **Key Concept Summaries** as a review of each part of the lesson. Students can also use the online **Vocab Flash Cards** to review key terms.

EVALUATE

Have students take the **Lesson Quiz.** For an alternate assessment, see the **EXAM**VIEW® Assessment Suite, Progress Monitoring Assessments, or SuccessTracker™.

E L L Support

1 Content and Language
Write Cloze sentences for students to complete with the vocabulary terms for the lesson.

Lab zone Inquiry Path
Hands-on learning in the Lab zone

ENGAGE AND EXPLORE

To teach this lesson with an emphasis on inquiry, begin with the **Inquiry Warm-Up activity.** Students will determine criteria for constructing and dividing a time scale. The **After the Inquiry Warm-Up worksheet** sets up a discussion about timelines. Have volunteers share their answers to question 4 about which is the better tool for presenting a person's history: a timeline or a list of key events.

EXPLAIN AND ELABORATE

Focus on the **Inquiry Skill** for the lesson. Remind students that classifying is grouping together items that are alike in some way. How could classification be used in the **Inquiry Warm-Up Activity?** *(Sample: Grouping events that occurred during a particular segment of time)* **Build Inquiry** by allowing students to compare and contrast amphibians and reptiles. Have students do the **Quick Lab** to graph the ranges of various life forms.

Review the information about reptiles in the Triassic Period and about reptiles and birds in the Jurassic Period before beginning the **Apply It activity.** Have students share their results. Do the **Build Inquiry** to allow students to develop hypotheses about why flowering plants became the dominant plants after the end of the Mesozoic Era. Have students do the **Quick Lab** to model how an asteroid impact might have affected life in the oceans.

Explore the Big Q using **Figure 6** to discuss the landmark events and life forms in each era. **Build Inquiry by** having students research prehistoric life forms and present their findings to the class. Do the **Quick Lab** to have students make a timeline of major events in the Cenozoic Era. Students can use the online **Vocab Flash Cards** to review key terms.

EVALUATE

Have students take the **Lesson Quiz.** For an alternate assessment, see the **EXAM**VIEW® Assessment Suite, Progress Monitoring Assessments, or SuccessTracker™.

Digital Path
Online learning at MY SCIENCE ONLINE.com

ENGAGE AND EXPLORE

Teach this lesson using digital resources. Begin by having students explore real-world connections to early Earth at **My Planet Diary** online. Have them access the Chapter Resources to find the **Unlock the Big Question activity.** There they can answer the questions and refine their responses as they continue through the lesson. You can re-assign the activity and have students submit their work so you can track their progress.

EXPLAIN AND ELABORATE

Students reading above, at, or below the lexile measure of this lesson can access basic content readings at their level at **My Reading Web.** Encourage students to use the online **Vocab Flash Cards** to preview key terms. Have students do the **Quick Lab** to graph the ranges of various life forms.

Assign the **Apply It activity** online and have students submit their work to you. Have students do the **Quick Lab** to model how an asteroid impact might have affected life in the oceans and then share their results.

Explore the Big Q using **Figure 6** to discuss the landmark events and life forms in each era. Use the **Art in Motion activity** online to give students the opportunity to explore geologic changes and the development of life over time. Do the **Quick Lab** to have students make a timeline of major events in the Cenozoic Era. The **Key Concept Summaries** online allow students to read a summary and see an image associated with each part of the lesson. Online remediation is available at **My Science Coach.**

EVALUATE

Have students take the **Lesson Quiz.** For an alternate assessment, see the **EXAM**VIEW® Assessment Suite, Progress Monitoring Assessments, or SuccessTracker™.

2 Frontload the Lesson

Use the section headings to preview the lesson. Have students refer back to the scale in Lesson 4 before they read each section to clarify the era's position on the Geologic Time Scale.

3 Comprehensible Input

Divide the class into five groups and have each complete a Frayer Model diagram for one of the following key terms: *invertebrate, vertebrate, amphibian, reptile,* and *mammal.* It should include the definition, characteristics, an example, and a nonexample of the term. Have each group teach their word to the class.

4 Language Production

Pair or group students with varied language abilities to complete labs collaboratively for language practice. Have each student copy the completed written lab for personal reference.

5 Assess Understanding

Divide the class into small groups. Have each student identify a key concept from the lesson to discuss in his or her group. After the discussions, have students talk about the key concepts as a group.

LESSON 8.6

Eras of Earth's History

Establish Learning Objectives

After this lesson, students will be able to:

🗝 Describe the major events in the Paleozoic Era.

🗝 Describe the major events in the Mesozoic Era.

🗝 Describe the major events in the Cenozoic Era.

Engage

Activate Prior Knowledge

MY PLANET DIARY Read *Mystery Metal* with the class. Point out that the extinction of the dinosaurs has fascinated scientists for many centuries. Ask: **According to the inferences of some scientists, was the impact of an asteroid a direct cause or an indirect cause of dinosaurs dying out? Explain.** *(Indirect; Scientists infer that the asteroid's impact caused a vast dust-cloud that lingered for years. Because the cloud blocked the sun, plants and animals died off.)*

BIG IDEAS OF SCIENCE REFERENCE LIBRARY 📖
Have students look up the following topics:
Dinosaurs, Eryops, Extinction, Giant Mammals.

Explore

Lab Resource: Inquiry Warm-Up 🧪

L2 DIVIDING HISTORY Students will divide a famous person's life into blocks of time and compare to how geologic time is divided.

---

6 Eras of Earth's History

🗝 What Happened in the Paleozoic Era?

🗝 What Happened in the Mesozoic Era?

🗝 What Happened in the Cenozoic Era?

MY PLANET DIARY

Mystery Metal

The rock layers in the photo hold evidence in one of the great mysteries of science: What killed the dinosaurs?

Find the thin, pale layer of rock marked by the ruler. This layer formed at the end of the Cretaceous period. It contains unusually high amounts of the metal iridium. At first, scientists could not explain the amount of iridium in this layer.

Iridium is more common in asteroids than on Earth. Many scientists now infer that an asteroid struck Earth. The impact threw dust into the air, blocking sunlight for years. About half the plant and animal species on Earth—including the dinosaurs—died out.

 Do the Inquiry Warm-Up *Dividing History.*

FUN FACT

Think about what you know about fossils and Earth's history as you answer these questions.

1. What have many scientists inferred from the iridium found at the Cretaceous boundary?
   An asteroid containing relatively large amounts of iridium struck Earth.

2. What are some questions you have about the history of life on Earth?
   Sample: I would like to know when birds first appeared on Earth.

▶ PLANET DIARY Go to **Planet Diary** to learn more about mass extinctions.

270 A Trip Through Geologic Time

SUPPORT ALL READERS

Lexile Measure = 890L   **Lexile Word Count = 1911**

Prior Exposure to Content: Many students may have misconceptions on this topic

Academic Vocabulary: *classify, develop, evidence, identify*

Science Vocabulary: *amphibian, invertebrate, mammal, reptile, vertabrate*

Concept Level: Generally appropriate for most students in this grade

Preteach With: My Planet Diary "Mystery Metal" and Figure 2 activity

Go to **My Reading Web** to access leveled readings that provide a foundation for the content.

my science online.com

Vocabulary
- invertebrate • vertebrate
- amphibian • reptile
- mass extinction • mammal

Skills
- Reading: Identify Supporting Evidence
- Inquiry: Classify

What Happened in the Paleozoic Era?

The extinction of the dinosaurs is one of the most famous events in Earth's history, but it is just one example of the changes that have taken place. Through most of Earth's history, the only living things were single-celled organisms.

Near the end of Precambrian time, more complex living things evolved. Feathery, plantlike organisms anchored themselves to the seafloor. Jellyfish-like organisms floated in the oceans. Scientists have found fossils of such organisms in Australia, Russia, China, and southern Africa. But a much greater variety of living things evolved during the next phase of geologic time—the Paleozoic Era.

The Cambrian Explosion During the Cambrian Period, life took a big leap forward. **At the beginning of the Paleozoic Era, a great number of different kinds of organisms evolved. For the first time, many organisms had hard parts, including shells and outer skeletons.** Paleontologists call this event the Cambrian Explosion because so many new life forms appeared within a relatively short time.

FIGURE 1 ··

Cambrian Life
The photo below shows a fossil of a Cambrian organism called *Anomalocaris*. The illustration shows one artist's idea of what *Anomalocaris* (the large organism) and other organisms looked like.
✎ **Interpret Photos** What does the fossil tell you about what *Anomalocaris* looked like?

<u>Sample: Anomalocaris had many</u>
<u>small segments.</u>

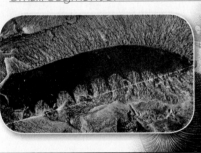

Explain —————

Introduce Vocabulary
Explain to students that the key to understanding the difference between an *invertebrate* and a *vertebrate* can be found in the prefix *in-*, which means "not." A *vertebrate* is an animal with a backbone, and an invertebrate is an animal without a backbone.

Teach Key Concepts 🔑
Explain to students that the beginning of the Paleozoic Era was marked by dramatic changes in life forms. Ask: **Until near the end of Precambrian time, what were most living things?** (*Single-celled organisms*) **What was new about many of the organisms that evolved during the Cambrian Period?** (*Many organisms had hard parts, including shells and outer skeletons.*) **Why do paleontologists use the term Cambrian Explosion to describe this time?** (*Because so many new life forms appeared within a relatively short period of time*)

21st Century Learning

L3 **INFORMATION LITERACY** Have students research the scientific explanations for the explosion in diversity of life during the Cambrian Period. Remind students that they should carefully evaluate the reliability of the information they find during their research. Encourage volunteers to present their findings to the class.

My Planet Diary provides an opportunity for students to explore real-world connections to early Earth.

my science online | Paleozoic Era

Explain

Teach Key Concepts 🗝

Remind students that the earliest life forms lived in Earth's oceans. Ask: **What dramatic change in life forms occurred during the Devonian Period?** *(Animals began to spread from the seas to land.)* **What were these early land animals?** *(Vertebrates—lungfish and amphibians)* **What is an amphibian?** *(A vertebrate that lives part of its life on land and part of its life in water)*

🔄 **Identify Supporting Evidence** Tell students that identifying the supporting evidence for a hypothesis or scientific idea can help them understand the hypothesis or idea itself. Explain that evidence consists of facts—information whose accuracy can be confirmed by testing or observation.

Lead a Discussion

EVENTS DURING THE PALEOZOIC ERA Remind students that the different geologic eras are based on the major events that occurred in each. Have students refer to the Geologic Time Scale. Point out that the Paleozoic Era lasted from about 544 million years ago to about 245 million years ago and consisted of six periods. Ask: **What major event marked the beginning of the Paleozoic Era?** *(Many different kinds of organisms evolved.)* **What major events occurred after the end of the Cambrian Period?** *(The first vertebrates evolved, animals and plants began to live on land, reptiles evolved, and giant forests developed.)* **Why do you think that scientists have found many more fossils from the Cambrian Period than from Precambrian Time?** *(Organisms from the Cambrian Period had hard body parts, such as shells and outer skeletons, and were more likely to form fossils than organisms with only soft body parts.)*

did you know?

In 1938, a fisherman in South Africa caught a fish he'd never seen before: a coelacanth (SEE luh kanth). Coelacanths evolved during the Devonian Period, but scientists thought they had been extinct for at least 65 million years. Since 1938, more of these "living fossils" have been found living deep in the Indian Ocean.

FIGURE 2 ·······························

Changing Landscapes

✏ **Summarize** Based on the text and illustrations, describe the organisms in each period and how they differed from those in the previous period.

Silurian <u>Sample: In the Silurian, plants grew near the ground. All animals lived in the sea. The animals included trilobites and brachiopods.</u>

Invertebrates Develop At this time, all animals lived in the sea. Many were animals without backbones, or **invertebrates**. Invertebrates such as jellyfish, worms, and sponges made their home in the Cambrian ocean.

Brachiopods and trilobites were also common in the Cambrian seas. Brachiopods resembled modern clams, but are only distantly related to them. Trilobites were a huge and varied group of arthropods (AR thru pahds), animals with jointed legs and many body segments.

New Organisms Arise Invertebrates soon shared the seas with a new type of organism. During the Ordovician (awr duh VISH ee un) Period, the first vertebrates evolved. A **vertebrate** is an animal with a backbone. Jawless fishes with suckerlike mouths were the first vertebrates.

The First Land Plants Until the Silurian (sih LOOR ee un) Period, only one-celled organisms lived on the land. But during the Silurian Period, plants became abundant. These first, simple plants grew low to the ground in damp areas. By the Devonian Period (dih VOH nee un), plants that could grow in drier areas had evolved. Among these plants were the earliest ferns.

Early Fishes Both invertebrates and vertebrates lived in the Devonian seas. Even though the invertebrates were more numerous, the Devonian Period is often called the Age of Fishes. Every main group of fishes was present in the oceans at this time. Most fishes now had jaws, bony skeletons, and scales on their bodies. Sharks appeared in the late Devonian Period.

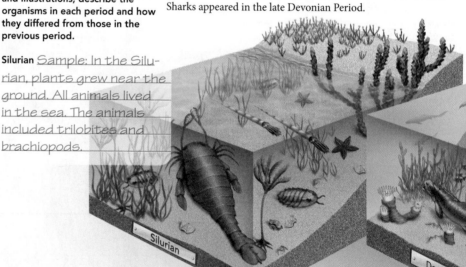

Animals Reach Land

The Devonian Period was also when animals began to spread widely on land. The first insects evolved during the Silurian Period, but vertebrates reached land during the Devonian. The first land vertebrates were lungfish with strong, muscular fins. The first amphibians evolved from these lungfish. An **amphibian** (am FIB ee un) is an animal that lives part of its life on land and part of its life in water.

The Carboniferous Period

Throughout the rest of the Paleozoic, other vertebrates evolved from amphibians. For example, small reptiles developed during the Carboniferous Period. **Reptiles** have scaly skin and lay eggs that have tough, leathery shells.

During the Carboniferous Period, winged insects evolved into many forms, including huge dragonflies and cockroaches. Giant ferns and cone-bearing plants formed vast swampy forests called coal forests. The remains of the coal-forest plants formed thick deposits of sediment that changed into coal over hundreds of millions of years.

Identify Supporting Evidence Underline the evidence that supports the statement, "The Devonian Period was also when animals began to spread widely on land."

Devonian Sample: In the Devonian, land plants were more diverse. Many fishes lived in the sea. Animals were beginning to reach land.

Carboniferous Sample: In the Carboniferous, many kinds of trees and other plants grew. Insects, reptiles, and amphibians lived on land.

273

Elaborate

Build Inquiry

L1 COMPARING AND CONTRASTING AMPHIBIANS AND REPTILES

Materials frog, lizard, separate containers for each

Time 20 minutes

Remind students that amphibians appeared on Earth before reptiles. Bring a frog and a reptile to class in separate containers. Have students write a description of each, noting similarities and differences. If live animals are not available, a series of photographs showing details of each animal's body can be used instead.

Ask: **How are these organisms alike and different?** (A typical answer might suggest that their body shapes are similar. An amphibian has thinner, moist skin and webbed feet, and a reptile has scaly skin and, except for snakes, clawed feet.) **Which is better adapted for living in water, and which is better adapted for living on land?** (An amphibian is better adapted for water because of its webbed feet and moist skin. A reptile is better adapted for land because its rough, scaly covering helps keep water inside and its claws help it hold on to land surfaces.)

21st Century Learning

INFORMATION LITERACY Provide students with a map of the United States. Challenge them to use reference materials to locate the general area of coal deposits in North America that formed during the Carboniferous Period and to list what the coal deposits are used for today.

Differentiated Instruction

L3 Research Precambrian Time
Encourage interested students to investigate conditions during Precambrian Time. Have them research the time periods into which Precambrian Time is divided and how Earth changed during those spans.

L1 Draw Pictures Show students examples or photos of ferns, horsetails, and club mosses. Point out that the vast swamp forests of the Carboniferous Period contained giant ancestors of these modern plants. Allow students to examine (and feel, if possible) the plants and then to make drawings of what a swamp forest might have looked like.

Explain

Teach Key Concepts 🔑

Explain to students that in a mass extinction, many types of living things become extinct at the same time. Ask: **When did a mass extinction occur on Earth?** *(At the end of the Permian Period)* **What are two hypotheses for the cause of this mass extinction?** *(The extinctions were caused by an asteroid striking Earth. The extinctions were caused by massive volcanic eruptions.)* **What other change in Earth took place during the Permian Period?** *(The continents moved together to form a supercontinent.)* **What is the name scientists have given to this supercontinent?** *(Pangaea)*

Elaborate

21st Century Learning

CREATIVITY Have students read *Eryops* in the **Big Ideas of Science Reference Library.** Ask students to make two drawings showing how they think Eryops looked 1) as a water-dwelling fish and 2) while it was evolving into the air-breathing amphibian shown in the pages. They should label the key features in each drawing and explain why changes to the features were necessary for the animal's survival.

Lab Resource: Quick Lab 🔬

L2 GRAPHING THE FOSSIL RECORD Students will graph the ranges of various life forms.

Evaluate

Assess Your Understanding

After students answer the questions, have them evaluate their understanding by completing the appropriate sentence.

RTI Response to Intervention

1a. If students cannot name the periods of the Paleozoic Era, **then** have them scan the material under the red heads *The Cambrian Explosion, New Organisms Arise,* and *The Carboniferous Period,* keeping an eye out for capitalized terms.

 b. If students need help with sequencing organisms, **then** have them scan the section to find references to these organisms.

 c. If students have trouble identifying possible causes of mass extinction, **then** have them review the final paragraph of the section.

MY SCIENCE COACH Have students go online for help in understanding the main events of the Paleozoic Era.

What two effects did the formation of Pangaea have?

Deserts expanded in the tropics and sheets of ice covered land close to the South Pole.

Pangaea During the Permian Period, between 299 and 250 million years ago, Earth's continents moved together to form a great landmass, or supercontinent, called Pangaea (pan JEE uh). The formation of Pangaea caused deserts to expand in the tropics. At the same time, sheets of ice covered land closer to the South Pole.

Mass Extinction 🔑 **At the end of the Permian Period, most species of life on Earth died out.** This was a **mass extinction,** in which many types of living things became extinct at the same time. Scientists estimate that about 90 percent of all ocean species died out. So did about 70 percent of species on land. Even widespread organisms like trilobites became extinct.

Scientists aren't sure what caused this extinction. Some think an asteroid struck Earth, creating huge dust clouds. Massive volcanic eruptions spewed carbon dioxide and sulfur dioxide into the atmosphere. Temperatures all over Earth rose during this time, too. The amount of carbon dioxide in the oceans increased and the amount of oxygen declined, though scientists aren't sure why. All these factors may have contributed to the mass extinction.

FIGURE 3
Permian Trilobite
Throughout the Paleozoic, trilobites such as this Permian example were one of the most successful groups of organisms. But no species of trilobites survived the Permian mass extinction.

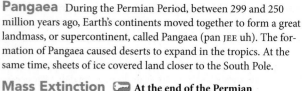
Do the Quick Lab *Graphing the Fossil Record.*

🔑 Assess Your Understanding

1a. List What are the periods of the Paleozoic Era?
Cambrian, Ordovician, Silurian, Devonian, Carboniferous, and Permian

b. Sequence Number the following organisms in order from earliest to latest appearance.
amphibians *4*   jawless fishes *2*
trilobites *1*   bony fishes *3*

c. Relate Cause and Effect Name two possible causes of the mass extinction at the end of the Paleozoic.
Sample: Volcanic eruptions and increased carbon dioxide in the oceans

got it?

○ **I get it!** Now I know that the main events in the Paleozoic Era were *the development of invertebrates, early vertebrates, and land plants.*

○ **I need extra help with** *See TE note.*

Go to MY SCIENCE COACH online for help with this subject.

What Happened in the Mesozoic Era?

When you think of prehistoric life, do you think of dinosaurs? If so, you're thinking of the Mesozoic Era.

The Triassic Period Some living things managed to survive the Permian mass extinction. Plants and animals that survived included fish, insects, reptiles, and cone-bearing plants called conifers. 🔑 **Reptiles were so successful during the Mesozoic Era that this time is often called the Age of Reptiles.** The first dinosaurs appeared about 225 million years ago, during the Triassic (tri AS ik) Period.

Mammals also first appeared during the Triassic Period. A **mammal** is a vertebrate that can control its body temperature and feeds milk to its young. Mammals in the Triassic Period were very small, about the size of a mouse.

The Jurassic Period During the Jurassic Period (joo RAS ik), dinosaurs became common on land. Other kinds of reptiles evolved to live in the ocean and in the air. Scientists have identified several hundred different kinds of dinosaurs.

One of the first birds, called *Archaeopteryx*, appeared during the Jurassic Period. The name *Archaeopteryx* means "ancient winged one." Many paleontologists now think that birds evolved from dinosaurs.

apply it!

The illustrations show a flying reptile called *Dimorphodon* and one of the earliest birds, *Archaeopteryx*.

❶ Identify two features the two animals have in common.

Sample: Wings, bill-like structures, claws on their legs

❷ Identify one major difference between the two animals.

Sample: One has feathers, and the other does not.

❸ ◢ Classify Which animal is *Archaeopteryx*? How do you know it is related to birds?

Sample: The second picture shows Archaeopteryx. It has feathers, as modern birds do.

275

Differentiated Instruction

L3 **Compare *Archaeopteryx* to Present-Day Birds** Challenge students to find a library book or magazine article that compares a bird skeleton with a dinosaur skeleton. Have volunteers research why many paleontologist think birds evolved from dinosaurs and prepare a presentation for the class.

Explain

Teach Key Concepts 🔑

Explain to students that reptiles became widespread during the Triassic Period of the Mesozoic Era.
Ask: **What do reptiles have in common with fish, insects, and conifers?** (All survived the mass extinction at the end of the Permian Period.) **When did the first dinosaur appear?** (About 225 million years ago) Point out that dinosaurs are a type of reptile. Stress that familiar dinosaurs did not necessarily live at the same time. For example, *Apatosaurus* lived during the Jurassic Period, whereas *Tyrannosaurus* lived during the Cretaceous Period.
Ask: **What other life form that is dominant today first appeared during this era?** (Mammals) **What event ended the Mesozoic Era?** (A mass extinction in which over half of all plant and animal groups were wiped out, including the dinosaurs.)

Elaborate

21st Century Learning

COMMUNICATION Organize students into small groups, and have each group brainstorm a list of questions about dinosaurs. Questions might include: *How large was the largest dinosaur? Were all dinosaurs giants? Did dinosaurs live in herds, or were they solitary? What did dinosaurs eat? Did they care for their young?* When groups have finished, have them read their questions to the class. Write the most interesting questions on the board, and invite volunteers to find the answers and report back to the class.

Apply It!

L1 Review the information about reptiles in the Triassic Period and about reptiles and birds in the Jurassic Period before beginning the activity.

◢ **Classify** Remind students that classifying is grouping together items that are alike in some way.
Ask: **What are the two organisms that are being classified in this activity?** (Archaeopteryx and Dimorphodon)

Digital Lesson: Assign the *Apply It* activity online and have students submit their work to you.

my science online | Mesozoic Era

Explain

Teach Key Concepts

Explain to students that scientists used large, dramatic events or changes in life forms to guide them in dividing Earth's geologic history into eras and periods. Point out that a mass extinction is the event that marks the end of the Permian Period of the Paleozoic Era. Ask: **What event marks the end of the Cretaceous Period about 65 million years ago?** *(Another mass extinction)* **What do scientists believe caused this event?** *(An asteroid striking Earth)*

Elaborate

Build Inquiry

L2 DEVELOP HYPOTHESES

Materials small potted evergreen plant, small flowering plant

Time 10 minutes

Point out that flowering plants, which first appeared in the Cretaceous Period, include all the leafy trees and grasses that dominate Earth today. Have students compare and contrast characteristics of gymnosperms (seed plants with exposed seed, usually in a cone) and angiosperms (flowering plants with seeds in a fruit). Have students observe, make sketches, and write a description of each kind of plant.

Ask: **Why do you think flowering plants became the dominant plant after the end of the Mesozoic Era?** *(Seeds in flowering plants are protected by fruits and are better able to survive than the seeds of cone-bearing plants.)*

Lab Resource: Quick Lab

L2 MODELING ASTEROID IMPACT Students will model an asteroid impact and observe the effects of the impact.

Evaluate

Assess Your Understanding

Have students evaluate their understanding by completing the appropriate sentence.

RTI Response to Intervention

If students cannot explain developments in the Mesozoic Era, **then** have them reread the material in this section and create an outline to organize the information.

my science COACH Have students go online for help in understanding the main developments in the Mesozoic Era.

FIGURE 4

The End of the Dinosaurs
Many scientists hypothesize that an asteroid hit Earth near the present-day Yucatán Peninsula, in southeastern Mexico.

CHALLENGE Write a short story summarizing the events shown in the illustration.

Students' stories should describe how an asteroid struck Earth, spread dust throughout the atmosphere, and caused climate change that led to the death of the dinosaurs.

The Cretaceous Period Reptiles, including dinosaurs, were still widespread throughout the Cretaceous Period (krih TAY shus). Birds began to replace flying reptiles during this period. Their hollow bones made them better adapted to their environment than the flying reptiles, which became extinct.

Flowering plants first evolved during the Cretaceous. Unlike conifers, flowering plants produce seeds that are inside a fruit. The fruit helps the seeds spread.

Another Mass Extinction At the close of the Cretaceous Period, about 65 million years ago, another mass extinction occurred. Scientists hypothesize that this mass extinction occurred when an asteroid from space struck Earth. This mass extinction wiped out more than half of all plant and animal groups, including the dinosaurs.

When the asteroid hit Earth, the impact threw huge amounts of dust and water vapor into the atmosphere. Dust and heavy clouds blocked sunlight around the world for years. Without sunlight, plants died, and plant-eating animals starved. The dust later formed the iridium-rich rock layer you read about at the beginning of the lesson. Some scientists think that climate changes caused by increased volcanic activity also helped cause the mass extinction.

THE DEATH OF THE DINOSAURS

BY TERRY DACTYL

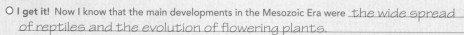

Do the Quick Lab
Modeling an Asteroid Impact.

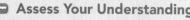

Assess Your Understanding

got it?

○ I get it! Now I know that the main developments in the Mesozoic Era were *the wide spread of reptiles and the evolution of flowering plants.*

○ I need extra help with *See TE note.*

Go to **my science COACH** *online for help with this subject.*

What Happened in the Cenozoic Era?

During the Mesozoic Era, mammals had to compete with dinosaurs for food and places to live. **The extinction of dinosaurs created an opportunity for mammals. During the Cenozoic Era, mammals evolved to live in many different environments—on land, in water, and even in the air.**

The Paleogene and Neogene Periods During the Paleogene and Neogene periods, Earth's climates were generally warm and mild, though they generally cooled over time. In the oceans, mammals such as whales and dolphins evolved. On land, flowering plants, insects, and mammals flourished. Grasses first began to spread widely. Some mammals became very large, as did some birds.

The Quaternary Period Earth's climate cooled and warmed in cycles during the Quaternary Period, causing a series of ice ages. Thick glaciers covered parts of Europe and North America. The latest warm period began between 10,000 and 20,000 years ago. Over thousands of years, most of the glaciers melted.

In the oceans, algae, coral, mollusks, fish, and mammals thrived. Insects and birds shared the skies. Flowering plants and mammals such as bats, cats, dogs, cattle, and humans became common. The fossil record suggests that modern humans may have evolved as early as 190,000 years ago. By about 12,000 to 15,000 years ago, humans had migrated to every continent except Antarctica.

FIGURE 5 ·······················
Giant Mammals
Many giant mammals evolved in the Cenozoic Era. This *Megatherium* is related to the modern sloth shown to the right, but was up to six meters tall.
✎ **Measure** About how many times taller was *Megatherium* than a modern sloth? _6_

Explain ———————

Teach Key Concepts 🗝

Explain to students that sometimes two or more species compete in a single habitat. Remind students that the Cenozoic Era is sometimes called the Age of Mammals. Have students refer to the Geologic Time Scale. Point out that the Cenozoic Era consists of three periods. Ask: **What major event marked the end of the Mesozoic Era?** *(Mass extinction of many plant and animal groups)* **How did conditions change for mammals during the Cenozoic Era?** *(After the extinction of the dinosaurs, mammals were able to live in a greater variety of environments.)* **How did the climate during the Paleogene and Neogene periods affect the types of life that evolved?** *(The warm and mild climate allowed whales, dolphins, and many grass-eating mammals to evolve.)* **How might the ice ages have affected the kinds of animals that lived during this era?** *(Some animals may not have been able to survive because of the cold climate or lack of food, and these animals may have become extinct.)*

LESSON 8.6

Differentiated Instruction

L1 Reptiles of the Mesozoic Era
Provide students with discarded science magazines or art supplies, and have them prepare a poster showing the different types of reptiles that lived during this era. Encourage students to find examples of present-day organisms that resemble reptiles in this era.

Elaborate

Explore the Big Q ❓ UbD

GEOLOGIC HISTORY Tell students to look at **Figure 6.** Remind students that this figure covers these two pages as well as the next two pages. Invite volunteers to read aloud the items in each column. Have students ask questions about the landmark events and life forms of that time. Write any questions that you might not be able to answer immediately on the chalkboard, and assign a student volunteer to find the answer or explanation in reference books. Ask **What major event happened about 3.8 million years ago?** *(The first sedimentary rocks formed.)*

Point out that the supercontinent Pangaea formed in the Permian Period and that this had a great effect on global climate. Ask: **In general, how is the climate of a region near an ocean different from the climate of a region far inland?** *(A typical answer might suggest that temperatures are more extreme inland compared to the climate near an ocean, where ocean winds produce moderate temperatures.)*

Explain that when the continents came together to form Pangaea, much coastal area was lost as smaller land masses moved into one another. At some point, there were no longer oceans between continents, and as a consequence, the climate changed throughout the world. Ask: **How could a change of climate affect an animal that was well adapted to a previous climate?** *(Sample: The animal might not live as easily in the new climate. For example, plants that the animal depended on for food might not grow in the new climate.)*

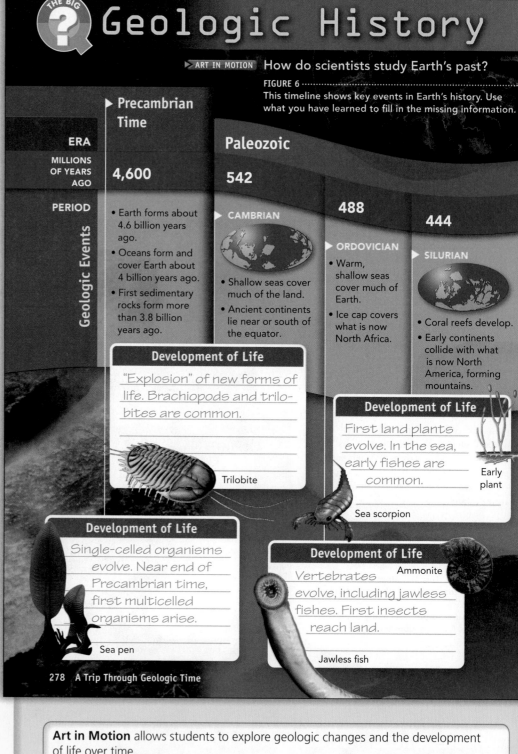

> EXPLORE THE BIG ❓

Geologic History

▶ ART IN MOTION How do scientists study Earth's past?

FIGURE 6 ·····
This timeline shows key events in Earth's history. Use what you have learned to fill in the missing information.

▶ **Precambrian Time**

Paleozoic

ERA				
MILLIONS OF YEARS AGO	4,600	542	488	444
PERIOD		CAMBRIAN	ORDOVICIAN	SILURIAN

Geologic Events

- Earth forms about 4.6 billion years ago.
- Oceans form and cover Earth about 4 billion years ago.
- First sedimentary rocks form more than 3.8 billion years ago.

CAMBRIAN
- Shallow seas cover much of the land.
- Ancient continents lie near or south of the equator.

ORDOVICIAN
- Warm, shallow seas cover much of Earth.
- Ice cap covers what is now North Africa.

SILURIAN
- Coral reefs develop.
- Early continents collide with what is now North America, forming mountains.

Development of Life

"Explosion" of new forms of life. Brachiopods and trilobites are common.

Trilobite

Development of Life

First land plants evolve. In the sea, early fishes are common.

Early plant

Sea scorpion

Development of Life

Single-celled organisms evolve. Near end of Precambrian time, first multicelled organisms arise.

Sea pen

Development of Life

Vertebrates evolve, including jawless fishes. First insects reach land.

Ammonite

Jawless fish

278   A Trip Through Geologic Time

Art in Motion allows students to explore geologic changes and the development of life over time.

my SCIENCE online.com Cenozoic Era

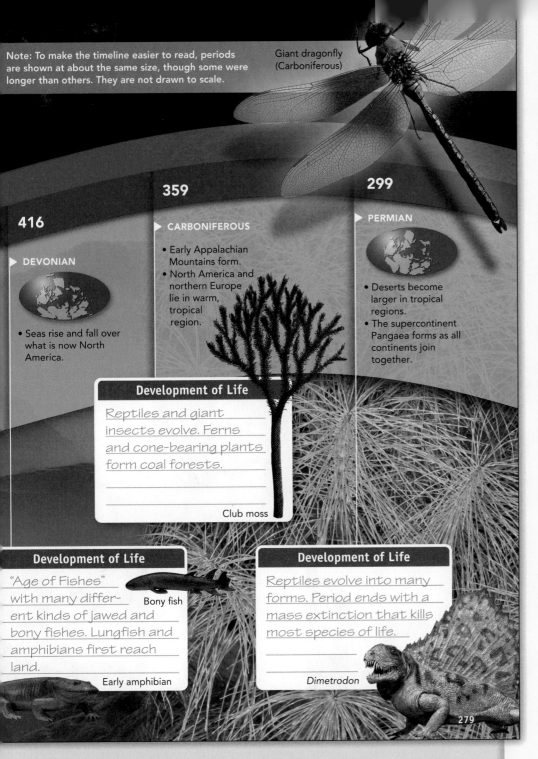

Note: To make the timeline easier to read, periods are shown at about the same size, though some were longer than others. They are not drawn to scale.

Giant dragonfly (Carboniferous)

416

DEVONIAN

• Seas rise and fall over what is now North America.

359

CARBONIFEROUS

• Early Appalachian Mountains form.
• North America and northern Europe lie in warm, tropical region.

299

PERMIAN

• Deserts become larger in tropical regions.
• The supercontinent Pangaea forms as all continents join together.

Development of Life

Reptiles and giant insects evolve. Ferns and cone-bearing plants form coal forests.

Club moss

Development of Life

"Age of Fishes" with many different kinds of jawed and bony fishes. Lungfish and amphibians first reach land.

Bony fish

Early amphibian

Development of Life

Reptiles evolve into many forms. Period ends with a mass extinction that kills most species of life.

Dimetrodon

279

Elaborate

Build Inquiry 🔬Lab zone

L2 PREHISTORIC LIFE FORMS

Materials reference books, poster board, art materials, printouts and pictures from the Internet (optional)

Time 1 class period for research (could be assigned as homework); 1 class period for presentations

Remind students that during each of the three geologic eras, major life forms evolved and disappeared. Tell students that they will research a major life form during one era. Ask them to work in pairs or small groups to choose one group of animals or plants, research its evolution, and prepare a poster showing the changes. Guide students in choosing a variety of organisms so that most students are not researching dinosaurs. Students might choose to focus on a large group, such as fishes or insects, or the evolution of a specific organism, such as trilobites or horses. Encourage students to make a "tree" that shows evolution through time. Allow students class time to present their posters as you go through each of the geologic periods in Earth's history.

As students make their presentations, ask them to explain how the evolution of their organism or group was made possible by other developments. *(Example: Animals were able to move from the oceans to land because plant life developed on land.)*

Differentiated Instruction

L3 Illustrating Time Periods
Encourage students to choose one or two periods shown in **Figure 6** to illustrate more extensively. Students can go back to the appropriate section of text about the particular period in order to locate one or more details that could be illustrated and added to the timeline. Invite several students to work collaboratively in order to cover all or many of the periods shown in **Figure 6.**

Explain

Address Misconceptions

L1 **GEOLOGIC TIME SPANS** Students may have a difficult time grasping the enormous spans of time represented by each geologic period. As a consequence, they might think that all the organisms listed and shown in each period lived at the same time. Tell students that the organisms shown in **Figure 6** did not necessarily appear and live for the same number of years within a particular period. Point out that *Coelophysis* first appeared at the end of the Triassic Period. *Barosaurus* did not appear until about 50 million years later (150 million years ago). In the Cretaceous Period, flowering plants first appeared 125 million years ago, but *Tyrannosaurus rex* did not appear until 85 million years ago and then died out about 65 million years ago. Ask: **How would you compare and contrast the geologic history of flowering plants and Tyrannosaurus rex?** *(Both evolved in the Cretaceous Period. However, whereas Tyrannosaurus rex disappeared 65 million years ago, flowering plants have continued to thrive.)*

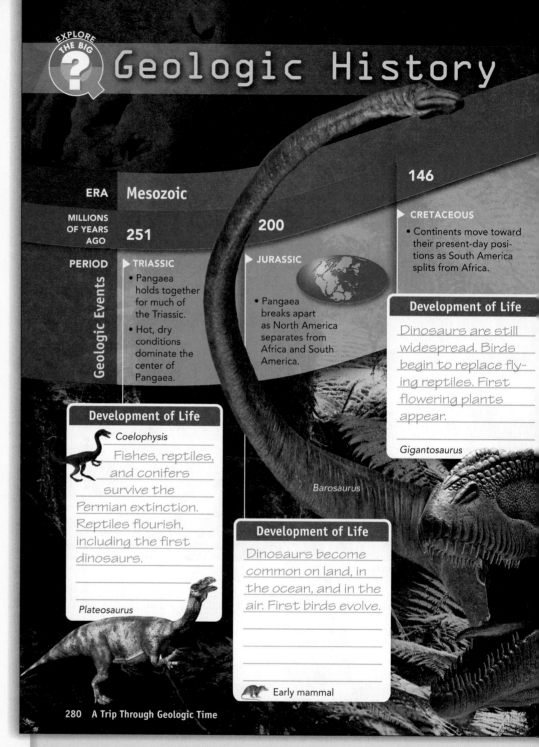

EXPLORE THE BIG

Geologic History

ERA	Mesozoic		
			146
MILLIONS OF YEARS AGO	251	200	▶ CRETACEOUS
PERIOD	▶ TRIASSIC	▶ JURASSIC	

▶ CRETACEOUS
- Continents move toward their present-day positions as South America splits from Africa.

Geologic Events

TRIASSIC
- Pangaea holds together for much of the Triassic.
- Hot, dry conditions dominate the center of Pangaea.

JURASSIC
- Pangaea breaks apart as North America separates from Africa and South America.

Development of Life

Dinosaurs are still widespread. Birds begin to replace flying reptiles. First flowering plants appear.

Gigantosaurus

Development of Life

Coelophysis

Fishes, reptiles, and conifers survive the Permian extinction. Reptiles flourish, including the first dinosaurs.

Plateosaurus

Development of Life

Dinosaurs become common on land, in the ocean, and in the air. First birds evolve.

Early mammal

Barosaurus

280   A Trip Through Geologic Time

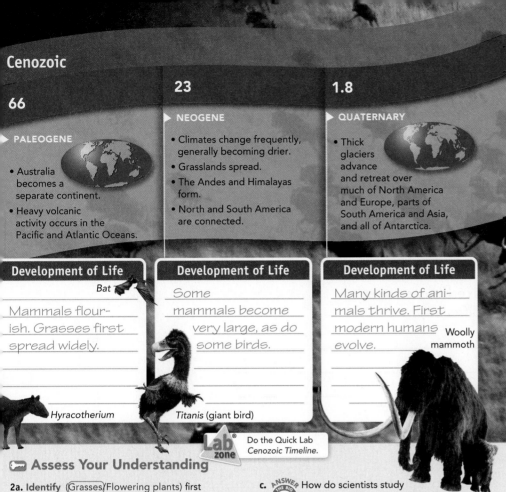

Cenozoic

66

PALEOGENE

- Australia becomes a separate continent.
- Heavy volcanic activity occurs in the Pacific and Atlantic Oceans.

23

▶ NEOGENE

- Climates change frequently, generally becoming drier.
- Grasslands spread.
- The Andes and Himalayas form.
- North and South America are connected.

1.8

▶ QUATERNARY

- Thick glaciers advance and retreat over much of North America and Europe, parts of South America and Asia, and all of Antarctica.

Development of Life

Bat

Mammals flourish. Grasses first spread widely.

Hyracotherium

Development of Life

Some mammals become very large, as do some birds.

Titanis (giant bird)

Development of Life

Many kinds of animals thrive. First modern humans evolve.

Woolly mammoth

Do the Quick Lab *Cenozoic Timeline.*

🔑 Assess Your Understanding

2a. Identify (Grasses/Flowering plants) first spread widely in the Cenozoic Era.

b. Explain What factors allowed new organisms to spread during the Cenozoic Era?

The disappearance of the dinosaurs led to many opportunities for mammals. Earth's climate was also warm and mild.

c. ANSWER How do scientists study Earth's past? Use an example from this chapter in your answer.

Sample: Scientists study fossils and rock layers to learn about Earth's past. For example, they found fossils of dinosaurs with feathers.

got it? ....

○ **I get it!** Now I know that important events in the Cenozoic Era included the spread of mammals and grasses and the evolution of humans.

○ **I need extra help with** See TE note.

Go to **my science COACH** *online for help with this subject.*

281

Explain
Make Analogies

L1 DIFFERENT PARTS OF THE SAME CENTURY
To help students understand the idea that two organisms from the same geologic period did not necessarily live at the same time, provide the following analogy. Modern time periods are often viewed in terms of a century, such as the 21st century or the 20th century. However, all of the people in the 20th century did not live at the same time. Ask: **What is the name of an American president who lived early in the 20th century and the name of an American president who lived late in the 20th century?** *(Sample: Theodore Roosevelt, Bill Clinton)* Point out that though these two individuals lived in the same century, they were never alive at the same time.

Elaborate

Lab Resource: Quick Lab

L2 CENOZOIC TIMELINE Students will make a timeline of major events in the Cenozoic Era.

Evaluate

Assess Your Understanding

After students answer the questions, have them evaluate their understanding by completing the appropriate sentence.

Answer the Big Q ❓ UbD

To help students focus on the Big Question, lead a class discussion about how scientists study Earth's past.

RTI Response to Intervention

2a. If students need help with choosing the correct type of plants, **then** have them review their answers in **Figure 6.**

b. If students have trouble explaining the spread of new organisms, **then** have them reread the first two paragraphs in this section.

c. If students cannot explain scientists' methods, **then** have them skim the chapter, using illustrations as well as lesson and section titles to guide their review.

my science COACH Have students go online for help in understanding the important events of the Cenozoic Era.

Differentiated Instruction

L1 Create a Display Encourage students to investigate the giant mammals, or megafauna, that lived during the Pliocene and Pleistocene epochs of the quaternary Period. These mammals included woolly mammoths, large rhinoceroses, saber-toothed tigers, giant camels, and moose-sized deer called Irish elk. Suggest that students include the mastodons and other animals found preserved in the ice of northern Siberia. Have students create a bulletin board display with illustrations and captions explaining the evolution of such animals.

Name ________________ Date ________ Class ________

Lab zone® After the Inquiry Warm-Up

Eras of Earth's History

Inquiry Warm-Up, *Dividing History*

In the Inquiry Warm-Up, you investigated criteria for constructing and dividing a time scale. Using what you learned from that activity, answer the questions below.

1. **COMPARE AND CONTRAST** How are the two timelines constructed by you and another student similar and how are they different?

2. **COMMUNICATE** Why do timelines exclude some details about the event listed for each date?

3. **SEQUENCE** Take the events on your timeline and list them in order of importance, instead of by dates. How does the order differ from your timeline order by dates?

4. **COMMUNICATE** Which method of showing information, a timeline or a list of key events, would you use to present a person's history? Explain.

Place the outside corner, the corner away from the dotted line, in the corner of your copy machine to copy onto letter-size paper.

Name _____ Date _____ Class _____

Eras of Earth's History

What Happened in the Paleozoic Era?

1a. LIST What are the periods of the Paleozoic Era?

_____

_____

b. SEQUENCE Number the following organisms in order from earliest to latest appearance.

amphibians ___   jawless fishes ___

trilobites ___   bony fishes ___

c. RELATE CAUSE AND EFFECT Name two possible causes of the mass extinction at the end of the Paleozoic Era.

_____

_____

_____

got_it? ···

○ **I get it!** Now I know that the main events in the Paleozoic Era were _____

_____

○ **I need extra help with** _____

_____

Eras of Earth's History

What Happened in the Mesozoic Era?

got _{it}**?** ··

○ **I get it!** Now I know that the main developments in the Mesozoic Era were _____

_____

○ **I need extra help with** _____

_____

What Happened in the Cenozoic Era?

2a. IDENTIFY (Grasses/Flowering plants) first spread widely in the Cenozoic Era.

b. EXPLAIN What factors allowed new organisms to spread during the Cenozoic Era?

_____

_____

c. ANSWER How do scientists study Earth's past? Use an example from this chapter in your answer.

_____

_____

_____

got _{it}**?** ··

○ **I get it!** Now I know that important events in the Cenozoic Era included _____

_____

○ **I need extra help with** _____

_____

Name _____ Date _____ Class _____

Eras of Earth's History

What Happened in the Paleozoic Era?

Through most of Earth's history, the only living things were single-celled organisms. **At the beginning of the Paleozoic Era, a great number of different kinds of organisms evolved. For the first time, many organisms had hard parts, including shells and outer skeletons.** At this time, all animals lived in the sea. Many were **invertebrates,** or animals without backbones. Later, the first vertebrates evolved. A **vertebrate** is an animal with a backbone. Later, simple plants began to grow on land and became abundant. During the Devonian Period, often called the Age of Fishes, every main group of fishes was present in the oceans. **The Devonian Period was also when animals began to spread widely on land.** An **amphibian** is an animal that lives part of its life on land and part of its life in water. As time went on, other vertebrates including reptiles evolved from amphibians. **Reptiles** have scaly skin and lay eggs that have tough, leathery shells. During the Permian Period, Earth's continents moved together to form a great land mass called Pangaea. **At the end of the Permian Period, most species of life on Earth died out.** Scientists are not sure what caused this **mass extinction,** in which many types of living things became extinct at the same time.

What Happened in the Mesozoic Era?

Fish, insects, reptiles, and conifers survived the mass extinction. **Reptiles were so successful during the Mesozoic Era that this time is often called the Age of Reptiles.** Dinosaurs and mammals first appeared in the Triassic Period. A **mammal** is a warm-blooded vertebrate that feeds milk to its young. Birds and flowering plants evolved during the Cretaceous Period. **At the close of the Cretaceous Period, about 65 million years ago, another mass extinction occurred. Scientists hypothesize that this mass extinction occurred when an asteroid from space struck Earth.**

What Happened in the Cenozoic Era?

The extinction of dinosaurs created an opportunity for mammals. During the Cenozoic Era, mammals evolved to live in many different environments—on land, in water, and even in the air. Earth's climates were generally warm, allowing whales and dolphins to evolve. In the Quaternary Period, the Earth experienced a series of ice ages. Modern humans may have evolved as early as 190,000 years ago.

On a separate sheet of paper, explain how several different life forms have developed on Earth.

Review and Reinforce

Eras of Earth's History

> ## Understanding Main Ideas
> Fill in the blank with the correct era or period to complete each statement.

1. Until the _____, only one-celled organisms lived on land, but during this period, plants became abundant.

2. At the start of the _____, many organisms evolved with hard parts including shells and outer skeletons.

3. During the _____ animals began to spread widely on land.

4. At the end of the _____, most species of life on Earth died.

5. Reptiles were so successful that the _____ is often called the Age of Reptiles.

6. At the close of the _____, about 65 million years ago, a second mass extinction occurred.

7. The first dinosaurs appeared during the _____.

8. During the _____, mammals evolved to live in many different environments—on land, in water, and even in the air.

9. The fossil record suggests that humans migrated to most continents during the

_____.

> ## Building Vocabulary
> Match each definition with its term by writing the letter of the correct term in the right column on the line beside the definition in the left column.

10. ___ animal with a backbone   a. reptile

11. ___ animal without a backbone   b. mammal

12. ___ animal that evolved from lungfish   c. invertebrate

13. ___ animal with strong legs and eggs with thick shells   d. mass extinction

14. ___ an event in which many types of living things die out at once e. amphibian

15. ___ animal that feeds its young with milk   f. vertebrate

Enrich

Eras of Earth's History

> Read the passages below. Then answer the questions that follow on a separate sheet of paper.

The End of an Era

What happened at the close of the Mesozoic Era to cause the extinction of dinosaurs and many other types of organisms? There is more than one theory. Each uses evidence from fossils and from analysis of rock layers.

Theory 1: An Asteroid Impact

About 65 million years ago, an asteroid about 10 kilometers in diameter collided with Earth. The impact had the force of millions of atomic bombs. Sediment and particles of the asteroid blasted into the atmosphere. A dust cloud blocked the sun for months or longer. Plants and other organisms that performed photosynthesis died, and many animals that depended on those plants for food died, too. Blocking the sun also dropped Earth's temperature, changing the climate. Animals that couldn't adapt became extinct. Evidence for this theory includes the fossil record, which shows that many organisms died out suddenly at the end of the Cretaceous Period. Scientists also discovered an impact crater in the Gulf of Mexico. Other evidence includes a thin layer of rock around Earth that is enriched with the rare element iridium— and that is 65 million years old. Asteroids contain iridium.

Theory 2: Volcanic Eruptions

About 65 millions years ago, huge volcanic eruptions occurred on the Indian subcontinent of south Asia. Movements of Earth's continents caused these eruptions. Lava poured over a large area, equal in size to about half of Europe. Volcanic dust spewed into the atmosphere, and dark clouds encircled Earth. For months or longer, the volcanic dust blocked the sun's energy from reaching Earth's surface, causing plants, and then animals, to die. Evidence for this theory includes a fossil record, which shows many organisms died suddenly at the end of the Cretaceous Period. Geologists identified a huge area of volcanic rock 65 million years old on the Indian subcontinent. Also a thin rock layer enriched with iridium around Earth dates back 65 million years. Eruptions produce dust-containing iridium.

1. What is the evidence for the asteroid-impact theory?
2. What is the evidence for the volcanic-eruptions theory?
3. In each theory, what causes the extinction of plants and animals?
4. What evidence would be needed to prove one of the theories true?
5. Which theory makes the most sense to you? Give reasons.

Name _____ Date _____ Class _____

Eras of Earth's History

If the statement is true, write *true*. If the statement is false, change the underlined word or words to make the statement true.

1. _____ Near the end of <u>Precambrian Time</u>, single-celled organisms were joined by more complex living things.

2. _____ A(n) <u>vertebrate</u> is an animal without a backbone.

3. _____ During the Silurian Period, plants and <u>insects</u> became abundant on Earth's land.

4. _____ A(n) <u>amphibian</u> is an animal that lives part of its life on land and part of its life in water.

5. _____ Reptiles are <u>invertebrates</u> that evolved from amphibians.

6. _____ Between 299 and 250 million years ago, Earth's continents formed a vast <u>landmass</u> called Pangaea.

Fill in the blank to complete each statement.

7. A(n) _____ occurs when many types of living things die out at the same time.

8. The Mesozoic Era is often called the Age of _____ because of the success of these animals.

9. The Triassic Period saw the rise of _____, or warm-blooded vertebrates that feed milk to their young.

10. The geologic period in which we are living is called the

_____.

Eras of Earth's History

Answer Key

After the Inquiry Warm-Up

1. Answers will vary. Both students' timelines may show segments are divided into similar periods, or that the timelines represent a person in the same type of profession, such as an athlete or scientist. They may show different time sections and different types of events that represent the person they chose.

2. Answers will vary. Sample: Timelines are outlines of events during certain periods of time. Details about each event would make the timeline too cumbersome.

3. Answers will vary. Students may show key accomplishments that appear in a different order from how they occurred in time.

4. Answers will vary. Students may choose a timeline because it shows the order in time that the events happened. Some students may choose the event list to show the most important items first.

Key Concept Summaries

For much of Earth's history, the only form of life was single-celled organisms. Finally invertebrates and vertebrates developed. Plants, fishes, amphibians, and reptiles followed. Mammals, birds, and flowering plants evolved before human beings developed on Earth.

Review and Reinforce

1. Silurian Period
2. Paleozoic Era
3. Devonian Period
4. Permian Period
5. Mesozoic Era
6. Cretaceous Period
7. Triassic Period
8. Cenozoic Era
9. Quaternary Period
10. f
11. c
12. e
13. a
14. d
15. b

Enrich

1. Evidence includes the fossil record, which shows many organisms died out 65 million years ago, an impact crater near the Yucatán Peninsula, and a layer of rock around Earth that is enriched with iridium.

2. Evidence includes the fossil record, which shows many organisms died out 65 million years ago, a huge area of volcanic rock on the Indian subcontinent from 65 million years ago, and a layer of rock around Earth that is enriched with iridium.

3. In each theory, a dust cloud blocks the energy from the sun from reaching Earth's surface for months or longer. This causes plants, which use energy from the sun to make food, to die, which in turn, causes animals to die.

4. Answers may vary. A typical answer might suggest that there is no evidence that could prove absolutely that one or the other of these theories is true.

5. Answers may vary. A typical answer might suggest that the asteroid theory makes more sense because volcanic eruptions in recent times have not caused similar extinctions.

Lesson Quiz

1. true
2. invertebrate
3. true
4. true
5. vertebrates
6. true
7. mass extinction
8. Reptiles
9. mammals
10. Quaternary Period

Study Guide

Review the Big Q ? UbD

Have students complete the statement at the top of the page. This Key Concept supports their understanding of the chapter's Big Question. Have students return to the chapter opener question. What is different about how students view the image of the fly now that they have completed the chapter? Thinking about this will help them prepare for the *Apply the Big Q* activity in the Review and Assessment.

Partner Review

Have partners review definitions of vocabulary terms by using the Study Guide to quiz each other. Students could read the key statements and leave out words for their partner to fill in, or change a statement so that it is false and then ask their partner to correct it.

Class Activity: Poster

Have students work in groups to create a large poster that shows six aspects of A Trip Through Geologic Time. For each of the chapter's six lessons, students should include an illustration or diagram, an explanation of how the lesson's title relates to the Big Idea, and a list of key terms and concepts. Ask students to use the following questions to help them organize their ideas:
- What are fossils?
- How old are rock layers?
- What is radioactive dating?
- What is the geologic time scale?
- How did Earth form?
- What happened in the Paleozoic, Mesozoic, and Cenozoic eras?

My Science Coach allows students to complete the *Practice Test* online.

The Big Question allows students to complete the *Apply the Big Q* activity about how scientists study Earth's past.

Vocab Flash Cards offer a way to review the chapter vocabulary words.

my science online .com ▷ **A Trip Through Geologic Time**

Study Guide

Scientists study <u>fossils</u> in order to draw inferences about how <u>organisms and environments</u> have changed over time.

LESSON 1 Fossils

🔑 Most fossils form when sediment hardens into rock, preserving the shapes of organisms.

🔑 Fossils include molds, casts, petrified fossils, carbon films, trace fossils, and preserved remains.

🔑 Fossils provide evidence about Earth's history.

Vocabulary
- fossil • mold • cast • petrified fossil
- carbon film • trace fossil • paleontologist
- evolution • extinct

LESSON 2 The Relative Age of Rocks

🔑 In horizontal sedimentary rock layers, the oldest layer is generally at the bottom. Each layer is younger than the layers below it.

🔑 Gaps in the geologic record and folding can change the position in which rock layers appear.

Vocabulary
- relative age • absolute age
- law of superposition • extrusion • intrusion
- fault • index fossil • unconformity

LESSON 3 Radioactive Dating

🔑 During radioactive decay, the atoms of one element break down to form atoms of another element.

🔑 In radioactive dating, scientists compare the amount of a radioactive element in a rock with the amount of the stable element into which the radioactive element decays.

Vocabulary
- radioactive decay
- half-life

LESSON 4 The Geologic Time Scale

🔑 Because the time span of Earth's past is so great, geologists use the geologic time scale to show Earth's history.

Vocabulary
- geologic time scale
- era
- period

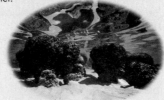

LESSON 5 Early Earth

🔑 Scientists think that Earth began as a ball of dust, rock, and ice in space. Gravity pulled this mass together.

Vocabulary
- comet

LESSON 6 Eras of Earth's History

🔑 During the Paleozoic Era, a great number of different organisms evolved.

🔑 Reptiles spread widely during the Mesozoic Era.

🔑 During the Cenozoic Era, mammals evolved to live in many different environments.

Vocabulary
- invertebrate • vertebrate • amphibian • reptile
- mass extinction • mammal

ELL Support

4 Language Production

Divide the students into six pairs or small groups. Each group will present an oral report that summarizes the information in each of the lessons. Each group's report should incorporate the Key Concepts for the lesson, use relevant vocabulary terms, and rely on visual aids. Have students verbalize their understanding of the lesson before they begin to write their reports.

Beginning
LOW/HIGH Allow students to work on the visual aids for the oral report. Encourage them to label and caption.

Intermediate
LOW/HIGH Have students present the oral reports to the class.

Advanced
LOW/HIGH Have students act as recorders for their groups when planning the reports.

Review and Assessment

LESSON 1 Fossils

1. A hollow area in sediment in the shape of all or part of an organism is called a
(a.) mold.   **b.** cast.
c. trace fossil.   **d.** carbon film.

2. A series of dinosaur footprints in rock are an example of a(n) ___trace___ fossil.

3. Develop Hypotheses Which organism has a better chance of leaving a fossil: a jellyfish or a bony fish? Explain.
A bony fish has a better chance, because a jellyfish has no hard parts.

Use the picture below to answer Questions 4–5.

4. Classify What type of fossil is shown?
Cast

5. Infer This fossil was found in a dry, mountainous area. What can you infer about how the area has changed over time?
At the time the fossil formed, the area must have been under water. The land has become higher and drier.

6. Write About It Suppose you are developing a museum exhibit about fossils. Write a guide for visitors to your exhibit explaining how fossils form and what scientists can learn from them.
See TE rubric.

LESSON 2 The Relative Age of Rocks

7. A gap in the geologic record that occurs when sedimentary rocks cover an eroded surface is called a(n)
a. intrusion.   (b.) unconformity.
c. fault.   **d.** extrusion.

8. A geologist finds an area of undisturbed sedimentary rock. The ___lowest___ layer is most likely the oldest.

9. Apply Concepts A geologist finds identical index fossils in a rock layer in the Grand Canyon in Arizona and in a rock layer in northern Utah, more than 675 kilometers away. What can she infer about the ages of the two rock layers?
The two rock layers are about the same age.

LESSON 3 Radioactive Dating

10. The time it takes for half of a radioactive element's atoms to decay is its
a. era.   (b.) half-life.
c. relative age.   **d.** absolute age.

11. Calculate The half-life of carbon-14 is 5,730 years. A basket has 25% of its carbon-14 remaining. About how old is the basket?
11,460 years

12. Solve Problems Uranium-235 has a half-life of 713 million years. Would uranium-235 or carbon-14 be more useful for dating a fossil from Precambrian time? Explain.
Uranium-235 would be more useful. There would be too little carbon-14 left to be useful.

Review and Assessment

Assess Understanding

Have students complete the answers to the Review and Assessment questions. Have a class discussion about what students find confusing. Write key concepts on the board to reinforce knowledge.

RTI Response to Intervention

3. If students cannot determine which organism has a better chance of leaving a fossil, **then** have them reread the section titled *What Are Fossils?*

7. If students need help with defining *unconformity*, **then** have them scan the text for the highlighted term and reread the definition.

11. If students have trouble calculating the age of the basket, **then** have them review the *Do the Math* activity.

Alternate Assessment

L1 MAKE A MODEL Challenge students to create a physical model of rock layers in the Earth. Students should present the model in such a way that viewers can easily see sedimentary rock layers, an extrusion, an intrusion, and fossils. Students should label the model and prepare a written guide that helps viewers understand various components.

CHAPTER 8

Write About It	Assess student's writing using this rubric.			
SCORING RUBRIC	**SCORE 4**	**SCORE 3**	**SCORE 2**	**SCORE 1**
Explanation of fossil formation	Student correctly explains fossil formation.	Student partially explains fossil formation.	Student includes an inaccurate explanation of fossil formation.	Student does not explain how fossils are formed.
Explanation of use to scientists	Student gives detailed explanation of use to scientists.	Students gives good overview of use to scientists.	Student gives incomplete overview of use to scientists.	Student does not explain what scientists can learn from fossils.

Review and Assessment, Cont.

RTI Response to Intervention

13. If students cannot identify how the geologic time scale is subdivided, **then** have them reread the section titled *Dividing Geologic Time*.

18. If students need help with explaining how oceans formed on Earth, **then** have them reread the section titled *The Oceans* and paraphrase the information to a partner.

22. If students have trouble judging the accuracy of the movie, **then** have them reread the sections on the Mesozoic and Cenozoic eras and review the time line of geologic history to determine when dinosaurs became extinct and when early humans first appeared.

Apply the Big Q ? UbD

TRANSFER Students should be able to demonstrate understanding of how scientists study Earth's past by answering this question. See the scoring rubric below.

Connect to the Big Idea ? UbD

BIG IDEA Earth is 4.6 billion years old and the rock record contains its history.

Send students back to the Big Ideas of Science at the beginning of their student edition. Have them read what they wrote about Earth's history before they started the chapter. Lead a class discussion about how their thoughts have changed. If all chapters have been completed, have students fill in the bottom section for the Big Idea.

L3 WRITING IN SCIENCE Ask students to write a television interview with a geologist that explores how scientists have determined that our planet is 4.6 billion years old by studying the rock record.

Review and Assessment

LESSON 4 The Geologic Time Scale

13. The geologic time scale is subdivided into
- **a.** relative ages.
- **b.** absolute ages.
- **c.** unconformities.
- **(d.)** eras and periods.

14. Scientists developed the geologic time scale by studying <u>rock layers and index fossils.</u>

15. Sequence Which major division of geologic time came first?
<u>Precambrian Time</u>

Which period of geologic time occurred most recently?
<u>Quaternary Period</u>

LESSON 5 Early Earth

16. Which of the following was found in Earth's first atmosphere?
- **a.** carbon dioxide
- **(b.)** hydrogen
- **c.** oxygen
- **d.** ozone

17. Over time, Earth's rock hardened and formed land called <u>continents.</u>

18. Explain How do scientists think that Earth's oceans formed?
<u>As Earth cooled, water vapor condensed into rain. The rain collected to form oceans.</u>

19. **Write About It** Do you agree or disagree with the following statement? "Without photosynthesis, land animals and plants could not have evolved." Use evidence to justify your answer. *See TE rubric.*

LESSON 6 Eras of Earth's History

20. The earliest multicelled organisms were
- **(a.)** invertebrates.
- **b.** land plants.
- **c.** vertebrates.
- **d.** bacteria.

21. Explain How did Earth's environments change from the Neogene to the Quaternary Period?
<u>The climate began to cool, causing ice ages.</u>

22. Evaluate Science in the Media If you see a movie in which early humans fight dinosaurs, how would you judge the scientific accuracy of that movie? Give reasons for your judgment.
<u>Sample: The movie is not accurate. Dinosaurs became extinct at the end of the Mesozoic Era. Humans did not evolve until the Cenozoic Era.</u>

APPLY How do scientists study Earth's past?

23. Look at the fossil below. What can you infer about the organism and its environment? Be sure to give evidence for your inferences.

<u>Sample: Based on its shape as shown in the fossil, the organism was related to turtles. It probably lived in a wet area, because most modern turtles live in or near water.</u>
<u>See TE rubric.</u>

| **Write About It** | Assess student's writing using this rubric. |

SCORING RUBRIC	SCORE 4	SCORE 3	SCORE 2	SCORE 1
Explanation of view of statement and use of evidence to justify answer	Student explains role of photosynthesis in evolution of land animals and plants and gives detailed evidence to justify answer.	Student explains photosynthesis but does not relate it to evolution of land animals and plants. Gives some evidence to justify.	Student does not explain the role of photosynthesis in evolution of land animals and plants or give evidence.	Student does not indicate agreement or disagreement with the statement or give evidence.

? How do scientists study earth's past?
Assess student's response using this rubric.

SCORING RUBRIC	SCORE 4	SCORE 3	SCORE 2	SCORE 1
Inference about organism and environment	Student makes an appropriate inference based on the fossil.	Student makes a relatively accurate inference based on the fossil.	Student makes an inaccurate inference based on the fossil.	Student does not make an inference based on the fossil.
Use of evidence to support inference	Student gives detailed evidence to justify answer.	Student gives some evidence to justify answer.	Student includes inaccuracies in evidence to support answer.	Student does not give evidence to justify answer.

Standardized Test Prep

Multiple Choice

Circle the letter of the correct answer.

1. Use the table to answer the question.

Geologic Time Scale

Time Period	Duration (Millions of Years)
Cenozoic Era	66
Mesozoic Era	185
Paleozoic Era	291
Precambrian Time	about 4,058

A class is designing an outdoor model to show the geologic time scale from Precambrian Time through the present. If they use a scale of 1 m = 100 million years, how long will their model be?

A   46,000 m   B   460 m
Ⓒ   46 m   D   4.6 m

2. A leaf falls into a shallow lake and is rapidly buried in the sediment. The sediment changes to rock over millions of years. Which type of fossil would *most likely* be formed?

Ⓐ   carbon film
B   cast
C   preserved remains
D   trace fossil

3. What change in Earth's atmosphere allowed organisms to live on land?

A   a collision with a comet
Ⓑ   the development of the ozone layer
C   a strong burst of particles from the sun
D   the absorption of carbon dioxide by oceans

4. Which of the following organisms lived during the Paleozoic Era?

A   dinosaurs
B   flowering plants
C   grasses
Ⓓ   trilobites

5. Scientists can determine the absolute age of rocks using

A   fault lines.
B   index fossils.
Ⓒ   radioactive dating.
D   the law of superposition.

Constructed Response

Use the diagram below and your knowledge of science to answer Question 6. Write your answer on a separate sheet of paper.

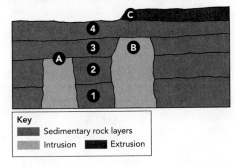

Key
- Sedimentary rock layers
- Intrusion
- Extrusion

6. Write the order in which the rock areas shown formed. Justify your answer using evidence from the diagram.
   See TE note.

Standardized Test Prep

Test-Taking Skills

READING ALL THE ANSWER CHOICES Multiple-choice questions sometimes take the form of an actual question. However, sometimes they take the form of a sentence that is completed by the correct answer. For this style of test item, it is a good idea to read the question stem along with each answer choice. By placing each possible answer in the context of the sentence, you may be able to eliminate one or more answer choices. This method also helps you take note of any idea or detail in the question stem that relates to the correct answer.

Constructed Response

6. Sample: The areas formed in the order 1, 2, A, 3, B, 4, C. Layer 1 is the oldest because it is on the bottom and the intrusions A and B both cut through it. Layer 2 is on top of layer 1, and both intrusions cut through it. Layer 3 is younger than layer 2. Intrusion A is older than layer 3 because it cuts through layers 1 and 2 but not layer 3. Intrusion B is younger than layer 3 because it cuts through layers 1, 2, and 3. Layer 4 is younger than both intrusions. Extrusion C is the youngest layer because it is on top of all the other layers.

Additional Assessment Resources

Chapter Test
EXAMVIEW® Assessment Suite
Performance Assessment
Progress Monitoring Assessments
SuccessTracker™

ⒺⓁⓁ Support

5 Assess Understanding

Have ELLs complete the Alternate Assessment. Provide guidelines on the information it must cover, and a rubric for assessment. You may wish to have students work in small groups to complete the activity.

Beginning

LOW/HIGH Pair beginning speakers with advanced speakers that have the same native language to help students complete the written guide.

Intermediate

LOW/HIGH Allow students extra time to complete their models and written guides. You may also wish to permit students to refer to their books or notes when writing their guides.

Advanced

LOW/HIGH Challenge students to use as many vocabulary words in their labels and written guides as possible.

Remediate If students have trouble with...

QUESTION	SEE LESSON	STANDARDS
1	6	
2	1	
3	5	
4	4	
5	3	
6	2	

Science Matters

Think Like a Scientist

Have students read *Putting the Puzzle Together.* Point out that paleontology includes the study of all prehistoric life, organisms' interactions with each other, and their interactions with their environments. Paleontology incorporates elements of biology, geology, and archeology. Tell students that fossils are the best clues paleontologists have about what prehistoric life was like.

Explain that many factors make reconstruction difficult. In addition to incomplete skeletons, sometimes fossilized bones of different dinosaurs are found mixed together at the same site. Tell students that other types of fossils can help scientists figure out things about what dinosaurs looked like. For example, whether there is a trace fossil made by the dinosaur's tail can tell scientists whether the tail was held in the air or dragged on the ground. Footprint fossils can tell about how the dinosaur stood and walked. Explain that scientists can use computer models to test their theories about what the animal looked like. They can create a simulation of the animal and use it in engineering experiments to see if the animal could function and be properly balanced if it looked the way the scientists imagined.

As students research T. rex reconstructions, have them note the differences between the version they chose and what they imagine the T. rex looked like.

Ask: **How do virtual fossils help with reconstruction?** (*Computers can create virtual fossils to use in the model based on an existing fossil.*) **Why do different reconstructions vary in appearance?** (*Fossils don't have information about muscle size and shape or coloring of the animal.*)

SCIENCE MATTERS

Think Like a Scientist

PUTTING THE PUZZLE TOGETHER

Imagine you are putting together a puzzle, but you don't have all the pieces. That's the problem for scientists trying to determine exactly what an animal looked like. Paleontologists may find only some of the bones of a prehistoric animal. They may find bones from more than one of the same kind of animal.

Scientists build reconstructions of the animals based on the fossils they have and observations of living relatives of the animal. Computed tomography (CT) scans help scientists make virtual fossils. They start with the pieces they have and then fill in the rest of the puzzle virtually. For example, if the scientists have found a fossil of the right jaw bone, the computers are able to help them model the left jaw bone, and build virtual models of the entire head.

Bones tell a story that scientists can understand. It's much harder to figure out the size and shape of the muscles or the color of the animal. Different scientists will build slightly different reconstructions of the same kind of animal. Because so many pieces of the puzzle are missing, it may be impossible to have a perfectly accurate reconstruction. Because the organisms are extinct, scientists may never know for sure.

Write About It Research the different ways in which paleontologists have reconstructed *Tyrannosaurus rex*. Choose one change and explain how it differed from a previous reconstruction. Why did paleontologists think this was a good change?

Paleontologist Jack Horner can use CT scans to create a 3-D model of this Lambeosaur skull. ▶

Quick Facts

In the late 1990s, producers at the British Broadcasting Company were looking for a new show about paleontology to appeal to a wide range of people. A producer named Tim Haines came up with the idea of recreating life-sized models of dinosaurs to show how they lived. Working with paleontologists, they created almost 20 dinosaur models and used them to film 6 episodes of a mini-series. Later, they created a live show called Walking with Dinosaurs in which the life-sized dinosaur recreations interact with each other and the audience. Each dinosaur model is operated by two puppeteers and a driver. The show has toured in the United States, the United Kingdom, and Europe. Have students research what dinosaurs are featured in the show. Ask them to choose a dinosaur and find out what the audience might have seen it do in the show.

Teen Finds Fossils

In early 2007, sixteen-year-old Sierra Sarti-Sweeney went for a walk at Boca Ciega Millennium Park in Seminole, Florida. She wanted to take some nature pictures. She did not expect to stumble on a mammoth!

During her walk, Sierra noticed bones in a stream bed. With her older brother, Sean, she brought the bones to local scientists. The bone Sierra found was the tooth of a prehistoric Columbian mammoth. Archaeologists say that the tooth and other fossils Sierra found could be as much as 100,000 years old!

Since Sierra's find, digging at the site has uncovered even more bones, including those from prehistoric camels, 2-meter turtles, and saber-toothed cats. According to scientists, the findings suggest that this part of Florida was once like the African savanna region.

For Sierra, the experience was exciting. She even had a call from a late-night television host. Finding the tooth confirmed Sierra's desire to be a zoologist and to keep looking at the world around her.

Design It Plan an exhibit of Sierra's findings. What would people want to know and see? Make a brochure advertising your exhibit and develop a presentation of the fossils found at Boca Ciega Millennium Park.

FROZEN EVIDENCE

In the giant ice cap at the South Pole, a continuous record of snow exists reaching back more than 800,000 years. Scientists have drilled 3.2 kilometers down into the ice. From the cores they pull up, scientists learn about the temperature and the different gases in the air when each layer was formed.

These cores show that temperatures go up and down in cycles. Long ice ages (about 90,000 years) follow short warm periods (about 10,000 years). The climate record also shows that temperatures and amounts of carbon dioxide change together. If carbon dioxide levels rise, temperatures also rise.

Research It Find at least three sources that explain the ice cores project. Write an essay critiquing the explanations provided. Note any bias, misinformation, or missing information.

Researchers extract samples from the ice at the South Pole. ▲

287

Kids Doing Science

Have students read *Teen Finds Fossils*. Tell students that Sarti-Sweeney's discovery inspired her whole community to come discover all the fossils in Boca Ciega Millenium Park. Park officials invited the public to come help with the dig, and people from ages 8 to 82 helped to recover thousands of fossils in four months.

Explain that fossils in this area are usually found farther below the surface. Scientists have many theories as to how these fossils surfaced, including erosion or storm water runoff from nearby roadwork. Tell students that Pleistocene fossils have been discovered at other sites on the east coast of Florida in Vero Beach and Melbourne. Show students a map of Florida and point out these areas.

Ask: **How do the fossils indicate what life in that area might have been like?** (*The different kinds of animals that lived there suggest the environment.*)

Hot Science

Have students read *Frozen Evidence*. Explain that scientists study the isotopes in water molecules to determine the temperature at the time the water sample became frozen. Water molecules that contain heavier isotopes will change from liquid to solid at a lower pressure. Therefore heavier water molecules freeze faster.

Tell students that ice cores are considered very valuable as a source of climatic proxies, or clues about climate variables. They provide more information about climate than studying tree rings or sediment layers because of the variety of information they contain.

Ask: **Would there be more heavy isotopes in an ice sample from an ice age or a warm period?** (*ice age*)

Energy Resources

Introduce the Big Q ❓ UbD

Have students look at the image and read the Engaging Question and description. Have students make hypotheses about the sources of energy in their lives. Point out that wind turbines like the ones shown on these pages have become dramatically more common in the United States in recent years.

Ask: **What is the source of the energy you used to get to school today?** *(Fossil fuels for gasoline, food for walking)* **What source of energy keeps your home warm?** *(Students may indicate oil, gas, wood, or electricity; accept all answers at this time.)* **What source of energy keeps you warm on a bright, clear summer afternoon?** *(The sun)*

Untamed Science Video

FARMING THE WIND Before viewing, invite students to suggest alternative energy resources to fossil fuels. Then play the video. Lead a class discussion and make a list of questions that the video raises. You may wish to have students view the video again after they have completed the chapter to see if their questions have been answered.

> To access the online resources for this chapter, search on or navigate to *Energy Resources.*
>
> **Untamed Science Video** compare wind energy to coal energy.
>
> **The Big Question** allows students to answer the Engaging Question about energy resources.

my science online.com ▶ **Energy Resources**

HOW CAN WIND KEEP YOUR LIGHTS ON?

❓ What are some of Earth's energy sources?

This man is repairing a wind turbine at a wind farm in Texas. Most wind turbines are at least 30 meters off the ground where the winds are fast. Wind speed and blade length help determine the best way to capture the wind and turn it into power. **Develop Hypotheses** Why do you think people are working to increase the amount of power we get from wind?

Sample: Wind energy captured by the turbine does not cause air pollution.

▶ UNTAMED SCIENCE Watch the **Untamed Science** video to learn more about energy resources.

Professional Development Note — From the Author

Humans are dependent on oil. The world uses energy at the rate of approximately 18 terawatts per second, most coming from dwindling reserves of fossil fuels. (For scale, one watt is about equal to lifting an apple up one meter each second. So human energy use equals 18 trillion apples going up and down each second.) What happens when fossil fuels run out? Well, potentially good news is around the corner: Earth receives about 7,000 times the total human energy use from the sun. This energy is unlimited and clean, and everybody has access to it. In the long term, our future could be very "bright."

✎ *Michael Wysession*

Energy Resources

Chapter at a Glance

CHAPTER PACING: 5–8 periods or $2\frac{1}{2}$–4 blocks

INTRODUCE THE CHAPTER: Engage students with the Engaging Question and the opening image. Activate prior knowledge and preteach vocabulary using the Getting Started pages.

Lesson 1: Fossil Fuels

Lesson 2: Alternative Sources of Energy

Lesson 3: Energy Use and Conservation

ASSESSMENT OPTIONS: Chapter Test, **EXAM**VIEW® Assessment Suite, Performance Assessment, Progress Monitoring Assessments, SuccessTracker™

Preference Navigator, in the online Planning tools, allows you to customize *Interactive Science* to your own teaching style. You can also edit lesson plans by selecting the Lesson Planner option.

Digital Teacher's Edition allows you to access your Teacher's Edition and Resource materials online.

my science online.com

my science online.com | Energy Resources | > UNTAMED SCIENCE > THE BIG QUESTION 289

Differentiated Instruction

L1 Interpret Visuals Help students understand that the photograph is taken from approximately 30 meters up in the air. Urge students to look at the structures in the distance to see that the photographer and the man doing repairs are on top of the pole that holds the blades of the turbine. Ask students whether they believe this location is appropriate for wind turbines, and why. *(High, open areas such as this one are ideal for gathering wind with turbines.)*

L3 Wind Turbines Challenge students to do research on the history and function of wind turbines. Students might include information about companies that manufacture such devices, various sizes and types of turbines, guidelines for placement and use, safety and health concerns, and what turbines require in terms of maintenance and repairs.

Getting Started

Check Your Understanding

This activity assesses students' understanding of the natural resources. Ask students to explain the difference between renewable and nonrenewable resources. After students have shared their answers, point out that all renewable and nonrenewable resources are natural resources.

Preteach Vocabulary Skills

Draw students' attention to the vocabulary listed in the *Chapter Preview*. Invite them to think about which of these terms might be considered high-use academic words. *Efficiency* might be an example. Have students look over the words *scarce* and *emit* with their meanings and examples in the chart. Then have them choose one word from the *Chapter Preview* and explain why they think it might have the characteristics of a high-use academic word. *(Students may indicate that words like* fuel, petroleum, efficiency, insulation, *and* energy conservation *are general enough to be used often in classrooms.)* Ask students to use these words in a sentence as they might be used in a classroom.

Getting Started

Check Your Understanding

1. **Background** Read the paragraph below and then answer the question.

> Aisha loves visiting her grandmother at work. Her grandmother says that the building she works in was designed to help conserve **natural resources.** Most of the building's electricity comes from **renewable resources,** such as sunlight and wind, instead of from **nonrenewable resources,** such as oil or coal.

- What is one example of a natural resource?

  Sample: wood, coal, water, oil, wind

> **MY READING WEB** If you had trouble completing the question above, visit **My Reading Web** and type in *Energy Resources.*

A **natural resource** is any material that occurs naturally in the environment and is used by people.

A **renewable resource** is either always available or is naturally replaced in a short time.

A **nonrenewable resource** is a resource that is not replaced within a useful time frame.

Vocabulary Skill

High-Use Academic Words High-use academic words are words that are used frequently in classrooms. Look for the words below as you read this chapter.

Word	Definition	Example
scarce	*adj.* rare; in limited supply	Tickets for the concert are becoming *scarce* because of the demand.
emit	*v.* to give off	When the oven is on, it *emits* heat, making the whole apartment warmer.

2. **Quick Check** Choose the word from the table above that best completes each sentence.

- Motor vehicles _emit_ chemicals that contribute to air pollution.
- As people continue to use oil faster than it can be replaced, it will become _scarce_.

My Reading Web offers leveled readings that provide a foundation for the chapter content.

Vocab Flash Cards offer extra practice with the chapter vocabulary words.

Digital Lesson
- Assign the *Check Your Understanding* activity online and have students submit their work to you.
- Assign the *Vocabulary Skill* activity online and have students submit their work to you.

my science online | Energy Resources

fossil fuel

solar energy

biomass fuel

energy conservation

Chapter Preview

LESSON 1
- fuel
- fossil fuel
- hydrocarbon
- petroleum
- refinery
- petrochemical
- 🔄 Summarize
- △ Communicate

LESSON 2
- solar energy
- hydroelectric power
- biomass fuel
- gasohol
- geothermal energy
- nuclear fission
- reactor vessel
- fuel rod
- control rod
- 🔄 Relate Cause and Effect
- △ Infer

LESSON 3
- efficiency
- insulation
- energy conservation
- 🔄 Identify the Main Idea
- △ Observe

▶ **VOCAB FLASH CARDS** For extra help with vocabulary, visit **Vocab Flash Cards** and type in *Energy Resources.*

291

CHAPTER 9

Preview Vocabulary Terms

Have students work together to create a word wall to display the vocabulary terms for the chapter. Be sure to discuss and analyze each term before posting it on the wall. As the class progresses through the chapter, the words can be sorted and categorized in different ways. A list of Academic Vocabulary for each lesson can be found in the Support All Readers box at the start of the lesson.

L1 Have students look at the images on this page as you pronounce each vocabulary word. Have students repeat the word after you. Then read the definition. Use the sample sentence in italics to clarify the meaning of the term.

fossil fuel *(FAWS ul   fyool)* An energy-rich substance formed from the remains of plants, animals, and other organisms. *Gasoline is a product made from a fossil fuel called oil.*

solar energy *(SOH lur   EN ur jee)* Energy from the sun. *Scientists have designed many devices to capture and distribute solar energy.*

biomass fuel *(BY oh mas   fyool)* A fuel made from living things. *Corn is one example of a biomass fuel that is used as a source of energy.*

energy conservation *(EN ur jee   kahn sur VAY shun)* Reducing energy use. *Riding a bike instead of driving a car is an effective form of energy conservation.*

Ⓔ Ⓛ Ⓛ Support

Provide students additional support when working with the word wall activity. You may wish to create more basic categories for the words, depending on students' language proficiencies.

Beginning
LOW Create a drawing or symbol to support the vocabulary term. If literate, develop a definition using the native language.

HIGH Write the word on the cards and introduce it to the class by pointing and saying it aloud.

Intermediate
LOW/HIGH Provide an example for each vocabulary term.

Advanced
LOW/HIGH Choose categories for the word wall based on grammar or etymology.

Fossil Fuels

What are some of Earth's energy sources?

Lesson Pacing: 1–2 periods or $\frac{1}{2}$–1 block

🕐 **SHORT ON TIME?** To do this lesson in approximately half the time, do the Activate Prior Knowledge activity followed by a discussion of the Key Concepts to familiarize students with the lesson content. Have students do the Quick Lab. The rest of the lesson can be completed by students independently.

Preference Navigator, in the online Planning tools, allows you to customize *Interactive Science* to your own teaching style. You can also edit lesson plans by selecting the Lesson Planner option.

Digital Teacher's Edition allows you to access your Teacher's Edition and Resource materials online.

my SCIENCE online.com

Lesson Vocabulary

- fuel
- fossil fuel
- hydrocarbon
- petroleum
- refinery
- petrochemical

Content Refresher
Professional Development Note

Fuel Supplies Fossil fuels take hundreds of millions of years to form, thus making their supplies limited. They form from the decomposing remains of plants and animals. Over time, the remains become buried under hundreds of meters of mud, rock, sand, and sometimes water. The type of fuel that forms—oil, coal, natural gas—is determined by the combination of the plant and animal matter that is present, how long the material is buried, and the temperature and pressure that exists while the remains decompose.

LESSON OBJECTIVES

 Name the three major fossil fuels.

Explain why fossil fuels are considered nonrenewable resources.

Blended Path
Active learning using Student Edition, Inquiry Path, and Digital Path

ENGAGE AND EXPLORE

Teach this lesson using a variety of resources. Begin by reading **My Planet Diary** as a class. Have students share ideas about how an energy crisis could impact their lives. Then have students do the **Inquiry Warm-Up activity.** Students will investigate and identify organic remains in a chunk of coal. The **After the Inquiry Warm-Up worksheet** sets up a discussion about the characteristics of coal which are developed during the formation process. Have volunteers share their answers to number 4 about how the layers of coal were formed.

EXPLAIN AND ELABORATE

Teach Key Concepts by explaining how the three major fossil fuels are developed and what they are made of. Use the **Support the Big Q** to identify some common uses for fossil fuels. **Lead a Discussion** about how coal is mined and the pros and cons of coal use. Use **Figures 3** and **4** to help students understand and visualize how coal and oil are formed over millions of years. Then have students practice the inquiry skill in the **Apply It activity. Lead a Discussion** about methane hydrates.

Continue to **Teach Key Concepts** by asking students what is likely to happen to fossil fuels if they continue to be used faster than they are formed. Hand out the **Key Concept Summaries** as a review of each part of the lesson. Students can also use the online **Vocab Flash Cards** to review key terms.

EVALUATE

Have students take the **Lesson Quiz.** For an alternate assessment, see the **EXAM**VIEW® Assessment Suite, Progress Monitoring Assessments, or SuccessTracker™.

Ⓔ Ⓛ Ⓛ Support

1 Content and Language

Explain that the Latin prefix *re-* means again and the Latin prefix *non-* means not. Write the words *renewable* and *nonrenewable* on the board. Using what they know about the prefixes ask students to define *renewable resource* and *nonrenewable resource*. A *renewable* resource is a resource that is replaced again and again. A *nonrenewable* resource is a resource that is not replaced after it has been used.

Inquiry Path
Hands-on learning in the Lab zone

Digital Path
Online learning at
my science online.com

ENGAGE AND EXPLORE

To teach this lesson with an emphasis on inquiry, begin with the **Inquiry Warm-Up activity**. Students will examine a piece of coal. Discuss any evidence of organic remains found in the coal sample. Have students do the **After the Inquiry Warm-Up worksheet**. Talk about the various stages of coal formation that occur over the course of millions of years. Have volunteers share their answers to number 4 about the layers in the coal samples.

EXPLAIN AND ELABORATE

Focus on the **Inquiry Skill** for the lesson. Explain that when you communicate, you share information, with others, in an organized format. What information did you communicate about fossil fuels in the **Inquiry Warm-Up?** (*There is evidence of organic remains in coal.*) Use the **Support the Big Q** to explain how fossil fuels are important sources of energy. The **Build Inquiry activity** allows students to replicate coal formation using everyday materials. During the second **Build Inquiry activity** students classify coal samples from different stages of the formation process. Use **Figure 4** and **5** to review how oil is formed and mined before beginning the **Apply It activity.** Ask volunteers to share their letters to the editor. The third **Build Inquiry activity** helps students to calculate and ponder the magnitude of the gas pipelines in the United States. Give students the chance to observe the consistency of crude oil by doing the **Quick Lab.**

Do the **Lab Investigation** to reinforce understanding of fossil fuels as nonrenewable resources. Students can use the online **Vocab Flash Cards** to review key terms.

EVALUATE

Have students take the **Lesson Quiz.** For an alternate assessment, see the **EXAM**VIEW® Assessment Suite, Progress Monitoring Assessments, or SuccessTracker™.

ENGAGE AND EXPLORE

Teach this lesson using digital resources. Begin by having students explore real-world connections to fossil fuels at **My Planet Diary** online. Have them access the Chapter Resources to find the **Unlock the Big Question activity.** There they can answer the questions and refine their responses as they continue through the lesson. You can re-assign the activity and have students submit their work so you can track their progress.

EXPLAIN AND ELABORATE

Students reading above, at, or below the lexile measure of this lesson can access basic content readings at their level at **My Reading Web.** Have students review the **Art in Motion** images to better understand how oil is formed below the ocean floor. Have students use the online **Vocab Flash Cards** to preview key terms. Use **Figure 4** to remind students how oil is formed under bodies of water before assigning the online **Apply It activity.** Ask volunteers to share their letters to the editor. Have students submit their work to you. Do the **Quick Lab** and then ask students to share their results.

Review *fossil fuels* before assigning the **Do the Math activity** online. Have students submit their work to you.

The **Key Concept Summary** online allows students to read a summary and see an image associated with each part of the lesson. Online remediation is available at **My Science Coach.**

EVALUATE

Have students take the **Lesson Quiz.** For an alternate assessment, see the **EXAM**VIEW® Assessment Suite, Progress Monitoring Assessments, or SuccessTracker™.

2 Frontload the Lesson
Preview the lesson visuals, labels, and captions. Ask students what they know about the term *fossil fuels*. Explain the specific meanings these words have in science.

3 Comprehensible Input
Have students study the visuals and their captions, as well as the graphic organizers, to support the key concepts of the lesson.

4 Language Production
Pair or group students with varied language abilities to complete labs collaboratively for language practice. Have each student copy the completed written lab for personal reference.

5 Assess Understanding
Make true or false statements using lesson content and have students indicate if they agree or disagree with a thumbs up or thumbs down gesture to check whole-class comprehension.

Fossil Fuels

LESSON 9.1

Establish Learning Objectives

After this lesson, students will be able to:

- Name the three major fossil fuels.
- Explain why fossil fuels are considered nonrenewable resources.

Engage

Activate Prior Knowledge

MY PLANET DIARY Read *Hurricane Energy Crisis* with the class. Invite students to think back and recall their own perceptions of Hurricane Katrina or other hurricanes. Ask: **How did Hurricane Katrina affect people directly?** *(It flooded cities and towns on the Gulf Coast. People lost their homes and left the area.)* **How did the storm affect people indirectly?** *(Factories and businesses were shut down. There were gas and oil shortages.)*

BIG IDEAS OF SCIENCE REFERENCE LIBRARY Have students look up the following topics: Coal, Energy Conservation.

Explore

Lab Resource: Inquiry Warm-Up

L1 WHAT'S IN A PIECE OF COAL? Students will make observations about a chunk of coal looking for evidence of organisms from which it was formed.

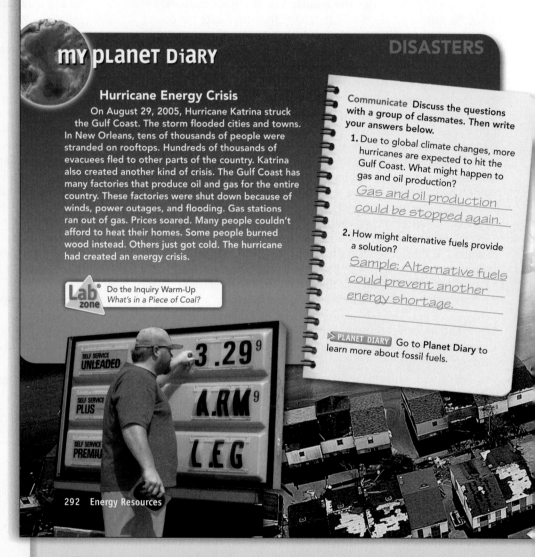

LESSON **1** Fossil Fuels

- What Are the Three Major Fossil Fuels?
- Why Are Fossil Fuels Nonrenewable Resources?

my planet Diary

DISASTERS

Hurricane Energy Crisis

On August 29, 2005, Hurricane Katrina struck the Gulf Coast. The storm flooded cities and towns. In New Orleans, tens of thousands of people were stranded on rooftops. Hundreds of thousands of evacuees fled to other parts of the country. Katrina also created another kind of crisis. The Gulf Coast has many factories that produce oil and gas for the entire country. These factories were shut down because of winds, power outages, and flooding. Gas stations ran out of gas. Prices soared. Many people couldn't afford to heat their homes. Some people burned wood instead. Others just got cold. The hurricane had created an energy crisis.

Lab zone Do the Inquiry Warm-Up What's in a Piece of Coal?

Communicate Discuss the questions with a group of classmates. Then write your answers below.

1. Due to global climate changes, more hurricanes are expected to hit the Gulf Coast. What might happen to gas and oil production?
   Gas and oil production could be stopped again.

2. How might alternative fuels provide a solution?
   Sample: Alternative fuels could prevent another energy shortage.

▶ PLANET DIARY Go to Planet Diary to learn more about fossil fuels.

292 Energy Resources

SUPPORT ALL READERS
Lexile Measure = 910L   Lexile Word Count = 1567

Prior Exposure to Content: Most students have encountered this topic in earlier grades

Academic Vocabulary: *communicate, summarize*

Science Vocabulary: *fossil fuel, hydrocarbon, petroleum, petrochemical*

Concept Level: Generally appropriate for most students in this grade

Preteach With: My Planet Diary "Hurricane Energy Crisis" and Figure 1 activity

Go to **My Reading Web** to access leveled readings that provide a foundation for the content.

my science online.com

Vocabulary
- fuel • fossil fuel • hydrocarbon
- petroleum • refinery
- petrochemical

Skills
- Reading: Summarize
- Inquiry: Communicate

What Are the Three Major Fossil Fuels?

Whether you travel in a car or a bus, walk, or ride your bike, you use some form of energy. The source of that energy is fuel. A **fuel** is a substance that provides energy, such as heat, light, motion, or electricity. This energy is the result of a chemical change.

Most of the energy used today comes from organisms that lived hundreds of millions of years ago. As these plants, animals, and other organisms died, their remains piled up. Layers of sand, rock, and mud buried the remains. Over time, heat and the pressure of the layers changed the remains into other substances. **Fossil fuels** are the energy-rich substances formed from the remains. **The three major fossil fuels are coal, oil, and natural gas.**

Fossil fuels are made of hydrocarbons. **Hydrocarbons** are chemical compounds that contain carbon and hydrogen atoms. When the fossil fuels are burned, the atoms react. They combine with oxygen to form new molecules. These reactions release energy in the forms of heat and light.

Burning fossil fuels provides more energy per kilogram than burning other fuels. One kilogram of coal, for example, can provide twice as much energy as one kilogram of wood. Oil and natural gas can provide three times as much energy as an equal mass of wood.

FIGURE 1 ·····················

Fossil Fuels in Everyday Life
Fossil fuels have many common uses.

✏ **Identify** Fill in the chart with ways that you or other people use the three fossil fuels in daily life.

Fossil Fuel	Common Uses	Uses in Your Life
Coal	• Used to generate half of all U.S. electricity • Used to make products like fertilizer and medicine • When heated, used to make steel	Sample: electricity
Oil	• As gasoline and diesel fuels, used to power vehicles • Used to heat homes • Used to make plastics and other petroleum products	Sample: cars, school bus, heat in home
Natural gas	• Used to generate electricity • Used to cook food • Used to heat homes	Sample: gas stove, heat in home

293

Explain

Introduce Vocabulary

Tell students that a *fuel* can be electricity, heat, motion, or light, as well as gasoline or oil. Point out that a fuel is a substance that provides energy.

Teach Key Concepts ⚷

Explain to students that the remains of dead organisms pile up and are buried under layers of sand, rock, and mud. Over hundreds of millions of years, the pressure of the layers change the remains into other substances that still contain the stored energy from the bodies of the dead organisms. Ask: **What three major fuels are formed from the remains of long-dead organisms?** *(Coal, oil, natural gas)* **What are these fuels made of?** *(Hydrocarbons)* **What are hydrocarbons?** *(Compounds that contain carbon and hydrogen atoms)*

Support the Big Q ❓ UbD

ENERGY FROM FUELS Remind students that burning fossil fuels releases energy. Ask: **How do fossil fuels compare to other fuels, such as wood?** *(Fossil fuels provide more energy per kilogram than wood does.)* **What are some ways hydrocarbons are used as an energy source?** *(They are burned to generate electricity, power vehicles, heat homes, and cook foods.)*

My Planet Diary provides an opportunity for students to explore real-world connections to fossil fuels.

my science online | Fossil Fuels

ELL Support

1 Content and Language
The word *plant* is used in two different ways. Help students understand that the word *plant* can mean "vegetative organism" as well as "factory."

2 Frontload the Lesson
Before reading this chapter, it will be helpful for students to understand the difference between renewable and nonrenewable resources. Draw a diagram that shows that natural resources can be divided into *renewable* and *nonrenewable*. Help students list examples of each.

3 Comprehensible Input
Students may be familiar with the term *deposit*, but not in a scientific sense. Explain that that when people save money, they *deposit* money in the bank so that, over time, their savings grows. Relate this to the way in which oil deposits form.

Explain

Lead a Discussion

COAL Most coal used in the United States is used to fuel electrical power plants. Point out that before natural gas and oil were used to heat homes, coal was the main fuel for heating homes. Ask: **How is coal removed from the ground?** *(It is chopped into pieces and lifted to the surface.)* **How is this done?** *(Miners use machines to lift coal from the ground)* **What makes working in a coal mine dangerous?** *(Miners can be killed in accidents or develop lung diseases because of the dust.)*

21st Century Learning

COMMUNICATION Have students read *Coal* in the **Big Ideas of Science Reference Library.** Students can demonstrate consumer literacy by researching causes of recent coal mining accidents. Then have them create a poster on safety precautions for coal miners. What equipment should they wear? What do they do in an emergency?

21st Century Learning

L3 CRITICAL THINKING Ask students to explain the sequence of events that must occur for coal to be used as a fuel. Students may wish to draw a diagram that shows the sequence of events from discovery of coal in a particular location, digging a mine, chopping chunks of coal, raising coal to the surface, and transportation of coal to places where it will be used as fuel.

Teach With Visuals

Tell students to look at **Figure 3.** Ask: **How would you describe the changes that happen on the land surface over time while plant matter below the surface is being transformed into peat and then into coal?** *(Sample response: A wet, swampy area changes gradually into a dry, wooded area.)*

Summarize Tell students that a summary is a short statement that presents the main ideas and most important details in a text. Summarizing can help students distinguish main ideas from the details that support those ideas.

FIGURE 2
Pros and Cons of Coal Use
Coal mining, shown above, is a dangerous job.
Compare and Contrast Fill in the chart below using information from the text.

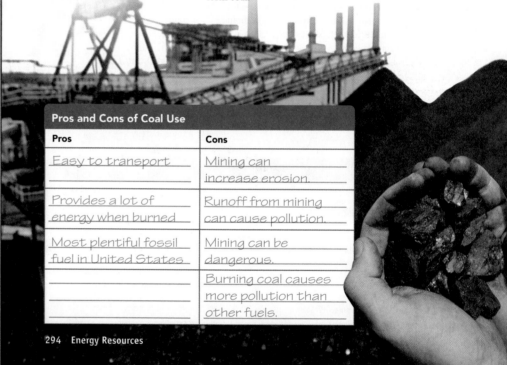

Coal People have burned coal to produce heat for thousands of years. For much of that time, wood was more convenient and cheaper than coal for most people. But during the 1800s, the huge energy needs of growing industries made it worthwhile to find, mine, and transport coal. Today, coal makes up about 22 percent of the fuel used in the United States. Most of that coal fuels electrical power plants.

Before coal can be used to produce energy, it has to be removed from the ground. Miners use machines to chop the coal into chunks and lift it to the surface. Coal mining can be a dangerous job. Thousands of miners have been killed or injured in mining accidents. Many more suffer from lung diseases. Fortunately, modern safety procedures and better equipment have made coal mining safer, although it is still very dangerous.

Coal is the most plentiful fossil fuel in the United States. It is fairly easy to transport and provides a lot of energy when burned. But coal also has some disadvantages. Coal mining can increase erosion. Runoff from coal mines can cause water pollution. Burning most types of coal results in more air pollution than using other fossil fuels. See **Figure 2.**

Figure 3 shows how plant remains build up over time and form coal.

Pros and Cons of Coal Use	
Pros	**Cons**
Easy to transport	Mining can increase erosion.
Provides a lot of energy when burned	Runoff from mining can cause pollution.
Most plentiful fossil fuel in United States	Mining can be dangerous.
	Burning coal causes more pollution than other fuels.

294 Energy Resources

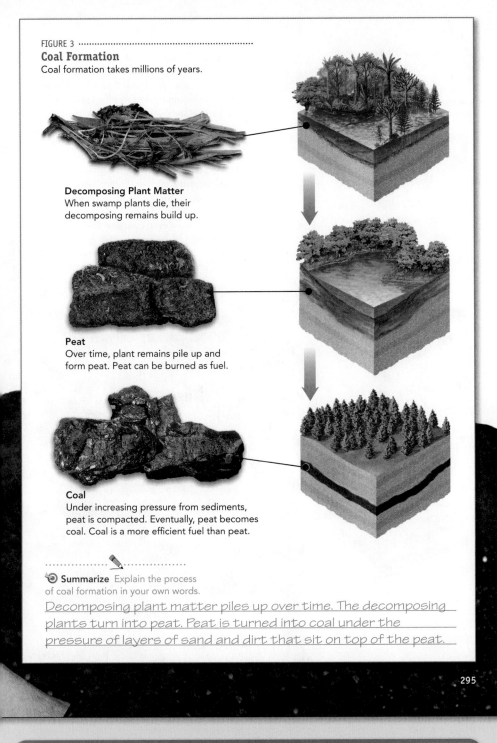

FIGURE 3 ·······························
Coal Formation
Coal formation takes millions of years.

Decomposing Plant Matter
When swamp plants die, their decomposing remains build up.

Peat
Over time, plant remains pile up and form peat. Peat can be burned as fuel.

Coal
Under increasing pressure from sediments, peat is compacted. Eventually, peat becomes coal. Coal is a more efficient fuel than peat.

················ ✎ ················

🔄 **Summarize** Explain the process of coal formation in your own words.

Decomposing plant matter piles up over time. The decomposing
plants turn into peat. Peat is turned into coal under the
pressure of layers of sand and dirt that sit on top of the peat.

295

Elaborate ───────────

Build Inquiry

L2 MODEL FOSSIL FUEL FORMATION

Materials clay, soil, sand, pebbles, leaves, colored paper, and books or heavy weights

Time 15 minutes

Challenge students to create a model showing how fossil fuels form over time. Models might include trapping materials such as leaves or colored paper between layers of soft material such as clay or soil, and then compressing these materials under heavy weights.

Ask: **What happens to buried materials that turns them into fossil fuels?** *(Over time, heat and pressure change the materials into hydrocarbons.)*

Build Inquiry

L3 CLASSIFY PEAT AND COAL

Materials samples of peat moss, lignite, bituminous coal, and anthracite; 2 small plastic bags; hand lenses

Time 10 minutes

Explain to students that peat is the decayed remains of plants—the early stage of coal formation. Give each group hand lenses, a plastic bag containing a sample of peat moss, and a second bag containing the three types of coal. **CAUTION:** *Rinse the coal thoroughly to remove any dust. Make sure students wash their hands after handling the samples.* Let students examine the samples, noting the similarities and differences between them. Then list the following names and characteristics on the board, and challenge students to identify each coal sample:
- *Lignite:* dark brown; layered; may contain recognizable fragments of plant remains
- *Bituminous coal:* denser than lignite; black; may have bands
- *Anthracite:* hardest type of coal; black; shiny

Ask: **Why are the coal samples darker and harder than the peat?** *(Coal has been buried longer than peat and therefore subjected to much greater pressure.)*

Differentiated Instruction

L1 The Use of Coal To solidify students' understanding of the extent to which coal is used as a fuel in the United States today, have students write a fraction that approximates how much of the fuel used in the United States today is coal.

L3 19th Century Uses of Coal
Challenge students to research what caused the huge energy needs that led to the mining and transportation of enormous amounts of coal during the 1800s. Students can write a short report or make an oral presentation of their findings.

L3 Illustrate Burning Fossil Fuels
Invite students to make a detailed illustration of the process of burning fossil fuels. Their illustrations should convey the composition of fossil fuels and of hydrocarbons, as well as the chain of causes and effects that create heat and light.

Explain

Teach With Visuals

Tell students to look at **Figure 4**. Ask: **What organisms shown in the first illustration will decompose on the ocean floor?** *(Fish, shellfish, plants)* **What processes are shown on the ocean floor and under the ocean floor in the second illustration?** *(More plants and shellfish will die and decompose on the ocean floor. Decomposition of earlier organisms proceeds below the ocean floor.)*

Make Analogies

L1 **VARIETIES OF REFINING** Explain that the process of refining crude oil is similar to the refining of other physical products, such as gold or sugar. Point out that the terms *crude* and *refined* are also used to describe aspects of human behavior. Ask: **What are examples of crude behavior at a dining table during a meal?** *(Talking with your mouth full, taking enormous portions of food, talking loudly and impolitely)* **What are examples of refined behavior at the table?** *(Eating quietly, offering food to others first and serving yourself afterwards, listening and speaking politely)*

FIGURE 4 ⋯⋯⋯⋯⋯⋯⋯⋯⋯⋯⋯⋯

▶ ART IN MOTION **Oil Formation**

Oil is formed in a process similar to coal.

✎ **Interpret Diagrams** Use what you know to fill in the steps of oil formation in the diagrams below.

300–400 million years ago

Sample: The remains of organisms pile up on the sea floor.

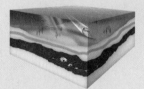

50–100 million years ago

Sample: Over time, layers of sand and dirt form over the remains.

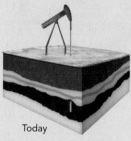

Today

Sample: Pressure and heat from the layers turn the remains into oil deposits.

296 Energy Resources

Oil Oil is a thick, black, liquid fossil fuel. It formed from the remains of small animals, algae, and other organisms that lived in oceans and shallow inland seas hundreds of millions of years ago. **Petroleum** is another name for oil. Petroleum comes from the Latin words *petra* (rock) and *oleum* (oil). Petroleum accounts for more than one third of the energy produced in the world. Fuel for most cars, airplanes, trains, and ships comes from petroleum. Many homes are heated by oil as well.

Most oil deposits are located underground in tiny holes in sandstone or limestone. **Figure 4** shows how oil is formed. The oil fills the holes somewhat like the way water fills the holes of a sponge. Because oil deposits are usually located deep below the surface, finding oil is difficult. Scientists can use sound waves to test an area for oil. Even using this technique, scientists may not always locate wells that will produce a usable amount of oil.

FIGURE 5 ⋯⋯⋯⋯⋯⋯⋯⋯⋯⋯

Oil Pipeline
Workers build an oil pipeline in Russia.

Art in Motion shows the gradual formation of oil deposits beneath the ocean floor.

Digital Lesson: Assign the *Apply It* activity online and have students submit their work to you.

mY SCIENCE online.com ▶ **Fossil Fuels**

When oil is first pumped out of the ground, it is called crude oil. To be made into useful products, crude oil must undergo a process called refining. A factory in which crude oil is heated and separated into fuels and other products is called a **refinery.** Many of the products that you use every day are made from crude oil. **Petrochemicals** are compounds that are made from oil. Petrochemicals are used to make plastics, paints, medicines, and cosmetics.

apply it!

Over 2,500 species of plants and animals live in Lake Baikal, in Russia. Eighty percent of these species live nowhere else on Earth. One of those species is the Baikal seal—one of only three freshwater seal species on Earth. The seal and other species were threatened when oil companies planned to build the world's longest oil pipeline within 800 meters of the lake's shore. The pipeline would bring oil from Russia's interior to China and ports along the Pacific Ocean. Citizens were concerned that oil leaks and spills would damage the lake. They worked together to convince the oil companies to move the pipeline 40 kilometers to the north. The design of the new pipeline protects the lake and also delivers oil to places that need it.

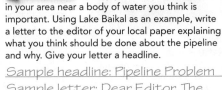

Communicate An oil pipeline is proposed in your area near a body of water you think is important. Using Lake Baikal as an example, write a letter to the editor of your local paper explaining what you think should be done about the pipeline and why. Give your letter a headline.

Sample headline: Pipeline Problem
Sample letter: Dear Editor, The proposed pipeline in our area threatens our local ecosystem. I think we can work together to have both the oil pipeline and the nature we enjoy. A similar problem happened near Lake Baikal, in Russia, when an oil company wanted to build a pipeline near the water. Because the company moved the pipeline away from the lake, many species are now better protected against oil spills. I think we can better design this pipeline to avoid harming nature in our area. That way, we can still transport oil and protect our ecosystem.

297

Elaborate

Apply It!

L1 Before students begin the *Apply It* activity, have them look carefully at the photograph of the lake. Invite them to name living things that live in and around the lake. Have them look again at **Figure 4** as a reminder of the process that leads to the formation of oil deposits under bodies of water. Encourage them to discuss how valuable resources lie beneath the lake as well as in and around the lake. Tell students that Lake Baikal, in Russia, holds 20 percent of the Earth's fresh water.

Communicate Remind students that their letter to the editor will be more effective if it contains a strong, clear main idea and supporting details.

21st Century Learning

INFORMATION LITERACY Have students research the Alaskan pipeline that reaches from Prudhoe Bay to Valdez and the environmental questions that were raised by its construction.

Differentiated Instruction

L1 Compare Formation of Coal and Oil Have students use a compare-and-contrast chart or a Venn diagram to show the similarities and differences between the formation of coal and the formation of oil under the surface of Earth.

L3 Research Crude Oil Refining Have students use reference materials to learn the basic processes involved in refining oil. Students should gather information about several products made by heating crude oil to greater temperatures (gasoline, jet fuel, heating oil, diesel fuel, grease and wax, asphalt).

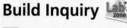
Explain

Lead a Discussion

METHANE HYDRATES Methane hydrates are located in ocean sediments and polar permafrost. Blake Ridge, located off of the coast of the southeastern United States, contains a volume of methane hydrate that is equal to 30 times the United States consumption of gas. As of 2009, there is no economically profitable technique by which to extract methane from methane hydrate deposits. Also, it is a greenhouse gas that is 10 times more effective than carbon dioxide in causing climate change. Ask: **Do you think it is worthwhile to investigate methods of extracting methane?** *(Students may say that it is worthwhile because it would provide a lot of energy. Other students may say that it is not worthwhile because it could harm the environment.)*

Elaborate

Build Inquiry

L2 CALCULATE LENGTHS OF GAS PIPELINE

Materials calculator

Time 5 minutes

Point out the text statement "If all the gas pipelines in the United States were connected, they would reach to the moon and back—three times!" Have students use the moon's average distance from Earth *(384,392 km)* to calculate the total length of U.S. gas pipelines *(384,392 km × 6 = 2,306,352 km)*.

Ask: **How does this distance compare to the width of your state?** *(Have that value ready.)*

Lab Resources: Quick Lab

L1 OBSERVING OIL'S CONSISTENCY Students will model the consistency of crude oil using molasses.

Evaluate

Assess Your Understanding

After students answer the questions, have them evaluate their understanding by completing the appropriate sentence.

RTI Response to Intervention

1a. If students cannot define *petrochemicals*, **then** have them skim the section to locate the boldfaced term and read the definition.

b. If students have trouble making judgments about pipelines, **then** have them review the *Apply It!* feature and the information they provided about the costs and benefits of natural gas.

MY SCIENCE COACH Have students go online for help in understanding the three major fossil fuels.

Natural Gas Natural gas is a mixture of methane and other gases. Natural gas forms from some of the same organisms as oil. Because it is less dense than oil, natural gas often rises above an oil deposit, forming a pocket of gas in the rock.

Pipelines transport natural gas from its source to the places where it is used. If all the gas pipelines in the United States were connected, they would reach to the moon and back—three times! Natural gas can also be compressed into a liquid and stored in tanks as fuel for trucks and buses.

Natural gas has several benefits. It produces large amounts of energy, but has lower levels of many air pollutants compared to coal or oil. It is also easy to transport once pipelines are built. One cost of natural gas is that it is highly flammable. A gas leak can cause explosions and fires. If you use natural gas in your home, you probably are familiar with the "gas" smell alerting you when there is unburned gas in the air. You may be surprised to learn that natural gas actually has no odor. What causes the strong smell? Gas companies add a chemical with a distinct smell to the gas so that people can detect a gas leak.

FIGURE 6
Natural Gas
A gas-top burner uses natural gas to cook food.
✎ **Analyze Costs and Benefits** Fill in the boxes with some costs and benefits of natural gas.

Costs of Natural Gas	Benefits of Natural Gas
Sample: highly flammable, still releases some air pollutants, could be expensive to find and extract through rock	Sample: produces fewer air pollutants than coal or oil, easy to transport if pipelines built

 Do the Quick Lab *Observing Oil's Consistency.*

🔑 Assess Your Understanding

1a. Define What are petrochemicals?
Compounds made from oil that are used to make plastics, paints, medicines, and cosmetics

b. Make Judgments Should the federal government decide where to build oil or natural gas pipelines? Explain.
Sample: No; they might not know people's needs in the local area.

got it?

○ I get it! Now I know that the three major fossil fuels are coal, oil, and natural gas.

○ I need extra help with See TE note.

Go to **MY SCIENCE COACH** online for help with this subject.

Why Are Fossil Fuels Nonrenewable Resources?

The many advantages of using fossil fuels as an energy source have made them essential to modern life. **Since fossil fuels take hundreds of millions of years to form, they are considered nonrenewable resources.** Earth's known oil reserves, or the amount of oil that can currently be used, took 500 million years to form. Fossil fuels will run out if they are used faster than they are formed.

Many nations that consume large amounts of fossil fuels have very small reserves or supplies. They have to buy oil, natural gas, and coal from nations with large supplies to make up the difference. The United States, for example, uses about one quarter of all the oil produced in the world. But only two percent of the world's oil supply is located in this country. The uneven distribution of fossil fuel reserves has often been a cause of political problems in the world.

Use the graph to answer the questions below.

1 Read Graphs Which energy source generates the most electricity in the United States? _Coal_

2 Calculate What percentage of the fuels in the graph are fossil fuels? _71.4%_

3 CHALLENGE How might this graph look in 50 years? Give reasons to support your answer. _Sample: Fossil fuel use will decrease as supplies become limited, and use of other fuels will increase._

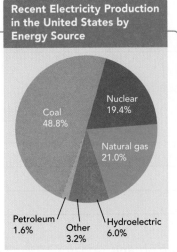

Recent Electricity Production in the United States by Energy Source

- Coal 48.8%
- Nuclear 19.4%
- Natural gas 21.0%
- Hydroelectric 6.0%
- Other 3.2%
- Petroleum 1.6%

Lab zone® Do the Quick Lab *Fossil Fuels.*

⚷ Assess Your Understanding

got it? ....

○ I get it! Now I know that fossil fuels are nonrenewable because _they take a very long time to form and are used up more rapidly than they are formed._

○ I need extra help with _See TE note._

Go to **my science ⊙ coach** *online for help with this subject.*

299

Differentiated Instruction

L1 Observe States of Matter Have students compare samples that represent the states of matter most commonly associated with the three fossil fuels: solid (chunks of coal), liquid (molasses to represent oil), and gas (closed, empty jar to represent natural gas). Make sure that students understand that the three fossil fuels are not the same substance in three different states. While they all are

hydrocarbons, each fuel is made up of different hydrocarbon compounds.

L3 Research Pipelines Challenge students to use reference books or online sources to find out where most natural gas pipelines are located in the United States. Have students learn how much natural gas moves through U.S. pipelines each day.

Explain

Teach Key Concepts 🔑

Explain to students that fossil fuels are unevenly distributed around the world. They are also nonrenewable resources. Ask: **What evidence do we have that our demand for fossil fuels might use up our supply of them?** *(Oil reserves take 500 million years to form. New reserves can't form quickly enough to replace those used up.)* **How might uneven distribution of fossil fuels contribute to global problems?** *(Students might indicate that fuel-rich and fuel-dependent nations may come into conflict.)*

Elaborate

Do the Math!

Point out that a circle graph can be used to show parts of a whole.

Ask: **If the entire circle represents 100 percent, what does one fourth of the circle represent?** *(Twenty-five percent)* **Why is a circle graph a good choice for this exercise?** *(Sample response: The graph emphasizes the differences between the proportions of the various energy sources.)*
See *Math Skill* and *Problem-Solving Activities* for support.

Lab Resource: Lab Investigation 🔬

L1 FOSSIL FUELS Students will make models comparing renewable and nonrenewable resources.

Evaluate

Assess Your Understanding

Have students evaluate their understanding by completing the appropriate sentence.

RTI Response to Intervention

If students have trouble classifying resources, **then** have them skim the section to find the Key Concept statement. Students should read the paragraph that includes this statement.

my science ⊙ coach Have students go online for help in understanding why fossil fuels are nonrenewable.

Digital Lesson: Assign the *Do the Math* activity online and have students submit their work to you.

my science online.com | Limited Fossil Fuels

Name _____ Date _____ Class _____

Fossil Fuels

> **Inquiry Warm-Up, *What's In A Piece of Coal?***
> In the Inquiry Warm-Up, you investigated evidence of organic remains in coal. Using what you learned from that activity, answer the questions below.

1. **SEQUENCE** What is coal called before it becomes lignite?

   _____

2. **INFER** Do you think it is easier or more difficult to see fossils in coal older than lignite? Explain.

   _____

   _____

   _____

   _____

3. **INFER** Do you think it is easier or more difficult to see organic remains in the coal using a microscope compared to a hand lens? Explain why.

   _____

   _____

   _____

   _____

4. **RELATE CAUSE AND EFFECT** If your coal sample has layers, explain how they were formed.

   _____

   _____

   _____

   _____

Fossil Fuels

What Are the Three Major Fossil Fuels?

1a. DEFINE What are petrochemicals? _____

_____

_____

b. MAKE JUDGMENTS Should the federal government decide
where to build oil or natural gas pipelines? Explain. _____

_____

_____

_____

got it? ....

○ **I get it!** Now I know that the three major fossil fuels are _____

_____

○ **I need extra help with** _____

_____

Why Are Fossil Fuels Nonrenewable Resources?

got it? ....

○ **I get it!** Now I know that fossil fuels are nonrenewable because _____

_____

○ **I need extra help with** _____

_____

Name _____ Date _____ Class _____

Fossil Fuels

What Are the Three Major Fossil Fuels?

A **fuel** is a substance that provides energy, such as heat, light, motion, or electricity. Most energy used today comes from organisms that lived hundreds of millions of years ago. **Fossil fuels** are the energy-rich substances formed from those remains. **The three major fossil fuels are coal, oil, and natural gas.** Fossil fuels are made of **hydrocarbons,** chemical compounds that contain carbon and hydrogen atoms. When the fossil fuels are burned, the atoms react and energy is released in the forms of heat and light. Burning fossil fuels provides more energy per kilogram than burning other fuels.

Coal is a solid fossil fuel that forms from plant remains. Before it can be used to produce energy, coal must be removed from the ground. Coal is the most plentiful fossil fuel in the United States. It is fairly easy to transport and provides a lot of energy when burned. However, mining coal causes erosion, and burning coal causes water and air pollution. **Petroleum** is another name for oil, a thick, black, liquid fossil fuel. It accounts for more than one third of the energy used in the world. Most oil deposits lie underground in tiny holes in sandstone or limestone. A factory in which crude oil is heated and separated into fuels and other products is called a **refinery.** **Petrochemicals** are compounds that are made from oil. They are used to make many common products, including plastics, paints, medicines, and cosmetics. Natural gas, a mixture of methane and other gases, forms from some of the same organisms as oil. Pipelines transport natural gas from its source to the places where it is used. Burning natural gas produces large amounts of energy and releases lower levels of many air pollutants than coal or oil, but it is highly flammable.

Why Are Fossil Fuels Nonrenewable Resources?

Fossil fuels are essential to modern life. **Since fossil fuels take hundreds of millions of years to form, they are considered nonrenewable resources.** Fossil fuels will run out if they continue to be used faster than they are formed. Fossil fuels are not necessarily located in the places where they are used the most. The uneven distribution of fossil fuel reserves is a cause of international conflicts in the world.

On a separate sheet of paper, explain the importance of fossil fuels today, as well as the challenges and conflicts relating to their use.

Fossil Fuels

Understanding Main Ideas
Answer the following questions on a separate sheet of paper.

1. What are the three major fossil fuels?
2. How do fossil fuels form?
3. How is energy produced from fossil fuels?
4. Why are fossil fuels considered nonrenewable?

Building Vocabulary
Write a definition for each of these terms on the lines below.

5. petroleum

_____

_____

6. hydrocarbons

_____

_____

7. refinery

_____

_____

8. petrochemicals

_____

_____

Name _____ Date _____ Class _____

Fossil Fuels

The tables show the amount of fossil fuels produced and used in the United States from 1957 to 2007. The numbers represent quadrillions of BTUs, British thermal units, used for measuring energy. Calculate the total amount of fossil fuels produced and used each year. Enter your results in the tables. Then answer the questions on a separate sheet of paper.

Fossil Fuel Production and Use

U.S. Fossil Fuel Production (in quadrillions of BTUs)

Year	Coal	Oil	Natural Gas	Total Produced
1957	13.1	15.2	10.6	1.
1967	13.8	18.7	17.9	2.
1977	15.8	17.5	19.6	3.
1987	20.1	17.7	17.1	4.
1997	23.2	13.6	19.5	5.
2007	23.5	10.8	19.8	6.

U.S. Fossil Fuel Use (in quadrillions of BTUs)

Year	Coal	Oil	Natural Gas	Total Produced
1957	10.8	17.9	10.2	7.
1967	11.9	25.3	17.9	8.
1977	13.9	37.1	19.9	9.
1987	18.0	32.9	17.7	10.
1997	21.4	36.3	22.6	11.
2007	22.8	39.8	23.6	12.

13. Use your totals to make a bar graph. Plot years on the horizontal axis and amounts of fossil fuels on the vertical axis. Make two bars for each year—showing total fuel production and total fuel use. Use colors or shading for the bars. Give your graph a title and key.

14. Compare the two bars for every year shown. What pattern do you see? Which type of fossil fuel was most responsible for that pattern?

15. What happens when the country produces less fossil fuel than it needs?

Place the outside corner, the corner away from the dotted line, in the corner of your copy machine to copy onto letter-size paper.

Name _____ Date _____ Class _____

Fossil Fuels

Fill in the blank(s) to complete each statement.

1. A fuel is a substance that provides _____.

2. _____ is a solid fossil fuel that forms from plant remains.

3. Petroleum is another name for the fossil fuel _____.

4. A factory in which crude oil is heated and separated into fuels and other products is called a _____.

If the statement is true, write *true*. If the statement is false, change the underlined word or words to make the statement true.

5. _____ Chemical compounds that contain carbon and hydrogen atoms are called <u>petrochemicals</u>.

6. _____ <u>Fossil fuels</u> are the energy-rich substances formed from the remains of long-dead organisms.

7. _____ The three major fossil fuels are coal, oil, and <u>petroleum</u>.

8. _____ <u>Oil</u> is the most plentiful fossil fuel in the United States.

9. _____ <u>Natural gas</u> forms from some of the same organisms as oil.

10. _____ Because fossil fuels are formed over hundreds of millions of years, they are considered <u>renewable</u> resources.

Fossil Fuels

Answer Key

After the Inquiry Warm-Up

1. peat

2. Sample: I think it should be more difficult because the fossils are altered and destroyed over time.

3. Sample: I think it is easier to see organic remains in coal using a microscope because a microscope has a higher resolution, so it can see finer and smaller details.

4. Students may say: Over many years, organic material is covered over by more organic material and compressed.

Key Concept Summaries

Answers will vary. Sample answer: Fossil fuels are important because they provide a majority of the energy used in the world for heating, electricity, and transportation today. However, the use of fossil fuels does present many problems. The mining of coal and pumping of oil and natural gas can lead to erosion and pollution of natural areas. The burning of fossil fuels also creates pollution. Because they are so heavily used and reserves are unevenly distributed throughout the world, fossil fuels can also be the source of international conflicts.

Review and Reinforce

1. coal, oil, natural gas

2. The remains of plants, animals, and other organisms become buried under layers of sand, rock, and mud. Over time, heat and the pressure of the layers turn the remains into other substances, such as fossil fuels.

3. Fossil fuels are made of hydrocarbons. When fossil fuels are burned, the atoms of hydrogen and carbon react and release energy in the form of heat and light.

4. Fossil fuels are considered nonrenewable because they take millions of years to form.

5. another name for oil

6. chemical compounds that contain carbon and hydrogen atoms

7. a factory in which crude oil is heated and separated into fuels and other products

8. compounds that are made from oil

Enrich

1. 38.9
2. 50.4
3. 52.9
4. 54.9
5. 56.3
6. 54.1
7. 38.9
8. 55.1
9. 70.9
10. 68.6
11. 80.3
12. 86.2

13. The graph should show that production and use were the same for 1957. After that, the bars for use are higher than the bars for production, with the difference increasing over time.

14. After 1957, the United States produced less fossil fuel than it needed. The difference between production and use generally increased over that period. Oil was most responsible for this pattern.

15. The country has to import fuels from other countries. Also, shortages may occur.

Lesson Quiz

1. energy
2. Coal
3. oil
4. refinery
5. hydrocarbons
6. true
7. natural gas
8. Coal
9. true
10. nonrenewable

Teacher Notes

Place the outside corner, the corner away from the dotted line, in the corner of your copy machine to copy onto letter-size paper.

Renewable Sources of Energy

What are some of Earth's energy sources?

Lesson Pacing: 2–3 periods or 1–1½ blocks

🕐 **SHORT ON TIME?** To do this lesson in approximately half the time, do the Activate Prior Knowledge activity followed by a discussion of the Key Concepts to familiarize students with the lesson content. Use the Explore the Big Q to help students identify pros and cons of Earth's energy sources. Do the Quick Labs and have students do the Interactive Art online. The rest of the lesson can be completed by students independently.

> **Preference Navigator,** in the online Planning tools, allows you to customize *Interactive Science* to your own teaching style. You can also edit lesson plans by selecting the Lesson Planner option.
>
> **Digital Teacher's Edition** allows you to access your Teacher's Edition and Resource materials online.

my science online .com

Lesson Vocabulary

- solar energy • hydroelectric power • biomass fuel • gasohol
- geothermal energy • nuclear fission • reactor vessel
- fuel rod • control rod

Content Refresher

Use of Renewable Energy Sources Renewable sources of energy exist in an inexhaustible or replaceable supply. They are generally considered less polluting than fossil fuels. In spite of these advantages, renewable energy sources are not widely used in the United States. Only 6 percent of the total U.S. energy consumed in 2007 was produced through renewable energy. In contrast, 40 percent of U.S. energy was produced with petroleum, 23 percent with natural gas, and 22 percent with coal.

Biomass Fuels Using biomass fuels helps reduce dependence on fossil fuels and waste-disposal problems. At the Mesquite Lake Resource Recovery Project in California, an electric power plant burns cow manure to produce enough electricity for thousands of homes. The manure would otherwise pose a disposal problem because of its high salt content and the presence of seeds that make it unsuitable for use as a fertilizer.

LESSON OBJECTIVES

- 🔑 Identify and describe renewable sources of energy.
- 🔑 Explain how a nuclear power plant produces electricity.

Blended Path
Active learning using Student Edition, Inquiry Path, and Digital Path

ENGAGE AND EXPLORE

Teach this lesson using a variety of resources. Begin by reading **My Planet Diary** as a class. Have students share ideas about fossil fuels as sources of energy and identify alternative sources of energy. Then have students do the **Inquiry Warm-Up activity.** Students will use water to capture energy from sunlight and monitor temperature changes. The **After the Inquiry Warm-Up worksheet** sets up a discussion about why certain areas are better than others for capturing solar energy. Have volunteers share their answers to number 4 about the temperature changes that occur when the water is exposed to sunlight for longer lengths of time.

EXPLAIN AND ELABORATE

Teach Key Concepts by identifying a variety of sources of energy used by people. **Lead a Discussion** about how solar energy is captured and converted using different devices. Use **Figure 2** to illustrate how passive and active solar heating can be used to power a building or home. Next, **Lead a Discussion** about hydroelectric power and wind energy. Discuss the benefits and downfalls of these two alternative sources of energy. Then **Lead a Discussion** about how biomass fuels are made from natural sources, used to produce electricity, and converted into other fuels. Then have students do the **Apply It activity.** Use **Figure 5** to show students how electricity is generated using geothermal power plants. **Lead a Discussion** about geothermal heat pumps. **Lead a Discussion** about why scientists are working to develop hydrogen power. Use the **Explore the Big Q** to scrutinize various sources of energy from the Earth. Discuss responses to the **Answer the Big Q** about Earth's energy sources.

Continue to **Teach Key Concepts** by explaining how nuclear power plants turn nuclear fission reactions into electricity. **Lead a Discussion** about the general process and specific components used to generate electricity in a nuclear power plant. Hand out the **Key Concept Summaries** as a review of each part of the lesson. Students can also use the online **Vocab Flash Cards** to review key terms.

EVALUATE

Have students take the **Lesson Quiz.** For an alternate assessment, see the **EXAM**VIEW® Assessment Suite, Progress Monitoring Assessments, or SuccessTracker™.

ELL Support

1 Content and Language

Define the term *solar*. *Solar* means related to the sun. Identify terms that include *solar*: solar energy, solar power, solar eclipse, solar cars, solar system, solar panels. Discuss how each term is related to the sun.

 **Inquiry Path** Hands-on learning in the Lab zone

ENGAGE AND EXPLORE

To teach this lesson with an emphasis on inquiry, begin with the **Inquiry Warm-Up activity.** Students will learn how solar energy is captured using a water-filled bag. Discuss how the location of the bag impacts the temperature of the water. Have students do the **After the Inquiry Warm-Up worksheet.** Talk about the temperature changes they recorded and where they captured the most solar energy. Have volunteers share their answers to number 4 about the impact of leaving the water in direct sunlight for a long duration of time.

EXPLAIN AND ELABORATE

Focus on the **Inquiry Skill** for the lesson. Point out that when you infer, you use evidence or logical thinking to draw a conclusion. **Build Inquiry** with students to observe how heat is trapped inside a passive solar object. Review the term *biomass* and how to read a line graph before beginning the **Apply It activity.** Ask volunteers to share their answers. **Explore the Big Q** by identifying energy sources represented in the illustrations. Have students work on the **Quick Lab** to reinforce understanding of how solar energy can warm food. Have students identify Earth's energy sources to **Answer the Big Q.**

Build Inquiry to help students understand the potential disadvantages of nuclear power. Have students complete the **Quick Lab** to understand how electricity is produced. Students can use the online **Vocab Flash Cards** to review key terms.

EVALUATE

Have students take the **Lesson Quiz.** For an alternate assessment, see the **EXAM**VIEW® Assessment Suite, Progress Monitoring Assessments, or SuccessTracker™.

Digital Path
Online learning at **my science online**.com

ENGAGE AND EXPLORE

Teach this lesson using digital resources. Begin by having students explore real-world connections to alternative energy sources at **My Planet Diary** online. Have them access the Chapter Resources to find the **Unlock the Big Question activity.** There they can answer the questions and refine their responses as they continue through the lesson. You can re-assign the activity and have students submit their work so you can track their progress.

EXPLAIN AND ELABORATE

Students reading above, at, or below the lexile measure of this lesson can access basic content readings at their level at **My Reading Web.** Have students use the online **Vocab Flash Cards** to preview key terms. Review the term biomass and how to interpret a line graph before assigning the online **Apply It activity.** Ask volunteers to share their interpretations of the graph. Have students submit their work to you. Use the **Interactive Art** to explore alternative energy sources. **Explore the Big Q** by identifying pros and cons of Earth's energy sources illustrated in **Figure 6.** Complete the **Quick Lab** to better understand how food can be cooked using solar energy. Discuss various sources of energy to **Answer the Big Q. My Science Coach** provides online support for students.

Have students do the online **Interactive Art activity** which illustrates how electricity is generated in nuclear power plants. Have students do the **Quick Lab** to explore how electricity is produced. The **Key Concept Summaries** online allow students to read a summary and see an image associated with each part of the lesson. Online remediation is available at **My Science Coach.**

EVALUATE

Have students take the **Lesson Quiz.** For an alternate assessment, see the **EXAM**VIEW® Assessment Suite, Progress Monitoring Assessments, or SuccessTracker™.

2 Frontload the Lesson

Preview the lesson visuals, labels, and captions. Ask students what they know about the terms *solar energy, hydroelectric power, biomass fuels, geothermal energy, nuclear fission, reactor vessel, fuel rod,* and *control rod.* Explain the specific meanings these words have in science.

3 Comprehensible Input

Have students study the visuals and their captions and diagrams to support the key concepts of the lesson.

4 Language Production

Encourage language practice by grouping students with diverse language abilities to collaboratively complete the labs. Have each student copy the completed written lab for personal reference.

5 Assess Understanding

Have students keep a content area log. Use a two-column format with the headings "What I Understand" and "What I Don't Understand." Follow up so that students can move items form the "Don't Understand" to the "Understand" column.

LESSON 9.2

Renewable Sources of Energy

Establish Learning Objectives

After this lesson, students will be able to:

- Identify and describe various renewable sources of energy.
- Explain how a nuclear power plant produces electricity.

Engage

Activate Prior Knowledge

MY PLANET DIARY Read *An Unlikely Decision* with the class. Point out that gas and oil deposits located beneath land in the United States have allowed American gas and oil companies to thrive for decades. Ask: **Why might someone who made their fortune in nonrenewable resources become involved in promoting renewable resources?** *(Students may say it is smart to look into renewable energy since nonrenewable sources won't be around forever.)*

BIG IDEAS OF SCIENCE REFERENCE LIBRARY
Have students look up the following topics: Biofuels, Solar Power.

Explore

Lab Resource: Inquiry Warm-Up

L1 CAN YOU CAPTURE SOLAR ENERGY? Students will use water to capture energy from sunlight and monitor temperature increases.

Renewable Sources of Energy

- What Are Some Renewable Sources of Energy?
- How Does a Nuclear Power Plant Produce Electricity?

my planet Diary

BIOGRAPHY

An Unlikely Decision

T. Boone Pickens's family taught him the value of hard work during the Great Depression of the 1930s. At 11, he delivered newspapers. By 26, he founded his own oil and gas company and became rich. In 2007, T. Boone Pickens surprised everyone by announcing plans to build the world's largest wind farm. He insisted the country must replace oil with wind and solar power. Even though he still promotes oil, he was one of the first oil businessmen to admit a change was needed. "I've been an oil man all my life," Pickens said, "but this is one emergency we can't drill our way out of."

Communicate Discuss these questions with a group of classmates. Write your answers below.

1. Why do you think Pickens's decision was so surprising?
   Sample: He made his fortune in oil and gas.

2. Do you think more focus should be put on finding sources of energy other than oil? Why or why not?
   Sample: Yes, because we might run out of oil.

> PLANET DIARY Go to **Planet Diary** to learn more about renewable energy.

Lab zone — Do the Inquiry Warm-Up Can You Capture Solar Energy?

What Are Some Renewable Sources of Energy?

Coal, oil, and natural gas are not the only energy options available on Earth. **Renewable sources of energy include sunlight, water, wind, nuclear power, biomass fuels, geothermal energy, and hydrogen.** Scientists are trying to find ways to put these energy resources to work to meet people's energy needs.

SUPPORT ALL READERS
Lexile Measure = 940L   Lexile Word Count = 2284

Prior Exposure to Context: Many students may have misconceptions on this topic

Academic Vocabulary: *cause, effect, infer*

Science Vocabulary: *biomass fuel, geothermal energy, nuclear fission*

Concept Level: Generally appropriate for most students in this grade

Preteach With: My Planet Diary "An Unlikely Decision" and Figure 2 activity

Go to **My Reading Web** to access leveled readings that provide a foundation for the content.

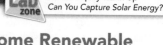

Vocabulary
- solar energy • hydroelectric power • biomass fuel
- gasohol • geothermal energy • nuclear fission
- reactor vessel • fuel rod • control rod

Skills
- Reading: Relate Cause and Effect
- Inquiry: Infer

Solar Energy The warmth you feel on a sunny day is **solar energy,** or energy from the sun. The sun constantly gives off energy in the forms of light and heat. Solar energy is the source, directly or indirectly, of most other renewable energy resources. In one hour, Earth receives enough solar energy to meet the energy needs of the world for an entire year. Solar energy does not cause pollution. It will not run out for billions of years.

So why hasn't solar energy replaced energy from fossil fuels? One reason is that solar energy is only available when the sun is shining. Another problem is that the energy Earth receives from the sun is very spread out. To obtain a useful amount of power, it is necessary to collect solar energy from a large area.

Solar Power Plants One way to capture the sun's energy involves using giant mirrors. In a solar power plant, rows of mirrors focus the sun's rays to heat a tank of water. The water boils. This creates steam. The steam can then be used to generate electricity.

Solar Cells Solar energy can be converted directly into electricity in a solar cell. When light hits the cell, an electric current is produced. Solar cells power some calculators, lights, and other small devices.

✏️ **Relate Cause and Effect**
Underline one way solar energy is collected and circle the way it is used.

did you know?

Photovoltaic cells, or solar cells, are named for the Greek word for light, *photo,* and electricity pioneer Alessandro Volta.

FIGURE 1 ·······················
Everyday Solar Power
Many objects, including calculators, street lights, and even backpacks that charge electronic devices, can be powered by the sun.

✏️ **Describe** What object in your everyday life would you like to run on solar power? Would you want the sun to be its only power source? Why?

Sample: I would want a solar-powered digital music player. I would also want a battery backup so I could still use it on cloudy days.

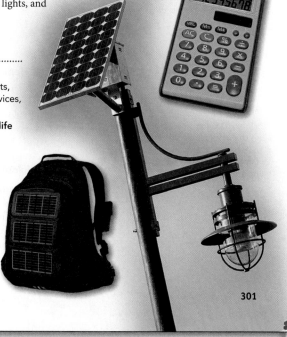

301

LESSON 9.2

Explain ——————

Introduce Vocabulary
Point out that two of the vocabulary words, *hydroelectric* and *geothermal* combine a Greek root with an adjective to form a new word. Explain that *hydroelectric* means "producing electricity with water" and that *geothermal* means "having to do with the heat inside the earth."

Teach Key Concepts 🔑
Explain to students that fossil fuels are the most common, but not the only, sources of energy available to people. Ask: **What are two sources of energy that relate to weather?** *(Wind, sunlight)* **What renewable source of energy is made from living things?** *(Biomass fuels)* **What other renewable sources of energy are scientists trying to develop further?** *(Water, nuclear, geothermal, and hydrogen)*

Lead a Discussion
SOLAR TECHNOLOGIES It's energizing! Different technologies associated with capturing solar energy involve different energy conversions. Ask: **Which solar technology converts light energy directly to electricity?** *(Solar cells)* **Which solar technology converts light energy to heat?** *(Solar power plant)* Explain to students that there are many solutions being sought, and some that are already in use, for ways to store energy when the sun is not shining. Some of these solutions are molten or liquid salt, pumping water uphill, and pumping air underground.

✏️ **Relate Cause and Effect** Tell students that a cause makes something happen. An effect is what happens. When students recognize that one event causes another, they are relating cause and effect.

My Planet Diary provides an opportunity for students to explore real-world connections to renewable energy sources.

my science online.com | Renewable Energy Sources

(ELL) Support

1 Content and Language
Write *bio-, mass, geo-,* and *thermal* on the board, defining each ("life," "physical quantity," "earth," and "heat"). Discuss how knowing these meanings can help students remember the meanings of the terms *biomass* and *geothermal.*

2 Frontload the Lesson
The key idea is full of new or unfamiliar terms, creating a very large language load for students. Write the key idea on

the board, while providing a partially filled-in outline that uses the section headings. As students complete each section, have them return to the key idea to determine which of the sources listed belong in each category.

3 Comprehensible Input
Create a Venn diagram to compare and contrast biomass fuels and fossil fuels. Ask volunteers to provide similarities and differences.

301

Explain

Teach With Visuals

Tell students to look at **Figure 2.** Review the passive and active solar heating systems in the illustration. Call on students to describe the various features labeled in the solar house. Ask: **Which of these solar-powered systems do you have in your own home?** *(Most students will probably identify passive interior heating and window design.)* **Where else in the community do you see examples of passive or active solar-powered systems?** *(Allow a day or two for students to report examples.)* If any students say that their homes are equipped with active solar-powered systems, invite those students to describe the devices and their operation to the class. Remind students that office buildings and institutions might use solar-powered systems, as well.

▲ **Infer** When students interpret an observation, they are inferring, or making an inference. Unlike a fact, an inference is one of many possible interpretations for an observation.

Elaborate

Build Inquiry

L1 **OBSERVE PASSIVE SOLAR HEATING**

Materials 2 thermometers, large glass jar

Time 10 minutes

Tell students that they can measure the difference in temperature inside and outside a passive solar object. Take students outdoors on a sunny day away from the pavement to a spot that receives direct sunlight. Have students note the temperatures of the two thermometers. Put one thermometer in a glass jar turned upside down on the ground and leave the other thermometer in open air. Have students compare the temperatures after several minutes.

Ask: **Why is the temperature higher inside the glass jar?** *(The glass allows light to pass into the jar but traps heat inside the jar.)*

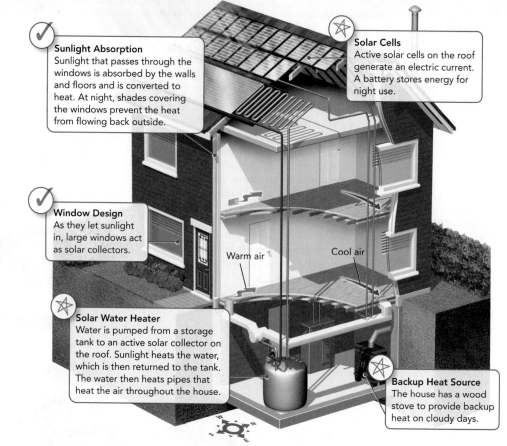

Sunlight Absorption
Sunlight that passes through the windows is absorbed by the walls and floors and is converted to heat. At night, shades covering the windows prevent the heat from flowing back outside.

Solar Cells
Active solar cells on the roof generate an electric current. A battery stores energy for night use.

Window Design
As they let sunlight in, large windows act as solar collectors.

Warm air   Cool air

Solar Water Heater
Water is pumped from a storage tank to an active solar collector on the roof. Sunlight heats the water, which is then returned to the tank. The water then heats pipes that heat the air throughout the house.

Backup Heat Source
The house has a wood stove to provide backup heat on cloudy days.

FIGURE 2 ....

Solar-Powered House

This house takes advantage of active and passive solar heating.

▲ **Infer** Draw a checkmark in the blank circles on the passive sources of solar energy. Draw a star in the blank circles on the active sources.

Passive Solar Heating Solar energy can be used to heat buildings with passive solar systems. A passive solar system converts sunlight into heat, or thermal energy. The heat is then distributed without using pumps or fans. Passive solar heating is what occurs in a parked car on a sunny day. Solar energy passes through the car's windows and heats the seats and other car parts. These parts transfer heat to the air, warming the inside of the car. The same principle can be used to heat a home.

Active Solar Heating An active solar system captures the sun's energy, and then uses pumps and fans to distribute the heat. First, light strikes the dark metal surface of a solar collector. There, it is converted to thermal energy. Water is pumped through pipes in the solar collector to absorb the thermal energy. The heated water then flows to a storage tank. Finally, pumps and fans distribute the heat throughout the building. Refer to **Figure 2.**

Hydroelectric Power

Solar energy is the indirect source of water power. In the water cycle, energy from the sun heats water on Earth's surface. The heat turns the water into water vapor. The vapor condenses and falls back to Earth as rain, sleet, hail, or snow. As the water flows over land, it provides another source of energy.

Hydroelectric power is electricity produced by flowing water. A dam across a river blocks the flow of water, creating a body of water called a reservoir. When a dam's gates are opened, water flows through tunnels at the bottom of the dam. As the water moves through the tunnels, it turns turbines (like a fan's blades). The turbines are connected to a generator. Once a dam is built, generating electricity is inexpensive. But dams can prevent some fish species from breeding. They can also damage aquatic habitats.

Capturing the Wind

Like water power, wind energy is also an indirect form of solar energy. The sun heats Earth's surface unevenly. As a result, different areas of the atmosphere have different temperatures and air pressures. The differences in pressure cause winds to form as air moves from one area to another.

Wind can be used to turn a turbine and generate electricity. Wind farms consist of many wind turbines. Together, the wind turbines generate large amounts of power. Wind is the fastest-growing energy source in the world. Wind energy does not cause pollution. In places where fuels are difficult to transport, wind energy is the major source of power if it is available.

Nuclear Power

Like water and wind power, nuclear power does not produce air pollution since no fuel is burned. Instead, the energy released from the splitting of atoms is used to create steam that turns turbines. This process can be dangerous and even cause explosions if too much energy is released. Wastes generated by nuclear plants can be dangerous if disposed of improperly.

FIGURE 3 ·······················
Hydroelectric and Wind Power
Hydroelectric and wind power do not rely on fossil fuels.
✎ **Compare and Contrast**
List similarities and differences between water and wind power in the Venn diagram.

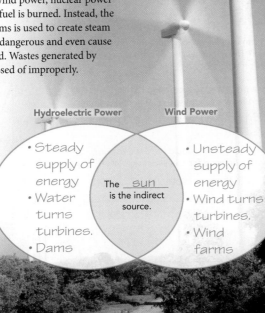

Hydroelectric Power
- Steady supply of energy
- Water turns turbines.
- Dams

The ___sun___ is the indirect source.

Wind Power
- Unsteady supply of energy
- Wind turns turbines.
- Wind farms

303

Explain

Lead a Discussion

POWER FROM WATER Go with the flow. Explain that the water cycle plays a role in generating electricity from flowing water and that hydroelectric power depends on the controlled flow of water through tunnels (spillways or gates) in dams. Ask: **What energy conversion takes place as flowing water turns turbines connected to a generator?** *(Mechanical energy is converted to electrical energy.)* **What are some negative effects that dams might have on the environment?** *(Sample: Dams can change ecosystems when they are built.)*

Lead a Discussion

WIND ENERGY Sun can lead to wind. Solar energy produces convection currents in the atmosphere that create wind. The sun also provides energy for the water cycle, which is essential to hydroelectric power. Tell students that, like the way flowing water produces electricity in a hydroelectric dam, wind generates power by moving turbines that are connected to generators. Ask: **What weather conditions are disruptive to harnessing wind energy?** *(Irregular winds; no winds; winds too strong; stagnant weather—no winds generated)* **Name two reasons why wind farms are best placed in remote locations.** *(Wind farms are noisy; they require a lot of space; other fuels may be difficult to transport to remote sites.)* Tell students that there once was concern over wind turbines causing harm to flying birds. However, modern turbines are larger and can generate the same amount of energy by moving slowly. This improvement reduces the chances of birds being injured.

21st Century Learning

COMMUNICATION Divide the class into two groups; assign one group water power and the other group wind power. Ask groups to consider the advantages of the assigned source of power, and why their community should adopt it. *(Students should consider climate and geographic restrictions, cost, potential environmental damage, and so on.)* Have each group give a brief presentation on its position.

Differentiated Instruction

L1 Illustrate a Solar Power Plant To reinforce students' understanding of the causes and effects that underlie the operation of a solar power plant, have them create an illustration showing the functions of the sun, a row of mirrors, a tank of water, and steam in the generation of electricity.

L3 Solar Power Timeline Challenge students to do research in order to create an annotated, illustrated timeline showing the history of solar energy.

Point out that human beings have been using energy from the sun since prehistoric times. Urge students to note developments and setbacks in the movement to make solar energy more widespread.

L3 Explain Solar Technologies Invite pairs of students to take turns explaining the principles underlying examples of technology that capture solar energy for human use.

303

Explain

Lead a Discussion

FUELS FROM LIVING THINGS Wood is a common *biomass fuel*. Explain that biomass can be burned as fuel and converted into other fuels. Ask: **What are five biomass products that can be burned as fuel?** *(Samples: trees/wood, corn, sugar cane, landfill wastes, leaves, manure, food wastes)* **Why do you think biomass fuels are commonly used in less developed nations?** *(They are easy to obtain and do not require special technology.)* Tell students that there are negative environmental impacts when food crops are used to produce biomass fuels. Ecosystems can be affected when large amounts of land are used to grow a single biomass fuel crop. A genetically similar crop may become more susceptible to diseases and pests, which can lead to crop failure. Growing biomass fuel crops requires machinery that runs on fossil fuels and petroleum-based pesticides and fertilizers. Biomass fuel crops also compete with food production. As U.S. farmers started to use corn crops for ethanol in 2006 and 2007, the amount of corn available for food decreased. This caused corn prices to increase. Ask: **Do you think the positive uses of biomass fuels outweigh the negative impacts?** *(Sample: Yes, because it helps to reduce our dependence on fossil fuels.)*

Address Misconceptions

L1 **NEW RENEWABLES?** Many people believe that renewable energy sources have been developed only recently as environment-friendly alternatives to fossil fuels, but this is not the case. Explain to students that renewable energy has been around for a long time. Also point out that hydroelectric power is the most widely used renewable source in the world, accounting for 19 percent of total electricity production.

Ask: **What types of energy were used before electricity?** *(Burning wood, peat, other biomass fuels; wind, water)* **Why did renewable sources become less popular?** *(Energy from fossil fuels is easier to obtain and more convenient.)*

Elaborate

Apply It!

L1 Before students begin the *Apply It!* activity, have them reread the section on biomass fuels and study the elements of the graph, noting the title, the labels on the sides of the graph, and the key. Point out the two curves, labeled "Demand" and "Supply." Explain that by tracking the relationship between the red line and the blue line, students will be able to see how supply and demand affect each another.

FIGURE 4 ....

Corn Power
Biomass fuels come from living things, such as corn. It takes about 11.84 kilograms of corn to make one gallon of fuel!

Biomass Fuels Wood was probably the first fuel ever used for heat and light. Wood belongs to a group of fuels called **biomass fuels.** Biomass fuels are made from living things. Other biomass fuels include leaves, food wastes, and even manure. As fossil fuel supplies shrink, people are taking a closer look at biomass fuels. For example, when oil prices rose in the early 1970s, Hawaiian farmers began burning sugar cane wastes to generate electricity.

In addition to being burned as fuel, biomass materials can be converted into other fuels. For example, corn, sugar cane, and other crops can be used to make alcohol. Adding alcohol to gasoline forms **gasohol.** Gasohol can be used as fuel for cars. Bacteria can produce methane gas by decomposing biomass materials in landfills. That methane can be used to heat buildings. And some crops, such as soybeans, can produce oil. The oil can be used as fuel, which is called biodiesel fuel.

Biomass fuels are renewable resources. But it takes time for new trees to replace those that have been cut down. And it is expensive to produce alcohol and methane in large quantities. As a result, biomass fuels are not widely used today in the United States. But as fossil fuels become scarcer, biomass fuels may provide another source for meeting energy needs.

apply it!

What can happen when a food crop is used for fuel? The relationship is plotted with two curves on the graph.

❶ **Interpret Graphs** According to the graph, as demand for corn increases, what happens to the supply?

It decreases.

❷ **CHALLENGE** How would the price of corn change as demand for fuel increases? Why?

Sample: It would increase because there would be a smaller supply of corn to go around and people would be willing to pay more.

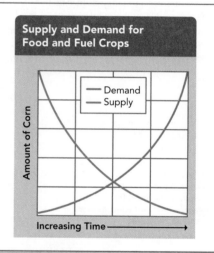

Supply and Demand for Food and Fuel Crops

— Demand
— Supply

Amount of Corn

Increasing Time ⟶

Digital Lesson: Assign the *Apply It* activity online and have students submit their work to you.

MY SCIENCE online.com   **Renewable Energy Sources**

Tapping Earth's Energy Below Earth's surface are pockets of very hot liquid rock called magma. In some places, magma is very close to the surface. The intense heat from Earth's interior that warms the magma is called **geothermal energy.**

In certain regions, such as Iceland and New Zealand, magma heats underground water to the boiling point. In these places, the hot water and steam can be valuable sources of energy. For example, in Reykjavík, Iceland, 90 percent of the homes are heated by water warmed underground in this way. Geothermal energy can also be used to generate electricity, as shown in **Figure 5.**

Geothermal energy does have disadvantages. There are only a few places where Earth's crust is thin enough for magma to come close to the surface. Elsewhere, very deep wells would be needed to tap this energy. Drilling deep wells is very expensive. Even so, geothermal energy is likely to become a good method for meeting energy needs for some locations in the future.

FIGURE 5 ·······························

Geothermal Power in Iceland

Geothermal power plants like the one shown here use heat from Earth's interior to generate electricity.

✎ **Infer** On the diagram below, draw Earth's crust and show where magma might be located in relation to Iceland's surface.

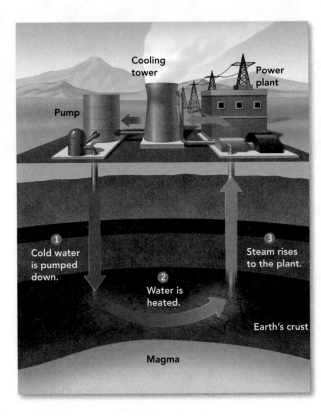

Cooling tower

Power plant

Pump

1 Cold water is pumped down.

2 Water is heated.

3 Steam rises to the plant.

Earth's crust

Magma

Earth's crust

Magma

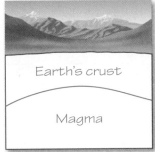

Earth's crust

Magma

305

Explain

Teach With Visuals

Have students look at **Figure 5.** Remind students that geothermal energy is the intense heat from Earth's interior. Ask: **How is electricity generated in a geothermal power plant?** (Cold water piped underground is heated by magma and turns into steam, which is used to generate electricity.) **Why do you think geothermal energy isn't more commonly used?** (Magma comes close to the surface only in a few areas; deep wells required in other places would be expensive.)

Lead a Discussion

HEAT PUMPS Students may not think that they live in an area that can benefit from geothermal energy. However, geothermal heat pumps can be used in any location where pipes can be drilled into the ground. Because the ground beneath six feet stays at roughly the same temperature (14 degrees Celsius) year-round, it can be used to store energy. In the winter, cold water is pumped into the ground where it is heated to 14 degrees Celsius. In the summer, warm water is pumped into the ground to be cooled to 14 degrees Celsius. While geothermal heat pumps are more expensive to install than conventional heating and cooling systems, they are becoming more common throughout the United States. Many schools are beginning to install geothermal heat pumps to reduce heating and cooling costs. Ask: **Do you think your school should investigate the use of a heat pump to reduce costs?** (Some students may think it is a good idea to help reduce costs in the long term. Other students may think it is a bad idea because of the cost in the short term.)

21st Century Learning

CRITICAL THINKING Have students reread the last paragraph on this page. Encourage students to note the specific information about two disadvantages of geothermal energy. (Limited number of places where Earth's crust is thin enough, expense of drilling deep wells) **What can you conclude about Earth's crust in Iceland and New Zealand?** (It must be thin.) **What do you think could make geothermal energy a good method for meeting energy needs in the future?** (Sample: Technological advances may make drilling less expensive.)

Differentiated Instruction

L1 Describe Geothermal Energy Have students summarize in their own words the process for generating electricity with geothermal energy. Let students share their summaries with the class in a follow-up discussion. Guide students to agree on a "best sentence" for each step in the process.

L3 Five Powerful Plants Have students research the five plants in Iceland that produce electricity. Over one-fourth of the electricity used in Iceland is produced by these plants.

Explain

Lead a Discussion

ENERGY FOR THE FUTURE Tell students that scientists want to develop hydrogen power because of its potential to provide huge amounts of energy. Ask: **What are the advantages and disadvantages associated with hydrogen power?** *(Advantages—abundant, burns cleanly, doesn't pollute air; disadvantages—expensive to produce, almost all hydrogen is combined with oxygen in water)* **What examples do we have of hydrogen power being supplied by fuel cells?** *(Experimental cars, space shuttle)* Students may have heard about electric cars. Tell students that like cars powered by hydrogen, some electric cars do not create air pollution. When electric cars are recharged using electricity generated by a renewable energy source, they cause no air pollutants. If an electric car is recharged using electricity generated by a nonrenewable energy source, then pollutants can be emitted from the power plant. However, all electric cars are considered zero-emission vehicles because they do not release any tailpipe pollutants.

Make Analogies

BENEFIT VS. COST To help students understand the idea that obtaining pure hydrogen takes more energy than is produced by burning hydrogen, invite students to think about other situations where a particular course of action is judged "not worth it" because it will "take more energy than it's worth," such as driving a relatively long distance to purchase an item that is on sale.

Elaborate

Explore the Big Q ? UbD

Direct students' attention to the particular objects (corn stalks, gas tank, hydrogen tank, wind turbines), atmospheric details (steam), and structures (dam, nuclear plant, house with solar panels) included in the illustration to represent each energy source. Ask: **Which energy sources are limited because they can only be found or gathered in certain locations?** *(Hydroelectric, fossil fuels, wind, geothermal)* **Which energy sources do not damage the environment?** *(Solar, wind, biomass, geothermal, hydrogen)*

Lab Resource: Quick Lab

L3 **DESIGN AND BUILD A SOLAR COOKER**
Students will design and build something to cook food. The cooker will be powered only by the sun.

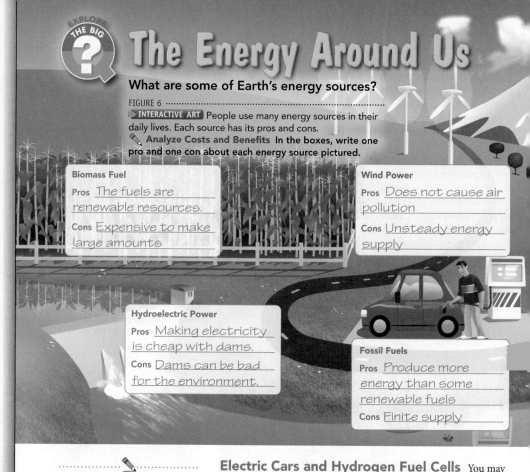

The Energy Around Us

What are some of Earth's energy sources?

FIGURE 6 ....

INTERACTIVE ART People use many energy sources in their daily lives. Each source has its pros and cons.

Analyze Costs and Benefits In the boxes, write one pro and one con about each energy source pictured.

Biomass Fuel
Pros _The fuels are renewable resources._
Cons _Expensive to make large amounts_

Wind Power
Pros _Does not cause air pollution_
Cons _Unsteady energy supply_

Hydroelectric Power
Pros _Making electricity is cheap with dams._
Cons _Dams can be bad for the environment._

Fossil Fuels
Pros _Produce more energy than some renewable fuels_
Cons _Finite supply_

Vocabulary High-Use Academic Words The word *emit* means "to give off." What do vehicles that run on hydrogen fuel cells emit?

Water vapor

_____

_____

_____

Electric Cars and Hydrogen Fuel Cells You may have heard about or even seen battery-powered electric cars. But what about cars that use hydrogen fuel cells? Both technologies, battery-powered electric cars and hydrogen fuel cells, have been developed to use renewable energy. See **Figure 6.**

Electric cars run entirely on batteries, and you plug them into an outlet to recharge them. The electricity used can be generated by power plants that use hydroelectric or solar energy. Some electric cars have adaptors that let you recharge them in minutes.

Some cars can run on hydrogen. They have tanks called hydrogen fuel cells that hold hydrogen instead of gasoline. Many power plants can use excess energy to break water molecules apart to make hydrogen. This hydrogen can then be pumped into cars. Cars that run on hydrogen fuel cells emit water vapor, not exhaust.

Interactive Art allows students to explore a hydroelectric power plant.

my science online .com   **Renewable Energy Sources**

Geothermal Energy

Pros Unlimited source

Cons Expensive to drill deep

Solar Power

Pros Will not run out for billions of years

Cons Only available when sun is shining

Nuclear Power

Pros Does not cause air pollution

Cons Nuclear waste damages environment.

Hydrogen Power

Pros Exists on Earth in large supply

Cons Takes more energy to create than what is made by burning it

Lab zone® Do the Lab Investigation *Design and Build a Solar Cooker.*

⚷ Assess Your Understanding

1a. Review What forms of energy are provided by the sun? Light and heat

b. Explain Are biomass fuels renewable? Why? Yes; crops can be replanted, although this takes time.

c. ANSWER THE BIG ? What are some of Earth's energy sources? Fossil fuels, solar power, hydroelectric power, wind power, nuclear power, biomass fuels, geothermal energy, and hydrogen

got it? ....

○ I get it! Now I know that alternative energy sources include sunlight, water, wind, nuclear power, biomass fuels, geothermal energy, and hydrogen.

○ I need extra help with See TE note.

Go to MY SCIENCE 🖥 COACH *online for help with this subject.*

307

Evaluate ⎯⎯⎯⎯⎯⎯

Assess Your Understanding

After students answer the questions, have them evaluate their understanding by completing the appropriate sentence.

Answer the Big Q ❓ UbD

To help students focus on the Big Question, lead a class discussion about Earth's energy sources.

RTI Response to Intervention

1a. If students have trouble listing forms of energy provided by the sun, **then** have them reread the first paragraph under the red head *Solar Energy*.

b. If students cannot explain what makes biomass renewable, **then** have them to review the last paragraph under the red head *Biomass Fuels*.

c. If students need help identifying energy sources, **then** have them to skim the entire chapter to find examples of energy sources.

MY SCIENCE 🖥 COACH Have students go online for help in understanding renewable energy sources.

Differentiated Instruction

L1 Illustrate Local Energy Use Invite students to create drawings, paintings, or murals that show local buildings, landforms, and other sites where energy use is evident. Students might include a gas station, a private home with solar panels, a wind turbine, a dam, and so on. Have students share their drawings with the rest of the class and call on other students to name the energy use that is illustrated.

L3 Hydrogen Power Plants Hydrogen is the simplest of the elements and the most plentiful gas in the universe. Have students research the planned use of hydrogen to power electrical plants. Have them prepare diagrams to support their findings.

Explain

Teach Key Concepts 🔑

Nuclear fission, the splitting of an atom's nucleus into two nuclei, is the basis for nuclear power. Ask: **What form of energy given off by nuclear fission is used in a power plant?** *(Heat)* **In a nuclear power plant, how is heat used?** *(It turns water into steam.)* **What happens next?** *(The steam turns the blades of a turbine to create electricity.)*

Lead a Discussion

HOW FISSION GENERATES ELECTRICITY Compare a nuclear power plant to other power plants. A nuclear power plant functions like other power plants: a heat source—in this case, fission—changes water into steam that powers turbines. Have students review **Figure 7.** Ask: **What are the three main components of a nuclear power plant?** *(The generator, the reactor vessel and the heat exchanger)* **Name two other energy sources that can create steam to turn turbines that generate electricity at a power plant.** *(Fossil fuels, especially coal; geothermal energy)*

How Does a Nuclear Power Plant Produce Electricity?

Nuclear power plants generate much of the world's electricity. They generate about 20 percent of the electricity in the United States and more than 70 percent in France. Controlled nuclear fission reactions take place inside nuclear power plants. **Nuclear fission** is the splitting of an atom's nucleus into two nuclei. The splitting releases a lot of energy. 🔑 **In a nuclear power plant, the heat released from fission reactions is used to turn water into steam. The steam then turns the blades of a turbine to generate electricity.** Look at the diagram of a nuclear power plant in **Figure 7.** In addition to the generator, it has two main parts: the reactor vessel and the heat exchanger.

Reactor Vessel The **reactor vessel** is the part of the nuclear reactor in which nuclear fission occurs. The reactor contains rods of radioactive uranium called **fuel rods.** When several fuel rods are placed close together, a series of fission reactions occurs.

If the reactor vessel gets too hot, control rods are used to slow down the chain reactions. **Control rods,** made of the elements cadmium, boron or hafnium, are inserted near the fuel rods. The elements absorb particles released during fission and slow the speed of the chain reactions. The control rods can then be removed to speed up the chain reactions again.

FIGURE 7 ·····································

▶ INTERACTIVE ART Nuclear **Power Plants**
Nuclear power plants are designed to turn the energy from nuclear fission reactions into electricity.

✎ **Interpret Diagrams** Where does nuclear fission occur in the plant?

In the reactor vessel

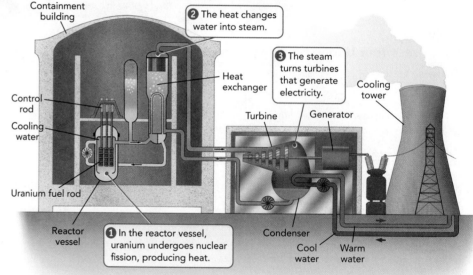

Containment building

2 The heat changes water into steam.

Heat exchanger

3 The steam turns turbines that generate electricity.

Cooling tower

Control rod

Cooling water

Turbine   Generator

Uranium fuel rod

Reactor vessel

1 In the reactor vessel, uranium undergoes nuclear fission, producing heat.

Condenser

Cool water   Warm water

Interactive Art allows students to understand the process that leads to the generation of electricity in nuclear power plants.

my science online.com

Nuclear Power

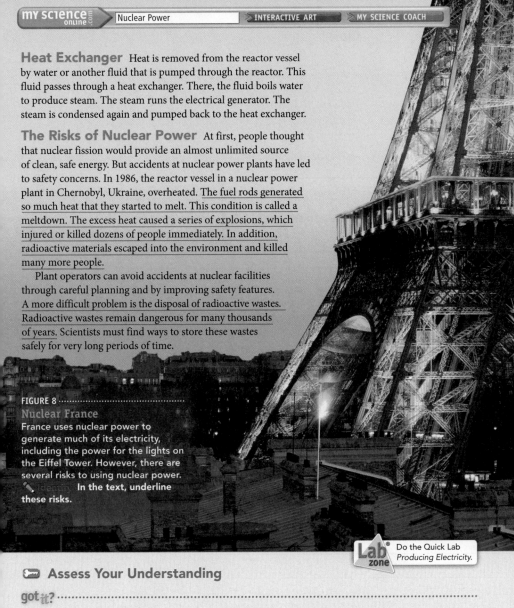

Heat Exchanger Heat is removed from the reactor vessel by water or another fluid that is pumped through the reactor. This fluid passes through a heat exchanger. There, the fluid boils water to produce steam. The steam runs the electrical generator. The steam is condensed again and pumped back to the heat exchanger.

The Risks of Nuclear Power At first, people thought that nuclear fission would provide an almost unlimited source of clean, safe energy. But accidents at nuclear power plants have led to safety concerns. In 1986, the reactor vessel in a nuclear power plant in Chernobyl, Ukraine, overheated. <u>The fuel rods generated so much heat that they started to melt. This condition is called a meltdown. The excess heat caused a series of explosions, which injured or killed dozens of people immediately. In addition, radioactive materials escaped into the environment and killed many more people.</u>

Plant operators can avoid accidents at nuclear facilities through careful planning and by improving safety features. <u>A more difficult problem is the disposal of radioactive wastes. Radioactive wastes remain dangerous for many thousands of years. Scientists must find ways to store these wastes safely for very long periods of time.</u>

FIGURE 8 ·················
Nuclear France
France uses nuclear power to generate much of its electricity, including the power for the lights on the Eiffel Tower. However, there are several risks to using nuclear power.
✎ **Identify** In the text, underline these risks.

Lab zone | Do the Quick Lab *Producing Electricity*.

📖 **Assess Your Understanding**

got it? ··························

○ I get it! Now I know that nuclear power plants produce energy by <u>using heat from nuclear fission reactions to make steam that generates turbines.</u>

○ I need extra help with <u>See TE note.</u>

Go to my science COACH *online for help with this subject.*

309

Differentiated Instruction

L1 Relate Cause and Effect Help students understand the process of producing power from nuclear fission by asking them to analyze the cause-and-effect relationships in the process. Have them create a flowchart beginning with nuclear fission and ending with electric current going to power lines.

L3 Identify Nuclear Accidents Challenge students to use reference books or online sources to learn the typical temperatures reached in a nuclear power plant's reactor vessel and then find the temperatures reached in the Chernobyl accident. Ask students to investigate and report on the occurrence of other nuclear accidents, such as Three Mile Island.

Elaborate

Build Inquiry Lab zone

L1 NUCLEAR POWER ACCIDENTS

Materials large world map

Time 15 minutes

Explain that radioactive fallout from the Chernobyl accident was spread by air currents. Display the map, and let volunteers locate Chernobyl (51° N, 30° about 130 km north of Kiev). Tell students that the force of the 1986 explosion carried radioactive materials high into the atmosphere, where they spread across the Northern Hemisphere and then settled back to Earth in what is called fallout. The heaviest fallout occurred in Ukraine, Belarus, Sweden, Norway, Denmark, France, and Switzerland. In addition, Finland, Lithuania, Germany, Poland, the Czech Republic, Slovakia, Austria, Hungary, Italy, and Great Britain suffered moderate fallout. Let students find all these countries on the map.

Ask: **Which affected country was farthest from Chernobyl?** *(Great Britain)* **What does this tell you about the dangers of nuclear power plants?** *(An accident can affect a huge area.)*

Lab Resource: Quick Lab

L1 PRODUCING ELECTRICITY Students will draw a model of a nuclear power plant to learn how it generates electricity.

Evaluate

Assess Your Understanding

Have students evaluate their understanding by completing the appropriate sentence.

RTI Response to Intervention

If students cannot explain how nuclear power plants work, **then** have them refer to **Figure 7** and read the numbered labels.

my science COACH Have students go online for help in understanding how nuclear power plants produce energy.

Lab zone **After the Inquiry Warm-Up**

Renewable Sources of Energy

> **Inquiry Warm-Up, *Can You Capture Solar Energy?***
> In the Inquiry Warm-Up, you investigated capturing solar energy with a water-filled bag. Using what you learned from that activity, answer the questions below.

1. **PREDICT** Assume you move a bag from a dark, shady area into an area with direct sunlight for 30 minutes and then back into the shade for 30 minutes. Draw a simple graph predicting the bag's temperature change over time.

2. **USE PRIOR KNOWLEDGE** Give at least one reason why solar energy cannot meet all of our energy needs.

   _____

   _____

3. **INFER** Explain your results for the temperature of the bag before and after you placed it in a dark area.

   _____

   _____

4. **PREDICT** Will the temperature of the water in the bag placed in direct sunlight be higher or lower if you leave it in direct sunlight for another 30 minutes?

   _____

   _____

Name _____ Date _____ Class _____

Renewable Sources of Energy

What Are Some Renewable Sources of Energy?

1a. REVIEW What forms of energy are provided by the sun? _____

_____

b. EXPLAIN Are biomass fuels renewable? Why? _____

_____

c. ANSWER What are some of Earth's energy sources?

_____

_____

got it? ···

○ **I get it!** Now I know that alternative energy sources include _____

_____

○ **I need extra help with** _____

_____

How Does a Nuclear Power Plant Produce Electricity?

got it? ···

○ **I get it!** Now I know that nuclear power plants produce energy by _____

_____

_____

○ **I need extra help with** _____

_____

Renewable Sources of Energy

What Are Some Renewable Sources of Energy?

Renewable sources of energy include sunlight, water, wind, nuclear power, biomass fuels, geothermal energy, and hydrogen. Solar energy is energy from the sun. In solar power plants, mirrors focus the sun's rays on a water tank, creating steam to generate electricity. In solar cells, light falling on the cell is converted to electric current. **Hydroelectric power** is electricity produced by flowing water. Inside a dam, flowing water turns turbines (like a fan's blades) to generate electricity. Wind can also be used to turn turbines and generate electricity.

In nuclear power, the energy released by splitting atoms creates steam that turns turbines. **Biomass fuels** such as wood, leaves, food wastes, and manure are made from living things. Biomass materials can be burned as fuels themselves or converted into other fuels, such as **gasohol,** a mix of alcohol and gasoline. The intense heat from Earth's interior that warms magma below Earth's surface is called **geothermal energy.** Water pumped into deep wells is heated by the magma to generate electricity. Hydrogen power may someday be a source of clean energy, but first scientists must find an inexpensive way to release hydrogen atoms from water.

How Does a Nuclear Power Plant Produce Electricity?

Nuclear power plants generate electricity through controlled **nuclear fission,** the splitting of an atom's nucleus into two nuclei. **In a nuclear power plant, the heat released from fission reactions is used to turn water into steam. The steam then turns the blades of a turbine to generate electricity.** The **reactor vessel** is the part of the nuclear reactor in which fission occurs. When rods of uranium called **fuel rods** are placed close together, fission reactions occur. If the reactor gets too hot, **control rods,** made of the metal cadmium, are inserted between the fuel rods to absorb particles released during fission and slow the reactions. Water or another fluid pumped through the reactor is heated by the reactions. It passes through a heat exchanger, where the heat boils water to generate electricity. Nuclear energy has two main drawbacks. Accidents at nuclear plants have led to safety concerns, and scientists have yet to find safe ways to store dangerous radioactive wastes for thousands of years.

Choose five renewable sources of energy and, on a separate sheet of paper, list one drawback for each.

Review and Reinforce

Renewable Sources of Energy

Understanding Main Ideas
Answer the following questions on a separate sheet of paper.

1. Some sources of energy are called *alternative sources*. To what sources of energy are they an alternative?
2. Name five alternative sources of energy.
3. Explain how wind and flowing water can be used to produce electricity.
4. Describe how electricity is produced inside a nuclear plant.

Building Vocabulary
Match each term with its definition by writing the letter of the correct definition in the right column on the line beside the term in the left column.

5. ___ solar energy

6. ___ nuclear fission

7. ___ hydroelectric power

8. ___ gasohol

9. ___ reactor vessel

10. ___ fuel rods

11. ___ biomass fuels

12. ___ geothermal energy

13. ___ control rods

a. a fuel made from a mix of alcohol and gasoline

b. the uranium rods inside a nuclear reactor that produce fission

c. a group of fuels made from living things

d. intense heat from Earth's interior that warms magma

e. the splitting of an atom's nucleus into two nuclei

f. energy from the sun

g. the cadmium rods inside a nuclear reactor that slow the reactions

h. the part of a nuclear reactor in which nuclear fission occurs

i. electricity produced by flowing water

Name _____ Date _____ Class _____

Renewable Sources of Energy

Wind generators are useful only in places where the wind blows steadily at 13 kilometers per hour or more. Could wind generators be used where you live? Try this activity to find out if the wind is strong enough to operate a wind generator.

Measuring Wind Speed

Materials

sewing needle

30 cm heavyweight thread

table-tennis ball

masking tape

protractor

Procedure

1. Tie a knot in one end of the thread. Carefully use the needle to pull the thread all the way though the table-tennis ball.

2. Tape the other end of the thread to the center mark on a protractor.

3. Choose a windy place outdoors. With your back to the wind, hold the protractor with its straight edge up and parallel to the ground.

4. Prepare a data table to record the date, time, angle of the thread, and wind speed. Put in enough rows to record data twice a day for one week.

5. Read and record the angle where the thread crosses the protractor's curved edge. Use the table on this page to convert the angle to wind speed.

6. Repeat your measurements twice a day for one week. Calculate the average wind speed for the week. Is the wind in your area strong enough to operate a wind generator?

Angle	Wind Speed (km/h)
90°	0
85°	6
80°	8
75°	10
70°	12
65°	13
60°	15
55°	16
50°	18
45°	20
40°	21
35°	23
30°	26
25°	29
20°	33

Tape
Protractor
Thread
Table-tennis ball
Knot

Place the outside corner, the corner away from the dotted line, in the corner of your copy machine to copy onto letter-size paper.

Lesson Quiz

Renewable Sources of Energy

If the statement is true, write *true*. If the statement is false, change the underlined word or words to make the statement true.

1. _____ Sunlight, water, wind, nuclear power, biomass fuels, geothermal energy, and hydrogen are all <u>nonrenewable</u> energy sources.

2. _____ The fastest-growing energy source in the world is <u>wind energy</u>.

3. _____ In order to harness <u>geothermal</u> energy, cool water is pumped down into deep wells.

4. _____ Inside a nuclear power plant, nuclear fission takes place within the <u>heat exchanger</u>.

5. _____ The radioactive wastes produced by nuclear fission remain dangerous for <u>dozens</u> of years.

Fill in the blank to complete each statement.

6. Energy from the sun is called _____.

7. _____ is electricity produced by flowing water.

8. _____ can also be converted into other fuels, such as gasohol, which is formed by adding alcohol to gasoline.

9. The intense heat from Earth's interior that warms the magma is called _____.

10. _____ is the splitting of an atom's nucleus into two nuclei.

Renewable Sources of Energy

Answer Key

After the Inquiry Warm-Up

1. Description: The graph should look like a bell—a curve moving from low temperature to a higher temperature and back to a low temperature again.

2. Accept all reasonable responses. Students may say: The sun doesn't always shine; i.e., at night, or during cloudy weather.

3. Sample: The temperature did not change because it absorbed little or no solar energy.

4. Sample: The temperature of the water should be higher after an additional 30 minutes in the sun.

Key Concept Summaries

Accept any five of the following: Solar energy is spread out across the face of Earth and is only available when and where the sun is shining. Hydroelectric power can damage ecosystems when rivers are dammed. Wind power is only available when and where there is wind blowing. Producing nuclear power includes some risk of releasing radioactivity and leaves radioactive wastes that are difficult to store safely. In most places on Earth, releasing geothermal energy would require digging very deep wells. Until scientists find a cheap method for producing hydrogen, producing it takes more energy than is released by burning it.

Review and Reinforce

1. fossil fuels, such as coal, oil, and natural gas

2. Accept any five of the following: sunlight, water, wind, nuclear power, biomass fuels, geothermal energy, and hydrogen

3. Wind energy can be used to turn turbines and generate electricity. Water flowing through tunnels inside a dam turns turbines that generate electricity.

4. Sample: Inside the reactor vessel of a nuclear reactor, uranium fuel rods are placed close together. Particles given off by the uranium cause nuclear fission, splitting the nuclei of the atoms and releasing energy in the form of heat. The heat is absorbed by water in the reactor vessel, which is pumped outside to a heat exchanger. Inside the heat exchanger, pipes containing the hot water from the reactor vessel heat more water, which is turned to steam. The steam turns turbines to produce electricity.

5. f	6. e
7. i	8. a
9. h	10. b
11. c	12. d
13. g	

Enrich

6. Wind speeds will vary. Students should answer Yes to the question if the wind is fairly steady and the average wind speed for the week is at least 13 km/h.

Lesson Quiz

1. alternative	2. true
3. true	4. reactor vessel
5. thousands	6. solar energy
7. Hydroelectric power	8. Biomass fuels
9. geothermal energy	10. Nuclear fission

Place the outside corner, the corner away from the dotted line, in the corner of your copy machine to copy onto letter-size paper.

Energy Use and Conservation

LESSON

3

 What are some of Earth's energy sources?

Lesson Pacing: 1–2 periods or $\frac{1}{2}$–1 block

🕐 **SHORT ON TIME?** To do this lesson in approximately half the time, do the Activate Prior Knowledge activity followed by a discussion of the Key Concepts to familiarize students with the lesson content. Have students do the Quick Labs. The rest of the lesson can be completed by students independently.

> **Preference Navigator,** in the online Planning tools, allows you to customize *Interactive Science* to your own teaching style. You can also edit lesson plans by selecting the Lesson Planner option.
>
> **Digital Teacher's Edition** allows you to access your Teacher's Edition and Resource materials online.
>
> **my science** online.com

Lesson Vocabulary

- efficiency
- insulation
- energy conservation

Content Refresher

Making Informed Decisions The federal government offers consumers a chance to make informed decisions when purchasing household appliances or homes. Appliances for homes earn the distinction of an "Energy Star" label when they meet energy efficiency standards established jointly by the Department of Energy and the U.S. Environmental Protection Agency (EPA). The Energy Star program estimates that a family can reduce its energy consumption by one third by choosing designated energy-efficient appliances.

According to the EPA, in 2008, Americans prevented 43 million metric tons of greenhouse gas emissions. That is equivalent to annual emissions by 29 million cars. Additionally, Americans saved over $19 billion dollars on utility bills by using Energy Star products and services.

LESSON OBJECTIVES

🔑 Explain how human energy use has changed over time.

🔑 Name ways to ensure that there will be enough energy for the future.

Blended Path
Active learning using Student Edition, Inquiry Path, and Digital Path

ENGAGE AND EXPLORE

Teach this lesson using a variety of resources. Begin by reading **My Planet Diary** as a class. Have students share what they know about various forms of insulation. Then have students do the **Inquiry Warm-Up activity.** Students will compare the efficiency of incandescent and fluorescent light bulbs. Discuss the characteristics of each type of light bulb. The **After the Inquiry Warm-Up worksheet** sets up a discussion about the benefits of using fluorescent light bulbs. Have volunteers share their answers to number 4 about the brightness of fluorescent and incandescent light bulbs.

EXPLAIN AND ELABORATE

Teach Key Concepts by explaining various ways that people created energy before using fossil fuels. Compare the energy sources shown on the timeline to **Support the Big Q.**

Continue to **Teach Key Concepts** by explaining the importance of conserving energy. Also discuss the importance of using energy efficiently. Use **Figures 1 and 2** to identify ways that human beings could conserve energy. **Lead a Discussion** about ways to increase the efficiency of our energy use in relation to heating and cooling systems, lighting, and transportation. Then have students complete the **Apply It activity.** Hand out the **Key Concept Summaries** as a review of each part of the lesson. Students can also use the online **Vocab Flash Cards** to review key terms.

EVALUATE

Have students take the **Lesson Quiz.** For an alternate assessment, see the **EXAM**VIEW® Assessment Suite, Progress Monitoring Assessments, or SuccessTracker™.

ⒺⓁⓁ Support

1 Content and Language

Identify the suffix in the terms *conservation* and *insulation*. When the Latin suffix *–ation* is added to a word it changes it from a verb to a noun. Determine the verb forms of *conservation* (to conserve) and *insulation* (to insulate). Identify similar nouns and their verb counterparts in this lesson: communication (to communicate); transportation (to transport); pollution (to pollute); suggestion (to suggest).

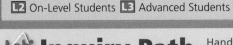 **Inquiry Path** Hands-on learning in the Lab zone

ENGAGE AND EXPLORE

To teach this lesson with an emphasis on inquiry, begin with the **Inquiry Warm-Up activity.** Students will investigate incandescent and fluorescent light bulbs. Discuss the differences in efficiency between the two bulbs. Have students do the **After the Inquiry Warm-Up worksheet.** Talk about why it is more efficient to use a fluorescent light bulb. Have volunteers share their answers to number 4 comparing the brightness of the two types of light bulbs.

EXPLAIN AND ELABORATE

Focus on the **Inquiry Skill** for the lesson. Point out that when you observe, you carefully watch something. **Support the Big Q** by using the timeline to identify various sources of energy used over the course of time. Have students do the **Quick Lab** to understand human energy use in the 20th century and then share their results.

Use the **Real World Inquiry** to identify ways that energy can be conserved in a home. **Build Inquiry** by discussing energy conservation and efficiency in relation to the real world. Review transportation and energy conservation before beginning the **Apply It activity.** Ask volunteers to share their posters and responses. Have students do the **Quick Lab** to learn how to increase efficiency of energy use and conserve energy. Students can use the online **Vocab Flash Cards** to review key terms.

EVALUATE

Have students take the **Lesson Quiz.** For an alternate assessment, see the **EXAM**VIEW® Assessment Suite, Progress Monitoring Assessments, or SuccessTracker™.

Digital Path Online learning at MY SCIENCE ONLINE.com

ENGAGE AND EXPLORE

Teach this lesson using digital resources. Begin by having students explore different forms of insulation at **My Planet Diary** online. Have them access the Chapter Resources to find the **Unlock the Big Question activity.** There they can answer the questions and refine their responses as they continue through the lesson. You can re-assign the activity and have students submit their work so you can track their progress.

EXPLAIN AND ELABORATE

Students reading above, at, or below the lexile measure of this lesson can access basic content readings at their level at **My Reading Web. Support the Big Q** by discussing past, present, and future sources of energy. Do the **Quick Lab** to understand current human energy use and then ask students to share their results.

Assign the online **Real World Inquiry** to help students understand how they can conserve energy in their homes. Review *energy conservation* in relation to transportation before assigning the online **Apply It activity.** Ask volunteers to share their posters and have students submit their work to you. Have students do the **Quick Lab** about increasing efficiency of energy use and conserving energy. Then ask students to share their results. The **Key Concept Summaries** online allow students to read a summary and see an image associated with each part of the lesson. Online remediation is available at **My Science Coach.**

EVALUATE

Have students take the **Lesson Quiz.** For an alternate assessment, see the **EXAM**VIEW® Assessment Suite, Progress Monitoring Assessments, or SuccessTracker™.

2 Frontload the Lesson
Preview the lesson visuals, labels, and captions. Ask students what they know about the words *conservation* and *efficiency*. Explain the specific meanings these words have in science.

3 Comprehensible Input
Have students help make a chart about ways to conserve energy and to use energy more efficiently.

4 Language Production
Pair or group students with varied language abilities to complete labs collaboratively for language practice. Have each student copy the completed written lab for personal reference.

5 Assess Understanding
Divide the class into small groups. Have each student identify a key concept from the lesson to discuss in his or her group. After the discussions, have students talk about the key concepts as a group.

Energy Use and Conservation

Establish Learning Objectives

After this lesson, students will be able to:

🔑 Explain how human energy use has changed over time.

🔑 Name ways to ensure that there will be enough energy for the future.

Engage

Activate Prior Knowledge

MY PLANET DIARY Read *House of Straw* with the class. Invite students to think about whether they have ever seen bales of straw in fields or piled near a barn. Explain that straw is hollow stalks of wheat, rye, or other cereal plants, that are left after the grain has been threshed out. Ask: **What materials used for insulation are less natural and environmentally safe than straw?** *(Much insulation used in exterior walls is made of fiberglass.)*

BIG IDEAS OF SCIENCE REFERENCE LIBRARY 📖
Have students look up the following topics: Energy Conservation, Light Bulbs.

Explore

Lab Resource: Inquiry Warm-Up 🧪

 WHICH BULB IS MORE EFFICIENT?
Students will compare the efficiency of incandescent and fluorescent light bulbs.

> **My Planet Diary** provides an opportunity for students to explore real-world connections to energy use and conservation.
>
> **my science** online.com `Energy Use`

LESSON
3 Energy Use and Conservation

🔑 How Has Energy Use Changed Over Time?

🔑 How Can We Ensure There Will Be Enough Energy for the Future?

my planet Diary   **TECHNOLOGY**

House of Straw

What was that first little pig thinking? Was he just lazy—building a house of straw as quickly as he could without much thought? Or was he helping the environment? It turns out that straw is one of the best materials for keeping warm air inside in cold weather and keeping hot air outside in hot weather. Builders place stacks of straw along the exterior walls of a building and then seal the straw with mud. Bales of straw are natural and cheap, since straw is left over after grain is harvested. It's no wonder that more and more people are using straw to insulate their homes!

Communicate Write your answers below.

1. How does using straw for insulation save energy?
   Sample: People will use less energy to heat and cool their homes.

2. Why is using straw for insulation good for the environment?
   Sample: Straw is cheap, and is a natural and renewable resource.

> **PLANET DIARY** Go to **Planet Diary** to learn more about energy use and conservation.

🧪 Do the Inquiry Warm-Up *Which Bulb Is More Efficient?*

310 Energy Resources

SUPPORT ALL READERS
Lexile Measure = 910L   Lexile Word Count = 960

Prior Exposure to Content: May be the first time students have encountered this topic

Academic Vocabulary: *observe, identify*

Science Vocabulary: *efficiency, energy conservation, insulation*

Concept Level: Generally appropriate for most students in this grade

Preteach With: My Planet Diary "House of Straw" and Figure 1 activity

Go to **My Reading Web** to access leveled readings that provide a foundation for the content.

my science online.com

Vocabulary
• efficiency • insulation
• energy conservation

Skills
Reading: Identify the Main Idea
Inquiry: Observe

How Has Energy Use Changed Over Time?

Energy, beyond using your own muscle power, is essential to the way most people live. The methods people use to obtain energy have changed, especially in the last 200 years. **For most of human history, people burned wood for energy. Only recently have fossil fuels become the main energy source.**

Eventually, people harnessed the power of other renewable resources. Ships used tall sails to capture wind energy. Flowing water turned wheels connected to stones that ground grain into flour.

Wood, wind, and water were also the main sources of energy in the United States until the nineteenth century. Coal gained in popularity as a fuel during the westward expansion of the railroads. Coal remained the dominant fuel until 1951, when it was replaced by oil and natural gas.

Today, scientists are continually looking for new and better fuels to meet the world's energy needs. As fossil fuel supplies continue to decrease, the interest in renewable energy sources has increased. With more focus on protecting the environment, scientists are working to meet our energy needs while reducing and eliminating many sources of pollution.

Identify the Main Idea
Energy use has changed over time. On the timeline, label and shade the periods in which coal and oil were the dominant fuel sources in the United States.

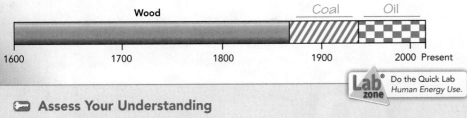

Wood   Coal   Oil

1600   1700   1800   1900   2000   Present

 Do the Quick Lab *Human Energy Use.*

Assess Your Understanding

got it?

○ **I get it!** Now I know that human energy use has *changed over time from mostly wood burning to burning fossil fuels.*

○ **I need extra help with** *See TE note.*

Go to **MY SCIENCE COACH** online for help with this subject.

311

Explain

Introduce Vocabulary

Tell students that the word *efficient* means "bringing about a desired result with the least waste of time, effort, or materials." It is the adjective form of *efficiency.*

Teach Key Concepts

Explain to students that the last few centuries have brought dramatic changes to the way human beings create energy. Ask: **Until about 200 years ago, what did people do to create heat, light, and energy?** *(Burn wood, use energy from wind and water.)* **During the last two centuries, what has become the most common source of energy?** *(Fossil fuels)*

Support the Big Q **UbD**

ENERGY SOURCES Have students look at the timeline. Ask: **What energy source do you think was used before 1600?** *(Wood)* Point out that wind and water were also used before 1600. Ask: **How will future energy sources likely be different from the sources shown on the timeline?** *(They will be renewable sources.)*

Identify the Main Idea Tell students that the main idea is the most important or biggest idea in a paragraph or section of text. The other information in the paragraph or section supports or further explains the main idea.

Elaborate

Lab Resource: Quick Lab

L2 HUMAN ENERGY USE Students will use a graph to analyze how energy and fuels were used during the second half of the 20th century.

Evaluate

Assess Your Understanding

Have students evaluate their understanding by completing the appropriate sentence.

RTI Response to Intervention

Provide additional exercises to reinforce this concept. **If** students have trouble describing changes in energy use, **then** have them locate and read the boldface Key Concept statement for this section.

L1 MY SCIENCE COACH Online remediation to assist students in understanding changes in human energy use.

---

1 Content and Language
Use **Figure 2** to help students understand the high-frequency vocabulary and phrases used to describe ways to conserve energy: *turn off, shut off, open,* and *close.* List these words and phrases to provide a word bank for the writing exercise in **Figure 3.**

2 Frontload the Lesson
Introduce the section by previewing the titles, visuals, and captions. Have

students predict what this section will be about. Make sure that students confirm their predictions after they have read the section.

3 Comprehensible Input
The words *preserve* and *conserve* are sometimes used interchangeably. Explain that to *preserve* something is to make sure it lasts, while to *conserve* something is to use it sparingly or in small amounts.

Explain ————————

Teach Key Concepts

Explain to students that human beings will exhaust the supply of fossil fuels in the future. Ask: **What is the difference between *efficiency* and *conservation* as the terms relate to energy?** *(Sample: Energy conservation means cutting back on the amount of energy we use. Energy efficiency involves improving the percentage of energy used for work.)*

Teach With Visuals

Tell students to look at **Figure 2.** Ask: **What is wasteful about the use of energy in the bathroom, bedroom, and attic of the house?** *(Lights, television, and a computer are left on when not in use.)* **Where is energy being wasted in the kitchen?** *(The refrigerator door has been left open.)*

▲ **Observe** When students use one or more of their five senses to gather information about the world, they are observing. Point out that an observation should be an accurate report of what the senses detect.

21st Century Learning

INFORMATION LITERACY Have students read *Energy Conservation* in the **Big Ideas of Science Reference Library.** Ask students to evaluate scientific claims by reading literature on compact fluorescent light bulbs and comparing a company's claim to information featured on either a government or academic website. Have them share their findings with a partner and submit a consumer alert report.

How Can We Ensure There Will Be Enough Energy for the Future?

What would happen if the world ran out of fossil fuels today? The heating and cooling systems in most buildings would stop functioning. Forests would disappear as people began to burn wood for heating and cooking. Cars, buses, and trains would be stranded wherever they ran out of fuel. About 70 percent of the world's electric power would disappear. Since televisions, computers, and telephones depend on electricity, communication would be greatly reduced. Lights and most home appliances would no longer work.

Although fossil fuels won't run out immediately, they also won't last forever. Most people think that it makes sense to use fuels more wisely now to avoid fuel shortages in the future. ⚷ **One way to preserve our current energy resources is to increase the efficiency of our energy use. Another way is to conserve energy whenever possible.** Refer to **Figure 1.**

FIGURE 1 ....
> **REAL-WORLD INQUIRY** **Wasting Energy**
Many things, such as lights and appliances, use energy. If people do not use these things properly, energy can be wasted.
🔺**Observe** Circle everything in this scene that is wasting energy.

Professional Development Note — Teacher to Teacher

Energy Resources To give historical context to human energy use, I have groups of students research the way(s) people have used energy resources. Early humans used wood to make fires for warmth. During the Renaissance, people learned to use windmills. Modern people use fossil fuels as well as solar, geothermal, tidal, nuclear, and biomass fuel sources. As we discuss natural, renewable, and nonrenewable resources, we further integrate our unit by having students identify civilizations that thrived because of their judicious use of energy resources.

✎ *Leslie Pohley*
Largo Middle School
Largo, Florida

Energy Efficiency One way to make energy resources last longer is to use fuels more efficiently. **Efficiency** is the percentage of energy that is actually used to perform work. The rest of the energy is "lost" to the surroundings, usually as heat. People have developed many ways to increase energy efficiency.

Heating and Cooling One method of increasing the efficiency of heating and cooling systems is insulation. **Insulation** is a layer of material that traps air. This helps block the transfer of heat between the air inside and outside a building. You have probably seen insulation made of fiberglass. It looks like pink cotton candy. A layer of fiberglass 15 centimeters thick insulates a room as well as a brick wall 2 meters thick!

Trapped air can act as insulation in windows too. Many windows consist of two panes of glass with space in between them. The air between the panes of glass acts as insulation.

Lighting Much of the electricity used for home lighting is wasted. For example, less than 10 percent of the electricity that an incandescent light bulb uses is converted into light. The rest is given off as heat. In contrast, compact fluorescent bulbs use about one fourth as much energy to provide the same amount of light.

FIGURE 2 ....
Solutions to Wasting Energy
There are many ways to save energy in a home.
✎ Explain Pick at least three of the things you circled in the scene and explain what people could do to stop wasting energy.

Ways to Conserve Energy

Sample: Wear warmer clothes instead of turning up the heat, turn lights off when you leave the room, and don't leave cars running idle.

313

Lead a Discussion

EFFICIENT USE OF ENERGY Remind students that when we say we are increasing the energy efficiency of a device that consumes energy, we mean that we are increasing the percentage of consumed energy the device uses to do work and decreasing the percentage of consumed energy that is lost to the surroundings. Explain that energy efficiency can be improved in many areas of our lives. Draw a chart on the board that will show types of energy use and ways to increase efficiency. Fill it in as students discuss. Ask: **What is the most common way to improve efficiency of heating and cooling?** *(Adding fiberglass insulation or a layer of air)*

Elaborate ——————

21st Century Learning

ACCOUNTABILITY Look over **Figure 2** with students, noting various details of energy loss in a group discussion. Then ask students to reflect on their own bedroom and their own home in order to make a generalization about how they and their families can better conserve energy. *(Sample: My family and I can better conserve energy by paying more attention to turning off lights and other electrical devices when they are not in use.)*

Real-World Inquiry allows students to explore energy conservation in and around a typical home.

my science online.com ▶ Energy Conservation

Differentiated Instruction

L1 **Identify Energy Efficiency** Pair students having difficulty with those who have a clear concept of energy efficiency. Have each pair of students compile a list of ways to individually improve energy efficiency on a daily basis.

L3 **The National Appliance Energy Conservation Act** Challenge students to find out about the National Appliance Energy Conservation Act, which sets energy-efficiency standards for appliances. As a result of this law, refrigerators built today use at least 80 percent less energy than those built in the 1980s.

Explain

Lead a Discussion

EFFICIENT USE OF ENERGY Continue filling in your chart by discussing energy use for transportation. Ask: **What are some ways that energy efficiency can be improved in transportation?** *(Transportation—better engines and tires, public transportation, carpooling; lighting—using compact fluorescent bulbs)* **How can you personally improve energy efficiency?** *(Take the bus or carpool, check on lighting and heating/cooling at home)* Remind students that the efforts of any one person to conserve energy always make a difference. Invite volunteers to share ways their families save energy at home.

Point out to students what the differences are between the different types of energy efficient vehicles on the market. Electric Vehicles (EVs) operate using an electric motor and rechargeable batteries. Plugging the batteries into an electrical outlet or other electrical source, such as a solar panel, can recharge them. Hybrid-Electric Vehicles (HEVs) combine the small combustion engine of a traditional vehicle with the electric motor and battery of an EV. Plug-in Hybrid-Electric Vehicles (PHEVs) are similar to the HEV, but use much larger batteries. The batteries in a PHEV have a longer all-electric range and can also be recharged by plugging them into an external power source.

Elaborate

Build Inquiry

L2 INTERPRET ILLUSTRATIONS

Materials For each group of students, photocopies of four pictures of energy use taken from newspapers or magazines, markers

Time 15 minutes

Review with students the types of objects and activities that function because of the burning of fossil fuels. Then ask them to use markers to identify particular examples of dramatic energy use and of energy loss in the photographs. Then have the students classify these examples into categories, such as heating and transportation, heating and cooling, lighting, and recreation.

Ask: **Why is it important for each individual to conserve energy and to increase energy efficiency?** *(Sample: If each individual conserves energy and increases energy efficiency in his or her own life, it will dramatically improve the energy situation for the entire planet.)*

Transportation Engineers have improved the energy efficiency of cars by designing better engines and batteries. For instance, many new cars use high-efficiency hybrid engines that go twice as far on a tank of fuel than other cars. Buses in some cities are now entirely electric, running on high-power rechargeable batteries. New kinds of batteries allow some electric cars to drive hundreds of kilometers before recharging.

Another way to save energy is to reduce the number of cars on the road. In many communities, public transit systems provide an alternative to driving. Other cities encourage carpooling and bicycling. Many cities now set aside lanes for cars containing two or more people.

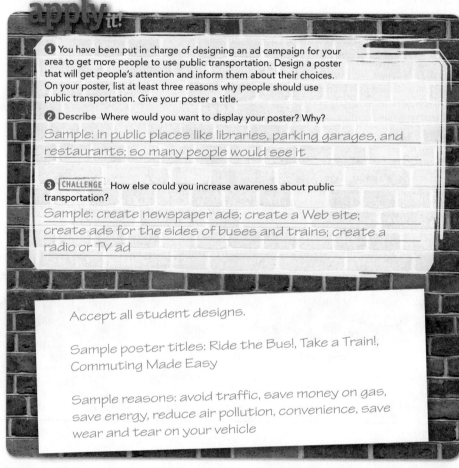

apply it!

1 You have been put in charge of designing an ad campaign for your area to get more people to use public transportation. Design a poster that will get people's attention and inform them about their choices. On your poster, list at least three reasons why people should use public transportation. Give your poster a title.

2 Describe Where would you want to display your poster? Why?

Sample: in public places like libraries, parking garages, and restaurants; so many people would see it

3 CHALLENGE How else could you increase awareness about public transportation?

Sample: create newspaper ads; create a Web site; create ads for the sides of buses and trains; create a radio or TV ad

Accept all student designs.

Sample poster titles: Ride the Bus!, Take a Train!, Commuting Made Easy

Sample reasons: avoid traffic, save money on gas, save energy, reduce air pollution, convenience, save wear and tear on your vehicle

Digital Lesson: Assign the *Apply It* activity online and have students submit their work to you.

my science online.com | Energy Conservation

Energy Conservation Another approach to making energy resources last longer is conservation. **Energy conservation** means reducing energy use.

You can reduce your personal energy use by changing your behavior in some simple ways. For example, if you walk to the store instead of getting a ride, you are conserving the gasoline it would take to drive to the store.

While these suggestions seem like small things, multiplied by millions of people they add up to a lot of energy saved for the future.

Sample: I could walk or ride my bike on short trips, recycle, use fans instead of air conditioners, and turn off lights and the television when I leave a room.

FIGURE 3 ·······················
Energy Conservation in Your Everyday Life
Even students like you can conserve energy.
✎ **Communicate** With a partner, think of ways you can conserve energy in your daily life. Write your answers in the notebook.

Lab zone ® Do the Quick Lab *Future Energy Use.*

🔑 **Assess Your Understanding**

1a. Define What does it mean to say that something is "energy efficient"?
Sample: It means that when compared to other products, more energy is used to perform work and is not lost to heat.

b. Solve Problems What are some strategies a city could use to increase energy conservation?
Sample: Invest in good public transportation and encourage energy-efficient building development.

got it? ·······················
○ **I get it!** Now I know that ensuring that the future has enough energy requires _increasing energy efficiency and conserving energy whenever possible._

○ **I need extra help with** _See TE note._

Go to MY SCIENCE ⑤ COACH *online for help with this subject.*

315

Lab zone® **After the Inquiry Warm-Up**

Energy Use and Conservation

Inquiry Warm-Up, *Which Bulb Is More Efficient?*
In the Inquiry Warm-Up, you investigated differences in efficiency between incandescent and fluorescent light bulbs. Using what you learned from that activity, answer the questions below.

1. **CALCULATE** You use only incandescent bulbs in your home, and your electric bill is $200. About how much will your bill be if you switch and use only fluorescent light bulbs? Base your answer on your response to question 2 in the Inquiry Warm-Up. Use the space below for your work if necessary.

_____

2. **INFER** Which type of light bulb is best to use in an aquarium with fish that are very sensitive to high temperatures? Explain.

_____

_____

3. **DRAW CONCLUSIONS** Which light bulb, a 40-watt fluorescent or a 40-watt incandescent, uses less energy? Which uses more energy? Explain.

_____

_____

_____

4. **PREDICT** Of the two 40-watt light bulbs in question 3 above, which would be brighter? Explain.

_____

_____

_____

Name _____ Date _____ Class _____

Energy Use and Conservation

> ## How Has Energy Use Changed Over Time?

got it? ··

○ **I get it!** Now I know that human energy use has _____

_____

○ **I need extra help with** _____

_____

> ## How Can We Ensure There Will Be Enough Energy for the Future?

1a. DEFINE What does it mean to say that something is "energy efficient"? _____

_____

_____

b. SOLVE PROBLEMS What are some strategies a city could use to increase energy conservation? _____

_____

_____

got it? ··

○ **I get it!** Now I know that ensuring that the future has enough energy requires _____

_____

○ **I need extra help with** _____

_____

Name _____ Date _____ Class _____

Energy Use and Conservation

How Has Energy Use Changed Over Time?

For most of human history, people burned wood for light, heat, and energy. Only recently have fossil fuels become the main energy source. For 200 years, wood, wind, and water were the main sources of energy in the American colonies that became the United States. Ships used sails to capture wind energy, and mills used flowing water to turn wheels and grind grain into flour. Then, in the nineteenth century, coal gained in popularity with the westward expansion of the railroads. Coal remained the dominant fuel until 1951, when it was replaced by oil and natural gas. As fossil fuel supplies decrease, interest in renewable energy sources has increased.

How Can We Ensure There Will Be Enough Energy for the Future?

If the world ran out of fossil fuels suddenly, most heating and cooling systems would stop functioning. Cars, buses, and trains would be useless. And because about 70 percent of the world's electric power would disappear, lights and most home appliances would no longer work. Communications—through televisions, computers, and telephones—would also be greatly reduced.

People have begun to take steps to try to use fuels more wisely as scientists seek new and better fuels. **One way to preserve our current energy resources is to increase the efficiency of our energy use. Another way is to conserve energy whenever possible.** One way to make energy resources last longer is to use fuels more efficiently. **Efficiency** is the percentage of energy that is actually used to perform work. The rest of the energy is "lost" to the surroundings, usually as heat. **Insulation,** a layer of material that traps air, is used to increase the efficiency of heating and cooling systems. Compact fluorescent light bulbs provide the same amount of light as incandescent bulbs but use about one fourth as much energy. Energy can be saved by reducing the number of motor vehicles on the road and the number of miles people drive, and by designing better engines and tires. Another way to make energy resources last longer is conservation. **Energy conservation** means reducing energy use.

Is interest in renewable resources new to the United States? Write and explain your answer on a separate sheet of paper.

Name _____ Date _____ Class _____

Energy Use and Conservation

Understanding Main Ideas
Answer the following questions in the spaces provided.

1. Until the nineteenth century, what were the three main sources of energy in the United States?

   _____

2. In the last two hundred years, what fuels have people used most?

   _____

3. Why are scientists looking for new fuels to replace fossil fuels?

   _____

   _____

4. What is energy efficiency, and why is increasing it important?

   _____

   _____

5. Why is a compact fluorescent light bulb more efficient than an incandescent bulb?

   _____

   _____

6. How can insulation in a building save energy?

   _____

   _____

Building Vocabulary
Fill in the blank to complete each statement.

7. _____ is the percentage of energy used to perform work.

8. A layer of material that traps air is _____.

9. Energy _____ means reducing energy use.

Place the outside corner, the corner away from the dotted line, in the corner of your copy machine to copy onto letter-size paper.

Enrich

Energy Use and Conservation

For a school project, Arturo Diaz wants to find out how much energy his family's home uses in a month. Their furnace uses oil. Their water heater and stove use natural gas. The table shows the data that Arturo collected for the month. Complete the table. On a separate sheet of paper, answer the questions that follow the table.

One Family's Household Energy Use

Energy Use Data

Energy Source	Meter/Gauge Readings		Difference in Readings
	Sept. 15	Oct. 15	
Electricity	76, 854 kWh	77,638 kWh	1.
Natural Gas	14, 786 ft³	15,073 ft³	2.
Fuel Oil	full tank (200 gal.)	3/4 tank (150 gal.)	3.

4. How many BTUs of electricity did the Diaz family use? (1 kWh = 3,413 BTUs)

5. How many BTUs of natural gas did the Diaz family use? (1 ft³ of gas produces 100 BTUs)

6. How many BTUs of fuel oil did the Diaz family use? (1 gallon of oil produces 144,000 BTUs)

7. What was the Diaz family's total energy use for the month from these three sources?

8. Calculate the percentage of each energy use.

9. Draw and label a circle graph to show the percentage of each energy use. (*Hint:* Divide the BTUs for each use by the total BTUs. Multiply each percentage by 360° to determine the arc of each wedge.)

Name _____ Date _____ Class _____

Energy Use and Conservation

Fill in the blank(s) to complete each statement.

1. Only recently have _____ become the main energy source in the U.S.

2. In the nineteenth century, with the westward expansion of railroads, _____ gained in popularity as a fuel.

3. One way to preserve our current energy resources is to increase the _____ of our energy use.

4. Another way to preserve those resources is to _____ energy whenever possible.

If the statement is true, write _true_. If the statement is false, change the underlined word or words to make the statement true.

5. _____ For most of human history, people <u>burned wood</u> for light, heat, and energy.

6. _____ In addition, people harnessed the power of renewable resources such as <u>wind and water</u>.

7. _____ In the mid-twentieth century, <u>wood and water</u> joined coal as the dominant fuels.

8. _____ As fossil fuel supplies decrease, interest has increased in looking for <u>nonrenewable</u> energy sources.

9. _____ <u>Insulation</u> is the percentage of energy that is actually used to perform work.

10. _____ <u>Energy conservation</u> means reducing energy use.

Energy Use and Conservation

Answer Key

After the Inquiry Warm-Up

1. about $50

2. A fluorescent light bulb is better to use because it gives off less heat for about the same amount of light.

3. Sample: They use the same amount of energy. The amount of energy used by a light bulb is expressed by its wattage. Since both bulbs have the same wattage, they use the same amount of energy.

4. The fluorescent bulb will be brighter because it is more efficient, giving off less energy as heat, than the incandescent light bulb.

Key Concept Summaries

For most of human history, people used renewable resources—wood, water, and wind—for light, heat, and energy. The use of fossil fuels has dominated people's energy use for the last two centuries. Today, people are growing interested again in renewable resources, since fossil fuel supplies are decreasing.

Review and Reinforce

1. wood, wind, and water

2. coal, oil, and natural gas

3. Fossil fuels are not renewable. Supplies are decreasing and will run out some day. Fossil fuels are also a major cause of pollution.

4. Energy efficiency is the percentage of energy that is used to perform work. Increasing energy efficiency is important because people and devices can use less energy to perform the same amount of work.

5. Compact fluorescent light bulbs use about one fourth as much energy to produce the same amount of light as an incandescent bulb.

6. Insulation helps block the transfer of heat between the air inside and outside a building. It saves energy by keeping the building cool in summer and warm in the winter.

7. Efficiency

8. insulation

9. conservation

Enrich

1. 784 kWh

2. 28,700 ft³

3. 50 gal

4. 2,675,792

5. 28,700,000

6. 7,200,000

7. 38,575,792

8. Natural gas, 74%; fuel oil, 19%; electricity, 7%.

9. Based on the percentages, wedge sizes are 266° for natural gas, 86° for fuel oil, and 25° for electricity—for a total of 359°. Sizes must be adjusted to total 360°.

Lesson Quiz

1. fossil fuels

2. coal

3. efficiency

4. conserve

5. true

6. true

7. oil and natural gas

8. renewable

9. Efficiency

10. true

Place the outside corner, the corner away from the dotted line, in the corner of your copy machine to copy onto letter-size paper.

Study Guide

Review the Big Q UbD

Have students complete the statement at the top of the page. These Key Concepts support their understanding of the chapter's Big Question. Have them return to the chapter opener pages. What is different about how students view the image of the wind turbine now that they have completed the chapter? Thinking about this will help them prepare for the *Apply the Big Q* activity in the Review and Assessment.

Partner Review

Have students review definitions of vocabulary terms by using the Study Guide to quiz each other. Students can read the Key Concept statements and leave out words for their partner to fill in, or change a statement so that it is false and then ask their partner to correct it.

Class Activity: Concept Map

Have students work in three groups to develop concept maps to show how the information in this chapter is related. Each group can focus on one lesson, brainstorming to identify Key Concepts, vocabulary, and examples and other details. Encourage each group to create its map on chart or poster paper using sticky notes. Explain that each concept map should begin at the top with Key Concepts. After each group has finished its work, bring the groups together to analyze how the maps relate to one another. Ask students to use the following questions to help them organize the information on their sticky notes:

• What are the three major fossil fuels?
• What is a nonrenewable resource?
• What are some renewable sources of energy?
• What have human beings used as fuel sources during the course of history?
• What steps can human beings take to preserve current energy resources?

My Science Coach allows students to complete the *Practice Test* online.

The Big Question allows students to complete the *Apply the Big Q* activity about what some of Earth's energy sources are.

Vocab Flash Cards offer a way to review the chapter vocabulary words.

my science online.com ▶ **Energy Resources**

REVIEW THE BIG ? Earth has many energy sources, including <u>fossil fuels</u> such as coal; the sun, which can be used for <u>solar energy</u>; and flowing water, which can be used for hydroelectric power.

LESSON 1 Fossil Fuels

🔑 The three major fossil fuels are coal, oil, and natural gas.

🔑 Since fossil fuels take hundreds of millions of years to form, they are considered nonrenewable resources.

Vocabulary
• fuel   • fossil fuel
• hydrocarbon
• petroleum   • refinery
• petrochemical

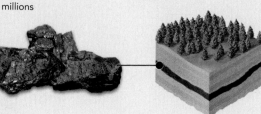

LESSON 2 Renewable Sources of Energy

🔑 Renewable sources of energy include sunlight, water, wind, nuclear power, biomass fuels, geothermal energy, and hydrogen.

🔑 In a nuclear power plant, the heat released from fission reactions is used to change water into steam. The steam then turns the blades of a turbine to generate electricity.

Vocabulary
• solar energy   • hydroelectric power   • biomass fuel   • gasohol
• geothermal energy   • nuclear fission
• reactor vessel   • fuel rod   • control rod

LESSON 3 Energy Use and Conservation

🔑 For most of human history, the main fuel source was wood. Only recently have fossil fuels become the main energy source.

🔑 One way to preserve our current energy resources is to increase the efficiency of our energy use. Another way is to conserve energy whenever possible.

Vocabulary
• efficiency   • insulation   • energy conservation

ELL Support

4 Language Production

Divide the class into small groups to create a poster or flyer promoting energy conservation at home and in school. Students should work together to create visually-engaging posters that persuade students to take a more active role in conserving energy.

Beginning
LOW/HIGH Allow students to work on the visuals for the posters.

Intermediate
LOW/HIGH Permit students to refer to their books or notes during the discussion.

Advanced
LOW/HIGH Have students write the text and captions for the poster.

Review and Assessment

LESSON 1 · Fossil Fuels

1. What is one similarity among oil, coal, and natural gas?

  a. They are all petrochemicals.

  b. They all must be processed in a refinery.

  c. They are all gases at room temperature.

  (d.) They are all formed from the remains of dead organisms.

2. Fossil fuels take hundreds of millions of years to form, and therefore are considered <u>nonrenewable</u> energy sources.

3. Compare and Contrast Describe one main use for each fuel: coal, oil, and natural gas.

<u>Sample: Coal can be used to produce electricity, oil can power vehicles, natural gas can be used in stoves.</u>

4. Sequence How does coal form?

<u>Sample: Coal forms from decomposing plant matter. Over time, the plant matter turns into peat under pressure. With more time and pressure, the peat becomes coal.</u>

5. Write About It Imagine a day without fossil fuels. Describe your day, from when you wake up until when you eat lunch. Identify each time you would have used energy from fossil fuels.

See TE rubric.

LESSON 2 · Renewable Sources of Energy

6. Which of the following is not a biomass fuel?

  a. gasohol   **b.** methane from landfills

  (c.) hydrogen   **d.** sugar cane wastes

7. Running water can be used as an energy source to produce <u>hydroelectric</u> power.

8. Apply Concepts Fill in the boxes with two benefits and two costs of hydrogen power.

Benefits	Costs
Sample: exists in large supply; does not cause smog	Sample: requires a lot of energy; expensive to produce

9. Interpret Photos Explain how a nuclear power plant, like the one pictured below, produces energy.

<u>Sample: Nuclear fission reactions generate heat. The heat turns water into steam. The steam turns turbines that generate electricity.</u>

Review and Assessment

Assess Understanding

Have students complete the answers to the Review and Assessment questions. Have a class discussion about what students find confusing. Write Key Concepts on the board to reinforce knowledge.

RTI Response to Intervention

1. If students need help explaining fossil fuels, **then** have them use their knowledge of the word *fossil* to remember that fossil fuels are formed from the decomposing matter of once-living organisms.

9. If students cannot explain how a power plant produces energy, **then** have them review **Figure 7**.

Alternate Assessment

L1 DESIGN FOR THE FUTURE Have students use a pencil, drawing paper, and a ruler as they design a home or a car of the future that operates entirely on renewable energy sources. Students should apply the concepts they have learned about the types of renewable energy sources that exist, the technology required to make practical use of those sources, and the sources' advantages over fossil fuels.

Write About It	Assess student's writing using this rubric.

SCORING RUBRIC	SCORE 4	SCORE 3	SCORE 2	SCORE 1
Describe day from waking to lunch	Student describes day from waking to lunch in vivid detail.	Student describes day from waking to lunch without much detail.	Student describes part of time between waking to lunch.	Student does not describe a day from waking to lunch.
Identify each time writer would have used fossil fuels	Student identifies every time he or she would have used fossil fuels.	Student identifies many times he or she would have used fossil fuels.	Student identifies a few times he or she would have used fossil fuels.	Student does not identify times he or she would have used fossil fuels.

RTI Response to Intervention

12. If students have trouble drawing a conclusion, **then** have them review the timeline.

Apply the Big Q ? UbD

TRANSFER Students should be able to demonstrate understanding of Earth's energy sources by answering this question. See the scoring rubric below.

Connect to the Big Idea ? UbD

BIG IDEA Living things interact with their environment.

Send students back to the Big Ideas of Science at the beginning of their student edition. Have them read what they wrote about interactions of living things and their environment before they started the chapter. Lead a class discussion about how their thoughts have changed. If all chapters have been completed, have students fill in the bottom section for the Big Idea.

L3 WRITING IN SCIENCE Ask students to write a blog entry about how this chapter's Big Question relates to the Big idea.

LESSON 3 Energy Use and Conservation

10. What is efficiency?

   a. the percentage of energy that is lost to the environment as heat

   b. the percentage of energy that is used to perform work

   c. the percentage of energy that is conserved when work is done

   d. the percentage of energy that is wasted when electronics are left on

11. <u>Energy conservation</u> involves using less energy, helping energy resources last longer.

12. Draw Conclusions How is energy use today different from energy use 200 years ago?
<u>Sample: Two hundred years ago, people mainly used wood to power their lives. Today, most energy comes from burning fossil fuels.</u>

13. Solve Problems Describe three actions a person can take to conserve energy.
<u>Sample: walk or bike instead of using a car, wear warmer clothing instead of turning up the heat, turn lights off when leaving a room</u>

APPLY THE BIG ? What are some of Earth's energy sources?

14. Earth's energy sources include both renewable and nonrenewable resources. Name at least three sources of energy that could be used in a classroom like the one below. Then describe the ideal energy source for generating most of your school's electricity and explain why you chose this source.

<u>Sample: Solar energy could be used to power the calculators. Natural gas or oil could be used to heat the building. Some of the electricity could be generated by wind power. I think wind power is an ideal source of energy for my school because it does not cause air pollution and I live in a windy area. See TE rubric.</u>

? What are some of Earth's energy sources?
Assess student's response using this rubric.

SCORING RUBRIC	SCORE 4	SCORE 3	SCORE 2	SCORE 1
Name three sources of energy	Student names more than three sources of energy.	Student names three sources of energy.	Student names one or two sources of energy.	Student does not name sources of energy.
Describe ideal energy source and explain choice	Describes ideal energy source in detail with thorough explanation	Describes ideal energy source in some detail with brief explanation	Describes ideal energy source with incomplete explanation	Does not describe source and gives no explanation

Standardized Test Prep

Multiple Choice

Circle the letter of the best answer.

1. Which statement is best supported by the table below?

2007 Global Oil Production and Use

Country	Oil production global rank	Oil use global rank
United States	3	1
Russia	1	6
China	5	3
Brazil	15	8

- A Brazil produces more oil than China.
- (B) Russia produces the most oil.
- C China consumes the most oil.
- D The United States consumes and produces the most oil in the world.

2. Which of the following is not a fossil fuel?
- A oil
- B coal
- C natural gas
- (D) wood

3. The interior of a car heats up on a sunny day because of
- A solar cells.
- B active solar heating.
- (C) passive solar heating.
- D direct solar heating.

4. Which explains why systems that transform energy are not completely efficient?
- A Increasing energy resources increases efficiency.
- B Doing less work gives off more heat.
- (C) Some energy is converted to heat that flows to surrounding material.
- D An increase in the amount of energy is needed to generate electricity.

5. How does a nuclear power plant produce energy?
- A with solar panels
- (B) through nuclear fission reactions
- C with geothermal heat
- D through nuclear meltdown reactions

Constructed Response

Use the diagram below and your knowledge of science to help you answer Question 6. Write your answer on a separate sheet of paper.

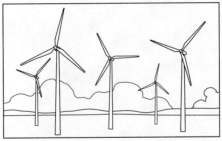

6. Describe how energy is produced in the diagram above. Then, describe one advantage and one disadvantage of this source.
See TE note.

Standardized Test Prep

Test-Taking Skills

INTERPRETING TABLES Tell students that when they answer questions like Question 1, which include tables, they should read all parts of the table carefully, including the title, the labels of vertical columns and horizontal rows, and the numbers. Point out that students should clarify the table's information in their own minds before reviewing how the table relates to the question as a whole.

Constructed Response

6. Wind turns the blades of the turbine. The turbine is connected to a generator. As the turbine turns, the generator creates electricity. Wind energy does not create air pollution like burning fossil fuels such as oil or coal. Wind turbines are loud, and some people may think they are unattractive on the landscape. They can also interrupt bird migrations.

Additional Assessment Resources

Chapter Test
EXAMVIEW® Assessment Suite
Performance Assessment
Progress Monitoring Assessments
SuccessTracker™

Remediate If students have trouble with...

QUESTION	SEE LESSON	STANDARDS
1	3	
2	1	
3	2	
4	3	
5	2	
6	2	

Science Matters

Think Like a Scientist

Have students read *How Low Is Low-Impact?*
Point out that technologies that are genuinely
low-impact generally collect energy from natural
renewable resources. For example, hydroelectric
dams harness the power of running rivers and turn
it into electricity. There is some initial impact on the
environment associated with the dam's construction,
but this is usually quickly offset by the amount of
energy produced by the dam.

Hybrid cars are an example of a product that claims
to be low-impact. They run primarily on electricity,
which means they do not rely on fossil fuels to power
them and do not produce pollution by burning those
fossil fuels. However the electricity used to power
these cars is often generated by burning coal or oil.
A truly low-impact mode of transportation that can
be used by everyone has not been invented yet, so
hybrid cars are a good step in the right direction,
since they generally use less fossil fuels.

As students discuss the costs and benefits of low-
impact technologies, suggest they make a two-
column list to organize their arguments for and
against. Remind them that time and money could
be considered costs of these technologies. If a
technology takes a long time to invent or is too
expensive for most people to use, it makes it less
viable.

Ask: **What are some examples of truly low-
impact technologies?** *(Sample: solar power,
wind power, hydroelectric power)* **What makes
a technology truly low-impact?** *(It provides
energy without having a harmful impact on the
environment.)*

SCIENCE MATTERS

Think Like a Scientist

How Low Is Low Impact?

▲ This electric car is charged
by attaching an electric
cord to an outlet. However,
the source of the electricity
may be a fossil fuel-based
power plant.

Hybrid engines, windmills, low-impact this,
alternative-energy that—everywhere you look,
people are trying to find ways to create energy by
using renewable resources. Sometimes, a technology
seems to conserve energy, but in reality it has hidden
costs. For example, electric cars do not release air
pollutants during use, but the method that is used
to generate the electricity for the car may cause
pollution. Is the electricity really "clean"?

Evaluating the costs and benefits of different
technologies is an important scientific skill. Use
the following questions to sharpen your decision-
making skills.

What is the source? What materials are used to
create or power the technology? How are they
obtained?

What are the products? What is produced when
the technology is created or used? How do these
products affect the environment? How are these
products stored, recycled, or disposed of?

How does it affect our lives? Does using a
technology encourage people to use more energy?
If it does, do the benefits of the technology
outweigh the environmental costs?

Every technology has costs and benefits. However, it
is important to be able to evaluate new technologies
to find out if the benefits outweigh the costs!

Write About It In a group, discuss the questions
listed above. Can you think of ways to add to them
or to change them? Then, create an Environmental
Decision-Making Guide and use it to evaluate two of
the energy technologies described in this chapter.

Quick Facts

You've probably seen a farm where crops are grown. You've probably seen
a farm where animals are raised. But have you seen a farm where wind is
farmed and energy is the result? On the land of a wind farm there are tall
fan-like structures called wind turbines. The wind turns the blades of these
turbines and the energy collected is sent to a generator to be converted to
electricity. Wind is a completely clean source of energy that doesn't pollute.
Wind is also a renewable resource. However, winds are not always reliable,
wind energy cannot be stored, and often wind farms are in rural areas far from
the cities that require the electricity. Scientists are hard at work to improve the
efficiency and use of wind power. Have students research where the closest
wind farm is and how their area might benefit from its energy.

Life on an Oil Rig

OFFSHORE PETROLEUM ENGINEER

This professional's office is on a huge steel platform that is half the area of a football field, surrounded by water. With much of Earth's oil located under the ocean floor, petroleum engineers must go where the oil is. Many of them work on offshore oil rigs—large drilling platforms that extract oil from under the ocean floor.

Conditions far out in the the ocean can be harsh or dangerous. Large equipment, fires, and even hurricanes threaten workers' safety. However, far out in the ocean, workers on oil rigs can see sharks, manta rays, and other marine life.

Petroleum engineers study geology, physics, and chemistry to understand the properties of rock formations that contain oil. They use high-tech remote sensing equipment to find oil and computer modeling software to figure out how to get the oil out of the ocean's floor.

Write About It Find out more about life on an offshore oil rig. Then, write a diary or blog entry that describes a week in the life of an offshore petroleum engineer.

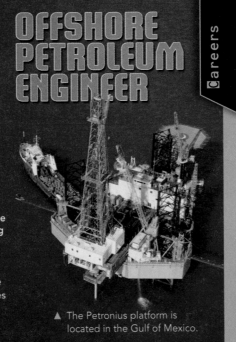
▲ The Petronius platform is located in the Gulf of Mexico.

Hydrokinetic Energy

Whirlpool! Maelstrom! Vortex! Do these words make you think of a rushing spiral of water, sucking fish and boats into its center? Not all vortexes sink ships. Fish and whales cause little vortexes when they swim. As the animals move, they create turbulence in the water. Turbulent water moves away from the animal and gives it a little push.

An engineer named Michael Bernitsas has developed a device that uses this effect to generate electricity. As currents push water around a cylindrical device, a vortex forms. As the vortex moves away from the device, the cylinder moves up and down. The device then converts that mechanical energy into electrical energy. Bernitsas has even improved the device by adding mechanical "fish tails" to the generators! Bernitsas is still testing his system, but he hopes that it can someday be used to help meet society's needs for a renewable source of energy.

Design It Find out more about how fish swim. Then, design a model that shows how the body of a fish moves in the water. In your model, show where a vortex would form as the fish swims.

321

Careers

Have students read *Offshore Petroleum Engineer*. Point out that because most of Earth's surface is covered by water, it makes sense that a lot of its oil would be beneath the ocean floor. Oil rig workers work out at sea for months.

Petroleum engineers are responsible for finding safe and environmentally responsible ways to extract the oil from the sea floor. As students work on their diary or blog entries, have them think about what fields of science they might need to think about.

Ask: **What are some factors that might make drilling for oil at sea different than on land?** *(Sample: the movement of the ocean, the water pressure)* **Why do petroleum engineers use remote equipment to study the sea floor?** *(The sea floor is a great distance below the surface in some places and they cannot study it in person.)*

Frontiers of Technology

Have students read *Hydrokinetic Energy*. Explain that turbulence in the water is much like turbulence in the air. Turbulent air pushes on the object moving through it. Ask students if they have ever been on an airplane that experienced turbulence.

When an object sinks into the water, a vortex is created around it. The power of this vortex can draw other things down into the water. That is why rescue or salvage boats must be careful when working near a boat that is sinking.

Ask: **Aside from an object moving through the water, what is another cause of vortexes?** *(Sample: weather phenomenons can cause vortexes to form.)* **How do you think the addition of fish tails help the cylindrical device developed by Bernitsas?** *(Sample: There are more moving parts so there are more places for vortexes to form.)*

Water

Introduce the Big Q ? UbD

Have students look at the image and read the Engaging Question and description. Ask them to write a hypothesis to explain where the water in the river came from and where it is going. Point out that, depending on where the river is located, the water may join with other rivers and become an even larger river or it might empty directly into the ocean. Ask: **Where does the water that flows out of your kitchen faucet come from?** *(Answers will vary depending on the water sources in your community. Some communities get water from local or distant reservoirs. Some individual homes rely on well water.)* **How do people get water from the ground?** *(Students familiar with wells will say that a hole is drilled in the ground down to the water table. The water is then pumped to the surface.)* **Where does the water in reservoirs and in the ground come from?** *(It comes from rain, snow, and other forms of precipitation.)*

Untamed Science Video

WATER CYCLISTS Before viewing, invite students to discuss bodies of water in or near your town or city. Then play the video. Lead a class discussion and make a list of questions that the video raises. You may wish to have students view the video again after they have completed the chapter to see if their questions have been answered.

> **To access the online resources for this chapter, search on or navigate to *Water*.**
>
> **Untamed Science Video** explains about water on Earth.
>
> **The Big Question** allows students to answer the Engaging Question about the water cycle on Earth.
>
> my science online.com `Water`

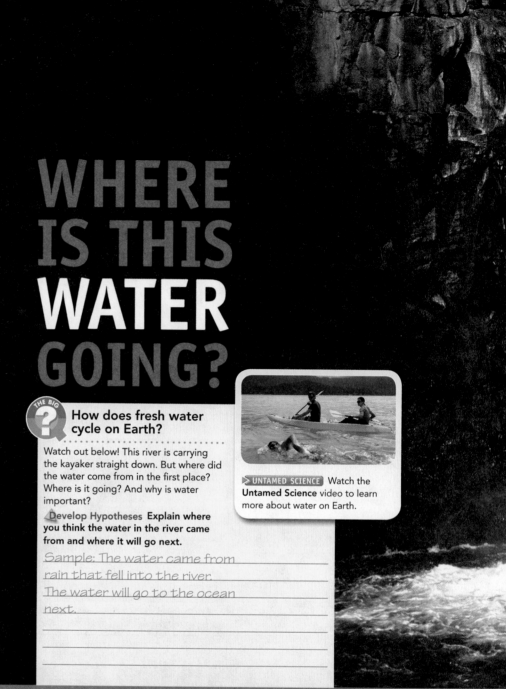

WHERE IS THIS WATER GOING?

THE BIG ?

How does fresh water cycle on Earth?

Watch out below! This river is carrying the kayaker straight down. But where did the water come from in the first place? Where is it going? And why is water important?

Develop Hypotheses Explain where you think the water in the river came from and where it will go next.

Sample: The water came from rain that fell into the river. The water will go to the ocean next.

> **UNTAMED SCIENCE** Watch the **Untamed Science** video to learn more about water on Earth.

Professional Development Note **From the Author**

Earth is the "water planet." We know of no other planet like it. The conditions required for water to coexist in all three phases (solid, liquid, gas) continuously for four billion years on a planet's surface are so remarkably stringent that there may be no other planet like Earth in the Milky Way. Fresh water is rapidly becoming a critical resource in very short supply. Roughly a third of the world's population goes to bed thirsty each night with either insufficient or inadequate water supplies. Wars may someday be fought over water.

✏ *Michael Wysession*

CHAPTER

Water 10

Chapter at a Glance

CHAPTER PACING: 10–16 periods or 5–8 blocks

INTRODUCE THE CHAPTER: Use the Engaging Question and the opening image to get students thinking about water. Activate prior knowledge and preteach vocabulary using the Getting Started pages.

Lesson 1: Water on Earth

Lesson 2: Surface Water

Lesson 3: Water Underground

Lesson 4: Exploring the Ocean

Lesson 5: Wave Action

Lesson 6: Currents and Climate

ASSESSMENT OPTIONS: Chapter Test, **EXAM**VIEW® Assessment Suite, Performance Assessment, Progress Monitoring Assessments, SuccessTracker™

Preference Navigator, in the online Planning tools, allows you to customize *Interactive Science* to your own teaching style. You can also edit lesson plans by selecting the Lesson Planner option.

Digital Teacher's Edition allows you to access your Teacher's Edition and Resource materials online.

my science online

CHAPTER 10

Differentiated Instruction

L1 Sequence Help students understand the sequential nature of continuous cycles. Explain that living things, such as plants, have events that occur in a certain order, or sequence, in their life cycles. Make simple drawings on separate index cards to show the stages of a plant life cycle (seed, seedling, flowering plant). Place the cards on a table and have students make paper arrows to link the drawings, showing they represent stages in continuous cycles.

L3 Rivers Have students research a major river of the world (Mississippi, Nile, Amazon, Yellow, and so on). Students should include information about the physical characteristics of the river, as well as information about the role the river plays in people's lives.

Getting Started

Check Your Understanding

This activity assesses students' understanding of how water vapor condenses into a liquid. After students have shared their answers, point out this is only part of the water cycle. Because the cycle is a continual process, water in its liquid form also evaporates into water vapor in the air. Ask students what the temperature is like on a misty day. Then ask them what happens to the water on the glass when the temperature rises. Lead them to connect that the state water exists in during each phase of the water cycle is related to the temperature of the air around the water.

Preteach Vocabulary Skills

Draw students' attention to the vocabulary listed in the *Chapter Preview*. Have students find the words that end in -*ation* and have them circle each one. (*Evaporation, transpiration, precipitation, eutrophication.*) Ask students to name some everyday words that have this same ending. (*Transportation, invitation, preparation, sanitation*)

---

10 Getting Started

Check Your Understanding

1. Background Read the paragraph below and then answer the question.

Have you ever sat at a window on a misty day? You might see **condensation** as drops of water form on the glass. These drops form when **water vapor** in the air cools and turns into a liquid. **Gravity** pulls the drops down the windowpane toward Earth's surface.

> **Condensation** occurs when a substance changes from a gas to a liquid.
>
> **Water vapor** is water in the gaseous state.
>
> **Gravity** is a force that attracts all objects toward each other.

• How do water drops form on the window?

  Water vapor in the air cools and
  condenses as a liquid on the glass.

> **MY READING WEB** If you had trouble completing the question above, visit **My Reading Web** and type in *Fresh Water*.

Vocabulary Skill

Latin Word Origins Many science words come to English from Latin. In this chapter you will learn the term *permeable*. *Permeable* comes from the Latin word parts *per-*, meaning "through"; *meare*, meaning "to go" or "to pass"; and *-bilis*, meaning "capable of."

$$\underset{\text{through}}{per\text{-}} + \underset{\text{go or pass}}{meare} + \underset{\text{capable of}}{\text{-}bilis} = \underset{\text{capable of going through}}{permeable}$$

Learn these Latin word parts to help you remember the vocabulary terms.

Latin Origin	Meaning	Example
trans-	across	transpiration, *n.*
spirare	to breathe	transpiration, *n.*
vapor	steam	evaporation, *n.*
videre	to separate	divide, *v.*

2. Quick Check Use the table to answer the question.

• Based on the table, predict the meaning of *transpiration*.

  Sample: breathing across

My Reading Web offers leveled readings related to chapter content.

Vocab Flash Cards offer extra practice with the chapter vocabulary words.

Digital Lesson

• Assign the *Check Your Understanding* activity online and have students submit their work to you.

• Assign the *Vocabulary Skill* activity online and have students submit their work to you.

my science online.com Water

groundwater

water cycle

wave

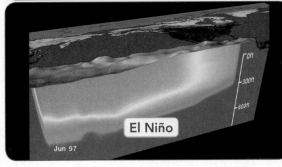
El Niño
Jun 97

Chapter Preview

LESSON 1
- habitat • groundwater
- water cycle • evaporation
- transpiration • precipitation
- Identify the Main Idea
- Observe

LESSON 2
- tributary • watershed
- divide • reservoir
- eutrophication
- Sequence
- Form Operational Definitions

LESSON 3
- permeable • impermeable
- unsaturated zone
- saturated zone • water table
- aquifer • artesian well
- Relate Cause and Effect
- Predict

LESSON 4
- salinity • sonar • seamount
- trench • continental slope
- continental shelf • abyssal plain
- mid-ocean ridge
- Identify the Main Idea
- Interpret Data

LESSON 5
- wave • wavelength • frequency
- wave height • tsunami
- longshore drift • rip current
- groin
- Relate Cause and Effect
- Form Operational Definitions

LESSON 6
- current • Coriolis effect
- climate • El Niño • La Niña
- Compare and Contrast
- Infer

> **VOCAB FLASH CARDS** For extra help with vocabulary, visit **Vocab Flash Cards** and type in *Water.*

325

Preview Vocabulary Terms

Have students create their own science glossaries for the vocabulary terms in this chapter. Be sure to discuss and analyze each term before students add it to their glossaries. As the class progresses through the chapter, students can include additional information that relates to the term or the concept it describes. A list of Academic Vocabulary for each lesson can be found in the Support All Readers box at the start of the lesson.

L1 Have students look at the images on this page as you pronounce the vocabulary word. Have students repeat the word after you. Then read the definition. Use the sample sentence in italics to clarify the meaning of the term.

groundwater *(GROWND Waw tur)* Water that fills the cracks and spaces in underground soil and rock layers. *Most of Earth's fresh water exists as groundwater, not surface water.*

water cycle *(WAW tur SY kul)* The continuous process by which water moves from Earth's surface to the atmosphere and back, driven by gravity and energy from the sun. *The total amount of water moving through Earth's water cycle has stayed fairly constant over millions of years.*

wave *(wayv)* The movement of energy through a body of water. *An ocean wave forms as a result of wind blowing over the water's surface.*

El Niño *(el NEEN yoh)* A climate event that occurs every two to seven years in the Pacific Ocean. *El Niño can cause weather hazards such as heavy rains, flooding, and tornadoes.*

CHAPTER 10

ELL Support

Have students complete the **Preview Vocabulary Terms** activity either alone or in pairs. Before students begin creating their science glossaries, write each word and introduce it to students by pointing and saying it aloud.

Beginning
LOW/HIGH Draw a picture for each vocabulary term in the glossary that helps associate the term with its definition.

Intermediate
LOW/HIGH Include English pronunciations for each term.

Advanced
LOW/HIGH For each vocabulary term in the glossary, write a sentence using the term correctly.

Water on Earth

1 ❓ How does fresh water cycle on Earth?

Lesson Pacing: 2–3 periods or 1–1½ blocks

🕐 **SHORT ON TIME?** To do this lesson in approximately half the time, do the Activate Prior Knowledge activity followed by a discussion of the Key Concepts to familiarize students with the lesson content. Have students do the Quick Lab. The rest of the lesson can be completed by students independently.

Preference Navigator, in the online Planning tools, allows you to customize *Interactive Science* to your own teaching style. You can also edit lesson plans by selecting the Lesson Planner option.

Digital Teacher's Edition allows you to access your Teacher's Edition and Resource online.

Lesson Vocabulary

- habitat
- groundwater
- water cycle
- evaporation
- transpiration
- precipitation

Content Refresher

Professional Development Note

Water Sources on Earth Most ice that makes up about three quarters of Earth's fresh water is found at the poles. The North Pole includes sea ice that covers the Arctic Ocean, as well as continental glaciers covering Greenland. But the continental glaciers on Antarctica contain 90% of the world's ice. Fresh water as ice is not available for human consumption. Not all Earth's groundwater is available for human use, either. Below a certain depth, it is not practical to raise groundwater to the surface. So, only shallow groundwater is available. Scientists estimate between Earth's surface and 4 km below the surface there are more than 8 million cubic km of fresh water. About half the U.S. population gets at least some fresh water from groundwater resources.

LESSON OBJECTIVES

- 🔖 State how people and other living things use water.
- 🔖 Describe how Earth's water is distributed.
- 🔖 Explain how Earth's water moves through the water cycle.

Blended Path
Active learning using Student Edition, Inquiry Path, and Digital Path

ENGAGE AND EXPLORE

Teach this lesson using a variety of resources. Begin by reading **My Planet Diary** as a class. Have students share ideas about how much water they believe they personally use each day. Then have students do the **Inquiry Warm-Up activity.** Students will observe the formation of condensation on glass. Discuss the relevance of the air and water temperature to the formation of condensation. The **After the Inquiry Warm-Up worksheet** sets up a discussion about the conditions necessary for water molecules to turn into water droplets. Have volunteers share their answers to number 4 about the sort of weather modeled in this activity.

EXPLAIN AND ELABORATE

Teach Key Concepts by explaining why water is important to all living things.

Continue to **Teach Key Concepts** by identifying the sources of saltwater and freshwater found on Earth's surface. **Lead a Discussion** about why salt water is not very useful to people.

Teach Key Concepts by using **Figure 3** to illustrate the movement of water from Earth's surface, into the atmosphere, and back. **Support the Big Q** by explaining how plants play an integral role in the water cycle. **Lead a Discussion** about what happens to precipitation when it falls to Earth. Then have students complete the **Apply It activity.** Hand out the **Key Concept Summaries** as a review of each part of the lesson. Students can also use the online **Vocab Flash Cards** to review key terms.

EVALUATE

Have students take the **Lesson Quiz.** For an alternate assessment, see the **EXAM**VIEW® Assessment Suite, Progress Monitoring Assessments, or SuccessTracker™.

ⒺⓁⓁ Support

1 Content and Language
Point out that the term *groundwater* is a compound word. It is made up of the words *ground*, meaning soil or earth and *water*, which is a liquid. Therefore by combining the two words and definitions it is possible to define *groundwater* as water that comes from the soil or earth.

 **Inquiry Path** Hands-on learning in the Lab zone

ENGAGE AND EXPLORE

To teach this lesson with an emphasis on inquiry, begin with the **Inquiry Warm-Up activity.** Students will investigate the formation of condensation. Discuss the circumstances that create condensation. Have students do the **After the Inquiry Warm-Up worksheet.** Talk about the role of temperature in the formation of condensation. Have volunteers share their answers to number 4 about what type of weather is modeled in the activity.

EXPLAIN AND ELABORATE

Focus on the **Inquiry Skill** for the lesson. Point out that when you observe, you use your senses to gather information. What observations were made about the formation of condensation in the **Inquiry Warm-Up activity?** *(If the air containing water molecules is warmer than the water molecules, condensation will form.)* Have students do the **Quick Lab** and then share their graphs about how Earth's water is used.

Do the **Quick Lab** to reinforce understanding of how water is distributed on Earth.

Support the Big Q by discussing the process of transpiration in plants. Review the terms *condensation* and *evaporation* before beginning the **Apply It activity.** Ask volunteers to give examples of a water cycle process they have observed. Have students complete the **Lab Investigation** to examine the process of transpiration and compute the mass of water. Students can use the online **Vocab Flash Cards** to review key terms.

EVALUATE

Have students take the **Lesson Quiz.** For an alternate assessment, see the **EXAM**VIEW® Assessment Suite, Progress Monitoring Assessments, or SuccessTracker™.

Digital Path Online learning at my science online.com

ENGAGE AND EXPLORE

Teach this lesson using digital resources. Begin by having students explore the amount of water used per person per day at **My Planet Diary** online. Have them access the Chapter Resources to find the **Unlock the Big Question activity.** There they can answer the questions and refine their responses as they continue through the lesson. You can re-assign the activity and have students submit their work so you can track their progress.

EXPLAIN AND ELABORATE

Students reading above, at, or below the lexile measure of this lesson can access basic content readings at their level at **My Reading Web.** Have students use the online **Vocab Flash Cards** to preview key terms. Do the **Quick Lab** and then ask students to share their graphs about how Earth's water is used.

Assign the **Do the Math activity** online and have students submit their work to you. Do the **Quick Lab** to model how water is distributed on Earth.

Use the **Support the Big Q** to help students understand how plants move the greatest amount of water in the water cycle. Have students do the online **Interactive Art activity** to explore the water cycle. Review *condensation* and *evaporation* before assigning the online **Apply It activity.** Ask volunteers to share which water cycle processes they have seen. Have students submit their work to you. The **Key Concept Summaries** online allow students to read a summary and see an image associated with each part of the lesson. Online remediation is available at **My Science Coach.**

EVALUATE

Have students take the **Lesson Quiz.** For an alternate assessment, see the **EXAM**VIEW® Assessment Suite, Progress Monitoring Assessments, or SuccessTracker™.

2 Frontload the Lesson

Preview the lesson questions. Ask students what they know about the importance of water, the location of water, and the water cycle. Explain these concepts using the lesson visuals, labels, and captions.

3 Comprehensible Input

Have students study the visuals and their captions to support the key concepts of the lesson.

4 Language Production

Pair or group students with varied language abilities to complete labs collaboratively for language practice. Have each student copy the completed written lab for personal reference.

5 Assess Understanding

Divide the class into small groups. Have each student identify a key concept from the lesson to discuss in his or her group. After the discussions, have students talk about the key concepts as a group.

Water on Earth

Lexile Measure = 890L

Establish Learning Objectives

After this lesson, students will be able to:

 State how people and other living things use water.

 Describe how Earth's water is distributed.

 Explain how Earth's water moves through the water cycle.

Engage

Activate Prior Knowledge

MY PLANET DIARY Read *How Much Water Do You Use?* with the class. Have students identify the various ways they use water each day. (Samples: bathing, drinking and cooking, washing clothes) Ask: **Why might water use vary from state to state?** *(Samples: States that have large farms use large amounts of water to irrigate plants. States that have factories that use water in the processing of their products would have higher water use.)*

BIG IDEAS OF SCIENCE REFERENCE LIBRARY Have students look up the following topic: Drinking Water.

Explore

Lab Resource: Inquiry Warm-Up

L1 **WHERE DOES THE WATER COME FROM?** Students will observe the process of condensation.

---

1 Water on Earth

 UNLOCK THE BIG ?

 Why Is Water Important?

Where Is Water Found?

What Is the Water Cycle?

MY PLANET DIARY

SCIENCE STATS

How Much Water Do You Use?

You take a shower. You brush your teeth. You take a big drink after soccer practice. All day long, you need water! How much water do you use in a day? How much do you think your whole state uses? The graph shows the water used per person in the ten states of the United States with the largest populations. The data include the water used for all purposes, including farming, industry, and electric power.

Water Use per Person per Day

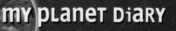

State (y-axis): California, Texas, New York, Florida, Illinois, Pennsylvania, Ohio, Michigan, Georgia, North Carolina

Gallons Used per Person per Day (x-axis): 0, 500, 1000, 1500

Study the graph. Then answer the questions below.

1. In which state is the water use per person greatest? In which state is it least?

   Greatest: California; least: New York

2. What do you think might explain the difference in water use between states?

   Sample: States that have more farms use more water.

▶ PLANET DIARY Go to **Planet Diary** to learn more about fresh water on Earth.

Lab zone Do the Inquiry Warm-Up *Where Does the Water Come From?*

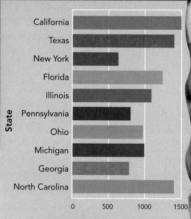

SUPPORT ALL READERS

Lexile Measure = 890L   Lexile Word Count = 1176

Prior Exposure to Content: Most students have encountered this topic in earlier grades

Academic Vocabulary: *observe, predict, classify, apply*

Science Vocabulary: *evaporation, precipitation, transpiration*

Concept Level: Generally appropriate for most students in this grade

Preteach With: My Planet Diary "How Much Water Do You Use?"

Go to **My Reading Web** to access leveled readings that provide a foundation for the content.

MY SCIENCE online.com

Vocabulary
- habitat • groundwater • water cycle • evaporation
- transpiration • precipitation

Skills
- ⟲ Reading: Identify the Main Idea
- △ Inquiry: Observe

Why Is Water Important?

What do you and an apple have in common? You both consist mostly of water! Water makes up nearly two thirds of your body's mass. That water is necessary to keep your body functioning. ⟪⟫ **All living things need water in order to carry out their body processes. In addition, many living things live in water.**

Body Processes Without water, neither you nor an apple could survive. Water allows organisms to break down food, grow, reproduce, and get and use materials they need from their environments. Animals obtain water by drinking it or by eating foods that contain water. Most animals cannot survive more than a few days without water.

Plants and other organisms that make their own food also need water. Algae and plants use water, along with carbon dioxide and energy from the sun, to make their own food in a process called photosynthesis (foh toh SIN thuh sis). Other organisms get food by eating the plants, or by eating organisms that eat the plants.

Habitats Water provides habitats for many living things. An organism's **habitat** is the place where it lives and obtains all the things it needs to survive. Some organisms cannot live out of water. You are probably familiar with large water-dwelling organisms such as sharks. But most such organisms are microscopic. In fact, aquatic, or water, habitats contain more types of organisms than land habitats do.

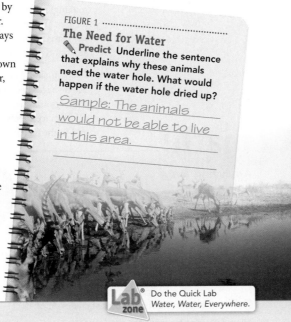

FIGURE 1 ....
The Need for Water
✏ **Predict** Underline the sentence that explains why these animals need the water hole. What would happen if the water hole dried up?

Sample: The animals would not be able to live in this area.

Lab zone
Do the Quick Lab
Water, Water, Everywhere.

⟪⟫ Assess Your Understanding

got it? ....

○ **I get it!** Now I know that living things use water *to perform body processes that keep them alive and as a habitat.*

○ **I need extra help with** *See TE note.*

Go to MY SCIENCE ⟨s⟩ COACH online for help with this subject.

327

Explain ————

Introduce Vocabulary

To help students understand the meaning of *water cycle,* point out that *cycle* in *bicycle* refers to the round, or circular wheels. A wheel moves in a repeating circular pattern, and the processes that make up the water cycle are part of a repeating pattern.

Teach Key Concepts ⟪⟫

Explain to students that all living things must have water in order to survive and carry out their body processes. Also, water provides shelter for many living things. Ask: **Why do living things need water?** *(To carry out body processes; some living things use water for shelter)* **Plants and other organisms that make their own food need water for what process?** *(Photosynthesis)* **What are two examples of water habitats?** *(Sample: ocean, pond)*

Elaborate ————

Lab Resource: Quick Lab

L2 **WATER, WATER, EVERYWHERE** Students will research and make a circle graph showing how Earth's water is used.

Evaluate ————

Assess Your Understanding

Have students evaluate their understanding by completing the appropriate sentence.

ⓇⓉⒾ Response to Intervention

If students have trouble identifying why water is important to living things, **then** have them review the concept that animals and plants use water for body processes by discussing how to care for pets and houseplants.

MY SCIENCE ⟨s⟩ COACH Have students go online for help in understanding why water is important to living things.

My Planet Diary provides an opportunity for students to explore real-world connections to Earth's water.

Explain

Teach Key Concepts 🔑

Explain to students that most of Earth's surface water is salt water. Ask: **What percentage of Earth's surface water is salt water?** *(97 percent)* **Where on Earth's surface would you find salt water?** *(Oceans)* You may wish to add that there are other saltwater bodies of water, such as the Great Salt Lake in Utah. Ask: **What percentage of Earth's surface water is fresh water?** *(3 percent)* **Where is the greatest amount of fresh water found?** *(In ice sheets that cover most of Greenland and Antarctica and in icebergs in the Arctic Ocean and in the North Atlantic Ocean)*

🔄 **Identify the Main Idea** The main idea tells what a section is about. It is the most important point the writer wants to make.

Lead a Discussion

OCEANS AND LAKES Discuss with students the fact that only a small percentage of water is available for human use. Also, about half of the volume of lakes (including "inland seas") is salt water. Ask: **Why is salt water less useful to people than fresh water?** *(Sample: Salt water cannot be used for drinking or to water crops.)* Explain that the technology for converting salt water to fresh water is expensive and impractical, so only a small percentage of water on Earth is readily available for human use.

Elaborate

Do the Math!

🔲 Point out that both the circle graph and the image of the water glass are ways of showing how much of Earth's water is found in different forms. Some students may have difficulty understanding the relationship between the circle graph and the water glass graph. Explain that the circle graph shows all the water on Earth—both salt water and fresh water. The glass represents just the 3% of the total water that is fresh water. Ask: **What makes up the smallest percent of liquid fresh water found on Earth?** *(Water found in lakes and rivers)*

See *Math Skill and Problem-Solving Activities* for support.

Where Is Water Found?

When you turn on the tap, it might seem that an endless supply of fresh water comes out! But Earth's freshwater supply is very limited. 🔑 **Most of Earth's surface water—roughly 97 percent—is salt water found in oceans. Only 3 percent is fresh water.**

Of that 3 percent, about two thirds is frozen in huge masses of ice near the North and South poles. About a third of the fresh water is underground. A tiny fraction of fresh water occurs in lakes and rivers. An even tinier fraction is found in the atmosphere, most of it in the form of invisible water vapor, the gaseous form of water.

Oceans Find the oceans on the map in **Figure 2**. Pacific, Atlantic, Indian, and Arctic are the names used for the different parts of the ocean. (Some scientists call the area around Antarctica the Southern Ocean.) But the waters are really all interconnected, making up one big ocean. The Pacific Ocean is the largest, covering an area greater than all the land on Earth. The Atlantic Ocean is next largest, though the Indian Ocean is deeper. The Arctic Ocean surrounds the North Pole. Smaller saltwater bodies are called seas.

Ice Much of Earth's fresh water is frozen into sheets of ice. Massive ice sheets cover most of Greenland and Antarctica. Icebergs are floating chunks of ice made of fresh water that break off from ice sheets. You could also find icebergs in the Arctic Ocean and in the North Atlantic.

✏️
✏ **Identify the Main Idea**
Underline the main idea in each paragraph on this page.

do the math!

Analyzing Data

These graphs show how much of Earth's water is found in different forms.

❶ **Read Graphs** Where is most water on Earth found? __In oceans and salt lakes__

❷ **Read Graphs** About what fraction of Earth's fresh water is in the form of ice? __About 2/3 (also accept 7/10)__

❸ **Interpret Data** How does the total amount of groundwater compare to the total amount of ice? __The total amount of groundwater is less than half the amount of ice.__

Salt water in oceans and salt lakes **97%**

Fresh water **3%**

Water vapor **0.04%**
Ice **69%**
Groundwater **30%**
Lakes and rivers **0.26%**

Professional Development Note

Teacher to Teacher

That's A Lot of Water! Put 100 index cards on a table that represents a fresh water source. Have students carry the cards one by one across the room to a table that represents their homes, timing how long it takes to collect approximately 100 gallons. Discuss the time and effort it took as a group to collect the water, the equivalent of about two bathtubs full. Students will be surprised to learn this is the amount of water the average person in the U.S. uses daily! Have students calculate the amount of water used by the entire school, city, and state first using gallons, and then convert to liters.

✏ *Emily Compton*
Park Forest Middle School
Baton Rouge, LA

Rivers and Lakes Look at **Figure 2.** All the rivers and lakes marked on the map contain fresh water, as do many other smaller rivers and lakes. North America's five Great Lakes contain about 20 percent of all the water in the world's freshwater lakes.

Groundwater To find some of the fresh water on Earth, you have to look underground. When it rains or snows, most water that doesn't evaporate soaks into the ground. This water trickles through spaces between particles of soil and rock. Water that fills the cracks and spaces in underground soil and rock layers is called **groundwater.** Far more fresh water is located underground than in all of Earth's rivers and lakes.

FIGURE 2 ··························
Earth's Major Waterways
The map shows Earth's oceans and some major freshwater sources.
✎ **Classify** Circle the names of three saltwater sources. Underline the names of three freshwater sources.

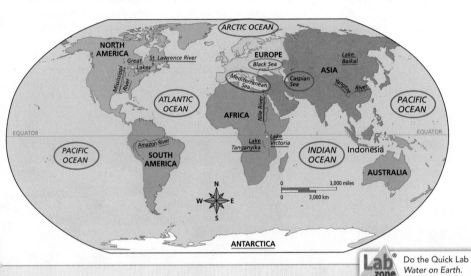

 Do the Quick Lab
Water on Earth.

🔑 **Assess Your Understanding**

1a. List What are the four main sources of fresh water on Earth?

<u>Ice, rivers, lakes, groundwater</u>

b. Make Judgments Which freshwater source do you think is most important to people? Why?

<u>Sample: rivers and lakes,</u>
<u>because they are the easiest</u>
<u>sources for people to reach</u>

got it? ·······························

○ **I get it!** Now I know that Earth's water is found in <u>oceans, ice, rivers, lakes, ground-</u>
<u>water, and water vapor in the atmosphere.</u>

○ **I need extra help with** <u>See TE note.</u>

Go to **my science COACH** online for help with this subject.

329

Lab Resource: Quick Lab Lab zone

L2 WATER ON EARTH Students will model the distribution of water on Earth.

Evaluate ————————

Assess Your Understanding

After students answer the questions, have them evaluate their understanding by completing the appropriate sentence.

𝗥𝗧𝗜 Response to Intervention

1a. If students cannot identify sources of fresh water, **then** have them skim the section to find the four red heads that identify sources of water. Then have them determine which of these are fresh water.

b. If students need help with identifying which freshwater source is most important to people, **then** have them review the information about sources of freshwater on Earth.

my science S COACH Have students go online for help in understanding where salt water and fresh water are found on Earth.

Digital Lesson: Assign the *Do the Math* activity online and have students submit their work to you.

Differentiated Instruction

L3 Your Community's Water Source
Have students do research to find out where your community's water comes from. Many water companies provide information about water sources and water quality on their Web sites. You may wish to provide the address for the Web site of your local water company. Remind students to follow prescribed Internet use guidelines.

L1 Bodies of Water Some students may find it difficult to locate the freshwater sources on the map in **Figure 2.** Display a classroom map of the world, and invite volunteers to point to freshwater sources and read the names aloud. Point out how much larger Earth's oceans are than the lakes and rivers.

Explain

Teach Key Concepts

Explain to students that the water cycle is the continuous movement of water among Earth's surface, living things, and the atmosphere. Ask: **If you hang wet clothing on a line to dry, where does the water go?** *(It evaporates, or becomes water vapor in the air.)* Point out that evaporation differs from boiling. Evaporation occurs only at the surface of a liquid and can happen at any temperature as long as the substance is a liquid at that temperature. Boiling occurs throughout a liquid and only occurs when the temperature is above the boiling point of that substance. Ask: **What drives the water cycle?** *(Gravity and energy from the sun)* **How does water move in a cycle?** *(Water moves from Earth's surface to the atmosphere and back to the surface.)*

Teach With Visuals

Tell students to look at **Figure 3**. Ask: **What are the steps in the water cycle?** *(Evaporation, condensation, precipitation, runoff, and transpiration)* **What are sources of water from which water evaporates?** *(Bodies of water such as oceans and lakes)* **In what state of matter is evaporated water?** *(Gaseous)* **How does water form clouds?** *(Water vapor in the atmosphere condenses.)* **How does water return to Earth's surface?** *(It falls as precipitation when the water droplets in clouds become larger and larger and finally heavy enough to fall.)*

Support the Big Q

Remind students that living things are part of the water cycle. Discuss the process of transpiration, with which students may not be familiar. Explain that water vapor moves out of a plant through tiny openings in the leaves. Point out that of all living things, plants move the greatest amount of water in the water cycle. Ask: **What form is water in when it leaves a plant through the process of transpiration?** *(Gas)*

What Is the Water Cycle?

Earth has its own built-in water recycling system: the water cycle. The **water cycle** is the continuous process by which water moves from Earth's surface to the atmosphere and back, driven by energy from the sun and gravity. In the water cycle, water moves between land, living things, bodies of water on Earth's surface, and the atmosphere.

Water Evaporates Where does the water in a puddle go when it disappears? It evaporates, becoming water vapor. **Evaporation** is the process by which molecules at the surface of a liquid absorb enough energy to change to a gaseous state. Water constantly evaporates from the surfaces of bodies of water such as oceans and lakes, as well as from soil and your skin. Plants play a role, too, in this step of the water cycle. Plants draw in water from the soil through their roots. Eventually the water is given off through the leaves as water vapor in a process called **transpiration**.

Vocabulary Latin Word Origins The letter *e* in *evaporation* comes from the Latin word *ex*, meaning "away." *Vapor* is Latin for "water vapor." What do you predict that *evaporation* means?

Sample: moving away into water vapor

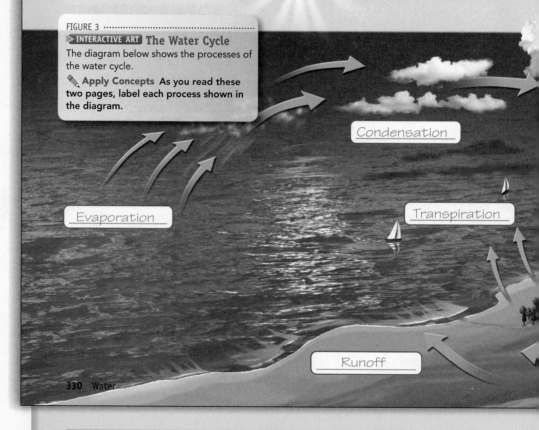

FIGURE 3
> INTERACTIVE ART The Water Cycle
The diagram below shows the processes of the water cycle.

Apply Concepts As you read these two pages, label each process shown in the diagram.

Condensation

Transpiration

Evaporation

Runoff

Interactive Art allows students to explore the water cycle.

my science online.com | Water Cycle

Condensation Forms Clouds After a water molecule evaporates, warm air can carry the water molecule upward. Air tends to become colder as it rises. Water vapor condenses more easily at lower temperatures, so some water vapor cools and condenses into liquid water. Droplets of liquid water clump around solid particles in the air, forming clouds.

Water Falls as Precipitation As more water vapor condenses, the water droplets grow larger. Eventually, they become so heavy that they fall back to Earth. Water that falls to Earth as rain, snow, hail, or sleet is called **precipitation.**

Most precipitation falls directly into the ocean. Of the precipitation that falls on land, most evaporates. A small amount of the remaining water runs off the surface into streams and lakes in a process called runoff, but most of it seeps into groundwater. After a long time, this groundwater may flow down to the ocean and evaporate again.

Precipitation is the source of almost all fresh water on and below Earth's surface. For millions of years, the total amount of water cycling through the Earth system has remained fairly constant—the rates of evaporation and precipitation are balanced.

Precipitation

apply it!

① **Observe** What water cycle process can you observe here?

Condensation

② **CHALLENGE** What other process or processes can you infer are also taking place?

Evaporation

③ Give an example of a water cycle process you have seen.

Sample: I have seen water falling as rain.

Lab zone Do the Lab Investigation *Water From Trees.*

Assess Your Understanding

2a. Identify What are the three major steps in the water cycle?

Evaporation, condensation, and precipitation

b. Sequence Start with a puddle on a sunny day. How might water move through the water cycle and eventually fall as rain?

Sample: Energy from the sun will cause water to evaporate. The water will condense in clouds, and then fall as precipitation.

got it?

○ **I get it!** Now I know that the water cycle is the set of processes by which water moves from Earth's surface to the atmosphere and back again.

○ **I need extra help with** See TE note.

Go to **my science COACH** *online for help with this subject.*

331

Lead a Discussion

PRECIPITATION Discuss with students what happens to water that falls to Earth as precipitation. Ask: **What happens to most precipitation?** *(It falls directly into the ocean.)* **What happens to most of the precipitation that falls on land?** *(It evaporates.)* **What happens to the small amount of remaining water that does not evaporate?** *(Most seeps into the ground, and the rest (a small amount) runs off into rivers and lakes.)*

Elaborate
Apply It!

L1 Review the concepts of condensation and evaporation before beginning the activity.

▲ **Observe** Remind students that observation is the process of using the senses to gather information. Direct students to look carefully at the photograph of the plastic drinking cup.

Lab Resource: Lab Investigation

L2 WATER FROM TREES Students will observe transpiration and will calculate the mass of water.

Evaluate
Assess Your Understanding

After students answer the questions, have them evaluate their understanding by completing the appropriate sentence.

RTI Response to Intervention

2a. If students cannot identify the three major steps in the water cycle, **then** have them review **Figure 3** and identify the processes of evaporation, condensation, and precipitation.

b. If students have trouble sequencing the path of water through the water cycle, **then** suggest they first draw a simple diagram showing the sequence of liquid water in a puddle evaporating due to energy from the sun, condensing as clouds, and falling as precipitation. Point out to students that more than one pathway is possible.

my science COACH Have students go online for help in understanding the water cycle.

Differentiated Instruction

L1 What Drives the Water Cycle? Although the water cycle is driven by gravity and energy from the sun, these two factors drive different aspects of the water cycle. Clarify this for students by asking them to identify two parts of the water cycle that are driven by gravity. If they need help, remind them that gravity causes objects to fall toward Earth. *(Precipitation falling to earth and runoff flowing downhill)* Ask students to identify two parts of the water cycle that

are driven by energy from the sun. *(Evaporation and transpiration)*

L3 Drinking Ancient Water Have students write a brief "History of a Drop of Water" It should be a fanciful story tracing a single drop of water from some a time and place in the past to the present day school water fountain.

Lab zone — After the Inquiry Warm-Up

Water on Earth

> **Inquiry Warm-Up, *Where Does the Water Come From?***
> In the Inquiry Warm-Up, you investigated how condensation appears on a glass. Using what you learned from that activity, answer the questions below.

1. **COMPARE AND CONTRAST** How did the temperature of the water compare to the temperature of the air in the room?

   _____

2. **PREDICT** Do you think the same result would have occurred with a glass of warm water? Explain your answer.

   _____

   _____

3. **RELATE CAUSE AND EFFECT** How could your observations apply to water molecules in the air?

   _____

4. **INFER** What sort of weather does this experiment model?

   _____

Assess Your Understanding

Water on Earth

Why Is Water Important?

got it? ··

○ **I get it!** Now I know that living things use water _____
_____
_____

○ **I need extra help with** _____
_____

Where is Water Found?

1a. LIST What are four main sources of fresh water on Earth?

_____
_____

b. MAKE JUDGMENTS Which freshwater source do you think is most
important to people? Why?

_____
_____
_____

got it? ··

○ **I get it!** Now I know that Earth's water is found in_____
_____
_____

○ **I need extra help with**_____
_____

Name _____ Date _____ Class _____

Water on Earth

What Is the Water Cycle

2a. IDENTIFY What are the three major steps in the water cycle?

_____

b. SEQUENCE Start with a puddle on a sunny day. How might water move through the water cycle and actually fall as rain?

_____

_____

_____

got it? ....

○ **I get it!** Now I know that the water cycle is _____

_____

_____

○ **I need extra help with** _____

_____

_____

Name _____ Date _____ Class _____

Key Concept Summaries

Water On Earth

Why Is Water Important?

All living things need water in order to carry out their body processes. Water allows organisms to break down food, grow, reproduce, and get and use materials they need from their environments. Plants and other organisms that make their own food also need water. Algae and plants use water, along with carbon dioxide and energy from the sun, to make their own food in a process called photosynthesis.

In addition, many living things use water for shelter. Water provides habitats for many living things. A **habitat** is the place where an organism lives and obtains all the things it needs to survive. Some organisms cannot live out of water.

Where Is Water Found?

Most of Earth's surface water—roughly 97 percent—is salt water found in oceans. Only 3 percent is fresh water. Of that 3 percent, about two thirds is frozen in huge masses of ice near the North and South Poles. Massive ice sheets cover most of Greenland and Antarctica.

Most of the rest of the fresh water is underground. Water that fills the cracks and spaces in underground soil and in rock layer is called **groundwater.** Far more fresh water is located underground than in all of Earth's rivers and lakes.

What Is the Water Cycle?

The **water cycle** is the continuous process by which water moves from Earth's surface to the atmosphere and back, driven by gravity and energy from the sun.

In the water cycle, water moves between land, living things, bodies of water on Earth's surface, and the atmosphere.

Processes included in the water cycle are **evaporation,** the process where molecules at the surface of a liquid absorb enough energy to change to a gaseous state,

and **transpiration,** the process of water taken in by plants and given off through the leaves as water vapor.

Water vapor in the air cools and condenses into liquid water, which eventually forms clouds. When the water droplets become heavy, they fall back to Earth as rain, snow, hail, or sleet, all of which are forms of **precipitation.**

On a separate sheet of paper, explain how fresh water cycles on Earth.

Name _____ Date _____ Class _____

Water on Earth

Understanding Main Ideas
Answer the following questions on a separate sheet of paper.

1. Identify two ways in which water is important to living things.
2. What is the percent of fresh water and salt water on Earth and where is each type found?

The diagram below shows the water cycle. Use the diagram to answer Questions 3–5.

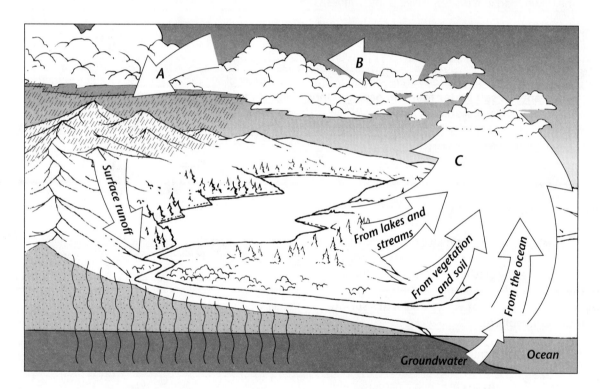

3. What process is shown at point A? _____
4. What process is shown at point B? _____
5. What process is shown at point C? _____

Building Vocabulary
On a separate sheet of paper, write a definition for each of these terms.

6. groundwater   7. water cycle   8. transpiration

Name _____ Date _____ Class _____

Enrich

Water on Earth

All the water on Earth flows through the water cycle. Read the passage and look at the diagram below. Then answer the questions that follow on a separate sheet of paper.

Evaporation, Precipitation, and Runoff

The diagram below shows the yearly global flow of water through the water cycle. The numbers represent the amounts of evaporation and precipitation over the oceans and over the land.

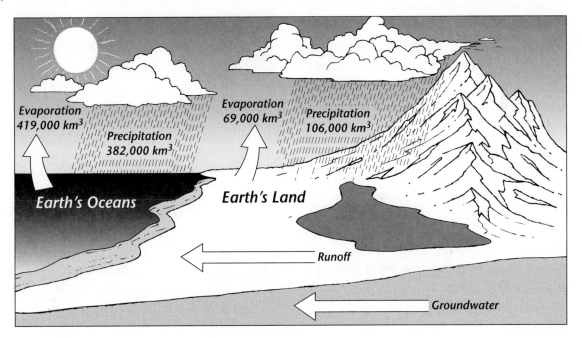

Evaporation 419,000 km³

Precipitation 382,000 km³

Evaporation 69,000 km³

Precipitation 106,000 km³

Earth's Oceans

Earth's Land

Runoff

Groundwater

1. What is the total amount of global evaporation?
2. What is the total amount of global precipitation?
3. How does the total amount of global precipitation compare to the total amount of global evaporation?
4. Where does more evaporation occur, from the oceans or from the land? Explain.
5. Where does more precipitation occur, over the oceans or over the land? Explain.
6. Do Earth's oceans gain or lose water, considering evaporation and precipitation together? How much?
7. Do Earth's continents gain or lose water, considering evaporation and precipitation together? How much?
8. Compare the differences in evaporation and precipitation over Earth's oceans and land. How are they related?

Lesson Quiz

Water On Earth

If the statement is true, write *true*. If the statement is false, change the underlined word or words to make the statement true.

1. _____ Plants use water, carbon dioxide, and energy to make food in a process called <u>transpiration</u>.

2. _____ The process by which water falls to Earth as rain, snow, hail, or sleet is called <u>condensation</u>.

3. _____ In the process of <u>evaporation</u>, water molecules at the surface of a liquid absorb enough energy to change to a gas called water vapor.

4. _____ In the process of <u>precipitation</u>, water vapor in air cools and becomes water droplets that clump around particles in air to form clouds.

5. _____ Plants give off water vapor through their leaves in a process called <u>photosynthesis</u>.

Fill in the blank to complete each statement.

6. About 97 percent of water on is Earth is found in _____ and salt lakes.

7. More freshwater exists as _____ than is found in all of Earth's rivers and lakes.

8. The water cycle is driven by energy from the sun and _____ .

9. The place in which an organism lives and obtains the things it needs to survive is its _____ .

10. Most of Greenland is covered by fresh water that is _____ .

Water on Earth

Answer Key

After the Inquiry Warm-Up

1. The water in the glass was colder than the air in the room.

2. Sample: No, because if the air and the water are the same temperature, there is no reason for the water to move.

3. If air containing water molecules becomes warmer than the water molecules, water droplets will form.

4. This experiment simulates how rain and other precipitation is formed.

Key Concept Summaries

Water evaporates from bodies of water on Earth's surface and water vapor is given off through plant leaves through transpiration. Water vapor in the atmosphere cools and condenses into liquid water, forming clouds. When the water droplets become heavy enough, they fall back to Earth as precipitation.

Review and Reinforce

1. Living things use water to perform body processes needed for survival and as a habitat

2. Salt water: 97%; Fresh water: 3%; salt water is found in oceans and salt lakes; fresh water is found in ice sheets and icebergs, in lakes and rivers, as groundwater, and as water vapor in the atmosphere.

3. precipitation

4. condensation

5. evaporation

6. water that soaks into the ground from precipitation and fills the cracks and spaces in underground soil and rock layers

7. the continuous process by which water moves from Earth surface to the atmosphere and back, driven by gravity and energy from the sun

8. the process by which plants give off water in the form of water vapor through their leaves

Enrich

1. $419,000 + 69,000 = 488,000$ km^3

2. $382,000 + 106,000 = 488,000$ km^3

3. Global evaporation equals global precipitation.

4. Much more evaporation occurs from the oceans (419,000 km^3 compared to 69,000 km^3), because much more of Earth's surface is covered by ocean than land.

5. Much more precipitation occurs over the oceans (382,000 km^3 compared to 106,000 km^3), because much more of the Earth's surface is covered by ocean than land.

6. Since 419,000 km^3 of water evaporate while only 382,000 km^3 of water fall as precipitation, Earth's oceans lose 37,000 km^3 of water.

7. Since 106,000 km^3 of water fall as precipitation, while only 69,000 km^3 of water evaporate, Earth's land gains 37,000 km^3 of water.

8. The oceans lose the same amount as the land gains. The water that flows into the oceans in runoff and groundwater balances the two out.

Lesson Quiz

1. photosynthesis
2. precipitation
3. true
4. condensation
5. transpiration
6. oceans
7. groundwater
8. gravity
9. habitat
10. frozen

Surface Water

How does fresh water cycle on Earth?

Lesson Pacing: 2–3 periods or 1–1½ blocks

🕐 **SHORT ON TIME?** To do this lesson in approximately half the time, do the Activate Prior Knowledge activity followed by a discussion of the Key Concepts to familiarize students with the lesson content. Use the Explore the Big Q to help students understand the cycle of fresh water on Earth. Do the Quick Labs and have students do the Real-World Inquiry online. The rest of the lesson can be completed by students independently.

Preference Navigator, in the online Planning tools, allows you to customize *Interactive Science* to your own teaching style. You can also edit lesson plans by selecting the Lesson Planner option.

Digital Teacher's Edition allows you to access your Teacher's Edition and Resource materials online.

my science online .com

Lesson Vocabulary

• tributary • watershed • divide • reservoir • eutrophication

Content Refresher
Professional Development Note

River Systems Tributaries in river systems form distinctive drainage patterns. The most common pattern, found in the major watersheds of the United States, is a *dendritic* (treelike) pattern, with streams flowing irregularly like branches on a tree. In a *radial* drainage pattern, all of the streams flow outward from a center point, like the spokes on a wheel. A radial pattern is most often found on isolated volcanic cones and domes of Earth's crust. A *rectangular* drainage pattern develops when the underlying bedrock is crisscrossed by joints and faults. The streams in this pattern form many right-angle bends and are almost parallel to one another, making the system look somewhat like a garden trellis. Other terms used to describe a river system are the stages of its development: youth, maturity, and old age. A single river system may include all three stages. At the headwaters, where the fast-moving water erodes the underlying land, the river is young. A young river has waterfalls, rapids, a narrow V-shaped valley, and a steep slope. A mature river erodes it sides more than its bottom, creating a flood plain. An old river has a flood plain that is much wider than the width of its meanders, and the river may shift course frequently.

LESSON OBJECTIVES

🔑 Tell what a river system is.

🔑 Explain how ponds and lakes form.

🔑 Describe the changes that occur in ponds and lakes.

Blended Path
Active learning using Student Edition, Inquiry Path, and Digital Path

ENGAGE AND EXPLORE

Teach this lesson using a variety of resources. Begin by reading **My Planet Diary** as a class. Have students share ideas about where rain goes after it falls on a mountain. Then have students do the **Inquiry Warm-Up activity.** Students will locate and classify surface water using a map of their state. Discuss the various bodies of water in their state. The **After the Inquiry Warm-Up worksheet** sets up a discussion about how water is absorbed by a sponge. Have volunteers share their answers to number 4 about the formation of watersheds.

EXPLAIN AND ELABORATE

Teach Key Concepts by explaining the term *tributary* and by having students identify rivers that are tributaries to the Mississippi River. **Lead a Discussion** about the various areas of watershed that feed the Mississippi River. Help students understand how natural barriers such as divides shed water in different directions.

Continue to **Teach Key Concepts** by distinguishing ponds and lakes from rivers. **Lead a Discussion** about the various types of lakes and how they are formed. Then have students do the **Apply It activity.** Ask volunteers to share the characteristics of ponds and lakes noted in their Venn diagrams.

Teach Key Concepts to explain that natural processes and human activities can cause lakes to change. Use **Figure 5** to illustrate the changes that occur in a lake over time and discuss the process of *eutrophication.* **Explore the Big Q** by using symbols to depict the water cycle. Have students **Answer the Big Q.** Allow volunteers to explain how fresh water cycles on Earth. Hand out the **Key Concept Summaries** as a review of each part of the lesson. Students can also use the online **Vocab Flash Cards** to review key terms.

EVALUATE

Have students take the **Lesson Quiz.** For an alternate assessment, see the **EXAM**VIEW® Assessment Suite, Progress Monitoring Assessments, or SuccessTracker™.

ⒺⓁⓁ Support

1 Content and Language
Eutrophication comes from the Greek word *eutrophos,* meaning "well-nourished" and the suffix *-ation,* meaning "a process." Explain that when algae, in a lake, is well nourished, the process of *eutrophication* begins.

Lab zone Inquiry Path
Hands-on learning in the Lab zone

ENGAGE AND EXPLORE

To teach this lesson with an emphasis on inquiry, begin with the **Inquiry Warm-Up activity.** Students will identify and classify surface water in their community using a map. Discuss the characteristics of the surface water in their community. Have students do the **After the Inquiry Warm-Up worksheet** about water absorption. Have volunteers share their answers to number 4 about the formation of watersheds.

EXPLAIN AND ELABORATE

Focus on the **Inquiry Skill** for the lesson. Point out that when you form operational definitions, you describe how a term can be defined. What definitions were made about the classifications in the **Inquiry Warm-Up activity?** *(Operational definitions for rivers, lakes, oceans)* Have students do the **Quick Lab** to model the river system in a watershed.

Review the characteristics of ponds and lakes before beginning the **Apply It activity.** Ask volunteers to share their Venn diagrams and operational definitions for lake. Use the **Teacher Demo** to point out similarities and differences between pond plants and pond algae. Have students do the **Quick Lab** to reinforce understanding of how lakes form.

Have students **Explore the Big Q** by drawing the water cycle using symbols. Assign the **Real-World Inquiry** for students to study issues regarding the Colorado River. Use the **Quick Lab** to show students the effects of algae on pond life. Have students share their responses to the **Answer the Big Q** about the fresh water cycle. Students can use the online **Vocab Flash Cards** to review key terms.

EVALUATE

Have students take the **Lesson Quiz.** For an alternate assessment, see the **EXAM**VIEW® Assessment Suite, Progress Monitoring Assessments, or SuccessTracker™.

Digital Path
Online learning at my science online.com

ENGAGE AND EXPLORE

Teach this lesson using digital resources. Begin by having students observe how rivers flow in Colorado's mountains at **My Planet Diary** online. Have them access the Chapter Resources to find the **Unlock the Big Question activity.** There they can answer the questions and refine their responses as they continue through the lesson. You can re-assign the activity and have students submit their work so you can track their progress.

EXPLAIN AND ELABORATE

Students reading above, at, or below the lexile measure of this lesson can access basic content readings at their level at **My Reading Web.** Have students use the online **Vocab Flash Cards** to preview key terms. Do the first **Quick Lab** to model the river system in a watershed.

Review what students know about ponds and lakes before assigning the online **Apply It activity.** Ask volunteers to share diagrams and definitions and submit their work to you. Have students do the next **Quick Lab** to model the formation of a lake.

Have students do the online **Real-World Inquiry** to uncover issues regarding the Colorado River. Use the **Explore the Big Q activity** to review the processes that make up the water cycle. Give students an opportunity to see how algae growth affects a pond in the last **Quick Lab.** Ask students to share their responses to **Answer the Big Q** about how fresh water cycles on Earth. The **Key Concept Summaries** online allow students to read a summary and see an image associated with each part of the lesson. Online remediation is available at **My Science Coach.**

EVALUATE

Have students take the **Lesson Quiz.** For an alternate assessment, see the **EXAM**VIEW® Assessment Suite, Progress Monitoring Assessments, or SuccessTracker™.

2 Frontload the Lesson
Preview the lesson visuals, labels, and captions. Ask students what they know about the terms *tributary, watershed,* and *reservoir.* Explain the specific meanings these words have in science.

3 Comprehensible Input
Have students make a chart that identifies which vocabulary words are associated with rivers and which vocabulary words are associated with ponds and lakes.

4 Language Production
Pair or group students with varied language abilities to complete labs collaboratively for language practice. Have each student copy the completed written lab for personal reference.

5 Assess Understanding
Have students submit their portfolio of notes and drawings or give oral presentations of the lesson content.

LESSON 10.2

Surface Water

Establish Learning Objectives

After this lesson, students will be able to:

🗝 Tell what a river system is.

🗝 Explain how ponds and lakes form.

🗝 Describe the changes that occur in ponds and lakes.

Engage

Activate Prior Knowledge

MY PLANET DIARY Read *So Near, So Far* with the class. Ask students to describe what happens when rain falls on a mound of soil. Elicit that many small trickles might connect to form larger streams of water. Compare this to what happens when water falls on mountains. Ask: **What kind of water flows in streams and rivers?** *(Fresh water)*

BIG IDEAS OF SCIENCE REFERENCE LIBRARY 📖 Have students look up the following topics: Amazon River, Great Lakes.

Explore

Lab Resource: Inquiry Warm-Up 🔺

L? **MAPPING SURFACE WATERS** Students will use a map of their state to locate and classify the surface waters in and near their community.

LESSON 2 Surface Water

🗝 What Is a River System?

🗝 What Are Ponds and Lakes?

🗝 How Can Lakes Change?

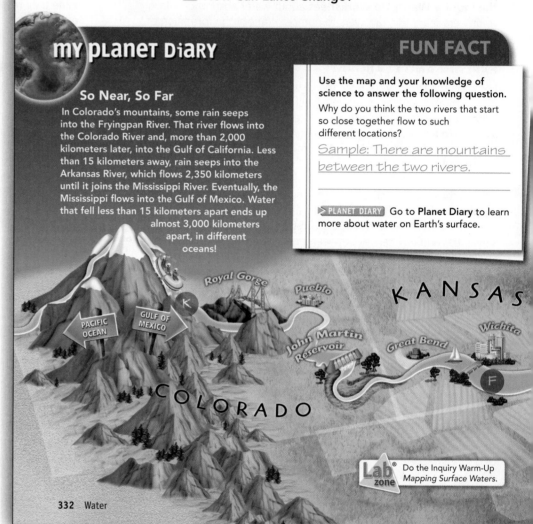

MY PLANET DIARY

FUN FACT

So Near, So Far

In Colorado's mountains, some rain seeps into the Fryingpan River. That river flows into the Colorado River and, more than 2,000 kilometers later, into the Gulf of California. Less than 15 kilometers away, rain seeps into the Arkansas River, which flows 2,350 kilometers until it joins the Mississippi River. Eventually, the Mississippi flows into the Gulf of Mexico. Water that fell less than 15 kilometers apart ends up almost 3,000 kilometers apart, in different oceans!

Use the map and your knowledge of science to answer the following question.

Why do you think the two rivers that start so close together flow to such different locations?

Sample: There are mountains between the two rivers.

▶ **PLANET DIARY** Go to **Planet Diary** to learn more about water on Earth's surface.

🔺 Do the Inquiry Warm-Up *Mapping Surface Waters.*

332 Water

SUPPORT ALL READERS

Lexile Measure = 920L   Lexile Word Count = 1208

Prior Exposure to Content: May be the first time students have encountered this topic

Academic Vocabulary: *operational definitions, sequence*

Science Vocabulary: *eutrophication, reservoir, tributary, watershed*

Concept Level: Generally appropriate for most students in this grade

Preteach With: My Planet Diary "So Near, So Far" and Figure 1 activity

Go to **My Reading Web** to access leveled readings that provide a foundation for the content.

MY SCIENCE online.com

Vocabulary
- tributary
- watershed
- divide
- reservoir
- eutrophication

Skills
- Reading: Sequence
- Inquiry: Form Operational Definitions

What Is a River System?

If you were hiking near the beginning of the Fryingpan and Arkansas rivers, you could observe tiny streams of water from melted snow. Gravity causes these tiny streams to flow downhill. As you follow one small stream, you would notice that the stream reaches another stream and joins it, forming a larger stream. That larger stream joins other streams until a small river forms.

Tributaries As you continue following the small river downhill, you might notice more streams joining the river. Eventually, the small river itself flows into a larger river. This river grows as more small rivers flow into it, before finally spilling into the ocean. The streams and smaller rivers that feed into a main river are called **tributaries.** Tributaries flow downward toward the main river, pulled by the force of gravity. 🔑 **A river and all the streams and smaller rivers that flow into it together make up a river system.**

Why is the Arkansas River considered a tributary of the Mississippi River?

The Arkansas River
flows into the Missis-
sippi River.

FIGURE 1 ....

The Arkansas River

✎ **Make Judgments** Put a K on the map where you might go kayaking. Put an F where you might get water for farming. Put an M where you might build a manufacturing plant. Explain why you chose the locations you did.

Sample positions are shown. Kayaking would be best
where the river is fast and steep, farming in flat areas,
and manufacturing near cities and dams.

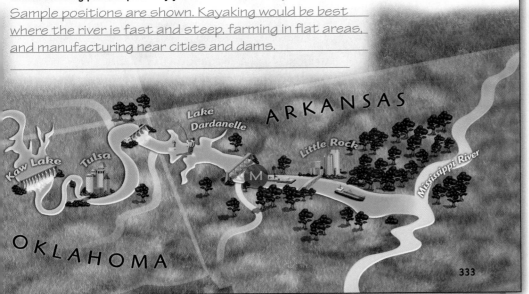

OKLAHOMA

Kaw Lake

Tulsa

Lake Dardanelle

ARKANSAS

Little Rock

Mississippi River

333

Explain

Introduce Vocabulary

Help students understand the meaning of *reservoir*. Explain that one meaning of the word *reserve* is "to keep back for future use." A reservoir is a place where water is stored for future use.

Teach Key Concepts 🔑

Explain to students that a river system can include many small rivers as well as the main river they flow into. Ask: **What is an example of a system?** *(Sample: Digestive organs make up the digestive system.)* Explain that just as an organ system is made up of parts, so a river system is made of parts. Ask: **What are some parts of a river system?** *(Streams, smaller rivers, larger rivers)* **Where does the water that makes up streams come from?** *(Precipitation)* **How might snowfall on a mountain contribute to the water in streams and rivers?** *(When snow on a mountain melts, some of the water flows downhill, forming or adding to water in streams and rivers.)* **What force causes the water in tributaries to flow?** *(Gravity)*

My Planet Diary provides an opportunity for students to explore real-world connections to rivers.

my science online | River Features

Explain

Lead a Discussion

WATERSHEDS Help students understand what a watershed is. Ask: **What sources of water can be tributaries?** *(Streams and smaller rivers)* Explain that streams start from precipitation that is not absorbed into the ground. The water that has reached the surface moves over the ground. In some places it forms grooves that join other grooves to form a channel called a stream. Streams flow downhill and form tributaries that make up a river. Ask: **What is the land area that supplies water to a river system called?** *(A watershed)* Have students look at **Figure 2** and identify the five watershed areas highlighted on the map. *(Columbia River Watershed, Colorado River Watershed, Missouri River Watershed, Mississippi River Watershed, and Ohio River Watershed)*

Make Analogies

L1 **SHEDDING WATER** Help students understand the meaning of *watershed* by breaking it into its two parts, *water* and *shed*. Ask: **What does it mean when an advertisement for a raincoat says that the coat's fabric "sheds water"?** *(It means water rolls off the coat.)* **What happens when water falls on sloped land, like the side of a mountain?** *(It runs downhill.)* Students should remember that land sheds much of the water that lands on it, and that water runs into streams and rivers. The land that sheds the water is the watershed.

Watersheds Just as all the water in a bathtub flows toward the drain, all the water in a river system drains into a main river. The land area that supplies water to a river system is called a **watershed.** Watersheds are sometimes known as drainage basins.

As you can see in **Figure 2,** the Missouri and Ohio rivers are quite long. Yet they flow into the Mississippi River. When rivers join another river system, the areas they drain become part of the largest river's watershed. The watershed of the Mississippi River covers nearly one third of the United States!

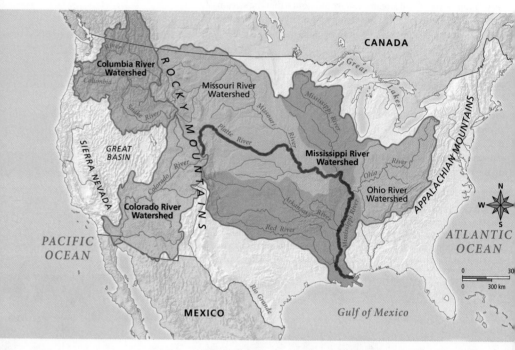

FIGURE 2

Major Watersheds of the United States
This map shows watersheds of several large rivers in the United States. ✎ **Interpret Maps** Draw the path that water would take from the Platte River's source to the ocean. Which watersheds would the water pass through?

Platte, Missouri, and Mississippi

Divides What keeps watersheds separate? One watershed is separated from another by a ridge of land called a **divide**. Streams on each side of the divide flow in different directions. The Great Divide (also called the Continental Divide) is the longest divide in North America. It follows the line of the Rocky Mountains. West of this divide, water flows toward the Pacific Ocean. Some water is trapped between the Rockies and the Sierra Nevadas, in the Great Basin. Between the Rocky and Appalachian mountains, water flows toward the Mississippi River and into the Gulf of Mexico.

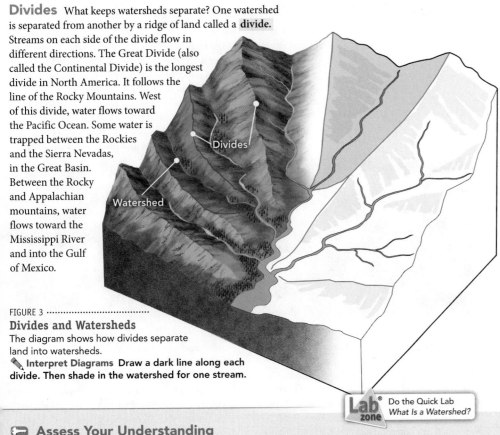

FIGURE 3 ·······················

Divides and Watersheds
The diagram shows how divides separate land into watersheds.

✎ **Interpret Diagrams** Draw a dark line along each divide. Then shade in the watershed for one stream.

Lab zone® Do the Quick Lab
What Is a Watershed?

335

🔑 **Assess Your Understanding**

1a. Identify A (divide/tributary) separates two watersheds.

b. Summarize How is a watershed related to a river system? _A watershed is the area of land that provides water for a river system._

c. Make Generalizations How can a stream be part of more than one watershed?
The area of land where water flows into the stream is its watershed. If the stream flows into another river, it becomes part of that river's watershed.

got it? ·······················

○ **I get it!** Now I know that a river system is _a river and all the smaller rivers and streams that flow into it._

○ **I need extra help with** _See TE note._

Go to MY SCIENCE 🔵s COACH *online for help with this subject.*

335

Elaborate

Lead a Discussion

DIVIDES Help students understand what a divide is. Ask: **Why don't all the watersheds bring water to just one large river?** (*Natural barriers called divides separate one watershed from another.*) **What is a divide?** (*A ridge of land between watersheds.*) **What is the Great Divide?** (*The longest divide in North America*) **Where does water flow west and east of the Great Divide?** (*West of the Great Divide water flows toward the Pacific Ocean. East of it, between the Rocky and Appalachian mountains, water flows toward the Mississippi River and into the Gulf of Mexico.*)

Lab Resource: Quick Lab

L2 **WHAT IS A WATERSHED?** Students will model the river system in a watershed.

Evaluate

Assess Your Understanding

After students answer the questions, have them evaluate their understanding by completing the appropriate sentence.

RTI Response to Intervention

1. If students have trouble identifying characteristics of a watershed, **then** have students look at the area they shaded on **Figure 3** and trace the path of water from the shaded watershed into the stream to the river.

MY SCIENCE 🔵s COACH Have students go online for help in understanding river systems.

Differentiated Instruction

L1 **Water Flows Downhill** Review the idea that water flows downhill because of gravity. Have students demonstrate this concept using a basin, a cup of water, and modeling clay formed in the shape of a mountain.

L1 **Model Watersheds and Divides** Fold a sheet of paper in half lengthwise and hold it up so the crease is on top and the folded paper looks like a tent.

Point to the crease. Explain that if the paper on either side of the crease represents two watersheds, the crease would represent the divide.

L3 **Name that Watershed** Have students to use a more detailed physical map to identify watersheds for the Rio Grande and other major rivers that are not labeled on the map on this page in their book.

335

Explain

Teach Key Concepts 🔑

Explain to students ponds and lakes form when water collects in hollows and low lying areas of land. Ask: **How are ponds and lakes different from a river?** *(The water in ponds and lakes is standing water whereas the water in rivers is flowing.)* **What two characteristics usually distinguish ponds from lakes?** *(Ponds are usually smaller and less deep than lakes.)*

21st Century Learning

CRITICAL THINKING Help students recall the main difference between a lake and a pond by drawing and labeling two cutaway views—one of a shallow body of water labeled *Pond* and one of a considerably deeper body of water labeled *Lake*. Show plants growing from all parts of the pond bottom. Show a few plants mostly distributed around the edges of the lake. Ask students to explain the reason for this difference in plant growth. *(The lake is deeper than the pond. Sunlight does not reach the deepest parts of the lake, so plants generally do not grow there.)*

Lead a Discussion

LAKE FORMATION Discuss with students some of the different ways in which lakes form. Ask: **How is an oxbow lake formed?** *(As a river bends and loops, it flows around obstacles and creates new channels. If the new channels cut off an existing loop, that loop may become an oxbow lake.)* **How did glacial lakes form?** *(Depressions created by ice sheets filled with water from the glaciers that melted at the end of the Ice Age.)* **When does a rift valley lake form?** *(Movements of Earth's crust form a long, deep valley that fills with water)* **What are two ways a volcanic lake can form?** *(A lava or mud flow from a volcano can block a river, forming a lake, or a lake can form in an volcanic empty crater.)*

Elaborate

Apply It!

L1 Review the descriptions under the photographs of a pond and a lake before beginning the activity. Suggest students make a list of ways in which the two bodies of water are similar and ways in which they are different. They should use their list to help them complete the Venn diagram.

🔺 **Form Operational Definitions** Remind students that an operational definition is a statement that describes how a term can be defined.

What Are Ponds and Lakes?

What makes a lake or pond different from a river? Unlike streams and rivers, ponds and lakes contain still water. In general, ponds are smaller and shallower than lakes. Sunlight usually reaches to the bottom of all parts of a pond. Most lakes have areas where the water is too deep for much sunlight to reach the bottom.

Where does pond and lake water come from? Some ponds and lakes are supplied by rainfall, melting snow and ice, and runoff. Others are fed by rivers or groundwater. 🔑 **Ponds and lakes form when water collects in hollows and low-lying areas of land.**

Exploring a Pond Because the water is shallow enough for sunlight to reach the bottom, plants grow throughout a pond. Bacteria and plantlike organisms called algae also live in the pond. The plants and algae produce oxygen as they use sunlight to make food. Fish and other animals in the pond use the oxygen and food provided by plants and algae. Some animals also use these plants for shelter.

Exploring a Lake Lakes are usually larger and deeper than ponds, so little sunlight reaches the bottom of a deep lake. Fewer plants can live in in the chilly, dark depths of such a lake. Mollusks and worms move along the lake's sandy or rocky bottom. They eat food particles that drift down from the surface. Young bony fishes such as pike and sturgeon eat the tiny bottom-dwellers, while the adult fish eat other fish.

apply it!

❶ Complete the Venn diagram to compare and contrast characteristics of lakes and ponds.

❷ 🔺 **Form Operational Definitions** Based on your answers, write an operational definition for *lake*.

<u>Sample: a body of still water</u>
<u>that is too deep for sunlight to</u>
<u>reach the bottom</u>

Ponds — Sample: Shallower, sunlight reaches the bottom, algae

Sample: Contains still water

Lakes — Sample: Deeper, darker, colder, large fish

Digital Lesson: Assign the *Apply It* activity online and have students submit their work to you.

my science online.com ▷ **Ponds and Lakes**

FIGURE 4 ....
Types of Lakes
The photos show examples of glacial, volcanic, and rift valley lakes. ✎ **Classify** Write *G* on the glacial lake, *V* on the volcanic lake, and *R* on the rift valley lake.

Lake Formation Lakes can form through several natural processes. A river, for example, may bend and loop as it encounters obstacles in its path. Eventually, a new channel might form, cutting off a loop. The cutoff loop may become an oxbow lake.

Some lakes, such as the Great Lakes, formed in depressions created by ice sheets that melted at the end of the Ice Age. Other lakes were created by movements of Earth's crust that formed long, deep valleys called rift valleys. In Africa, Lake Tanganyika lies in a rift valley. Volcanoes can also form lakes. Lava or mud from a volcano can block a river, forming a lake. Lakes can also form in the empty craters of volcanoes.

People can create a lake by building a dam. A lake that stores water for human use is called a **reservoir**.

Lab zone — Do the Quick Lab *Modeling How a Lake Forms.*

🔑 Assess Your Understanding

2a. Explain What is one major difference between a lake and a pond?
<u>Lakes are usually deeper than ponds.</u>

b. Compare and Contrast How is a reservoir different from other kinds of lakes?
<u>A reservoir is created by people to hold water for human use.</u>

got it?

○ I get it! Now I know that lakes and ponds are <u>areas of still water that collect in low-lying areas.</u>

○ I need extra help with <u>See TE note.</u>

Go to **my science COACH** *online for help with this subject.*

337

Teacher Demo 🔬 Lab zone

L2 OBSERVING PLANT LIFE

Materials pond algae, pond plants

Time 10 minutes

Provide specimens of common pond algae such as *Spirogyra* or *Cladophora*, and pond plants such as pondweeds, for students to examine.

Ask: **How are the plants different from the algae?** *(The plants have roots and leaves, the algae do not. The plants are larger.)* **How are they alike?** *(They both are green.)* **How are the plants and algae important parts of their habitats?** *(They are a source of food and oxygen for animals.)*

Elaborate ——————

Lab Resource: Quick Lab 🔬 Lab zone

L2 MODELING HOW A LAKE FORMS Students will model the formation of a lake.

Evaluate ——————

Assess Your Understanding

After students answer the questions, have them evaluate their understanding by completing the appropriate sentence.

RTI Response to Intervention

2. If students have trouble contrasting lakes, ponds, and reservoirs, **then** have students skim the section to locate these highlighted terms and read the definition of each term.

my science 🄢 COACH Have students go online for help in understanding the similarities and differences between lakes and ponds.

Differentiated Instruction

L1 Sequence an Oxbow Lake Formation Illustrate how an oxbow lake forms with simple drawings that show: 1. a straight river with a loop (meander) in the middle, that becomes straight again; 2. the neck of the loop coming together; 3. the loop cut off from the main channel of the river; 4. a U-shaped lake near the straight river channel.

L3 Temporary Ponds Point out that in some parts of the United States, some ponds appear only in the spring and are gone by midsummer. These ponds are called vernal ponds. Invite students to research vernal ponds. They should find out how and where these ponds form and what kinds of organisms inhabit them.

Explain

Teach Key Concepts 🔑

Explain to students that natural processes and human activities can cause lakes to change. Help students see the cause-and-effect relationships that lead to eutrophication and the eventual replacement of a lake with a meadow. Ask: **What causes nutrients to be released into lake waters?** *(Nutrients are released when bacteria break down the bodies of dead lake organisms.)* **What effect does the buildup of nutrients in a lake have on algae?** *(Algae use the nutrients for growth. As algae grow and reproduce, they form a layer on the surface of the lake.)* **How does this layer of algae affect plants in the lake?** *(The algae layer blocks sunlight, which causes the lake plants to die.)* **How are lake animals affected?** *(The death of lake plants decreases the amount of food and oxygen that the animals need.)* **What role do humans play in eutrophication?** *(Human activities can increase eutrophication by increasing the amount of nutrients that enters ponds and lakes.)*

🔄 **Sequence** Explain that a sequence is the order in which a series of events occurs. A flowchart or a cycle diagram can help students visualize the steps in a sequence.

Teach With Visuals

Tell students to look at **Figure 5**. Ask: **In the second image of the lake, what has caused the lake to become shallower?** *(Decaying matter from dead plant and animals has piled up on the lake bottom.)* **What does the final image show?** *(The lake is completely filled in and has been replaced by a meadow or field covered with plants.)*

How Can Lakes Change?

If you watch a lake or pond over many years, you will see it change. In time, the lake may shrink and become shallower. 🔑 **Natural processes and human activities can cause lakes to disappear.**

Eutrophication As lake organisms die, bacteria break down the bodies and release nutrients into the water. These nutrients, such as nitrogen and phosphorus, are chemicals that other organisms need. Over time, nutrients can build up in the lake in a process called **eutrophication** (yoo troh fih KAY shun). Algae use these nutrients and spread, forming a layer on the lake's surface.

Figure 5 shows how eutrophication can change a lake. When the algae layer becomes so thick that it blocks sunlight, plants cannot carry out photosynthesis, and they die. Without food and oxygen from the plants, animals die. Decaying material from dead organisms piles up on the bottom, making the lake shallower. As the area fills in, land plants grow in the mud. Eventually, the area fills with plants, and a meadow replaces the former lake.

The Human Role Though eutrophication occurs naturally, human activities can also cause or increase it. For example, fertilizer from farms runs off into ponds and lakes, providing extra nutrients to the algae. The extra nutrients speed up the growth of algae, leading to faster eutrophication.

🔄 **Sequence** Which of the following processes occurs first during eutrophication?
- ⦿ Nutrients build up in a lake.
- ◯ A lake is replaced by a meadow.
- ◯ Plants stop carrying out photosynthesis.

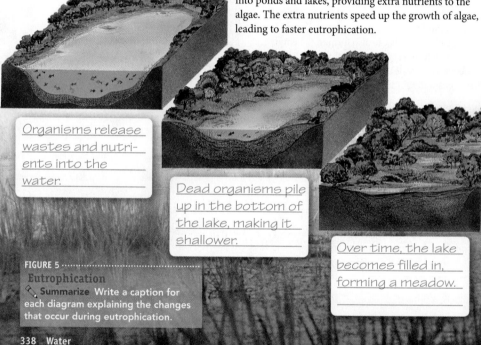

Organisms release wastes and nutrients into the water.

Dead organisms pile up in the bottom of the lake, making it shallower.

Over time, the lake becomes filled in, forming a meadow.

FIGURE 5
Eutrophication
✎ **Summarize** Write a caption for each diagram explaining the changes that occur during eutrophication.

338 Water

Real-World Inquiry allows students to explore issues regarding the Colorado River watershed.

my science online.com | **Changing Lakes**

An Endless Cycle

How does fresh water cycle on Earth?

FIGURE 6 ....
> REAL-WORLD INQUIRY Make a cycle diagram to show
how water cycles. Include the processes listed below.

Processes

Evaporation

Condensation

Transpiration

Precipitation

Runoff

Sample:

Clouds

Rain

Evaporation

Runoff to a river system and groundwater

Plants

Collects in lakes and oceans

Include examples of:
a river system
a lake or pond
an ocean
groundwater

Lab zone — Do the Quick Lab
How Can Algal Growth Affect Pond Life?

🗝 Assess Your Understanding

3a. Explain Eutrophication occurs when algae block sunlight in a lake or pond and plants cannot <u>carry out photosynthesis.</u>

b. ANSWER THE BIG ? How does fresh water cycle on Earth?
<u>Water forms river systems and also soaks into the ground. Through evaporation and transpiration, it moves into the atmosphere, from which it then falls as precipitation.</u>

got it?

○ I get it! Now I know that lakes can change due to <u>eutrophication and human activities.</u>

_____

_____

_____

○ I need extra help with <u>See TE note.</u>

Go to **MY SCIENCE COACH** *online for help with this subject.*

339

Explain

Explore the Big Q ? UbD

Direct students' attention to each process and its symbol. Help students review each process. Before making water-cycle diagrams, have students briefly identify each process and explain how the symbol shown represents that process. Ask: **What happens after evaporation?** *(Condensation)* **What happens to water that condenses?** *(It forms clouds and precipitation.)* **How does precipitation cycle back into the atmosphere?** *(Precipitation falls on the ground where it runs into bodies of water. This water evaporates and enters the atmosphere.)*

Lab Resource: Quick Lab

L1 HOW CAN ALGAL GROWTH AFFECT POND LIFE? Students will model the effect of algae population growth on ponds.

Evaluate

Assess Your Understanding

After students answer the questions, have them evaluate their understanding by completing the appropriate sentence.

Answer the Big Q ? UbD

To help students focus on the Big Question, lead a class discussion about how fresh water cycles on Earth.

RTI Response to Intervention

3a. If students cannot explain eutrophication in a lake or pond, **then** have them reread the definition of eutrophication and review the consequences of this process.

b. If students need help with describing the cycle of fresh water on Earth, **then** remind them that the water cycle is an endless cycle with no beginning or end. Have students' use their diagrams of the water cycle to review the processes.

MY SCIENCE COACH Have students go online for help in understanding eutrophication and the cycle of fresh water on Earth.

Differentiated Instruction

L1 Sequence Eutrophication Help students understand each step in the process that results in the filling in of a lake or pond as an end result of eutrophication. Students should be able to see that the lake is becoming smaller. As you focus students' attention on each diagram, review what is happening to the living and nonliving parts of the ecosystem.

L3 Fertilizers Explain to students that fertilizers used on farmland and in home gardens contain nitrates and phosphates. Have them discuss how fertilizers used on land can increase the rate of eutrophication in ponds and lakes. Encourage students to find out if their family uses fertilizers on a lawn or garden, and if so, what it contains.

Name ______________________ Date __________ Class __________

Lab zone® After the Inquiry Warm-Up

Surface Water

Inquiry Warm-Up, *Mapping Surface Waters*
In the Inquiry Warm-Up, you investigated surface waters in your state. Using what you learned from that activity, answer the questions below.

1. **INFER** Choose the largest body of water on your map. How do people use this body of water?

____

____

2. **RELATE CAUSE AND EFFECT** Why do you think the cities built near water were built there?

____

____

3. **PREDICT** How do you think the bodies of water in your state might change in the next one hundred years?

____

____

4. **INFER** How might excessive precipitation affect the bodies of water in your state?

____

____

Place the outside corner, the corner away from the dotted line, in the corner of your copy machine to copy onto letter-size paper.

Name _____ Date _____ Class _____

Surface Water

What Is a River System?

1a. **IDENTIFY** A (divide/tributary) separates two watersheds.

b. **SUMMARIZE** How is a watershed related to a river system? _____

_____

_____

c. **MAKE GENERALIZATIONS** How can a stream be part of more than one watershed?

_____

_____

got it? ....

○ **I get it!** Now I know that a river system is _____

_____

○ **I need extra help with** _____

_____

What Are Ponds and Lakes?

2a. **EXPLAIN** What is one major difference between a lake and a pond?

_____

b. **COMPARE AND CONTRAST** How is a reservoir different from other kinds of lakes?

_____

_____

got it? ....

○ **I get it!** Now I know that lakes and ponds are _____

_____

○ **I need extra help with** _____

_____

Name _____ Date _____ Class _____

Assess Your Understanding

Surface Water

How Can Lakes Change?

3a. EXPLAIN Eutrophication occurs when algae block
sunlight in a lake or pond and plants cannot _____

_____

b. ANSWER 🅱️ How does fresh water cycle on Earth?

_____

_____

_____

_____

_____

got it? ·

○ **I get it!** Now I know that lakes can change due to _____

_____

_____

○ **I need extra help with** _____

_____

Key Concept Summaries

Surface Water

What Is a River System?

The streams and smaller rivers that feed into a main river are **tributaries.** Tributaries flow toward the main river because they are pulled by the force of gravity. **A river and all the streams and smaller rivers that flow into it together make up a river system.**

The land area that supplies water to a river system is a **watershed,** or drainage basin. One watershed is separated from another by a ridge of land called a **divide.** The streams on each side of a divide flow in different directions.

What Are Ponds and Lakes?

Ponds and lakes form when water collects in hollows and in low-lying areas of land. Unlike rivers, ponds and lakes contain still or standing water. Ponds are usually smaller and shallower than lakes. Sunlight reaches to the bottom of all parts of a pond, but most lakes have some bottom areas that are too deep for much sunlight to reach them.

Lakes can form when a river bends as it encounters obstacles. A new channel forms that cuts off the bend. The cut-off bend becomes an oxbow lake. Some lakes formed from depressions created by ice sheets that melted at the end of the Ice Age. Others were created by movements of Earth's crust that formed long deep rift valleys. Lakes can form when a volcano blocks a river and they can form in the empty craters of volcanoes. By building a dam, people can create a lake called a **reservoir.**

How Can Lakes Change?

Natural processes and human activities can cause lakes to disappear. When lake organisms die, bacteria break down their bodies and release nutrients into the water. Over time, nutrients can build up in a lake in a process called **eutrophication.** Algae use the plentiful nutrients and grow into a thick layer that blocks sunlight from reaching lake plants. The lake plants die and the animals that eat them die as well. Decaying material piles up and the lake becomes shallower and eventually fills in.

Human activities can cause eutrophication or increase it. Fertilizer in runoff from farmland contains nutrients that increase eutrophication when the runoff enters ponds and lakes.

On a separate sheet of paper, explain how eutrophication can change a lake over time.

Surface Water

> **Understanding Main Ideas**
> Fill in the blank to complete each statement.

1. A small river flows into a larger one which eventually empties into

   the _____.

2. Tributaries flow downward toward the main river because of

   _____.

3. A river and all the streams and smaller rivers that flow into it

   together make up a _____.

4. A watershed is sometimes called a _____.

5. Water on each side of a divide flows in _____.

6. Ponds and lakes form when water collect in _____
   areas of land.

7. Ponds are smaller and _____ than lakes.

> **Building Vocabulary**
> Write a definition for each of these terms on the lines below.

8. tributary

   _____

9. divide

   _____

10. watershed

    _____

11. eutrophication

    _____

Surface Water

> Read each passage. Then choose one of the viewpoints below or another viewpoint of your own. On a separate sheet of paper, write a persuasive argument to support your viewpoint.

The Columbia River Debate

The Columbia River is the fourth largest river in North America. Its watershed includes seven northwestern states and two Canadian provinces. The Columbia River system is important to both the people and wildlife of the area, but sometimes their needs conflict. Government officials are now trying to decide how to balance the needs of humans and wildlife.

People need the Columbia River system. There are more than 100 dams along the Columbia and its tributaries. These dams help control flooding and create reservoirs that are used for swimming, boating, fishing, and other activities. Many of the dams generate inexpensive electric power for homes and businesses. This inexpensive power has encouraged the growth of industry in the area. The dams provide irrigation water that has turned arid land into productive farmland. The Columbia River also supplies water for cities and industries. In addition, the river system is used for shipping and for commercial salmon fishing, a $2 billion industry in the Northwest.

Salmon need the Columbia River system. Salmon reproduce in the Columbia's headwaters. The young fish, called smolts, swim downriver to the Pacific Ocean, where they grow to adulthood. The adults return to their birth–streams to reproduce and die. The river system's dams act as barriers to migrating smolts and adult salmon, since the fish cannot swim over or around them. Along some dams, people have built fish ladders so adult salmon can bypass the dams as they migrate upstream. Fish ladders are a series of steps in the water that allow fish to make several small jumps to get over the dam. But fish ladders do not help the smolts migrating downstream. They become stranded in lakes behind dams, are eaten by predators in the lakes, or are killed by the dams' turbines. Of every five smolts that start the downstream trip, only one reaches the ocean.

A. The Columbia River system is a valuable resource that should be used to meet the needs of the people.

B. The Columbia River system should be returned to its natural state so it can serve the needs of salmon and other wildlife.

Name _____ Date _____ Class _____

Surface Water

Write the letter of the correct answer on the line at the left.

1. ___ Lakes can disappear due to

   A condensation

   B transpiration

   C eutrophication

   D photosynthesis

2. ___ The streams and smaller rivers that feed into a main river are its

   A watersheds

   B tributaries

   C divides

   D reservoirs

3. ___ A stream that flows into two different rivers is part of two

   A reservoirs

   B tributaries

   C divides

   D watersheds

4. ___ Compared to lakes, ponds are usually

   A larger

   B deeper

   C shadier

   D shallower

Fill in the blank to complete each statement.

5. Though it occurs naturally, human activities can increase _____.

6. When a lake is created by the building of a dam, the lake is called a

   _____.

7. A river and all the streams and smaller rivers that flow into it together make up a

   _____.

8. A lake can form when a river is blocked by mud and lava from

   a _____.

9. Algae can overgrow a lake when the lake contains too many _____.

10. Nearly one third of the United States is covered by the Mississippi River

    _____.

Surface Water

Answer Key

After the Inquiry Warm-Up

1. Answers will vary based on the bodies of water in your state. Students may suggest recreation, transportation, or irrigation.

2. Answers may vary. Students may say cities were built near bodies of water used to transport raw materials to factories, to attract tourists, or to create hydroelectric power.

3. Answers will vary based on the bodies of water in your state. Students may say that shorelines would be eroded, courses of rivers might change, or lakes may grow or shrink.

4. Answers will vary based on the bodies of water in your state. Students may say rivers or lakes might be flooded.

Key Concept Summaries

As lake organisms die, their remains decay, releasing nutrients into the water. Over time, nutrients can build up in the lake. Algae use the nutrients to grow, eventually forming a layer so thick that it blocks sunlight and other plants die out. Animals that eat the plants die. Decayed material piles up on the lake bottom making the lake shallower. Over time, the area fills in and land plants grow in the mud. Finally, a meadow replaces the former lake.

Review and Reinforce

1. ocean
2. gravity
3. river system
4. drainage basin
5. different directions
6. low-lying
7. shallower
8. a stream or river that feeds into a main river
9. a ridge of land that separates one divide from another
10. the land area that supplies water to a river system
11. the buildup of nutrients in a lake over time due to the decayed remains of organisms

Enrich

Students' viewpoints and arguments they use to support them will vary. Accept and encourage all viewpoints supported with *specific details*. Some students may recognize that people holding Viewpoint A include those whose livelihoods depend on commercial salmon fishing.

Lesson Quiz

1. C
2. B
3. D
4. D
5. eutrophication
6. reservoir
7. river system
8. volcano
9. nutrients
10. watershed

Water Underground

 How does fresh water cycle on Earth?

Lesson Pacing: 1–2 periods or $\frac{1}{2}$–1 block

🕐 **SHORT ON TIME?** To do this lesson in approximately half the time, do the Activate Prior Knowledge activity followed by a discussion of the Key Concepts to familiarize students with the lesson content. Have students do the Quick Labs. The rest of the lesson can be completed by students independently.

Preference Navigator, in the online Planning tools, allows you to customize *Interactive Science* to your own teaching style. You can also edit lesson plans by selecting the Lesson Planner option.

Digital Teacher's Edition allows you to access your Teacher's Edition and Resource materials online.

MY SCIENCE online.com

Lesson Vocabulary

- permeable
- impermeable
- unsaturated zone
- saturated zone
- water table
- aquifer
- artesian well

 Content Refresher

Professional Development Note

Aquifer Depletion Taking more groundwater from an aquifer than can be naturally recharged is known as aquifer depletion. Dry wells are only one of the serious consequences of aquifer depletion. When water is depleted from an aquifer, the land above it may settle, a condition called subsidence. When groundwater is depleted in coastal areas, salt water is drawn into the aquifer. This makes the groundwater salty and unfit for drinking. Aquifer depletion results mainly from withdrawing water for irrigation. With traditional irrigation methods, more than 50 percent of the water applied to fields simply evaporates. Recent advances in irrigation technology are improving the efficiency of agricultural water use.

LESSON OBJECTIVES

🔖 Describe how water moves through underground layers of soil and rock.

🔖 Explain how people obtain water from an aquifer.

Blended Path
Active learning using Student Edition, Inquiry Path, and Digital Path

ENGAGE AND EXPLORE

Teach this lesson using a variety of resources. Begin by reading **My Planet Diary** as a class. Have students share ideas about why it is important to locate and protect groundwater. Then have students do the **Inquiry Warm-Up activity.** Students will observe water movement in various types of materials. Discuss how different materials absorb water. The **After the Inquiry Warm-Up worksheet** sets up a discussion about the properties of pebbles and sand. Have volunteers share their answers to number 4 about how water might interact with solid rock.

EXPLAIN AND ELABORATE

Teach Key Concepts by explaining the terms *permeable* and *impermeable.* Have students classify the gravel and clay in **Figure 1** as either *permeable* or *impermeable.* **Lead a Discussion** about the characteristics of unsaturated and saturated zones. Use the **Support the Big Q activity** to explain how groundwater is part of the water cycle.

Lead a Discussion about how an aquifer can provide water for people, crops, and livestock. Continue to **Teach Key Concepts** by explaining how the depth of a well is determined. Use **Figure 3** to helps students visualize the locations where people can get water from the aquifer using springs, wells, and artesian wells. **Lead a Discussion** about the benefits and downfalls of regular wells and artesian wells. Hand out the **Key Concept Summaries** as a review of each part of the lesson. Students can also use the online **Vocab Flash Cards** to review key terms.

EVALUATE

Have students take the **Lesson Quiz.** For an alternate assessment, see the **EXAM**VIEW® Assessment Suite, Progress Monitoring Assessments, or SuccessTracker™.

ⓔⓛⓛ Support

1 Content and Language

The word *saturated* means, "soaked." The prefix *un-* means, "not." When the *un-* prefix is added to *saturated,* the word becomes *unsaturated* meaning, "not soaked." List other words with the prefix *un-* and discuss their meanings.

Inquiry Path
Hands-on learning in the Lab zone

Digital Path
Online learning at **my science online**.com

ENGAGE AND EXPLORE

To teach this lesson with an emphasis on inquiry, begin with the **Inquiry Warm-Up activity.** Students will investigate water absorption in various types of soil. Discuss the movement of water in each type of soil. Have students do the **After the Inquiry Warm-Up worksheet.** Talk about the absorption of water in the sand versus in the pebbles. Have volunteers share their answers to number 4 about how they predicted water would interact with solid rock.

EXPLAIN AND ELABORATE

Focus on the **Inquiry Skill** for the lesson. Point out that when you predict, you use the available data to make a statement about your expectations. What prediction can students make about the movement of water in soil based on the data from the **Inquiry Warm-Up activity?** *(Since soil is similar to sand, the water will not move as quickly through soil as it does through pebbles.)* **Support the Big Q** by explaining how water from the soil is a part of the water cycle. Have students do the **Quick Lab** to model how various types of soil and rock layers affect water percolation. Ask them to share their results.

Do the last **Quick Lab** to help students understand how an artesian well works. Students can use the online **Vocab Flash Cards** to review key terms.

EVALUATE

Have students take the **Lesson Quiz.** For an alternate assessment, see the **EXAM**VIEW® Assessment Suite, Progress Monitoring Assessments, or SuccessTracker™.

ENGAGE AND EXPLORE

Teach this lesson using digital resources. Begin by having students explore how people locate and protect groundwater at **My Planet Diary** online. Have them access the Chapter Resources to find the **Unlock the Big Question activity.** There they can answer the questions and refine their responses as they continue through the lesson. You can re-assign the activity and have students submit their work so you can track their progress.

EXPLAIN AND ELABORATE

Students reading above, at, or below the lexile measure of this lesson can access basic content readings at their level at **My Reading Web.** Have students use the online **Vocab Flash Cards** to preview key terms. **Support the Big Q** by discussing the role of groundwater in the water cycle. Have students do the **Art in Motion activity** online to see how permeable and impermeable materials affect the water table. Do the **Quick Lab** and then ask students to share their results. Discuss how soil and rock layers affect the speed and direction of water percolation.

Assign the **Do the Math activity** online and have students submit their work to you. Ask volunteers to share their titles for the graph and their predictions. Assign the **Quick Lab** for students to model how an artesian well operates. The **Key Concept Summaries** online allow students to read a summary and see an image associated with each part of the lesson. Online remediation is available at **My Science Coach.**

EVALUATE

Have students take the **Lesson Quiz.** For an alternate assessment, see the **EXAM**VIEW® Assessment Suite, Progress Monitoring Assessments, or SuccessTracker™.

2 Frontload the Lesson
Preview the lesson visuals, labels, and captions. Ask students what they know about the words *permeable, impermeable, saturated,* and *unsaturated.* Explain the specific meanings these words have in science.

3 Comprehensible Input
Have students study the visuals and their captions to support the key concepts of the lesson.

4 Language Production
Pair or group students with varied language abilities to complete oral summaries collaboratively for language practice. Have each group share its summary with the class.

5 Assess Understanding
Have students keep a content area log. Use a two-column format with the headings "What I Understand" and "What I Don't Understand." Follow up so students can move items from the "Don't Understand" to the "Understand" column.

Water Underground

Establish Learning Objectives

After this lesson, students will be able to:

🔑 Describe how water moves through underground layers of soil and rock.

🔑 Explain how people obtain water from an aquifer.

Engage

Activate Prior Knowledge

MY PLANET DIARY Read *Looking for Water* with the class. Point out that Ms Oosting and her team use indirect methods to locate the source of water for a particular well. Ask: **How does the team use inference to determine where the water comes from?** *(They pump water out of the well that they are interested in. When the water level in surrounding wells drops, they then infer that these wells are in areas that contribute water to the first well.)*

BIG IDEAS OF SCIENCE REFERENCE LIBRARY 📖 Have students look up the following topic: Drinking Water.

Explore

Lab Resource: Inquiry Warm-Up 🔬

L1 **WHERE DOES THE WATER GO?** Students will observe how water moves through soil.

LESSON
3 Water Underground

🔑 **How Does Water Move Underground?**

🔑 **How Do People Use Groundwater?**

MY PLANET DIARY   CAREER

Looking for Water

How do you know where the water you drink comes from? Saskia Oosting could help you find out! Ms. Oosting works for a company that locates and protects groundwater supplies. She is a project manager, which means she coordinates the work of many other people.

One of her company's jobs is figuring out where the water in a particular well comes from. Scientists and engineers drill other wells near the well they're observing. Then they pump water out of the first well and watch the others to see where the level of groundwater drops. Once they've found the area that contributes water to the well, the company can help people who use that water keep the supply clean.

✏️ Communicate With a partner, discuss your answers to these questions.

1. How do engineers find out where the water in a well comes from?

   They drill more wells nearby, pump water out of the first well, and watch where the water level changes.

2. What kinds of science skills do you think Ms. Oosting needs to do her job?

   Sample: observing, making inferences, making predictions

▷ PLANET DIARY Go to **Planet Diary** to learn more about groundwater.

🔬 Lab zone Do the Inquiry Warm-Up *Where Does the Water Go?*

SUPPORT ALL READERS

Lexile Measure = 950L   Lexile Word Count = 1233

Prior Exposure to Content: May be the first time students have encountered this topic

Academic Vocabulary: *cause, effect, predict, communicate, interpret*

Science Vocabulary: *permeable, impermeable, aquifer*

Concept Level: Generally appropriate for most students in this grade

Preteach With: My Planet Diary "Looking for Water" and Figure 1 activity

Go to **My Reading Web** to access leveled readings that provide a foundation for the content.

my science online.com ▶

Vocabulary
- permeable • impermeable
- unsaturated zone • saturated zone
- water table • aquifer • artesian well

Skills
- Reading: Relate Cause and Effect
- Inquiry: Predict

How Does Water Move Underground?

Where does underground water come from? Like surface water, underground water generally comes from precipitation. Some precipitation soaks into the ground, pulled by gravity.

If you pour water into a glass full of pebbles, the water flows down around the pebbles until it reaches the bottom of the glass. Then the water begins to fill up the spaces between the pebbles. **In the same way, water underground trickles down between particles of soil and through cracks and spaces in layers of rock.**

Effects of Different Materials Different types of rock and soil have different-sized spaces, or pores, between their particles, as shown in **Figure 1.** The size of the pores and the connections between them determine how easily water moves. Because they have large and connected pores, materials such as sand and gravel allow water to pass through, or permeate. They are thus known as **permeable** (PUR mee uh bul) materials.

Other materials have few or no pores or cracks, or the pores are very small. Clay has very small pores and is less permeable than sand. Unless it is cracked, granite is **impermeable,** meaning that water cannot pass through easily.

FIGURE 1 ....

Permeable and Impermeable Materials
Compare how water moves in clay (left) and gravel (right).

✎ **Compare and Contrast**
Which material is more permeable? (gravel)/clay) **Why?**

There is more space between gravel particles than between clay particles.

341

Explain

Introduce Vocabulary
Explain that *permeable* comes from a Latin word that means "can be passed through." Point out that permeable materials are those that other materials, especially liquids, can pass through or permeate. Remind students that the prefix *im-* means "not," so *impermeable* describes a material that liquids cannot pass through.

Teach Key Concepts 🔑
Explain to students that water moves underground between particles of soil and through cracks and through spaces in layers of rock. Ask: **How does water fill up spaces underground?** *(It trickles down through spaces between particles of soil and through cracks in rock layers.)* **What term describes material through which water can pass?** *(Permeable)* Point out that when water seeps into the ground and reaches an impermeable layer, the water stops sinking. This occurs because the rock layer is made up materials that have few open spaces through which water can pass. Ask: **What term describes material through which water cannot pass?** *(Impermeable)*

Teach With Visuals
Tell students to look at the two photographs in **Figure 1.** Ask: **What visual clues help you determine whether clay or gravel material is more permeable?** *(Water is pooling on top of the clay and trickling down through the gravel, so gravel is more permeable than clay.)*

21st Century Learning

CREATIVITY Review the meaning of the terms permeable and impermeable. Have students identify materials in the classroom that are permeable, such as clothing fabric, and materials that are impermeable, such as the stone chalkboard or wood or metal furniture. Have students brainstorm to think of ways life might be different if the permeable objects were impermeable and vice versa.

My Planet Diary provides an opportunity for students to explore real-world connections to groundwater formation.

MY SCIENCE online.com | Groundwater Formation

Explain

Lead a Discussion

WATER ZONES Help students see the significance of knowing the depth of the water table. Ask: **How do the unsaturated and saturated zones of rock and soil layers differ?** *(The unsaturated top layer is made up of layers of rock and soil that contain air as well as water. So they are not filled with water. Below this zone is the saturated zone where the spaces in the ground are filled or saturated with water.)* **What is the top of the saturated zone called?** *(The water table)* **Why is knowing the depth of the water table helpful if you want to dig a well?** *(It tells you how deep you need to dig to reach groundwater.)*

Support the Big Q ? UbD

WATER IN SOIL Remind students that water that moves through soil is also part of the water cycle. Ask: **How does water enter the soil?** *(It soaks down through permeable layers of rock and soil.)* Point out that water in the soil is not static. It moves through the permeable layer and may emerge on the surface again.

Elaborate

Lab Resource: Quick Lab

L2 SOIL PERCOLATION Students will model the effect that various types of soil and rock layers have on the speed and direction of water percolation.

Evaluate

Assess Your Understanding

After students answer the questions, have them evaluate their understanding by completing the appropriate sentence.

RTI Response to Intervention

1a. If students cannot distinguish between permeable and impermeable material, **then** have them locate the highlighted terms and reread the paragraph that contains the terms and their definitions.

b. If students have trouble identifying the water table, **then** have them locate the highlighted term water table and read the definition. Students also should review **Figure 2.**

c. If students have trouble describing rock in the saturated zone, **then** have them review **Figure 2** and the definition of saturated zone.

my science COACH Have students go online for help in understanding permeability and the water table.

Water Zones Water from precipitation soaks down through permeable rock and soil layers. These layers contain air as well as water, so they are not saturated, or filled, with water. This top layer is thus called the **unsaturated zone.**

However, at some depth, the water reaches a level where the pores in the ground are saturated with water, called the **saturated zone.** The top of the saturated zone is the **water table.** If you know the depth of the water table in your area, you can tell how deep you must dig to reach groundwater.

The saturated zone often reaches deep into Earth, even though the rock becomes less permeable the deeper you go. Sometimes the direction of the water's flow is changed by impermeable layers, which the water has a harder time flowing through.

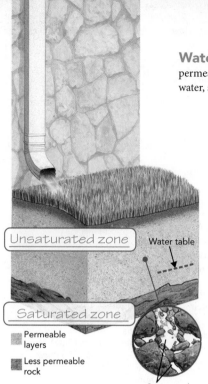

Unsaturated zone

Water table

Saturated zone

Permeable layers

Less permeable rock

Connected pores

FIGURE 2 ....

> ART IN MOTION **Groundwater Formation**
Upper areas of the soil contain both air and water, while lower areas, including less permeable rock, are saturated with water.

✎ **Interpret Diagrams** Label the saturated and unsaturated zones. Shade in the area where water will collect.

Water will collect below the water table (including in the less permeable rock layers).

Lab zone Do the Quick Lab Soil Percolation.

🔖 Assess Your Understanding

1a. Review Water slows down when it reaches (permeable/(impermeable)) material.

b. Explain What is the water table?
<u>The water table is the top of</u>
<u>the saturated layer.</u>

c. Infer The rock deep within the saturated zone most likely has (large/(small)) and (connected/(unconnected)) pores. Explain your answer.
<u>Since water does not pass</u>
<u>through easily, the pores must</u>
<u>be small or unconnected.</u>

got it? ....

○ I get it! Now I know that water moves through soil by <u>soaking through permeable</u> <u>materials until it reaches a saturated zone.</u>

○ I need extra help with <u>See TE note.</u>

Go to **my science COACH** online for help with this subject.

Art In Motion shows how permeable and impermeable materials affect the water table.

my science online.com ▶ | Groundwater Formation

How Do People Use Groundwater?

Suppose you live far from a river, lake, or pond. How could you reach groundwater for your needs? You might be in luck: The water table in your area might be only a few meters underground. In fact, in some places the water table actually meets the surface. Springs can form as groundwater bubbles or flows out of cracks in the rock.

Aquifers Any underground layer of permeable rock or sediment that holds water and allows it to flow is called an **aquifer.** Aquifers can range in size from a small patch to an area the size of several states. The huge Ogallala aquifer lies beneath the plains of the Midwest, from South Dakota to Texas. This aquifer provides water for millions of people, as well as for crops and livestock.

Aquifers are not unlimited sources of water. If people take water from the aquifer faster than the aquifer refills, the level of the aquifer will drop. As you'll see on the next page, this will make it more difficult to reach water in the future.

✏️ **Vocabulary** The Latin root *aqua-* is found in words such as *aquarium* and *aquatic* as well as *aquifer*. What do you think this root means?

<u>Water</u>

do the math!

Uses of Water

The graph shows water use in the United States. Use the graph to answer the questions below.

❶ **Read Graphs** What would be a good title for this graph? <u>Sample: Uses of Water in the United States</u>

❷ **Interpret Data** The two largest categories combine to make up about what percentage of the total water used in the United States? <u>83%</u>

❸ **Predict** How would an increase in the amount of land used for farms affect this graph? <u>The percentage of water used for agriculture would increase.</u>

❹ **Calculate** If the total daily usage of water in the United States is 1,280 billion liters, about how many liters are used by power plants? <u>About 600 billion liters</u>

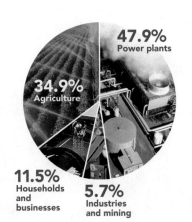

47.9% Power plants

34.9% Agriculture

11.5% Households and businesses

5.7% Industries and mining

343

Explain

Lead a Discussion

AQUIFERS Help students locate the aquifer in **Figure 3** on the next page. Ask: **What is an aquifer?** *(Any underground layer of permeable rock or sediment that holds water and allow it to flow)* **What is the consequence of taking water from an aquifer faster than the aquifer can refill?** *(The level of the aquifer can drop which could make it more difficult for people to reach the water in the aquifer.)*

Elaborate

21st Century Learning

COMMUNICATION Have students read *Drinking Water* in the **Big Ideas of Science Reference Library.** Ask them to do further research on the fluid requirements for two athletic activities, such as football and running, or others of their choosing. Interview the school's athletic director as part of your research. Recreate the interview with a partner who will play the role of the athletic director. Include dialogue on the dangers of both dehydration and over hydration.

Do the Math!

L1 Some students may have difficulty determining how to calculate the approximate number of liters of water used by power plants. Explain that multiplying 47.9 percent (.479) by the total daily usage (1,280 billion liters), they obtain the result 613 billion liters that can be rounded off to 600 billion liters.

🔺 **Predict** Remind students that a prediction is not a guess, but a statement of what is expected to happen based on available data.

See *Math Skill and Problem-Solving Activities* for support.

Digital Lesson: Assign the *Do the Math* activity online and have students submit their work to you.

my science online .com ▶ Water Underground

Differentiated Instruction

L3 Groundwater Contaminants Invite interested students to research and report on the relationship of one of the following to contamination of groundwater: improper disposal of motor oil, overuse of fertilizers on plants, improper disposal of hazardous chemicals. Students can share what they learn in the form of a poster showing how to avoid contaminating groundwater.

L1 Do the Math Read Question 2 aloud to students. Ask them to identify the clue in the question that lets them know they can estimate the answer. ("About what percentage") Then, ask students to identify the two largest categories and round the decimals to the nearest whole number before adding the amounts.

Elaborate

Teach Key Concepts 🔑

Tell students that to provide water, a well must be drilled below the water table. Point out that when the bottom of a well is in a saturated zone, the well will contain water. Ask: **What will happen to a well if the water table drops below the bottom of the well?** *(The well will run dry.)* **What are two ways that the well could become usable again?** *(The well would have to be made deeper to reach the lowered water table, or rainfall could naturally replenish the aquifer.)*

Teach With Visuals

Tell students to look at **Figure 3.** Ask: **What causes the spring to form?** *(Groundwater is flowing though cracks in the rock onto the surface.)* Note that there are many possible locations for students to draw the wells. Ask: **Where in the drawing could you put the regular well?** *(Anywhere, as long as it reaches below the current water table.)* **Do you have more or fewer places to put the artesian well? Explain your answer.** *(Fewer; it must be in a place where the water is trapped between rock layers and the level of water in the aquifer is higher than the top of the well.)*

21st Century Learning

INTERPERSONAL SKILLS Explain to students that in Yellowstone National Park, the water that collects around hot springs and geysers is often extremely clear. Have them work in pairs to make an inference about what the most likely reason for this is. *(The water that flows out of hot springs and that erupts from geysers is boiling hot. It is too hot to support the growth of algae or most kinds of bacteria. Without the growth of these and other organisms to cloud it, the water remains crystal clear.)*

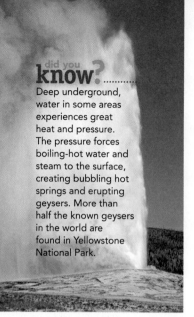

did you know?

Deep underground, water in some areas experiences great heat and pressure. The pressure forces boiling-hot water and steam to the surface, creating bubbling hot springs and erupting geysers. More than half the known geysers in the world are found in Yellowstone National Park.

Movement in Aquifers Do you picture groundwater as a large, still pool beneath Earth's surface? In fact, the water is moving, seeping through layers of rock or soil. The rate of motion depends largely on the slope of the water table and the permeability of the rocks. Some groundwater moves only a few centimeters a day. At that rate, the water moves about 10 meters a year. Groundwater may travel hundreds of kilometers and stay in an aquifer for thousands of years before coming to the surface again.

Wells The depth and level of a water table can vary greatly over a small area. Generally, the level of a water table follows the shape of the surface of the land, as shown in **Figure 3.** The level can rise during heavy rains or snow melts, and fall in times of dry weather.

Since ancient times, people have brought groundwater to the surface for drinking and other everyday uses. 🔑 **People can obtain groundwater from an aquifer by drilling a well below the water table.** When the bottom of the well is in a saturated zone, the well contains water. If the water table drops below the bottom of the well, the well will run dry and water cannot be obtained from it.

FIGURE 3 ·······

Springs and Wells

Suppose you are a farmer looking for water sources.

✏️ **Make Judgments** Draw lines showing where you would drill a regular well and an artesian well. Explain why you chose those locations.

Regular well

Spring

Water Table

Aquifer

Using Pumps
Long ago, people dug wells by hand. They used a bucket to bring up the water. People may also have used simple pumps. Today, however, most wells are dug with well-drilling equipment. Mechanical pumps bring up the groundwater.

Pumping water out of an aquifer lowers the water level near the well. If too much water is pumped out too fast, a well may run dry. The owners of the well will have to dig deeper to reach the lowered water table, or wait for rainfall to refill the aquifer.

Relying on Pressure
Another option for bringing up groundwater is an artesian well. In an **artesian well** (ahr TEE zhun), water rises on its own because of pressure within an aquifer.

In some aquifers, groundwater becomes trapped between two layers of impermeable rock or sediment. This water is under great pressure from the water extending back up the aquifer. If the top layer of rock is punctured, the pressure sends water spurting up through the hole. No pump is necessary—in an artesian well, water pressure does the job.

Artesian well

Sample: I would put the regular well in an area where the water table is near the surface, so the well would not have to be as deep. I would put an artesian well where there is an aquifer trapped in the rock, so there would be enough pressure to bring up the water without a pump.

⟲ Relate Cause and Effect
If the water table near a well is (raised/~~lowered~~), the well may run dry.

Do the Quick Lab
An Artesian Well.

🗨 Assess Your Understanding

2a. Describe What are three ways people can get water from an aquifer?

Springs, wells, and artesian wells

b. Infer Use **Figure 3** as a guide. Why is it important to know the depth of an aquifer before drilling a well?

The well must be deep enough to reach the aquifer.

c. Solve Problems During the winter, you draw your water from a well. Every summer, the well dries up. What might be the reason for the change?

Sample: The water table must drop during the summer. There may be less precipitation or more evaporation during the summer.

got it? ·········

○ **I get it!** Now I know that people reach underground water by _using springs or digging wells to reach aquifers._

○ **I need extra help with** _See TE note._

Go to **my science coach** online for help with this subject.

345

Differentiated Instruction

L1 Understanding Groundwater and Wells Pair students who are having difficulty with concepts in this section with more proficient students. Have each student pair construct a concept map that includes descriptions and explanations of the terms *aquifer, well, artesian well,* and *spring.*

L3 Geysers Encourage students to do research to find out what conditions are needed for a geyser to erupt. Students can report their findings in a labeled diagram.

Lead a Discussion

OBTAINING WATER Have students review how water from a regular well is mechanically pumped to the surface. Help them contrast this method with an artesian well, which relies on the water pressure in the aquifer to send water to the surface. Ask: **What is an advantage of an artesian well over a regular well?** *(No pump is needed with an artesian well.)* **Given this advantage, why aren't artesian wells used all the time?** *(They can only be used where conditions are right. The aquifer must be trapped between rock layers and the water must extend higher than the well.)*

 Cause and Effect Explain that relating a cause and its effect involves evaluating two events and deciding that one of them is the cause of the other. The event that results in a change is the cause. The change that occurs is the effect.

Elaborate
Lab Resource: Quick Lab
L2 AN ARTESIAN WELL Students will model how people get water from artesian wells.

Evaluate
Assess Your Understanding
After students answer the questions, have them evaluate their understanding by completing the appropriate sentence.

RTI Response to Intervention
2a. If students need help describing ways people get water from an aquifer, **then** have them review the three methods typically used to get water from an aquifer—springs, regular wells, and artisan wells.

b. If students cannot infer why it is important to know the depth of an aquifer before drilling a well, **then** have them look again at **Figure 3.**

c. If students have trouble identifying a possible cause of well drying up seasonally, **then** suggest that they consider the probability of a decrease in precipitation and an increase in evaporation that might occur in summer as compared with other seasons.

my science coach Have students go online for help in understanding wells.

Lab **zone** **After the Inquiry Warm-Up**

Water Underground

> **Inquiry Warm-Up, *Where Does the Water Go?***
> In the Inquiry Warm-Up, you investigated water absorption with different materials. Using what you learned from that activity, answer the questions below.

1. **OBSERVE** Which did the water move through more quickly, the sand or the pebbles?

   _____

2. **INFER** Why do you think it moved faster through that material?

   _____

3. **INFER** Why does the sand stay wet once the water has reached the bottom of the jar?

   _____

4. **PREDICT** If there were a layer of solid rock at the bottom of the jar, how would the water interact with the solid rock?

   _____

Assess Your Understanding

Water Underground

How Does Water Move Underground?

1a. **REVIEW** Water slows down when it reaches (permeable/impermeable) material.

b. **EXPLAIN** What is the water table?

_____

c. **INFER** The rock deep within the saturated zone most likely has (large/small) and (connected/unconnected) pores. Explain your answer.

_____

got**it?** ···

○ **I get it!** Now I know that water moves through soil by _____

_____

○ **I need extra help with** _____

_____

How Do People Use Groundwater?

2a. **DESCRIBE** What are three ways people can get water from an aquifer?

_____

b. **INFER** Use **Figure 3** as a guide. Why is it important to know the depth of an aquifer before drilling a well?

_____

_____

c. **SOLVE PROBLEMS** During the winter, you draw your water from a well. Every summer, the well dries up. What might be the reason for the change?

_____

_____

got**it?** ···

○ **I get it!** Now I know that people reach underground water by _____

_____

○ **I need extra help with** _____

_____

·····················

Water Underground

How Does Water Move Underground?

Underground water generally comes from precipitation, which soaks into the ground. **Water underground trickles down between particles of soil and through cracks and spaces in layers of rock.**

Because they have large and connected pores, materials such as sand and gravel allow water to pass through, or permeate and are called **permeable** materials. Other materials, such as clay have few or no pores or cracks or the pores are very small. These materials are less permeable than sand. Granite is **impermeable,** meaning that water cannot pass through easily.

The top layers of rock and soil contain air as well as water and are called the **unsaturated zone.** At some depth the water reaches the **saturated zone,** a level where the pores in the ground are saturated with water. The top of the saturated zone is called the **water table.** The saturated zone reaches deep into Earth even though the rock becomes less permeable the deeper you go.

How Do People Use Groundwater?

An underground layer of permeable rock or sediment that holds water and allows it to flow is called an **aquifer.** Aquifers do not have unlimited sources of water. The rate that water moves in an aquifer depends on the slope of the water table and the permeability of the rocks. The level of a water table generally follows the shape of the surface of the land. The level can rise during heavy rains or snow melts and fall during times of dry weather.

People can obtain groundwater from an aquifer by drilling a well below the water table. When the bottom of the well is in a saturated zone, the well contains water. Today most wells are dug with well-drilling equipment. Mechanical pumps bring up the groundwater. If too much water is pumped out too fast, a well may run dry.

In an **artesian well,** water rises on its own because of pressure within an aquifer. In some aquifers, groundwater becomes trapped between two layers of impermeable rock or sediment. This water is under great pressure from the water extending back up the aquifer. If the top layer of rock is punctured, the pressure sends water spurting up through the hole.

On a separate sheet of paper, describe the materials and zones water moves through underground.

Name _____ Date _____ Class _____

Water Underground

Understanding Main Ideas
Answer the following questions in the spaces provided.

1. Describe how water moves underground.

_____

_____

_____

2. How can people obtain groundwater from an aquifer?

_____

_____

3. What controls the rate of movement of groundwater?

_____

_____

4. Describe how an artesian well works.

_____

_____

_____

_____

Building Vocabulary
On a separate sheet of paper, write a definition for each of these terms.

5. permeable

6. impermeable

7. unsaturated zone

8. saturated zone

9. water table

10. artesian well

Enrich

Water Underground

> Below is a model of an aquifer a student made. Study the model, then answer the questions that follow in the spaces provided.

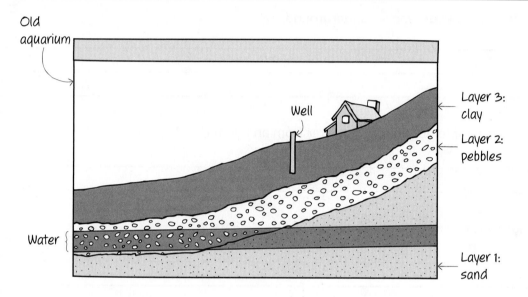

1. Study the layers in the diagram. How would Layer 3 affect runoff?

   _____

   _____

2. Would water collect where it is shown on the diagram? Explain your answer.

   _____

   _____

3. Would the well shown on the plan work in real life? Explain.

   _____

   _____

4. Redraw the plan for the model, showing any changes you would make. Include the underground layers, the well, and the water table. Label the layers to show the materials you would use if you were building the model.

Name _____ Date _____ Class _____

Lesson Quiz

Water Underground

Choose the best answer to the following questions.

1. ___ Which describes materials that have large and connected pores, such as sand and gravel?

   A   unsaturated

   B   impermeable

   C   saturated

   D   permeable

2. ___ By knowing the water table depth, you know how deep to dig to reach which of the following?

   A   granite

   B   springs

   C   groundwater

   D   pores

3. ___ Where can the water table be found?

   A   at the top of the saturated zone

   B   between layers of impermeable rock

   C   in the unsaturated zone

   D   below layers of clay soil

4. ___ Which is the best way to get water from an aquifer with a well?

   A   Drill below the water table.

   B   Drill below the aquifer.

   C   Drill near a dry well.

   D   Drill below impermeable rock.

Use the illustration below and a separate sheet of paper to answer Questions 5–10.

1. *layer of loose soil*

2. *layer of sand*

3. *layer of gravel*

4. *layer of hard clay*

5. *solid rock*

5. Which layers are permeable?

6. Which layers are impermeable?

7. Use a blue pencil or marker to add groundwater to the diagram. Put it in a logical place.

8. Label the saturated zone   9. Label the water table.   10. Label the unsaturated zone.

Water Underground

Answer Key

After the Inquiry Warm-Up

1. the pebbles

2. There is more space between the pebbles than between the grains of sand.

3. Sample: Some of the water stayed in the sand when the rest seeped through to the bottom of the jar, causing the sand to stay wet.

4. The rock would not absorb the water.

Key Concept Summaries

Materials that have large and connected pores that allow water to pass through are permeable. Materials with few or no pores does not allow water to pass through are impermeable. Water first passes through the unsaturated zone, which contains permeable layers. Then it reaches the saturated zone, where the pores in the ground are saturated with water. The water table is the top of the saturated zone.

Review and Reinforce

1. It trickles down between particles of soil and through cracks and spaces in layers of rock.

2. They can drill a well below the water table.

3. It depends largely on the slope of the water table and the permeability of the rocks.

4. In aquifers where groundwater becomes trapped between two layers of impermeable rock or sediment, the water is under great pressure. When the top layer of rock is punctured, the water pressure sends water spurting up through the hole.

5. materials such as sand and gravel allow water to pass through, or permeate

6. materials through which water cannot pass easily

7. the top layers of rock and soil that contain air as well as water

8. an underground level where the pores in the ground are saturated with water

9. the top of the saturated zone

10. a well in which water rises on its own because of pressure within an aquifer

Enrich

1. Since Layer 3 is clay, which is impermeable to water, runoff would flow over the land rather than sink into the ground.

2. No; sand is permeable and would not hold water in a layer as it is shown; the water would trickle down through the sand until it reached an impermeable layer.

3. No; the bottom of the well is in an impermeable layer and does not reach the water.

4. Students' drawings should at least include the following corrections: Move Layer 3 down (use clay for the bottom layer). The "band" of water should not extend into the clay. The bottom of the well should extend down past the water table in Layer 2.

Lesson Quiz

1. D
2. C
3. A
4. A
5. Layers 1, 2, and 3
6. Layers 4 and 5

7. Students drawings should include the most water drawn in the layer of gravel. They can include some water in the soil or sand, but there should be none in the layers of clay and rock.

8. Label for the saturated zone should be placed near the bottom of the diagram.

9. Label for the water table should be placed on the layer of gravel.

10. Label for the unsaturated zone should be placed near the top of the diagram.

Place the outside corner, the corner away from the dotted line, in the corner of your copy machine to copy onto letter-size paper.

Exploring the Ocean

How does fresh water cycle on Earth?

Lesson Pacing: 2–3 periods or 1–1½ blocks

🕐 **SHORT ON TIME?** To do this lesson in approximately half the time, do the Activate Prior Knowledge activity followed by a discussion of the Key Concepts to familiarize students with the lesson content. Use the Explore the Big Q to help students identify some characteristics of Earth's oceans. Do the Quick Labs and have students do the Interactive Art online. The rest of the lesson can be completed by students independently.

> **Preference Navigator,** in the online Planning tools, allows you to customize *Interactive Science* to your own teaching style. You can also edit lesson plans by selecting the Lesson Planner option.
>
> **Digital Teacher's Edition** allows you to access your Teacher's Edition and Resource materials online.

Lesson Vocabulary

- salinity
- sonar
- seamount
- trench
- continental slope
- continental shelf
- abyssal plain
- mid-ocean ridge

Content Refresher

Professional Development Note

Oxygen and Nitrogen in Ocean Water The air we breathe contains oxygen and nitrogen. At sea-level pressure, very little of the nitrogen we breathe in is absorbed into our blood. However, when divers are exposed to high pressure in deep water, their blood absorbs both nitrogen and oxygen. If a diver comes to the surface too quickly, the sudden pressure drop causes nitrogen dissolved in the blood to come out and forms bubbles. This causes a painful, even life-threatening, condition called the bends. To avoid the bends, divers going deeper than about 20 m must return to surface pressure slowly.

LESSON OBJECTIVES

- Identify characteristics of the ocean and ocean water.
- Identify the features and main sections of the ocean floor.

Blended Path
Active learning using Student Edition, Inquiry Path, and Digital Path

ENGAGE AND EXPLORE

Teach this lesson using a variety of resources. Begin by reading **My Planet Diary** as a class. Have students share ideas about what types of ocean conditions could be dangerous. Then have students do the **Inquiry Warm-Up activity.** Students will make inferences without their sense of sight. Discuss how they gathered information even without their sense of sight. The **After the Inquiry Warm-Up worksheet** sets up a discussion about characteristics of the object based on probing with straws. Have volunteers share their answers to number 4 about how this activity is similar to early ocean explorations.

EXPLAIN AND ELABORATE

Teach Key Concepts by explaining the three characteristics of oceans. Use **Figure 1** to illustrate the makeup of salinity in the ocean water. Continue to **Teach Key Concepts** by describing the temperature changes in ocean water. Explain to students that as you descend deeper into the water the pressure of the water increases. **Lead a Discussion** about the water pressure on a submersible vehicle at different depths. Then have students practice the inquiry skill in the **Apply It activity.**

Teach Key Concepts by asking students how the features of the ocean floor are formed. **Lead a Discussion** in which students compare the features of the ocean floor with those on the continents. Use the **Explore the Big Q** to illustrate the way that sonar information is used not just to map out the ocean floor but also to locate lost objects. Discuss students' responses to the **Answer the Big Q.** Hand out the **Key Concept Summaries** as a review of each part of the lesson. Students can also use the online **Vocab Flash Cards** to review key terms.

EVALUATE

Have students take the **Lesson Quiz.** For an alternate assessment, see the **EXAM**VIEW® Assessment Suite, Progress Monitoring Assessments, or SuccessTracker™.

ELL Support

1 Content and Language

Abyss comes from the Greek word *abyssos,* meaning "bottomless." When the suffix *–al,* meaning "pertaining to" is added to the word *abyss,* it becomes the adjective *abyssal,* describing a flat region of the ocean floor. Discuss phrases people use which include *abyss* or *abyssal.*

Lab zone Inquiry Path
Hands-on learning in the Lab zone

Digital Path
Online learning at **my science online**.com

ENGAGE AND EXPLORE

To teach this lesson with an emphasis on inquiry, begin with the **Inquiry Warm-Up activity.** Students will make inferences about a hidden object. Discuss what type of information they gathered without using their sense of sight. Have students do the **After the Inquiry Warm-Up worksheet.** Talk about what information they were able to gather using the straw probes. Have volunteers share their answers to number 4 about how this activity is similar to early explorations in the oceans.

EXPLAIN AND ELABORATE

Focus on the **Inquiry Skill** for the lesson. Point out that when you interpret data, you explain the importance of the facts, figures, and observations. What type of data was interpreted in the **Inquiry Warm-Up activity?** *(Data gained through observations to determine what was in the box)* Review how the depth of the ocean affects the temperature and pressure before beginning the **Apply It activity.** Ask volunteers to share their responses. Have students do the **Quick Lab** to better understand ocean conditions. Ask volunteers to share their results.

Build Inquiry to reinforce students' understanding of the various features of the ocean floor. Use the **Explore the Big Q activity** to help students interpret data relating to the characteristics of the ocean floor features. Do the **Quick Lab** to explore the profile of the ocean floor using a graph. Discuss student responses to the **Answer the Big Q activity.** Students can use the online **Vocab Flash Cards** to review key terms.

EVALUATE

Have students take the **Lesson Quiz.** For an alternate assessment, see the **EXAM**VIEW® Assessment Suite, Progress Monitoring Assessments, or SuccessTracker™.

ENGAGE AND EXPLORE

Teach this lesson using digital resources. Begin by having students explore the precautions taken during deep-sea escapes at **My Planet Diary** online. Have them access the Chapter Resources to find the **Unlock the Big Question activity.** There they can answer the questions and refine their responses as they continue through the lesson. You can re-assign the activity and have students submit their work so you can track their progress.

EXPLAIN AND ELABORATE

Students reading above, at, or below the lexile measure of this lesson can access basic content readings at their level at **My Reading Web.** The **Virtual Lab** online allows students to investigate characteristics of sea water. Have students use the online **Vocab Flash Cards** to preview key terms. Review the depth and temperature variations in the ocean water before assigning the online **Apply It activity.** Ask volunteers to share their interpretations of the data. Have students submit their work to you. Do the **Quick Lab** and then ask students to share their results.

Have students do the online **Interactive Art activity** to explore the features of the ocean floor. Use the **Explore the Big Q** by making predictions using the data provided. Assign the **Quick Lab** to make a graph of the ocean floor. Discuss student responses to the online **Answer the Big Q.** The **Key Concept Summaries** online allow students to read a summary and see an image associated with each part of the lesson. Online remediation is available at **My Science Coach.**

EVALUATE

Have students take the **Lesson Quiz.** For an alternate assessment, see the **EXAM**VIEW® Assessment Suite, Progress Monitoring Assessments, or SuccessTracker™.

2 Frontload the Lesson
Preview the lesson visuals, labels, and captions. Ask students what they know about the terms *continental slope, trench, seamount, continental shelf, abyssal plain,* and *mid-ocean range.* Explain the specific meanings of these words by comparing them to similar land features.

3 Comprehensible Input
Have students study the visuals and their captions to support the key concepts of the lesson.

4 Language Production
Pair or group students with varied language abilities to complete labs collaboratively for language practice. Have each student copy the completed written lab for personal reference.

5 Assess Understanding
Divide the class into small groups. Have each student identify a key concept from the lesson to discuss in his or her group. After the discussions, have students talk about the key concepts as a group.

Exploring the Ocean

Establish Learning Objectives

 Identify characteristics of the ocean and ocean water.

 Identify the features and main sections of the ocean floor.

Engage

Activate Prior Knowledge

MY PLANET DIARY Read *Deep-Sea Escape* with the class. Ask students who have been diving or snorkeling to share their experiences. Ask them what special precautions they took to stay safe. *(Samples: Swim with a partner; wear a wet suit.)* Ask: **What risks are there for people who need to escape from a submarine deep under the ocean?** *(The water is too cold for them and the pressure is so great their lungs could explode on the way up to the surface.)*

BIG IDEAS OF SCIENCE REFERENCE LIBRARY
Have students look up the following topic: Mid-Ocean Ridge.

Explore

Lab Resource: Inquiry Warm-Up

L2 WHAT CAN YOU LEARN WITHOUT SEEING?
Students will infer the shape of an object inside a shoebox.

Exploring the Ocean

 How Do Conditions Vary in Earth's Oceans?

 What Are Some Features of the Ocean Floor?

MY PLANET DIARY — SCIENCE AND TECHNOLOGY

Deep-Sea Escape

You've heard of how parachutes are used for escapes. But have you heard of a special suit that allows people to escape from a submarine 183 meters under water? The suit is designed to help sailors survive very cold temperatures and very high pressure. In an emergency, sailors put on this suit and enter a water-filled rescue chamber. Then the sailors shoot out, rising at two to three meters per second. If the suit tears, they have to exhale all the way to the surface so their lungs don't explode. At the surface, part of the suit inflates to become a life raft.

Discuss these questions with a classmate and write your answers below.

1. What technology was developed to help sailors escape a submarine accident?
   A special suit to protect them from deep-sea pressure and temperature

2. What would it feel like to escape from a submarine deep under water? How would you help your body adjust to the changing pressure?
   Sample: Cold and dark; I'd pop my ears.

> **PLANET DIARY** Go to **Planet Diary** to learn more about characteristics of the ocean.

Lab zone Do the Inquiry Warm-Up
What Can You Learn Without Seeing?

How Do Conditions Vary in Earth's Oceans?

People have explored the ocean since ancient times. For centuries, the ocean has provided food and served as a route for trade and travel. Modern scientists have studied the characteristics of the ocean's waters and the ocean floor. **The water in Earth's oceans varies in salinity, temperature, and depth.**

SUPPORT ALL READERS
Lexile Measure = 920L   Lexile Word Count = 1347

Prior Exposure to Content: Most students have encountered this topic in earlier grades

Academic Vocabulary: *data, interpret*

Science Vocabulary: *salinity, seamount, trench, abyssal plain*

Concept Level: Generally appropriate for most students in this grade

Preteach With: My Planet Diary "Deep-Sea Escape" and Figure 1 activity

Go to **My Reading Web** to access leveled readings that provide a foundation for the content.

my science online

Vocabulary

- salinity
- sonar
- seamount
- trench
- continental slope
- continental shelf
- abyssal plain
- mid-ocean ridge

Skills

- Reading: Identify the Main Idea
- Inquiry: Interpret Data

Salinity If you've ever swallowed a mouthful of water while you were swimming in the ocean, you know it's pretty salty. But just how salty? If you boiled a kilogram of ocean water in a pot until the water was gone, there would be about 35 grams of salt left in the pot. That's about two tablespoons of salt. **Salinity** is the total amount of dissolved salts in a sample of water. In most parts of the ocean, the salinity is between 34 and 37 parts per thousand.

The substance you know as table salt is sodium chloride. This salt is present in the greatest amount in ocean water. When sodium chloride dissolves in water, it separates into sodium and chloride particles called ions. Ocean water also contains smaller amounts of more than a dozen ions, including magnesium and calcium.

Near the ocean's surface, rain, snow, and melting ice add fresh water, lowering the salinity. Evaporation, on the other hand, increases salinity. Salt is left behind as the water evaporates. Salinity can also be higher near the poles. As the surface water freezes into ice, the salt is left behind in the remaining water.

Effects of Salinity Salinity affects ocean water in different ways. For instance, fresh water freezes at 0°C. But ocean water doesn't freeze until the temperature drops to about –1.9°C. The salt acts as a kind of antifreeze by interfering with the formation of ice. Salt water also has a higher density than fresh water. That means that the mass of one liter of salt water is greater than the mass of one liter of fresh water. Because its density is greater, seawater lifts, or buoys up, less dense objects floating in it.

> **Vocabulary Suffixes** Circle the correct word to complete the sentence below.
>
> Ocean water has a higher (salinity)/saline) than fresh water.

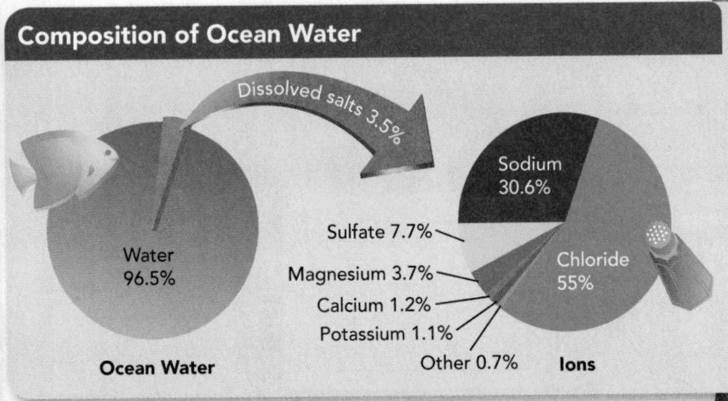

Composition of Ocean Water

Dissolved salts 3.5%

Water 96.5%

Ocean Water

Sodium 30.6%
Sulfate 7.7%
Magnesium 3.7%
Calcium 1.2%
Potassium 1.1%
Chloride 55%
Other 0.7%

Ions

FIGURE 1 ················
> **VIRTUAL LAB** Composition of Ocean Water
When salts dissolve, they separate into particles called ions.

✎ **Read Graphs** In ocean water, which ion is most common? Which salt?

Ion: chloride;
Salt: sodium
chloride

347

Explain

Introduce Vocabulary

Explain that *sonar* is an example of an acronym, a word formed from the initial letters or groups of letters of words in a phrase. *Sonar* is made up of parts of the words *SOund Navigation And Ranging*. It is a form of technology that uses sound waves to calculate the distance to an object.

Teach Key Concepts 🔑

Explain to students that the properties of the ocean are not the same everywhere. On the board, list *salinity, temperature,* and *depth.* Tell students that these are three characteristics of ocean water that vary, depending upon the part of the ocean. Ask: **What is salinity?** (*The total amount of dissolved salts in a sample of water*) **What is the main salt in ocean water?** (*Sodium chloride*)

Teach With Visuals

Tell students to look at **Figure 1.** Remind students that the circle graph on the left shows 100 percent of the composition of Earth's ocean water. The circle graph on the right shows 100 percent of the composition of only the salts dissolved in that ocean water. Each colored slice represents individual dissolved ions. All of the ions contribute to the water's salinity. Ask: **What percentage of ocean water is dissolved salts?** (*3.5%*) **Which element makes up 1.1% of the dissolved salts?** (*Potassium*)

> **My Planet Diary** provides an opportunity for students to explore real-world connections to ocean conditions.
>
> **Virtual Lab** allows students to investigate the characteristics of different temperatures and salinities of sea water.
>
> my science online.com | Ocean Conditions

(ELL) Support

1 Content and Language

Have students start a vocabulary notebook using the terms in this lesson. Suggest that they use their own words to define the terms and incorporate visuals whenever possible.

2 Frontload the Lesson

Rewrite the Key Concept statement as two separate sentences such as *The temperature at the surface of the ocean varies with location. The temperature at the surface of the ocean varies with the seasons.* Read each sentence aloud. Then challenge students to explain each sentence.

3 Comprehensible Input

To help students visualize the ocean's depth, suggest that they make a scale drawing of the three ocean zones. Have them use a scale of 500 m equals 1 cm.

Explain

Teach Key Concepts 🔑

Explain to students that the temperature of ocean water varies. It changes depending on where you are, how deep you go, and the time of year. Ask: **Where on Earth is ocean water the warmest?** *(Near the equator)* **What general statement can you make about the change in temperature as you go deeper in Earth's oceans?** *(Temperature decreases as depth increases.)* Invite students who have experienced swimming in the ocean or a lake to share their experiences with changing water temperature. Ask: **Why is the water often warmest at the surface?** *(The water at the surface is heated by the sun.)*

Teach Key Concepts 🔑

Explain to students that, for every 10 meters of ocean water you descend through, the pressure of the water increases by 1 bar. Remind them that pressure is the amount of force on a certain area. Ask: **Why does water exert force?** *(The force is the weight of the water above.)*

🔄 **Identify the Main Idea** Explain to students that each paragraph includes many ideas, but one of them is the most important idea. That idea is the main idea.

Lead a Discussion

WATER PRESSURE Have students look at the submersible vehicles shown in the *Apply It* activity. Ask: **How would the pressure change as the submersible descends?** *(Pressure would increase gradually.)* **In which zone would the submersible be under the least amount of pressure?** *(The surface zone)* **In which zone would the submersible be under the greatest amount of pressure?** *(The deep zone)*

348 Water

🔄 **Identify the Main Idea**
Underline the two changes that happen with depth.

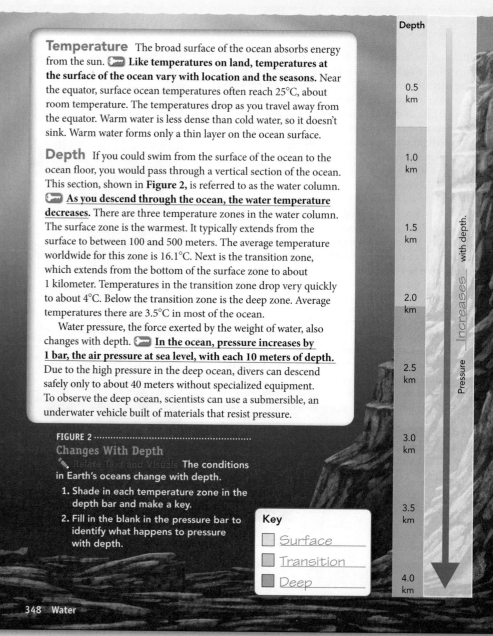

Temperature The broad surface of the ocean absorbs energy from the sun. 🔑 **Like temperatures on land, temperatures at the surface of the ocean vary with location and the seasons.** Near the equator, surface ocean temperatures often reach 25°C, about room temperature. The temperatures drop as you travel away from the equator. Warm water is less dense than cold water, so it doesn't sink. Warm water forms only a thin layer on the ocean surface.

Depth If you could swim from the surface of the ocean to the ocean floor, you would pass through a vertical section of the ocean. This section, shown in **Figure 2**, is referred to as the water column. 🔑 **As you descend through the ocean, the water temperature decreases.** There are three temperature zones in the water column. The surface zone is the warmest. It typically extends from the surface to between 100 and 500 meters. The average temperature worldwide for this zone is 16.1°C. Next is the transition zone, which extends from the bottom of the surface zone to about 1 kilometer. Temperatures in the transition zone drop very quickly to about 4°C. Below the transition zone is the deep zone. Average temperatures there are 3.5°C in most of the ocean.

Water pressure, the force exerted by the weight of water, also changes with depth. 🔑 **In the ocean, pressure increases by 1 bar, the air pressure at sea level, with each 10 meters of depth.** Due to the high pressure in the deep ocean, divers can descend safely only to about 40 meters without specialized equipment. To observe the deep ocean, scientists can use a submersible, an underwater vehicle built of materials that resist pressure.

FIGURE 2
Changes With Depth
✏️ Relate Text and Visuals The conditions in Earth's oceans change with depth.
1. Shade in each temperature zone in the depth bar and make a key.
2. Fill in the blank in the pressure bar to identify what happens to pressure with depth.

Key
⬜ Surface
⬜ Transition
⬜ Deep

Depth: 0.5 km, 1.0 km, 1.5 km, 2.0 km, 2.5 km, 3.0 km, 3.5 km, 4.0 km

Pressure _increases_ with depth.

348 Water

Professional Development Note

Teacher to Teacher

Science Controversy: The Breakdown of Ocean Currents Some evidence suggests that thermohaline circulation of the oceans, currents that bring warmth to northern latitudes, may be reduced or stop altogether because of great quantities of fresh water being added to oceans. This fresh water is a result of global warming melting sea ice. The result of global warming would be colder temperatures for many places that now enjoy moderate climates. Advanced computer models are conflicted as to the outcome. Introducing students to this type of debate in the scientific community gives them a new perspective on science as a whole.

✏️ *James Kuhl*
Central Square Middle School
Central Square, New York

apply it!

Each panel of dials provides information about conditions at various depths in the ocean.

1 Interpret Data Find the incorrect dial in each panel and correct its reading.

2 Label where in the ocean you might find each set of readings: surface zone, transition zone, or deep zone.

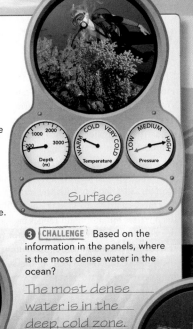

Surface

3 CHALLENGE Based on the information in the panels, where is the most dense water in the ocean?

The most dense water is in the deep, cold zone.

Transition

Deep

did you know?

The Deep Flight Super Falcon is the first winged submersible available to the public. It can "fly" quickly and easily to depths of more than 100 meters.

Lab zone
Do the Quick Lab
Ocean Conditions.

Assess Your Understanding

got it?

O I get it! Now I know that the water in Earth's oceans varies in *salinity, temperature, and depth.*

O I need extra help with *See TE note.*

Go to MY SCIENCE COACH *online for help with this subject.*

349

Elaborate

21st Century Learning

CRITICAL THINKING Remind students that as depth increases in an ocean, water temperature decreases and pressure increases. Ask: **Where are you likely to find cold water in a deep equatorial ocean?** *(At the bottom, or in the deep zone)* **Where is the water pressure the greatest in a swimming pool?** *(At the deepest place in the pool)*

Apply It!

L1 Summarize the relationships between depth and temperature and between depth and pressure before beginning the activity.

△ **Interpret Data** Remind students that data include facts, figures, and other information gathered through observations. Make sure students understand what each dial in the pictures represents. Remind them that one out of every set of three dials shows a reading that is incorrect for that particular zone.

Lab Resource: Quick Lab

L1 OCEAN CONDITIONS Students will identify differences in density between salt and fresh water.

Evaluate

Assess Your Understanding

Have students evaluate their understanding by completing the appropriate sentence.

RTI Response to Intervention

If students have trouble summarizing ocean conditions, **then** have them work in pairs to summarize ways in which ocean water conditions vary.

MY SCIENCE COACH Have students go online for help in understanding variations in ocean water conditions.

Digital Lesson: Assign the *Apply It* activity online and have students submit their work to you.

MY SCIENCE online.com Ocean Conditions

Differentiated Instruction

L1 Make a Scale Drawing To help students visualize the ocean's depth, suggest that they make a scale drawing of the three zones. Have them use a scale of 500 m equals 1 cm. After students finish their drawings, have them calculate the scale height of the 442-m-high Sears Tower. *(0.88 cm)*

L3 Investigate Submersibles Have students research and report on submersibles such as *Alvin* and *Trieste*.

L3 Describe the Ocean On a blank postcard, have students write a message describing the ocean to a pen pal who has never seen it. Descriptions should include how conditions vary in Earth's oceans. Then have students draw a picture of the ocean on the opposite side of the postcard.

Explain

Teach Key Concepts 🔑

Explain to students that the ocean floor is not a smooth, curved, basin. It has varying relief made up of different features similar to the landforms found on continents. These features include the continental shelf, continental slope, abyssal plain, mid-ocean ridge, and trenches. The movements of Earth's plates help form the features of the ocean floor. Review with students the concepts related to plate tectonics. Ask: **What is a plate?** (*A piece of Earth's lithosphere that slowly moves*) **At which ocean-floor feature do plates move apart?** (*Mid-ocean ridge*) **At which ocean-floor feature do plates move together?** (*Trench*)

Lead a Discussion

EXPLORE THE OCEAN FLOOR Have students imagine a journey across the Great Plains, over the Rocky Mountains, past the Cascade volcanoes, and ending at the Grand Canyon. Tell them that the ocean floor has features that are even more spectacular. Then work with students to develop a list of descriptive adjectives for each of the following terms: *abyssal plain, seamount, mid-ocean ridge,* and *trench.* Have students compare these features to similar features on the continents. Ask: **How are ocean floor features more spectacular than those on the continents?** (*Ocean floor features generally are longer, wider, taller, or deeper than features on the continents.*)

21st Century Learning

CRITICAL THINKING Explain that features on the ocean floor and on the continents are alike because they often form in similar ways. Ask: **How are mid-ocean ridges like the Appalachians?** (*Both are long chains of mountains.*) **Which two ocean floor features are like a coastal plain, with flat or gently rolling land?** (*An abyssal plain and continental shelf.*)

What Are Some Features of the Ocean Floor?

The ocean is very deep—3.8 kilometers deep on average. That's more than twice as deep as the Grand Canyon. Humans can't survive the darkness, cold temperatures, and extreme pressure of the deep ocean. So scientists have developed technology to study the ocean floor. A major advance in ocean-floor mapping was **sonar,** SOund NAvigation and Ranging. This system uses sound waves to calculate the distance to an object. A ship's sonar system sends out pulses of sound that bounce off the ocean floor. The equipment then measures how quickly the sound waves return to the ship.

Once scientists mapped the ocean floor, they discovered that the deep waters hid mountain ranges bigger than any on land, as well as deep canyons. 🔑 **Major ocean floor features include trenches, the continental shelf, the continental slope, the abyssal plain, and the mid-ocean ridge. These features have all been formed by the interaction of Earth's plates.** You can see these feaures in **Figure 3.**

FIGURE 3 ....
Ocean Floor
✏ **Relate Text and Visuals**
Match the descriptions below with the ocean floor features in the image. Write the number for each description in the corresponding circles.
(Image not to scale. To show major ocean floor features, thousands of kilometers have been squeezed into one illustration.)

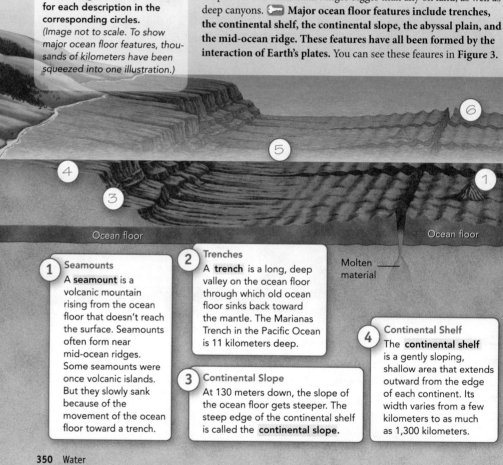

Ocean floor

Ocean floor

Molten material

1 Seamounts
A **seamount** is a volcanic mountain rising from the ocean floor that doesn't reach the surface. Seamounts often form near mid-ocean ridges. Some seamounts were once volcanic islands. But they slowly sank because of the movement of the ocean floor toward a trench.

2 Trenches
A **trench** is a long, deep valley on the ocean floor through which old ocean floor sinks back toward the mantle. The Marianas Trench in the Pacific Ocean is 11 kilometers deep.

3 Continental Slope
At 130 meters down, the slope of the ocean floor gets steeper. The steep edge of the continental shelf is called the **continental slope.**

4 Continental Shelf
The **continental shelf** is a gently sloping, shallow area that extends outward from the edge of each continent. Its width varies from a few kilometers to as much as 1,300 kilometers.

350 Water

Interactive Art allows students to explore the structures and topography of the ocean floor.

MY SCIENCE ONLINE.com | The Ocean Floor

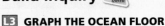

LOST AT SEA

EXPLORE THE BIG ?

FIGURE 4

▶ **INTERACTIVE ART** What are some characteristics of Earth's oceans?

✎ **Predict** Your ship has been radioed by a submarine that has lost the use of its navigation instruments. Based on the information in their last transmission, where might the vessel be? What might the conditions of the water be at this depth? Discuss your prediction with a partner.

Last transmission from sub: "Depth reading 3,000 meters; passed over a flat plain...sonar returned waves quickly; possibly approaching mountains."

The sub could be approaching the mid-ocean ridge. At 3,000 meters, they'd be in the deep zone. It would be too dark to see. The water would be very cold, and the water pressure would be high.

Lab zone Do the Quick Lab *The Shape of the Ocean Floor.*

5 Abyssal Plain
The **abyssal plain** (uh BIHS ul) is a broad area covered with thick layers of mud and silt. It's a smooth, nearly flat region of the ocean.

6 Mid-Ocean Ridges
Mid-ocean ridges are long chains of mountains on the ocean floors. Along the ridges, lava erupts and forms new ocean floor. Because of convection currents inside Earth, the ocean floor slowly moves toward a trench and sinks into the mantle.

🔑 Assess Your Understanding

1a. List What are four features of the ocean floor?

Continental shelf and slope, abyssal plain, mid-ocean ridge

b. Explain Why has investigation of the ocean been difficult?

High pressure, depth, cold

c. ANSWER THE BIG ? What are some characteristics of Earth's oceans?

Salinity, temperature zones, ocean floor features

got it? ....

○ **I get it!** Now I know that the ocean floor has many different features formed by ____ *the interaction of Earth's plates.*

○ **I need extra help with** *See TE note.*

Go to **MY SCIENCE ⓢ COACH** online for help with this subject.

351

Differentiated Instruction

L3 Research Guyots In **Figure 3,** point out the volcanic islands, which are volcanic mountains that rise from the sea floor to above the ocean surface. Have students research guyots and find out how they are related to volcanic islands. *(Guyots are flat-topped volcanic islands now below the ocean surface. The flat tops formed as a result of wave action.)*

L1 Locate Features Provide students with a map or globe that shows the ocean floor and have them locate features shown in **Figure 3.**

Elaborate

Build Inquiry **Lab zone**

L3 GRAPH THE OCEAN FLOOR

Materials graph paper, metric ruler

Time 20 minutes

Challenge students to make a scale drawing of a continental shelf, continental slope, abyssal plain, mid-ocean ridge, and deep–ocean trench. Give them the typical depth for each feature: shelf, 0 to 200 m; slope, 200 m to 3.8 km; abyssal plain, 3.8 km; mid-ocean ridge, 2.5 km; trench, 9 km. Ask: **How many times deeper is a trench than a continental shelf?** *(About 45 times deeper)* **How many times deeper is a trench than an abyssal plain?** *(From 2 to 3 times deeper)*

Explore the Big Q ❓ UbD

Direct students' attention to the instructions for the red skill head *Predict* and the vessel's transmission. Remind them to read both sets of text. Ask: **How many kilometers is 3,000 m?** *(3 km)* **Which of the three temperature zones in the ocean extends to 3 km?** *(The deep zone)*

Lab Resource: Quick Lab **Lab zone**

L2 THE SHAPE OF THE OCEAN FLOOR Students will explore plotting data on a graph to produce a profile of the ocean floor.

Evaluate

Assess Your Understanding

After students answer the questions, have them evaluate their understanding by completing the appropriate sentence.

Answer the Big Q ❓ UbD

To help students focus on the Big Question, lead a class discussion about the characteristics of Earth's oceans.

R T I Response to Intervention

1a. If students have trouble listing ocean floor features, **then** have them review **Figure 3.**

b. If students need help explaining the challenge of ocean investigation, **then** have them reread the first paragraph under the blue head *What Are Some Features of the Ocean Floor?*

c. If students cannot list ocean characteristics, **then** have them reread the Key Concept statements.

MY SCIENCE ⓢ COACH Have students go online for help in understanding ocean characteristics and ocean floor features.

Exploring the Ocean

Inquiry Warm-Up, *What Can You Learn Without Seeing?*
In the Inquiry Warm-Up, you investigated observations you can make about an object without seeing it. Using what you learned from that activity, answer the questions below.

1. **INFER** How can you relate how far you moved the straws to the size of the object?

   _____
   _____
   _____

2. **DRAW CONCLUSIONS** What can you tell about the material the object is made of, based on how much resistance it had against the straws?

   _____
   _____

3. **PREDICT** Assume there is a marble in the box. What observations would you expect to make based on using the straw probes?

   _____
   _____

4. **DEVELOP HYPOTHESIS** How could this experiment be similar to early explorations of Earth's oceans?

   _____
   _____

Assess Your Understanding

Exploring the Ocean

How Do Conditions Vary in Earth's Oceans?

got:it? ....

○ **I get it!** Now I know that the water in Earth's oceans varies in _____

_____

○ **I need extra help with** _____

_____

What Are Some Features of the Ocean Floor?

1a. LIST What are four features of the ocean floor?

_____

b. EXPLAIN Why has investigation of the ocean been difficult?

_____

_____

c. ANSWER What are some characteristics of Earth's oceans?

_____

_____

got:it? ....

○ **I get it!** Now I know that the ocean floor has many different features formed by

_____

_____

○ **I need extra help with** _____

_____

Key Concept Summaries

Exploring the Ocean

How Do Conditions Vary in Earth's Oceans?

The water in Earth's oceans varies in salinity, temperature, and depth. Salinity is the total amount of dissolved salts in a sample of water. Salinity affects the temperature and density of water. Saltwater freezes at a lower temperature and has a higher density than freshwater.

Like temperatures on land, temperatures at the surface of the ocean vary with location and the seasons. The temperature drops as you travel away from the equator. **As you descend through the ocean, the water temperature decreases.** There are three temperature zones in the water column: the surface zone, the transitions zone, and the deep zone.

Water pressure, the force exerted by the weight of water, also changes with depth. **In the ocean, pressure increases by 1 bar, the air pressure at sea level, with each 10 meters of depth.**

What Are Some Features of the Ocean Floor?

Scientists have developed technology to study the ocean floor. A major advance in ocean-floor mapping was **sonar,** sound navigation and ranging. This system uses sound waves to calculate the distance to an object.

Major ocean floor features include trenches, the continental shelf, the continental slope, the abyssal plain, and the mid-ocean ridge. These features have all been formed by the interaction of Earth's plates.

A **seamount** is a volcanic mountain rising from the ocean floor. **Mid-ocean ridges** are long chains of mountains on the ocean floor. The **continental shelf** is a gently sloping shallow area that extends outward from the edge of each continent. The steep edge of the continental shelf is called the **continental slope.** The **abyssal plain** is a broad area covered with thick layers of mud and silt. A **trench** is a long, deep valley on the ocean floor through which old ocean floor sinks back toward the mantle.

On a separate sheet of paper, tell how the ocean water and floor change as you go from the continental shelf to the abyssal plain.

Review and Reinforce

Exploring the Ocean

Understanding Main Ideas
Fill in the spaces in the table below.

The Ocean Water Column

	Depth Zone	Depth Range	Average Temperature (°C)
1.	Surface	0 to 500 m	
2.	Transition		4
3.		1 km and deeper	3.5

Answer the following questions on a separate sheet of paper.

4. What are three ways in which ocean water varies?
5. Which condition of ocean water varies with the location and seasons?
6. How does water temperature change as you move from the ocean floor to the surface?
7. What prevents scuba divers from going deeper than 40 meters below the surface?
8. How do ocean floor features such as trenches and mid-ocean ridges form?

Building Vocabulary
On a separate sheet of paper, write a definition for each of these terms.

9. continental shelf
10. salinity
11. trench
12. sonar
13. continental slope
14. mid-ocean ridge
15. abyssal plain
16. seamount

Enrich

Exploring the Ocean

Saltwater is made up of many different elements. Read the passage below. Follow the steps below the table to complete the third and fourth columns. Then, use a separate sheet of paper to make a circle graph about the composition of ocean water. To review how to make a circle graph, see the Skills Handbook at the back of your textbook.

The Composition of Ocean Water

On average, one kilogram of ocean water contains about 35 grams of salts. That is, salts make up about 3.5 percent of the mass of ocean water. Although sodium chloride is the most abundant and familiar salt in seawater, many other salts are also dissolved in seawater. The table below lists the salts that a scientist recovered by evaporating a 100-gram sample of ocean water. The second column of the table lists the mass of each salt recovered.

Major Salts From a Sample of Ocean Water			
Salts	Mass (g of salt recovered from 100 g of ocean water)	Number of Degrees on Circle Graph	Percentage of Total Salts
Sodium chloride	2.72		
Magnesium chloride	0.38		
Magnesium sulfate	0.17		
Calcium sulfate	0.13		
Potassium sulfate	0.08		
Calcium carbonate	0.01		
Magnesium bromide	0.01		

1. Use this equation to fill in the third column of the table.

$$\frac{\text{Mass of salt}}{\text{Total mass of salts (3.5 g)}} = \frac{x}{\text{Total number of degrees in circle (360)}}$$

2. Use this equation to fill in the fourth column of the table.

$$\text{Percentage of total salts} = \frac{\text{Number of degrees in circle graph}}{360} \times 100\%$$

3. Use a protractor and the data in the table to make a circle graph showing the percentage of each salt recovered from the sample of ocean water. Label each section of the graph.

Name _____ Date _____ Class _____

Lesson Quiz

Exploring the Ocean

If the statement is true, write *true*. If the statement is false, change the underlined word or words to make the statement true.

1. _____ Ocean water freezes at a <u>higher</u> temperature than fresh water.

2. _____ A <u>seamount</u> is a volcanic mountain that forms near a mid-ocean ridge.

3. _____ A gently sloping continental <u>slope</u> extends from the edge of each continent.

4. _____ Freshwater has a <u>lower</u> density than salt water.

5. _____ As you go deeper below the ocean surface the <u>temperature</u> decreases.

Fill in the blank to complete each statement.

6. How much sodium chloride and other salts are dissolved in a water sample is the water's _____.

7. Old ocean floor sinks toward the mantle at a(n) _____.

8. The _____ plain is a smooth, nearly flat region of the ocean floor.

9. Scientists use _____, a form of technology that uses sound waves, to help them map the ocean floor.

10. Water _____ increases with depth in the ocean because the weight of water above increases.

Place the outside corner, the corner away from the dotted line, in the corner of your copy machine to copy onto letter-size paper.

Exploring the Ocean

Answer Key

After the Inquiry Warm-Up

1. Accept all reasonable responses. Students may say that the straw moved very far when inserted into the box before touching the object, so it must be small. Or they may say the straw did not move very far before touching the object, so it must be large.

2. Accept all reasonable responses. Students may say the object did not resist the straws much when probed, so it must be made of soft material. Or that the object did resist when probed, so it must be made of hard material.

3. Sample: Some straws inserted into the holes would not touch the object, so it must be small. A straw that did touch it would resist the object, so it must have a hard surface. By dragging the straw along the surface of the object, we learn it has a smooth, rounded surface. By moving the object with a straw, we learn that it can roll.

4. Ocean water is very deep and dark, people could not see very deep into the ocean. Early ocean explorers could have dropped poles or ropes into the ocean and observed what those poles or ropes touched in the ocean.

Key Concept Summaries

The ocean floor gets deeper, changing from a gentle to a steep slope and then to a flat area. As the water gets deeper, its salinity varies, its temperature decreases, and its pressure increases.

Review and Reinforce

1. 16.1

2. 500 m to 1 km

3. Deep

4. It varies in salinity, temperature, and depth.

5. temperature

6. Temperature increases.

7. the pressure of the water

8. They form by the interaction of Earth's plates.

9. a gently sloping shallow area that extends outward from the edge of each continent

10. the total amount of dissolved salts in a sample of water

11. a long, deep valley on the ocean floor where old ocean floor sinks back toward the mantle

12. the system of sound navigation and ranging that uses sound waves to calculate the distance to an object on the ocean floor

13. the steep edge of the continental shelf

14. a long chain of mountains on the ocean floor

15. a broad area covered with thick layers of mud and silt

16. a volcanic mountain rising from the ocean floor

Enrich

1. Sodium chloride: 280°; magnesium chloride: 39°; magnesium sulfate: 17°; calcium sulfate: 13°; potassium sulfate: 8.2°; calcium carbonate: 1.0°; magnesium bromide: 1.0°

2. Sodium chloride: 78%; magnesium chloride: 11%; magnesium sulfate: 4.7%; calcium sulfate: 3.6%; potassium sulfate: 2.3%; calcium carbonate: 0.28%; magnesium bromide: 0.28%

3. Students' graphs should show the correct percentages for each salt as given above, with each section of the graph clearly labeled with the name of each salt.

Lesson Quiz

1. lower
2. true
3. shelf
4. true
5. true
6. salinity
7. trench
8. abyssal
9. sonar
10. pressure

Place the outside corner, the corner away from the dotted line, in the corner of your copy machine to copy onto letter-size paper.

Wave Action

5

 How does fresh water cycle on Earth?

Lesson Pacing: 1–2 periods or $\frac{1}{2}$–1 block

🕐 **SHORT ON TIME?** To do this lesson in approximately half the time, do the Activate Prior Knowledge activity followed by a discussion of the Key Concepts to familiarize students with the lesson content. Have students do the Quick Labs. The rest of the lesson can be completed by students independently.

Preference Navigator, in the online Planning tools, allows you to customize *Interactive Science* to your own teaching style. You can also edit lesson plans by selecting the Lesson Planner option.

Digital Teacher's Edition allows you to access your Teacher's Edition and Resource materials online.

my science online.com

Lesson Vocabulary

- wave
- wavelength
- frequency
- wave height
- tsunami
- longshore drift
- rip current
- groin

 ## Content Refresher

Wave Power and Tsunamis In the late 1800s, buoys with wave-powered whistles transformed the energy of waves. A float was used to transfer kinetic energy to a piston that operated a whistle. In the twentieth century British scientist, Dr. Stephen Salter, found a way to generate electricity with waves. Now, there are wave-generated power stations along the coasts of Britain, Norway, Japan, and India.

Tsunamis are the strongest, biggest waves ever recorded. An 1883 tsunami that struck Java and Sumatra was more than 34 m high—taller than a ten-story building. In 2004, an undersea earthquake, with a magnitude between 9.1 and 9.3, caused the deadliest tsunami in recorded history. This tsunami affected the coasts of most landmasses bordering the Indian Ocean with waves about 30 m high. The worldwide community donated more than $7 billion dollars in humanitarian aid to help those affected by the tsunami. In 2011, an undersea earthquake of magnitude 9.0 off the Japanese coast near Honshu produced a 10-meter high tsunami that destroyed villages and damaged several nuclear reactors.

LESSON OBJECTIVES

🔑 Explain how waves form and change and describe the characteristics of waves.

🔑 Describe how waves affect shorelines and beaches.

Blended Path
Active learning using Student Edition, Inquiry Path, and Digital Path

ENGAGE AND EXPLORE

Teach this lesson using a variety of resources. Begin by reading **My Planet Diary** as a class. Have students identify what they know about waves. Then have students do the **Inquiry Warm-Up activity.** Students will model waves and beach erosion. Discuss how the tongue depressor changes the wave activity. The **After the Inquiry Warm-Up worksheet** sets up a discussion about how waves change a beach. Have volunteers share their answers to number 4 about ways to prevent beach erosion.

EXPLAIN AND ELABORATE

Teach Key Concepts by explaining the term *energy* and having students identify how wind conditions impact the formation of waves. **Lead a Discussion** about how wave height, wavelength, and wave frequency are measured. Use **Figure 2** to reinforce understanding of wave characteristics. Use **Figure 3** to help students visualize the movement of water particles. Then have students practice the lesson's inquiry skill in the **Apply It activity.** Continue to **Teach Key Concepts** by explaining how wave characteristics change based on depth of the water. Use the **Support the Big Q** to illustrate how the shape of waves changes as it approaches the shore. Use **Figure 5** to show students how a tsunami develops.

Teach Key Concepts by explaining to students how a sandbar is formed. Continue to **Teach Key Concepts** by explaining how erosion occurs on a beach and what structures and landforms can protect a beach from erosion. **Lead a Discussion** about how the direction of the wind, in relation to the beach, impacts sand movement. Hand out the **Key Concept Summaries** as a review of each part of the lesson. Students can also use the online **Vocab Flash Cards** to review key terms.

EVALUATE

Have students take the **Lesson Quiz.** For an alternate assessment, see the **EXAM**VIEW® Assessment Suite, Progress Monitoring Assessments, or SuccessTracker™.

Ⓔ Ⓛ Ⓛ Support

1 Content and Language

Rogue can be a noun, verb, or adjective. The adjective *rogue,* meaning "hazardous and damaging", is used to describe unexpected waves of great heights. List other adjectives that could be used to describe rogue waves.

Inquiry Path
Hands-on learning in the Lab zone

ENGAGE AND EXPLORE

To teach this lesson with an emphasis on inquiry, begin with the **Inquiry Warm-Up activity.** Students will investigate how waves can erode a beach. Discuss the movement of the sand based on the speed at which the tongue depressor moves. Have students do the **After the Inquiry Warm-Up worksheet.** Talk about what students observed about the effects of beach waves on the sand. Have volunteers share their answers to number 4 about ways to counteract the effects of waves on beaches.

EXPLAIN AND ELABORATE

Focus on the **Inquiry Skill** for the lesson. Point out that when you form operational definitions, you describe how a term can be defined. What could an operational definition of erosion be based on the **Inquiry Warm-Up activity?** (*Erosion is the wearing away of sand by waves.*) Review the characteristics of waves before beginning the **Apply It activity.** Ask volunteers to share their operational definitions. Do the **Teacher Demo** to model wave energy. **Support the Big Q** by discussing how waves change as they approach the shore. Have students do the **Quick Lab** to simulate waves.

Build Inquiry to reinforce understanding of how grains of sand are moved by a longshore drift. Continue to **Build Inquiry** to model how wave energy is changed using barrier beaches. Students will explore a model of rip currents in the last **Quick Lab.** Students can use the online **Vocab Flash Cards** to review key terms.

EVALUATE

Have students take the **Lesson Quiz.** For an alternate assessment, see the **EXAM**VIEW® Assessment Suite, Progress Monitoring Assessments, or SuccessTracker™.

Digital Path
Online learning at MY SCIENCE ONLINE.com

ENGAGE AND EXPLORE

Teach this lesson using digital resources. Begin by having students explore the myth and the reality of rogue waves at **My Planet Diary** online. Have them access the Chapter Resources to find the **Unlock the Big Question activity.** There they can answer the questions and refine their responses as they continue through the lesson. You can re-assign the activity and have students submit their work so you can track their progress.

EXPLAIN AND ELABORATE

Students reading above, at, or below the lexile measure of this lesson can access basic content readings at their level at **My Reading Web.** Have students use the online **Vocab Flash Cards** to preview key terms. Review characteristics of waves before assigning the online **Apply It activity.** Ask volunteers to share the operational definitions they wrote for scientific terms. Have students submit their work to you. Have students do the online **Interactive Art activity** to explore the motion of water on the ocean's surface. **Support the Big Q** by discussing breakers. Have student do the **Quick Lab** to simulate waves.

Do the **Quick Lab** to model rip currents and then ask students to share their observations. The **Key Concept Summaries** online allow students to read a summary and see an image associated with each part of the lesson. Online remediation is available at **My Science Coach.**

EVALUATE

Have students take the **Lesson Quiz.** For an alternate assessment, see the **EXAM**VIEW® Assessment Suite, Progress Monitoring Assessments, or SuccessTracker™.

2 Frontload the Lesson
Preview the lesson visuals, labels, and captions. Ask students what they know about the words *wavelength, wave height,* and *frequency.* Explain the specific meanings these words have in science.

3 Comprehensible Input
Have students choose three vocabulary words and draw images that represent their meanings.

4 Language Production
Pair or group students with varied language abilities to complete labs collaboratively for language practice. Have each student copy the completed written lab for personal reference.

5 Assess Understanding
Have students keep a content area log. Use a two-column format with the headings "What I Understand" and "What I Don't Understand." Follow up so that students can move items from the "Don't Understand" to the "Understand" column.

Lexile Measure = 920L

Wave Action

Establish Learning Objectives

Explain how waves form and change and describe the characteristics of waves.

Describe how waves affect shorelines and beaches.

Engage

Activate Prior Knowledge

MY PLANET DIARY Read *Rogue Waves* with the class. Encourage students who have been to a beach or wave pool to describe the waves they experienced. Ask: **How are rogue waves different than ordinary waves?** *(They are much larger and more destructive.)*

BIG IDEAS OF SCIENCE REFERENCE LIBRARY Have students look up the following topic: Surfing.

Explore

Lab Resource: Inquiry Warm-Up

L1 HOW DO WAVES CHANGE A BEACH? Students will model waves and beach erosion.

Wave Action

How Do Waves Form and Change?

How Do Waves Affect the Shore?

MY PLANET DIARY

DISASTER

Rogue Waves

For hundreds of years, sailors have returned from the sea to tell of 30-meter-high waves that appeared out of nowhere. These waves, they said, plunged the largest ships into the ocean depths. For hundreds of years, these tales were taken no more seriously than the Scottish legend of the Loch Ness monster. Ships were sunk, scientists said, in storms.

Then, in 1995, an oil rig in the North Sea was struck by a rogue wave. Instruments on board measured the wave's height at 26 meters. As a result, the European Union set up a project to study these rogue waves using satellites. What the scientists found was shocking. Within three weeks, they tracked ten different giant waves.

Discuss these questions with a classmate and write your answers below.

1. Why did people begin to believe in rogue waves?

   In 1995, instruments on board an oil rig measured a huge wave.

2. How might you track a rogue wave?

   Sample: with satellites

> PLANET DIARY Go to **Planet Diary** to learn more about wave action.

  Do the Inquiry Warm-Up *How Do Waves Change a Beach?*

SUPPORT ALL READERS

Lexile Measure = 920L   Lexile Word Count = 1757

Prior Exposure to Content: May be the first time students have encountered this topic

Academic Vocabulary: *operational definitions*

Science Vocabulary: *wavelength, frequency, tsunami, groin*

Concept Level: Generally appropriate for most students in this grade

Preteach With: My Planet Diary "Rogue Waves" and Figure 1 activity

Go to **My Reading Web** to access leveled readings that provide a foundation for the content.

MY SCIENCE online.com

Vocabulary
- wave • wavelength • frequency • wave height
- tsunami • longshore drift • rip current • groin

Skills
🔁 Reading: Relate Cause and Effect
△ Inquiry: Form Operational Definitions

How Do Waves Form and Change?

When you watch a surfer's wave crash onto a beach, you are seeing the last step in the development of a wave. A **wave** is the movement of energy through a body of water. Wave development usually begins with wind. Without the energy of wind, the surface of the ocean would be as smooth as a mirror. 🔑 **Most waves form when winds blowing across the water's surface transmit their energy to the water.**

The size of a wave depends on the strength of the wind and on the length of time it blows. A gentle breeze creates small ripples on the surface of the water. Stronger winds create larger waves. The size of a wave also depends on the distance over which the wind blows. Winds blowing across longer distances build up bigger waves. That's why small ponds have ripples but the Great Lakes have waves you can surf!

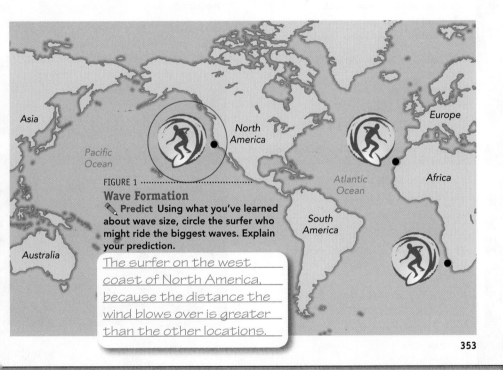

FIGURE 1 ....
Wave Formation
✏️ **Predict** Using what you've learned about wave size, circle the surfer who might ride the biggest waves. Explain your prediction.

The surfer on the west coast of North America, because the distance the wind blows over is greater than the other locations.

353

Explain

Introduce Vocabulary

Tell students that not all words in science have their origins in Greek or Latin. For example, *tsunami* is Japanese in origin, derived from the words *tsu* meaning "harbor" and *nami* meaning "wave."

Teach Key Concepts 🔑

Explain to students that energy is the ability to do work, such as move something. When wind blows across a body of water, some of the energy of the moving air gets transferred to the water, and waves form. Ask: **What is the cause of most waves?** *(The transfer of energy from wind)* **Why does a sailboat move?** *(Energy from the wind is transferred to the boat.)* Explain that the size of the waves that form depends on the amount of energy transferred to the water from the wind. Larger or higher waves have more energy. Ask: **Which wind could give more energy to water—a strong wind or a gentle breeze?** *(A strong wind)* **A wind that blows over a long distance or a wind that blows over a short distance?** *(A wind that blows over a long distance)* **What wind conditions would cause the largest waves to form in a body of water?** *(Very strong winds that blow over a very long distance)*

21st Century Learning 📖

CREATIVITY Have students read *Surfing* in the **Big Ideas of Science Reference Library** and create a collage displaying what they learned.

My Planet Diary provides an opportunity for students to explore real-world connections to wave action.

 Wave Action

1 Content and Language
Have students write sentences describing the relationships shown in **Figure 2.** For example, *Wave height is greater and wave length is shorter in the first diagram.*

2 Frontload the Lesson
Preview the lesson with students by calling attention to the titles, visuals, captions, and vocabulary terms.

3 Comprehensible Input
Demonstrate the motion of waves. Have two students each hold one end of a length of rope. One student repeatedly moves his or her arm up and down to create waves along the length of rope. Have students identify the different characteristics of waves that they see along the length of rope.

Explain

Lead a Discussion

WAVE CHARACTERISTICS Remind students that the height of an object is measured in a vertical direction and that the length of an object is measured in a horizontal direction. Ask: **What is the name for the distance between the crest and trough of a wave?** *(Wave height)* **What is the name for the distance from the crest of one wave to the crest of the next?** *(Wavelength)* **What term would you use to describe how many waves pass a point in a certain time period?** *(Frequency)*

Teach With Visuals

Tell students to look at **Figure 2.** Ask: **Which of the two diagrams shows waves with a long wavelength and low wave height?** *(The bottom diagram)* **In comparison, how would you describe the waves in the top diagram?** *(Shorter wavelength and higher wave height)*

Teach With Visuals

Tell students to look at **Figure 3.** Make sure they understand that the circular arrows show the movement of an individual particle of water moved by the energy of the wave as it passes. Ask: **In your own words, how can you describe the motion of a particle of water at the surface?** *(Possible answer: In a circular pattern, it moves up and forward, down, and then back up to where it started.)* **Which moves in a larger circle, a particle just below the surface or a particle on the surface of the ocean?** *(One on the surface)*

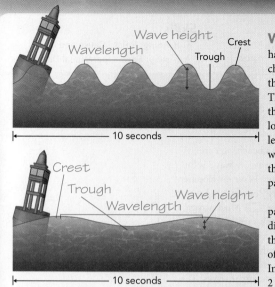

Wave Characteristics Scientists have a vocabulary to describe the characteristics of waves. The name for the highest part of a wave is the crest. The horizontal distance between crests is the **wavelength.** Long, rolling waves with lots of space between crests have long wavelengths. Short, choppy waves have shorter wavelengths. Waves are also measured by their **frequency,** the number of waves that pass a point in a certain amount of time.

As you can see in **Figure 2,** the lowest part of a wave is the trough. The vertical distance from the crest to the trough is the **wave height.** The energy and strength of a wave depend mainly on its wave height. In the open ocean, most waves are between 2 and 5 meters high. During storms, waves can grow much higher and more powerful.

FIGURE 2

Wave Characteristics
There are many different types of waves, but they have similar characteristics.

✏ **Read the text and complete the activity.**

1. **Identify** Find and label wavelength, wave height, crest, and trough on the diagrams. *Hint:* One diagram is started.

2. **Compare and Contrast** How does the frequency of the waves compare in the two diagrams?

The waves in the top image have a higher frequency. There are more waves in the same time.

Conditions at sea are constantly changing.

❶ Use the scientific vocabulary you learned above to describe the conditions at sea in the photo.

Sample: The crests are close so the wavelengths are short. This makes the wave height high. The frequency of the waves looks high, too.

❷ **Form Operational Definitions** Write your own definition for one of the scientific terms you used above.

Sample: wavelength—the distance between the crests of two waves

354 Water

Digital Lesson: Assign the *Apply It* activity online and have students submit their work to you.

Interactive Art allows students to explore the motion of water on the ocean's surface.

my science online.com **Wave Action**

Wave Energy Waves may appear to carry water toward shore, but water doesn't actually move forward in deep water. If it did, ocean water would eventually pile up on the coasts of every continent! The energy of the wave moves toward shore, but the water itself remains in place. You can test this by floating a cork in a bowl of water. Use a spoon to make a wave in the bowl. As the wave passes, the cork lurches forward a little; then it bobs backward. It ends up in almost the same spot where it started.

Water Motion What happens to the water as a wave travels along? Notice in **Figure 3** that as the wave passes, water particles move in a circular path. They swing forward and down with the energy of the wave, then back up to their original position. Deeper water particles move in smaller circles than those near the surface. At a depth equal to about one half the wavelength, water particles are not affected by the surface wave.

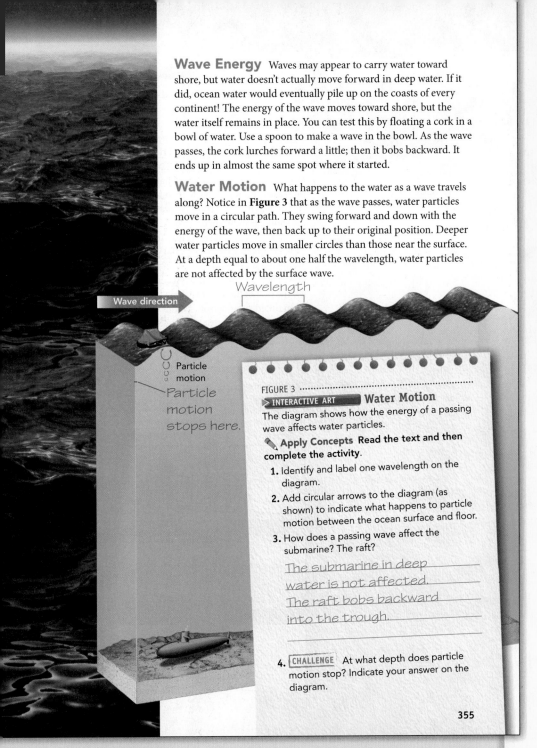

Wavelength

Wave direction

Particle motion

Particle motion stops here.

FIGURE 3 ....
> INTERACTIVE ART · Water Motion

The diagram shows how the energy of a passing wave affects water particles.

✏ **Apply Concepts** Read the text and then complete the activity.

1. Identify and label one wavelength on the diagram.

2. Add circular arrows to the diagram (as shown) to indicate what happens to particle motion between the ocean surface and floor.

3. How does a passing wave affect the submarine? The raft?

   The submarine in deep
   water is not affected.
   The raft bobs backward
   into the trough.

4. CHALLENGE At what depth does particle motion stop? Indicate your answer on the diagram.

355

Elaborate

Apply It!

L1 Review the boldface terms related to wave characteristics before beginning the activity.

🔺 **Form Operational Definitions** When students form an operational definition, they use what they know to summarize the meaning of a term. Suggest that, to write new definitions, students use different words then those in the sentences that contain the boldface terms. For example, they might replace *crest* or *horizontal* with words or phrases that mean the same thing.

Teacher Demo

L1 ENERGY AND WAVES

Material rope

Time 5 minutes

Remind students that it is energy and not water that moves in a wave. Then tie one end of a rope to a chair or other stationary object. Have a volunteer move the free end of the rope up and down.

Ask: **Does the rope move closer to the chair?** *(No.)* **How does this activity model wave energy?** *(The waves travel to the chair, but the rope does not.)*

Differentiated Instruction

L1 Communicate Have students take turns explaining to a partner how wavelength and wave height are alike and different. *(Both are characteristics of a wave that describe distance. Wavelength is the distance between the crests, whereas wave height is the distance between the crest and trough.)*

L3 Act Out Waves Challenge partners to work together to pantomime passing waves and their effect on water particles at different depths.

Explain

LESSON 10.5

Teach Key Concepts 🔑

Explain to students that waves change as they move from the deep ocean water to the shore. The distance from crest to trough gets longer. The distance from crest to crest gets shorter. Ask: **What is the distance from crest to trough called?** *(Wave height)* **How does it change as a wave approaches the shore?** *(It increases.)* **What is the distance from crest to crest called?** *(Wavelength)* **How does it change as a wave approaches the shore?** *(It decreases.)*

🔄 **Relate Cause and Effect** Explain to students that a cause is an event that makes an effect happen. An effect happens as a result of the cause.

Support the Big Q ❓ UbD

BREAKING WAVES Discuss with students how waves change as they approach the shore. Ask: **Why do waves slow down close to the shore?** *(Because the waves touch the ocean floor)* **What happens to the tops of waves when the bottoms slow down?** *(The tops keep moving forward until the waves topple over.)*

Point out that although the energy of a wave always moves toward shore, this is the only time that the water from a wave actually moves forward.

Address Misconceptions

UNDERTOW VS. RIP CURRENT Many students may assume that an undertow is the same thing as rip current. Both are caused by waves breaking on the shore, but a rip current is much more dangerous to swimmers. An undertow can pull someone underwater, but the person will be alright if he or she remains calm and swims to the surface. A rip current, however, can carry a swimmer out to sea.

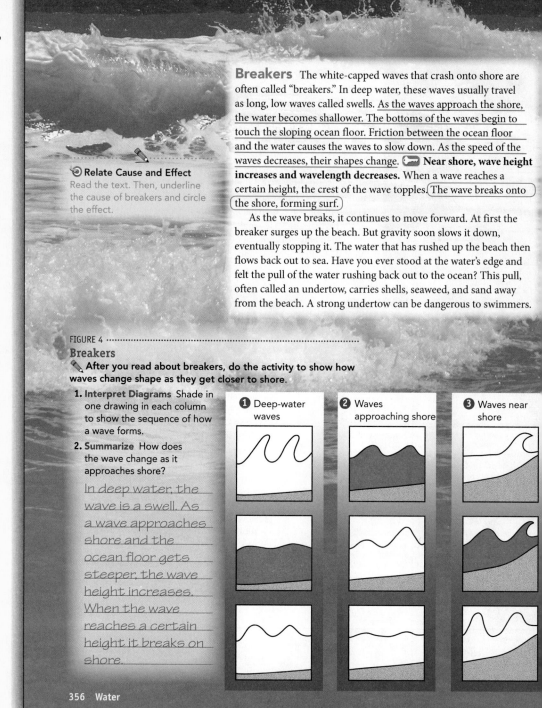

🔄 **Relate Cause and Effect**
Read the text. Then, underline the cause of breakers and circle the effect.

Breakers The white-capped waves that crash onto shore are often called "breakers." In deep water, these waves usually travel as long, low waves called swells. <u>As the waves approach the shore, the water becomes shallower. The bottoms of the waves begin to touch the sloping ocean floor. Friction between the ocean floor and the water causes the waves to slow down. As the speed of the waves decreases, their shapes change.</u> 🔑 **Near shore, wave height increases and wavelength decreases.** When a wave reaches a certain height, the crest of the wave topples. (The wave breaks onto the shore, forming surf.)

As the wave breaks, it continues to move forward. At first the breaker surges up the beach. But gravity soon slows it down, eventually stopping it. The water that has rushed up the beach then flows back out to sea. Have you ever stood at the water's edge and felt the pull of the water rushing back out to the ocean? This pull, often called an undertow, carries shells, seaweed, and sand away from the beach. A strong undertow can be dangerous to swimmers.

FIGURE 4
Breakers
After you read about breakers, do the activity to show how waves change shape as they get closer to shore.

1. **Interpret Diagrams** Shade in one drawing in each column to show the sequence of how a wave forms.

2. **Summarize** How does the wave change as it approaches shore?

In deep water, the wave is a swell. As a wave approaches shore and the ocean floor gets steeper, the wave height increases. When the wave reaches a certain height it breaks on shore.

❶ Deep-water waves
❷ Waves approaching shore
❸ Waves near shore

356 Water

Tsunami So far you've been reading about waves that are caused by the wind. But another kind of wave forms far below the ocean surface. This type of wave, called a **tsunami**, is usually caused by an earthquake beneath the ocean floor. The ocean floor's abrupt movement sends pulses of energy through the water, shown in the diagram below.

Despite the huge amount of energy a tsunami carries, people on a ship at sea may not even realize a tsunami is passing. How is this possible? A tsunami in deep water may have a wavelength of 200 kilometers or more, but a wave height of less than a meter. When the tsunami reaches shallow water near the coast, friction with the ocean floor causes the long wavelength to decrease suddenly. The wave height increases as the water "piles up." Some tsunamis have reached heights of 20 meters or more—taller than a five-story building!

Tsunamis are most common in the Pacific Ocean, often striking Alaska, Hawaii, and Japan. In response, nations in the Pacific have developed a warning system, which can alert them if a tsunami forms. On March 11, 2011, an enormous Tsunami devastated Japan. But not all tsunamis occur in the Pacific Ocean. On December 26, 2004, a major earthquake in the Indian Ocean caused tremendous tsunamis that hit 11 nations. Tragically, these tsunamis took the lives of more than 230,000 people. Several nations are now developing a warning system for the Indian Ocean.

FIGURE 5 ....

Tsunami

✏ **Communicate** Use the diagram below, showing how a tsunami forms, to help you develop a tsunami warning system. Include how you would warn people living in remote areas.

<u>Accept all reasonable</u>
<u>answers.</u>

An Indonesian village hit by the 2004 tsunami

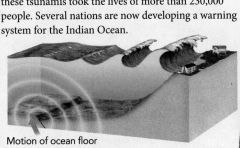

Motion of ocean floor

 Do the Quick Lab *Making Waves.*

🔑 **Assess Your Understanding**

got it? ....

○ I get it! Now I know that waves change as they approach shore because <u>friction between</u> <u>the ocean floor and water slows the waves down.</u>

○ I need extra help with <u>See TE note.</u>

Go to **my science COACH** online for help with this subject.

357

Differentiated Instruction

L1 Ask Questions Have students read the first three sentences about tsunamis. Then have them ask questions about what they would like to know about tsunamis. Write their questions on the board. Have students respond to each question after they have read the remainder of the section.

L3 Research Tsunamis Have students find out and share the answers to any unanswered questions from the activity above.

Teach With Visuals

Tell students to look at **Figure 5.** Review with them what happens during an underwater earthquake. *(Blocks of rock move on either side of a fault. Underwater landslides are sometimes triggered.)* Ask: **What is the source of energy in most tsunamis?** *(The energy in most tsunamis is from movement related to earthquakes on the ocean floor.)* **How is this different from a regular wave?** *(The energy in a regular ocean wave is from wind blowing across the water.)* **Why do you think tsunamis are most common in the Pacific Ocean?** *(Earthquakes are most common in that region.)*

21st Century Learning

L1 CRITICAL THINKING Point out that tsunamis can also be caused by volcanic eruptions and underwater landslides. Ask: **How are these events like the earthquakes that cause tsunamis?** *(Both involve the abrupt movement of rock material, either solid or molten, which sends energy through the surrounding ground and water.)* Tell students that the eruption of Krakatoa in 1883 caused a tsunami in the Indian Ocean that killed 36,000 people in Java. Large underwater landslides are particularly dangerous in the Atlantic.

Elaborate

Lab Resource: Quick Lab 🔬

L2 MAKING WAVES Students will use rope to simulate waves.

Evaluate

Assess Your Understanding

Have students evaluate their understanding by completing the appropriate sentence.

RTI Response to Intervention

If students need help explaining why waves change, **then** have them reread the paragraph following the red head *Breakers.*

my science COACH Have students go online for help in understanding how waves change.

Explain

Teach Key Concepts 🔑

Explain to students that deposition is the process by which sediment is laid down, or dropped, in new places. Waves deposit sand when they slow down near the shore. Ask: **What forms as a result of this wave deposition?** *(Sandbars)* **What is a sandbar?** *(A long ridge of deposited sand)* **What kind of current is associated with sandbars?** *(Rip current)*

Teach Key Concepts 🔑

Explain to students that erosion is the process of wearing down and carrying away rocks, including the sand along a shore. Waves change beaches by wearing down and carrying away rocks and sand. Ask: **Which natural landforms protect against erosion?** *(Barrier beaches and dunes)* **Why do these landforms protect the coastline?** *(Waves break against barrier beaches instead of the mainland. Vegetation on dunes holds sand in place.)* **What structures do people build to reduce beach erosion?** *(Groins)* **How do groins work?** *(They catch sand being moved by the longshore current.)* **Why might building groins be controversial in some communities?** *(Erosion is increased downcurrent from a groin.)*

Lead a Discussion

SHIFTING SANDS Remind students that wind rarely blows from a direction that is perpendicular to the shore. Ask: **If wind blows at an angle to the shore, how will the waves come in?** *(At an angle)* **Which way does gravity pull the water after a wave washes onto shore?** *(Straight back down the sloping beach toward the ocean.)* **If a sand grain was being moved by the water, what path would it take?** *(A zig-zag path along the beach)* **What would happen if something blocked the sand that was moving along the beach?** *(Sand would build up on one side of the barrier.)*

How Do Waves Affect the Shore?

As waves approach and crash onto the shore, the beach can change. Wave direction at sea is determined by the wind. Waves usually roll toward shore at an angle. But as they touch bottom, the shallower water slows the shoreward side of the wave first. The rows of waves gradually turn and become more nearly parallel to the shore.

Longshore Drift As waves come into shore, water washes up the beach at an angle, carrying sand grains, as shown in **Figure 6**. The water and sand then run down the beach. This movement of sand along the beach is called **longshore drift**. 🔑 **As the waves slow down, they deposit the sand they are carrying on the shallow, underwater slope, forming a long ridge called a sandbar.**

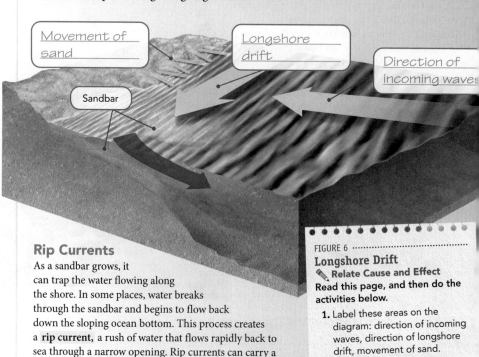

Movement of sand

Longshore drift

Direction of incoming waves

Sandbar

Rip Currents

As a sandbar grows, it can trap the water flowing along the shore. In some places, water breaks through the sandbar and begins to flow back down the sloping ocean bottom. This process creates a **rip current,** a rush of water that flows rapidly back to sea through a narrow opening. Rip currents can carry a swimmer out into deep water. Because rip currents are narrow, a strong swimmer can usually escape by swimming across the current, parallel to the beach.

FIGURE 6 ·····················
Longshore Drift
✎ **Relate Cause and Effect**
Read this page, and then do the activities below.

1. Label these areas on the diagram: direction of incoming waves, direction of longshore drift, movement of sand.

2. Draw an arrow in the area where a rip current would form.

Beach Erosion If you walk on the same beach every day, you might not notice that it's changing. But if you visit a beach just once each year, you might be startled by the changes you see. 🔑 **Waves shape a beach by eroding the shore in some places and building it up in others.**

Barrier Beaches Long sand deposits called barrier beaches form parallel to the shore and are separated from the mainland by a shallow lagoon. Waves break against the barrier beach, protecting the mainland from erosion. For this reason, people are working to preserve barrier beaches along the Atlantic coast from Georgia to Massachusetts.

Sand Dunes Hills of windblown sand, called sand dunes, can make a beach more stable and protect the shore from erosion. The strong roots of dune plants hold the sand in place and help slow erosion. Without them, sand dunes can be easily washed away by wave action.

Groins Many people like to live near the ocean, but erosion can threaten buildings near the beach. One way to reduce beach erosion is to build a wall of rocks or concrete, called a **groin,** outward from the beach. Sand carried by the water piles up on one side of the groin instead of moving down shore. However, groins increase erosion farther down the beach.

FIGURE 7 ....

Beach Erosion
✏️ **Evaluate the Impact on Society** Your community planning board wants to limit beach erosion. Do you vote to protect the dunes from being built on or to construct a groin instead? Why?

Sample: I would protect the dunes because it would reduce erosion and preserve the natural habitat of living things.

 Do the Quick Lab Modeling Currents.

🔑 **Assess Your Understanding**

got it? ....

○ I get it! Now I know that waves shape the beach by _eroding some areas and building up others._

○ I need extra help with _See TE note._

Go to **MY SCIENCE COACH** online for help with this subject.

359

Differentiated Instruction

L1 Rip Current Safety Have students look at **Figure 6** and locate the break in the sandbar. This is where a rip current could flow out toward deeper water. Ask students what would happen if they tried to swim against the current. (*They would be carried away from shore.*) Point out that if they swam only a short distance parallel to the beach, they would be over the sandbar and out of the rip current.

L3 Write a Beach Story Encourage students use their imaginations to write a fictional account of a trip to the beach. Have them use the highlighted terms in this section. They should also include the following terms in their story: *sandbar, barrier beach,* and *sand dune.* Have students compile their stories into a Beach Notebook for the class to read.

Elaborate

Build Inquiry

L2 LONGSHORE DRIFT

Materials piece of plywood (about 60 cm square), marble, small wood block

Time 20 minutes

Remind students that beaches tilt toward the water. The angle of tilt varies. Have students place a wood block under one end of a piece of plywood so that the plywood tilts at about a 10° angle. Then tell them to roll the marble up the plywood ramp and observe as the marble rolls straight back down the incline. Have students repeat this procedure to model longshore drift. Ask: **What does the marble represent in this model?** (*A grain of sand*)

Build Inquiry

L2 MODEL BARRIER BEACHES

Materials shallow pan, spoon, water, wood block

Time 25 minutes

Have students fill a shallow pan to about 1 cm depth with water. Students then should place the wood block so that it extends part of the way across the pan. Tell students that the wood block represents a barrier beach. Have students use a spoon to make waves at one end of the pan. They should compare waves along the other end of the pan and notice that the barrier beach stops most of the wave energy. Ask: **Other than groins, how could people use human-made barriers to reduce beach erosion?** (*Structures could be placed offshore to absorb wave energy.*)

Lab Resource: Quick Lab

L2 MODELING CURRENTS Students will explore rip currents by using a model.

Evaluate

Assess Your Understanding

Have students evaluate their understanding by completing the appropriate sentence.

RTI Response to Intervention

If students cannot describe how waves shape beaches, **then** have them reread the two Key Concept statements and the paragraphs that contain them.

MY SCIENCE COACH Have students go online for help in understanding how waves affect beaches.

359

Lab Zone — After the Inquiry Warm-Up

Wave Action

Inquiry Warm-Up, *How Do Waves Change a Beach?*

In the Inquiry Warm-Up, you investigated how waves change a beach. Using what you learned from that activity, answer the questions below.

1. **PREDICT** What would happen to the waves if you moved the tongue depressor faster? What would happen to the beach?

   _____

   _____

2. **INFER** What kind of conditions might you be simulating if you moved the tongue depressor faster?

   _____

   _____

3. **DRAW CONCLUSIONS** What can you tell about the effect of ocean waves on beaches from this experiment?

   _____

   _____

4. **DEVELOP HYPOTHESES** What are some ways you might counteract the effect of ocean waves on beaches?

   _____

   _____

Place the outside corner, the corner away from the dotted line, in the corner of your copy machine to copy onto letter-size paper.

Assess Your Understanding

Wave Action

> ### How Do Waves Form and Change?

got it? ....

○ **I get it!** Now I know that waves change as they approach shore because _____
_____

○ **I need extra help with** _____
_____

> ### How Do Waves Affect the Shore?

got it? ....

○ **I get it!** Now I know that waves shape the beach by _____
_____

○ **I need extra help with** _____
_____

Wave Action

How Do Waves Form and Change?

A **wave** is the movement of energy through a body of water. **Most waves form when wind blowing across the surface transmit their energy to the water.** The size of a wave depends on the strength of the wind and on the length of time it blows.

The name for the highest part of a wave is the crest. The horizontal distance between crests is the **wavelength.** Waves are also measured by their **frequency,** the number of waves that pass a point in a certain amount of time. The lowest part of a wave is the trough. The vertical distance from the crest to the trough is the **wave height.** The energy and strength of a wave depend mainly on its wave height.

The energy of a wave moves toward the shore, but the water itself remains in place. As a wave passes, water particles move in a circular path. Deeper water particles move in smaller circles than those near the surface.

Near shore, wave height increases and wavelength decreases. When a wave reaches a certain height, the crest of the wave topples. The wave breaks onto the shore, forming surf.

A wave that forms far below the ocean surface, called a **tsunami,** is usually caused by an earthquake beneath the ocean floor. Some have reached heights of 20 meters or more.

How Do Waves Affect the Shore?

The movement of sand along a beach is called **longshore drift. As the waves slow down, they deposit the sand they are carrying on the shallow, underwater slope, forming a long ridge called a sandbar.**

Water may break through a sandbar and begin to flow back down the sloping ocean bottom. This process creates a **rip current,** a rush of water that flows rapidly back to sea through a narrow opening.

Waves shape a beach by eroding the shore in some places and building it up in others. One way to reduce beach erosion is to build a wall of rocks or concrete, called a **groin,** outward from the beach.

On a separate sheet of paper, describe how ocean waves form and affect the shore.

Review and Reinforce

Wave Action

Understanding Main Ideas
Fill in the spaces in the drawing below.

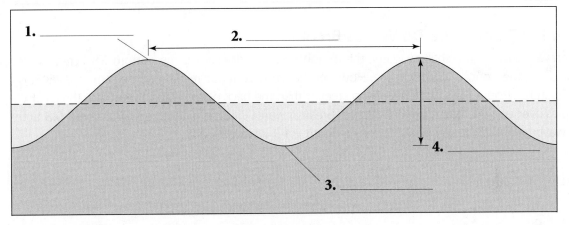

Answer the following questions on a separate sheet of paper.

5. How does a wave change when it enters shallow water near shore?
6. How do waves change a beach?
7. What are three ways to prevent beach erosion?

Building Vocabulary
If the statement is true, write *true*. If the statement is false, change the underlined word or words to make the statement true.

8. _____ A <u>wave</u> is created by the movement of energy through water.

9. _____ The number of waves that pass a point in a given amount of time is called <u>rip current</u>.

10. _____ <u>Sideways</u> drift is the movement of sand down a beach.

11. _____ A <u>surf</u> is a wave caused by an earthquake on the ocean floor.

12. _____ A wall of rocks or concrete built outward from a beach to prevent erosion is called a <u>groin</u>.

13. _____ A <u>tsunami</u> is a rush of water that flows out from the shore through a narrow opening.

14. _____ The distance between crests is called <u>wave width</u>.

Enrich

Wave Action

As waves approach the shore, the bottom of the ocean becomes closer to the surface, affecting the waves. Read the passage below and look at the diagram. Then answer the questions on a separate sheet of paper.

How Far From Shore Do Waves Break?

When waves move into shallow water, the troughs begin to drag along the bottom. This creates friction and causes the troughs to slow down. However the crests continue moving at the same speed. This results in the front of the wave becoming steeper than the back of the wave. Eventually, the crest topples over and the wave "breaks." Waves break in water that has a depth equal to about 0.3 times the wave height. Or, waves beak when the depth = 1.3 × wave height.

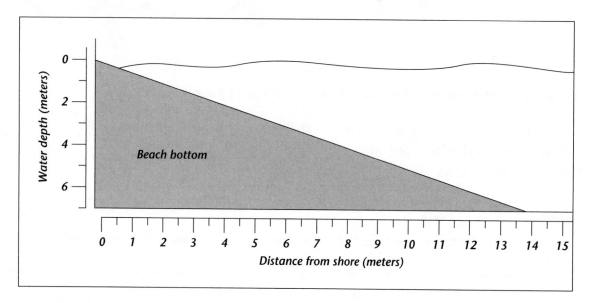

1. If a wave has a wave height of 5 meters, in what depth of water would it begin to break?

2. In what depth of water would a wave begin to break if it had a wave height of 3 meters?

3. According to the diagram, how far from shore would a wave break if it had a wave height of 3 meters?

4. How high must a wave be to break in water that is 7.8 meters deep?

5. If the wind picked up and caused an increase in wave height, would wave break farther from shore or closer to shore? Why?

Name _____ Date _____ Class _____

Wave Action

Fill in the blank to complete each statement.

1. Winds that blow over longer distances build up bigger _____.

2. Longshore drift is the movement of sand along a(n) _____.

3. Wavelength _____ and wave height increases as waves approach the shore.

4. Waves that form as a result of earthquakes are called _____.

5. Only a wave's _____ moves toward shore, not the water itself.

6. A backward rush of water called a _____ current can carry a swimmer out into deep water.

Write the letter of the correct answer on the line at the left.

7. ___ What is the horizontal distance between wave crests called?
   A wave height
   B trough
   C wavelength
   D frequency

8. ___ What causes most waves to form?
   A Earth's rotation
   B boats
   C rain
   D wind

9. ___ Which is a human-made structure that reduces beach erosion?
   A sandbar
   B groin
   C barrier beach
   D sand dune

10. ___ Which term best describes the path of movement of water particles in a wave?
   A circular
   B straight
   C sinking
   D rising

Wave Action

Answer Key

After the Inquiry Warm-Up

1. The waves would be bigger, faster, and stronger. The beach would be eroded more quickly.

2. A hurricane or other large storm

3. When waves crash on beaches, they carry some of the sand from the beach out deeper into the ocean.

4. Accept all reasonable responses. Students may describe barrier beaches, sand dunes, or groins, without calling those features by name.

Key Concept Summaries

Ocean waves form as a result of wind blowing across the ocean surface. They erode the shore in some places and build it up in others.

Review and Reinforce

1. crest

2. wavelength

3. trough

4. wave height

5. Its wave height increases, and its wavelength decreases.

6. by eroding the beach in some places and building it up in others

7. building groins, stabilizing sand dunes, and protecting barrier beaches

8. true   9. frequency

10. longshore   11. tsunami

12. true   13. rip current

14. wavelength

Enrich

1. at a depth equal to 1.3 times the wave height or 6.5 meters

2. at a depth of 3.9 meters

3. where the depth was 3.9 meters, which is about 8 meters from shore

4. 6 meters high

5. Higher waves break farther from shore because as waves get higher, the water depth in which they will break becomes deeper.

Lesson Quiz

1. waves   2. beach

3. decreases   4. tsunamis

5. energy   6. rip

7. C   8. D

9. B   10. A

Place the outside corner, the corner away from the dotted line, in the corner of your copy machine to copy onto letter-size paper.

Currents and Climate

LESSON

6

 How does fresh water cycle on Earth?

Lesson Pacing: 2–3 periods or 1–1$\frac{1}{2}$ blocks

⏱ SHORT ON TIME? To do this lesson in approximately half the time, do the Activate Prior Knowledge activity followed by a discussion of the Key Concepts to familiarize students with the lesson content. Have students do the Quick Lab. The rest of the lesson can be completed by students independently.

> **Preference Navigator,** in the online Planning tools, allows you to customize *Interactive Science* to your own teaching style. You can also edit lesson plans by selecting the Lesson Planner option.
>
> **Digital Teacher's Edition** allows you to access your Teacher's Edition and Resource materials online.

my science online.com

Lesson Vocabulary

- current
- Coriolis effect
- climate
- El Niño
- La Niña

 ## Content Refresher

El Niño One of the largest El Niños on record occurred during the years 1997 and 1998. Although the massive warm-water current was already shrinking by January of 1998, it was still 1.5 times the size of the continental United States. Because it was so large, the 1997-1998 El Niño brought some of the most unusual weather ever recorded in the United States. Many regions had unusually wet or dry conditions. Storms battered the coast of California. Regions outside of the United States also were affected. Torrential downpours occurred in parts of eastern and central Africa that are usually arid, and drought conditions existed in northeastern Brazil, Indonesia, and Australia, where it is usually wet.

El Niño is Spanish for "the boy" and refers to the periodic warming that occurs in the Pacific near South America around Christmas. La Niña is Spanish for "the girl." El Niño is the warm phase of oscillation and La Niña is the cold phase.

LESSON OBJECTIVES

🔑 Identify what causes surface currents and explain how surface currents affect climate.

🔑 Identify the causes of deep currents and describe the effects that deep currents have.

Blended Path
Active learning using Student Edition, Inquiry Path, and Digital Path

ENGAGE AND EXPLORE

Teach this lesson using a variety of resources. Begin by reading **My Planet Diary** as a class. Have students share ideas about how scientists study ocean currents. Then have students do the **Inquiry Warm-Up activity.** Students will model the effect wind blowing has on movement of surface and deep water currents. The **After the Inquiry Warm-Up worksheet** sets up a discussion about the density and temperature of ocean waters. Have volunteers share their answers to number 4 about how water density changes as the temperature of the water changes.

EXPLAIN AND ELABORATE

Teach Key Concepts by explaining the term *current* and asking how currents are different from waves. Use the **Support the Big Q** to illustrate the movement of the Gulf Stream current using **Figure 1.** Continue to **Teach Key Concepts** by discussing how ocean currents impact coastal regions climates. Then have students practice the inquiry skill in the **Apply It activity.** Use **Figure 2** to model the effects that El Niño winds can have on water temperatures. **Lead a Discussion** about how ocean activity causes short-term climate changes.

Teach Key Concepts by asking students what causes deep currents to flow in the ocean. Hand out the **Key Concept Summaries** as a review of each part of the lesson. Students can also use the online **Vocab Flash Cards** to review key terms.

EVALUATE

Have students take the **Lesson Quiz.** For an alternate assessment, see the **EXAM**VIEW® Assessment Suite, Progress Monitoring Assessments, or SuccessTracker™.

ⒺⓁⓁ Support

1 Content and Language

The word *climate* has more than one meaning. *Climate,* means "the typical weather in a specific area." *Climate,* also means "the environment during a specific period or place in time." Have students write statements using the different definitions of *climate.*

DIFFERENTIATED INSTRUCTION KEY
L1 Struggling Students or Special Needs
L2 On-Level Students **L3** Advanced Students

LESSON PLANNER 10.6

Lab zone Inquiry Path
Hands-on learning in the Lab zone

Digital Path
Online learning at **my science online**.com

ENGAGE AND EXPLORE

To teach this lesson with an emphasis on inquiry, begin with the **Inquiry Warm-Up activity.** Students will model wind effects on the movement of surface and deep currents. Discuss the characteristics of warm and cold waters. Have students do the **After the Inquiry Warm-Up worksheet.** Talk about how this activity relates to the waters in an ocean. Have volunteers share their answers to number 4 about how the density changes as the water warms up or cools down.

EXPLAIN AND ELABORATE

Focus on the **Inquiry Skill** for the lesson. Point out that when you infer, you use the available data to draw a conclusion. What could be inferred about the density and temperature of ocean waters in the **Inquiry Warm-Up activity?** *(The surface water is warmer and less dense while the deep ocean water is cooler and more dense.)* Review characteristics of the Gulf Stream before beginning the **Apply It activity.** Ask volunteers to share their inferences about the climate in Trondheim. Have students complete the **Lab Investigation** to help them visualize ocean currents.

Have students do the **Quick Lab** to explore the way temperature affects the movement of deep currents and then ask them to share their results. Students can use the online **Vocab Flash Cards** to review key terms.

EVALUATE

Have students take the **Lesson Quiz.** For an alternate assessment, see the **EXAM**VIEW® Assessment Suite, Progress Monitoring Assessments, or SuccessTracker™.

ENGAGE AND EXPLORE

Teach this lesson using digital resources. Begin by having students explore real-world connections to ocean currents at **My Planet Diary** online. Have them access the Chapter Resources to find the **Unlock the Big Question activity.** There they can answer the questions and refine their responses as they continue through the lesson. You can re-assign the activity and have students submit their work so you can track their progress.

EXPLAIN AND ELABORATE

Students reading above, at, or below the lexile measure of this lesson can access basic content readings at their level at **My Reading Web.** Have students use the online **Vocab Flash Cards** to preview key terms. Review what they know about how currents affect climates before assigning the online **Apply It activity.** Ask volunteers to share their inferences. Students should submit their work to you. Have students do the online **Art in Motion activity** to learn about ocean temperature during an El Niño event.

Assign the **Do the Math activity** online and have students submit their work to you. Do the **Quick Lab** about explore the way temperature affects the movement of deep currents then ask students to share their results. The **Key Concept Summaries** online allow students to read a summary and see an image associated with each part of the lesson. Online remediation is available at **My Science Coach.**

EVALUATE

Have students take the **Lesson Quiz.** For an alternate assessment, see the **EXAM**VIEW® Assessment Suite, Progress Monitoring Assessments, or SuccessTracker™.

2 Frontload the Lesson
Preview the lesson questions. Ask students if there are any words they do not understand. Explain the specific meanings these words have in science.

3 Comprehensible Input
Have students study the visuals and their captions to support the key concepts of the lesson.

4 Language Production
Pair or group students with varied language abilities to complete labs collaboratively for language practice. Have each student copy the completed written lab for personal reference.

5 Assess Understanding
Divide the class into small groups. Have each student identify a key concept from the lesson to discuss in his or her group. After the discussions, have students talk about the key concepts as a group.

Currents and Climate

Establish Learning Objectives

🔑 Identify what causes surface currents and explain how surface currents affect climate.

🔑 Identify the causes of deep currents and describe the effects that deep currents have.

Engage

Activate Prior Knowledge

MY PLANET DIARY Read *Ducky Overboard* with the class. Ask students whether they have heard stories about someone finding a message in a bottle that was thrown into the ocean at a faraway location.
Ask: **How do you think the bottle got there?** *(Some students might know that ocean currents exist and that a current transported the bottle.)*

BIG IDEAS OF SCIENCE REFERENCE LIBRARY 📖 Have students look up the following topic: Ocean Currents.

Explore

Lab Resource: Inquiry Warm-Up 🧪

L1 **BOTTOM TO TOP** Students will observe the effect of wind blowing on the movement of surface and deep water currents.

---

6 Currents and Climate

🔑 **What Causes Surface Currents?**

🔑 **What Causes Deep Currents?**

my planet diary   EVERYDAY SCIENCE

Ducky Overboard

What happens when a ship loses its cargo at sea? Is it gone forever? You might think so. One ship traveling from Hong Kong to Tacoma, Washington, lost 29,000 plastic toys. They fell overboard in a storm and were considered lost at sea. But when hundreds of the toys began washing up on distant shores, scientists got excited.

One way scientists study ocean currents is by releasing empty bottles into the ocean. But of 500 to 1,000 bottles released, scientists might only recover 10. That doesn't give them much data. The large number of floating toys could give scientists better data from more data points.

The first toys were spotted off the coast of Alaska. Then beachcombers began finding them in Canada, in Washington, and even as far away as Scotland.

Discuss these questions with a classmate and write your answers below.

1. Why was the plastic toy spill so helpful to scientists studying ocean currents?

   The toy spill resulted in a large number of data points.

2. Have you ever found objects on the beach? What data would scientists need from you for their research?

   Yes; a description of the object and the time and place it was found

▶ PLANET DIARY Go to **Planet Diary** to learn more about ocean currents.

🧪 **Lab zone** Do the Inquiry Warm-Up *Bottom to Top.*

360 Water

SUPPORT ALL READERS

Lexile Measure = 940L   Lexile Word Count = 1315

Prior Exposure to Content: May be the first time students have encountered this topic

Academic Vocabulary: *compare, contrast, infer*

Science Vocabulary: *Coriolis effect, El Niño, La Niña*

Concept Level: Generally appropriate for most students in this grade

Preteach With: My Planet Diary "Ducky Overboard" and Figure 1 activity

Go to **My Reading Web** to access leveled readings that provide a foundation for the content.

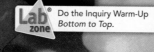

Vocabulary
- current
- climate
- Coriolis effect
- El Niño
- La Niña

Skills
- Reading: Compare and Contrast
- Inquiry: Infer

What Causes Surface Currents?

A **current** is a large stream of moving water that flows through the oceans. Unlike waves, currents carry water from one place to another. Some currents move water at the surface of the ocean. Other currents move water deep in the ocean.

🔑 **Surface currents affect water to a depth of several hundred meters. They are driven mainly by winds.** Surface currents follow Earth's major wind patterns. They move in circular patterns in the five major oceans. Most of the currents flow east or west, then double back to complete the circle, as shown in **Figure 1**.

Coriolis Effect Why do the currents move in these circular patterns? If Earth were standing still, winds and currents would flow in more direct paths between the poles and the equator. But as Earth rotates, the paths of the winds and currents curve. This effect of Earth's rotation on the direction of winds and currents is called the **Coriolis effect** (kawr ee OH lis). In the Northern Hemisphere, the Coriolis effect causes the currents to curve clockwise. In the Southern Hemisphere, the Coriolis effect causes the currents to curve counterclockwise.

FIGURE 1 ....

Surface Currents
✎ **Infer** The toys that fell overboard washed up in many places. Two of the locations are marked with ducks below. Circle the currents that you think moved the toys to these spots. Discuss your answer with a classmate.

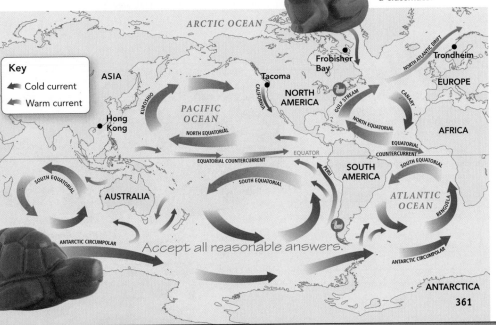

Accept all reasonable answers.

361

Explain

Introduce Vocabulary
Remind students that many science words come to English from other languages. Explain that *El Niño* means "the child" in Spanish.

Teach Key Concepts 🔑
Explain to students that like waves, surface currents are driven by the wind. But unlike waves, currents are streams of water that flow from place to place in the ocean. Ask: **How are currents different than waves?** *(Ocean water is moved great distances by currents, but not by waves.)* **How deep do some surface currents reach?** *(As much as several hundred meters)* Tell students that the Coriolis effect causes wind-formed currents to curve to the right in the northern hemisphere and to the left in the southern hemisphere. Ask: **If water currents kept curving, what path would they follow?** *(The currents would follow large circular paths.)* **How would the direction of rotation be different in the two hemispheres?** *(Rotation would be clockwise in the northern hemisphere and counterclockwise in the southern hemisphere.)* **If currents rotate clockwise in the northern hemisphere, which side of a continent would have a warm current?** *(East side)* **Which side would have a cold current?** *(West side)*

Support the Big Q ❓ UbD
GULF STREAM Have students locate the Gulf Stream in **Figure 1**. Point out how the current parallels the coast of North America before crossing to northern Europe. Ask: **Where does the warm water in the Gulf Stream come from?** *(Gulf of Mexico and Caribbean Sea)* **What ocean does the Gulf Stream flow through?** *(Atlantic Ocean)* **What is the Gulf Stream called when it crosses the Atlantic Ocean?** *(North Atlantic Drift)*

My Planet Diary provides an opportunity for students to explore real-world connections to surface currents.

my science online | Surface Currents

LESSON 10.6

ⒺⓁⓁ Support

1 Content and Language
Point out that some English words have more than one meaning. *Current* can mean something that is happening in the present. It can also mean the flow of electricity. Have students define the term as it is used in this lesson.

2 Frontload the Lesson
Have students write sentences using different meanings of the word *current*. After students finish the lesson, have

them write a sentence that uses the word *current* based on the lesson.

3 Comprehensible Input
Have students look at the map of ocean currents on this page. Have students draw the path they think one of the ducks might have traveled.

Explain

Teach Key Concepts 🔑

Explain to students that different coastal areas of North America have different climates. Their climates are affected by the different temperatures of nearby ocean currents that warm or cool the air and land.
Ask: **How is a town near a warm ocean current likely to be affected?** *(Its climate would be warmer and wetter.)* **How is a town near a cold ocean current likely to be affected?** *(Its climate would be colder and drier.)*

↪ **Compare and Contrast** Remind students that when they compare and contrast, they identify ways in which two objects or events are the same and different.

Teach With Visuals

Tell students to look at **Figure 2.** Explain that the diagram shows a cross section of the Pacific Ocean, with the left side of the diagram representing the western Pacific and the right side representing the eastern Pacific along the South American coast. Have a student read the caption as the class listens. Then explain that the colors show the relative water temperature from warmest to coldest as follows: red, orange, yellow, green and blue. Ask: **What dates are represented in the image?** *(January and June of 1997)* **In the eastern Pacific in January of 1997, at what depth do the coldest waters in dark blue begin to occur?** *(About 100 ft or 30.48 m)* **In the eastern Pacific in June of 1997, at what depth do the coldest waters in dark blue begin to occur?** *(About 300 ft or 91.44 m)* **Why does this change occur?** *(El Niño winds caused warmer water from the western Pacific to move to the eastern Pacific.)*

Elaborate

Apply It!

L1 Review the characteristics of the Gulf Stream before beginning the activity.

△ **Infer** Explain to students that inferring involves interpreting an observation or other information. On **Figure 1,** point out for students the location of the towns pictured. Help students locate the current arrows near the town. Ask them to infer a relationship between the arrows and the climates.

✎ **Compare and Contrast** Use the space below to compare and contrast the effects of warm and cold currents on climate.

Warm ocean currents warm the air above them. They can make an area humid and mild. Cold ocean currents cool the air above them making nearby land areas cooler and drier.

Gulf Stream The Gulf Stream is the largest and most powerful surface current in the North Atlantic Ocean. This current is caused by strong winds from the west. It is more than 30 kilometers wide and 300 meters deep. The Gulf Stream moves warm water from the Gulf of Mexico to the Caribbean Sea. It then continues northward along the east coast of the United States. Near Cape Hatteras, North Carolina, it curves eastward across the Atlantic, as a result of the Coriolis effect. When the Gulf Stream crosses the Atlantic it becomes the North Atlantic Drift.

Effects on Climate The Gulf Stream has a warming effect on the climate of nearby land areas. **Climate** is the pattern of temperature and precipitation typical of an area over a long period of time. The mid-Atlantic region of the United States, including North Carolina and Virginia, has a more moderate climate because of the Gulf Stream. Winters are very mild and summers are humid.

Currents affect climate by moving cold and warm water around the globe. Currents generally move warm water from the tropics toward the poles and bring cold water back toward the equator. 🔑 **A surface current warms or cools the air above it. This affects the climate of land near the coast.** Winds pick up moisture as they blow across warm-water currents. This explains why the warm Kuroshio Current brings mild, rainy weather to the southern islands of Japan. Cold-water currents cool the air above them. Cold air holds less moisture than warm air. So cold currents tend to bring cool, dry weather to land areas in their path.

apply it!

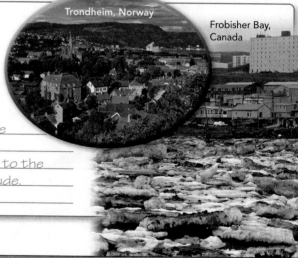

Trondheim, Norway

Frobisher Bay, Canada

Trondheim, Norway, and Frobisher Bay, Canada, are shown here in July. They are at roughly the same latitude, but they have very different climates.

△ **Infer** Why does Trondheim have a mild climate? *Hint:* Refer to the map on the previous page.

Trondheim is affected by the Gulf Stream. This warm current brings mild weather to the region despite its high latitude.

362 Water

Digital Lesson: Assign the *Apply It* activity online and have students submit their work to you.

Art in Motion shows what happens to the temperature of the ocean during an El Niño event.

my science online.com ⟩ **Surface Currents**

El Niño Changes in wind patterns and currents can have a major impact on the oceans and nearby land. One example of such changes is **El Niño,** a climate event that occurs every two to seven years in the Pacific Ocean. El Niño begins when an unusual pattern of winds forms over the western Pacific. This causes a vast sheet of warm water to move east toward the South American coast, as shown in **Figure 2.** This warm water prevents the cold deep water from moving to the surface. El Niño conditions can last for one to two years before the usual winds and currents return.

El Niño causes shifts in weather patterns. This leads to unusual and often severe conditions in different areas. A major El Niño occurred between 1997 and 1998. It caused an especially warm winter in the northeastern United States. It was also responsible for heavy rains, flooding, and mudslides in California, as well as a string of deadly tornadoes in Florida.

La Niña When surface waters in the eastern Pacific are colder than normal, a climate event known as **La Niña** occurs. A La Niña event is the opposite of an El Niño event. La Niña events typically bring colder than normal winters and greater precipitation to the Pacific Northwest and the north central United States.

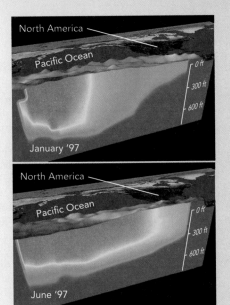

FIGURE 2 ....

> **ART IN MOTION** Warming Sea Temperature
The images show what happens to temperature below the surface of the ocean during an El Niño event. Red indicates a warmer sea surface temperature.

✎ **Draw Conclusions** What happened to the the water temperature over six months?

The area of warm water flat-
tened out and moved east.

Assess Your Understanding

> **Lab zone** Do the Lab Investigation
> *Modeling Ocean Currents.*

1a. Define What is a current?

A large stream of water mov-
ing through the ocean

b. Describe What causes surface currents?

Wind causes surface currents.

got it? ....

○ **I get it!** Now I know that currents are driven mainly by _wind and are affected by the_
Coriolis effect.

○ **I need extra help with** _See TE note._

Go to **MY SCIENCE COACH** *online for help with this subject.*

c. **CHALLENGE** Why is it helpful to a community to be able to predict an El Niño event?

They can prepare for the
weather events El Niño brings.

363

Elaborate

Lead a Discussion

SHORT-TERM CLIMATE CHANGE Explain to students that, during normal years, easterly winds keep a low mound of very warm water in the western Pacific. During El Niño years, these winds weaken and the warm water flows east. One result is short-term climate changes like heavy rains, flooding, and mudslides in California. Ask: **How could changes in the western Pacific Ocean affect the United States?** *(The ocean and atmosphere are connected and affect one another. Changes in ocean surface temperature can affect climate over a large region, even temporarily.)* **How do you think scientist know when El Niño or La Niña occur?** *(They use equipment floating in the ocean and satellites to measure water temperatures.)*

Lab Resource: Lab Investigation

L2 **MODELING OCEAN CURRENTS** Students will use rheostatic fluid in a pan to model ocean currents.

Evaluate

Assess Your Understanding

After students answer the questions, have them evaluate their understanding by completing the appropriate sentence.

RTI Response to Intervention

1a. If students have trouble defining current, **then** have them reread the sentence that contains the boldface term.

b. If students cannot describe the cause of surface currents, **then** have them reread the Key Concept statement.

c. If students need help inferring the need for predictions, **then** have them reread the paragraph following the red head *El Niño* and look for the effects of this event.

MY SCIENCE COACH Have students go online for help in understanding surface currents.

Differentiated Instruction

L1 **Currents and Geography** Display a classroom map of the world and help students locate the places discussed in this section. You may wish to have students use removable tape or sticky notes to add ocean current arrows to the map.

L3 **News Article** Have students research the most recent El Niño or La Niña occurrence. They should look for interesting or unusual ways in which these events affected climate. Students should choose one effect and write a news article about it. Remind them that a good news article answers the following questions: *Who? What? Where? When? Why?* and *How?* Have students compile their articles into a class newspaper.

Explain

Teach Key Concepts 🔧

Explain to students that ocean water varies in salinity. Remind them that salinity is the total amount of dissolved salts in a sample of water. As the salinity of ocean water increases, so does density. Differences in density are what cause deep currents to flow in the ocean. Ask: **What causes the salinity of ocean water to increase?** *(Ice forming near the poles)* **What do you think would cause the salinity of ocean water to decrease?** *(Possible answers: Ice near the poles melting; an increase in freshwater flowing into the ocean from rivers, runoff, etc.)* **How quickly do deep currents flow?** *(They flow very slowly.)*

21st Century Learning

CRITICAL THINKING Tell students that although deep currents and surface currents can be related, these currents are very different. Ask: **Where do surface currents flow?** *(In the upper few hundred meters of ocean water)* **Where do deep currents flow?** *(At greater depth)* **What causes surface currents to flow?** *(Wind)* **What causes deep currents to flow?** *(Differences in density)* **Which type of current could form in the North Atlantic Ocean, sink, and then flow south along the ocean floor?** *(A deep current)*

What Causes Deep Currents?

Deep below the ocean surface, another type of current causes chilly waters to creep slowly across the ocean floor. 🔧 **Deep currents are caused by differences in the density of ocean water.** Recall that cold water is more dense than warm water.

Salinity When a warm surface current moves from the equator toward one of the poles, it gradually cools. As ice forms near the poles, the salinity of the water increases from the salt left behind during freezing. As the water's temperature decreases and its salinity increases, the water becomes denser and sinks. Then, the cold water flows back along the ocean floor as a deep current. Deep currents are affected by the Coriolis effect, which causes them to curve.

🔧 **Deep currents move and mix water around the world. They carry cold water from the poles toward the equator.** Deep currents flow slowly. They may take as long as 1,000 years to circulate between the oceans back to where they started.

Global Ocean Conveyor The simplified pattern of ocean currents in **Figure 3** looks like a conveyor belt, moving water between the oceans. This pattern of ocean currents results from density differences due to temperature and salinity. The currents bring oxygen into the deep ocean that is needed for marine life.

The ocean's deep currents mostly start as cold water in the North Atlantic Ocean. This is the same water that moved north across the Atlantic as part of the Gulf Stream. This cold, salty water, called the North Atlantic Deep Water, is dense. It sinks to the bottom of the ocean and flows southward toward Antarctica. From there it flows northward into both the Indian and Pacific oceans. The deep cold water rises to the surface in the Indian and Pacific oceans, warms, and eventually flows back along the surface into the Atlantic.

Atlantic Ocean

Cold

Warm

FIGURE 3 ....

Global Conveyor

✏️ **Predict** What might happen if the global conveyor stopped?

Sample: Marine life would be severely affected. They would not get the oxygen they need.

Digital Lesson: Assign the *Do the Math* activity online and have students submit their work to you.

my science online.com | **Deep Currents**

do the math! Analyzing Data

Calculating Density

Temperature affects the density of ocean water. To calculate the density of a substance, divide the mass of the substance by its volume.

$$\text{Density} = \frac{\text{Mass}}{\text{Volume}}$$

· · · · · · · · · · · · · · · Practice Problem · · · · · · · · · · · · · · ·

Calculate Find the density of the following 1-L samples of ocean water. Sample A has a mass of 1.01 kg; Sample B has a mass of 1.06 kg. Which sample is likely to have the higher salinity? Why?

Sample A, 1.01 kg/L; Sample B, 1.06 kg/L;
Sample B probably has the higher salinity.
Salt increases the density of water.

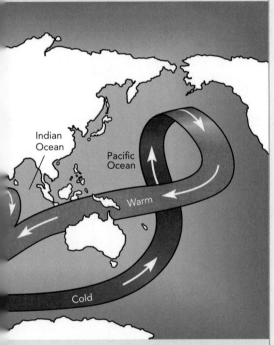

Indian Ocean
Pacific Ocean
Warm
Cold

Lab zone® Do the Quick Lab *Deep Currents.*

🔑 Assess Your Understanding

2a. Review What causes deep currents?

Differences in the density of
ocean water

b. Explain How does the temperature of ocean water affect its density?

If temperature increases,
density decreases. Water
near poles is colder, denser
than water near equator.

got it? ·

○ I get it! Now I know how the global ocean conveyor moves: *Deep, cold* *water flows from the poles* *and rises to the surface in* *the Indian and Pacific oceans.*

○ I need extra help with *See TE note.*

Go to MY SCIENCE ⑤ COACH *online for help with this subject.*

365

Differentiated Instruction

L3 Surface and Deep Currents Have students work in pairs. One student writes a sentence telling how surface currents and deep currents are alike. The partner takes the sentence and adds a second sentence telling how surface currents and deep currents are different. Students should continue taking turns adding sentences until they have used as many ways as they can think of to compare and contrast the two kinds of currents.

Elaborate

Make Analogies

L1 OCEAN CURRENT CONVEYOR BELT Explain to students what a conveyor belt is. Have them picture an assembly line along which a product is made. The product moves from place to place in a manufacturing plant by rolling along a conveyor belt. Ask: **How is a deep current like a global conveyor belt?** *(Like a conveyor belt moving a product throughout a manufacturing plant, a deep current moves water throughout the world's oceans.)*

Do the Math!

L1 Remind students that differences in the density of ocean water cause deep currents to flow. Also, remind them that density is the ratio of the mass of a substance to its volume.

See *Math Skill and Problem-Solving Activities* for support.

Lab Resource: Quick Lab

L2 DEEP CURRENTS Students will explore the way temperature affects the movement of deep currents.

Evaluate

Assess Your Understanding

After students answer the questions, have them evaluate their understanding by completing the appropriate sentence.

R T I Response to Intervention

2a. If students cannot review the cause of deep currents, **then** have them reread the Key Concept statement.

 b. If students need help explaining how temperature affects density, **then** have them reread the paragraph following the red head *Salinity.*

MY SCIENCE ⑤ COACH Have students go online for help in understanding deep currents.

Lab zone | **After the Inquiry Warm-Up**

Currents and Climate

> **Inquiry Warm-Up, *Bottom to Top***
> In the Inquiry Warm-Up, you investigated the densities of warm and cold water. Using what you learned from that activity, answer the questions below.

1. **PREDICT** What would have happened if you boiled colored water and added it to the original warm water sample?

   _____

   _____

2. **PREDICT** What would happen if you added a different color to even colder water and added that to the mixture you made?

   _____

   _____

3. **INFER** What can this experiment tell you about temperature and density of water in the ocean?

   _____

   _____

4. **DRAW CONCLUSIONS** What will happen as the cold water warms up and the warm water cools down?

   _____

   _____

Name _____ Date _____ Class _____

Currents and Climate

What Causes Surface Currents?

1a. DEFINE What is a current?

_____

b. DESCRIBE What causes surface currents?

_____

c. CHALLENGE Why is it helpful to a community to be able to predict an El Niño event?

_____

got it? ··

○ **I get it!** Now I know that currents are driven mainly by _____

_____

○ **I need extra help with** _____

_____

What Causes Deep Currents?

2a. REVIEW What causes deep currents?

_____

b. EXPLAIN How does the temperature of ocean water affect its density?

_____

_____

got it? ··

○ **I get it!** Now I know how the global ocean conveyor moves: _____

_____

_____

○ **I need extra help with** _____

_____

Key Concept Summaries

Currents and Climate

What Causes Surface Currents?

A **current** is a large stream of moving water that flows through the oceans. Unlike waves, currents carry water from one place to another. **Surface currents affect water to a depth of several hundred meters. They are driven mainly by winds.**

As Earth rotates, the paths of winds and currents curve. This effect of Earth's rotation on the direction of winds and currents is called the **Coriolis effect.**

The Gulf Stream is the largest and most powerful surface current in the North Atlantic Ocean. It has a warming effect on the climate of nearby land areas. **Climate** is the pattern of temperature and precipitation typical of an area over a long period of time. **A surface current warms or cools the air above it. This affects the climate of land near the coast.**

Changes in wind patterns and currents can have a major impact on the oceans and neighboring land. One example of such changes is **El Niño,** a climate event that occurs every two to seven years in the Pacific Ocean. When El Niño occurs, unusual wind patterns cause a vast sheet of warm water to move east toward South America. When surface waters in the eastern Pacific are colder than normal, a climate event known as **La Niña** occurs.

What Causes Deep Currents?

Deep currents are caused by differences in the density of ocean water. When a surface current moves toward the poles, its water temperature decreases and its salinity increases. The water becomes denser and sinks. Then, the cold water flows back along the ocean floor as a deep current.

Deep currents move and mix water around the world. They carry cold water from the poles toward the equator. The pattern of ocean currents looks like a conveyor belt, moving water between the oceans. This pattern of ocean currents is called the thermohaline circulation.

On a separate sheet of paper, contrast the two main types of ocean currents and their causes.

Place the outside corner, the corner away from the dotted line, in the corner of your copy machine to copy onto letter-size paper.

Currents and Climate

Understanding Main Ideas
Fill in the spaces in the table below.

	Type of Current	Cause
1.		Winds
2.	Deep	

Answer the following questions in the spaces provided.

3. How do surface currents affect climate?

_____

_____

4. How do deep currents affect the oceans?

_____

_____

_____

Building Vocabulary
Fill in the blank to complete each statement.

5. _____ is a climate event that occurs when surface waters in the eastern Pacific are colder than normal.

6. _____ is an abnormal climate event that occurs every 2 to 7 years in the Pacific Ocean.

7. _____ are large streams of moving water that flow through the oceans.

8. The effect of Earth's rotation on the direction of winds and currents is called the

_____.

9. _____ is the pattern of temperature and precipitation typical of an area over a long period of time.

Currents and Climate

> The Sargasso Sea is a unique part of the Atlantic Ocean that is affected by its currents. Read the passage below. Then answer the questions that follow it on a separate sheet of paper.

The Sargasso Sea

The Sargasso Sea is an oval-shaped region in the North Atlantic Ocean. The Sargasso Sea gets its name from the Portuguese word for seaweed. This is because brown seaweed covers most of its surface.

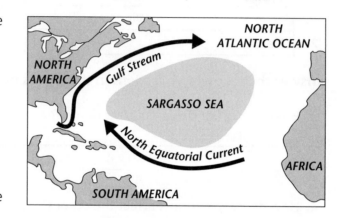

The Sargasso Sea was first described by Christopher Columbus in 1492. He was afraid that rocks might lie hidden below the seaweed and damage his ships. However, it was also the seaweed that encouraged Columbus to continue on his voyage. Because seaweed usually grows close to shore, he thought land must be near. Since Columbus' time, many legends about the Sargasso Sea have spread. The seaweed covering its surface was believed to be so thick that no ship could escape from it. Early writers described ancient ghost ships, rotting away as they remained trapped forever in the seaweed.

The legends about the Sargasso Sea are simply that. The seaweed is not thick enough to interfere with the movement of ships. Still, the Sargasso Sea has several unusual features. Its waters are exceptionally clear, allowing light to penetrate as deep as 1 kilometer. In addition, the waters of the Sargasso Sea are very calm, warm, and salty.

The unusual features of the Sargasso Sea result in part of its great depth, which averages almost 5 kilometers. The sea's location plays a role as well. It is surrounded by fast-moving currents—the Gulf Stream and the North Equatorial Current—that keep its waters from mixing with the rest of the Atlantic Ocean. The Sargasso Sea also lies in a region where temperatures are very warm. Precipitation is low and evaporation is high in this region.

1. Why do you think early navigators tried to avoid the Sargasso Sea?
2. How do the waters of the Sargasso Sea differ from the waters of the rest of the North Atlantic?
3. What keeps the waters of the Sargasso Sea from mixing with the rest of the Atlantic Ocean?
4. Suggest an explanation for the high salinity of the Sargasso Sea.

Lesson Quiz

Currents and Climate

Write the letter of the correct answer on the line at the left.

1. ___ Which of the following is caused by differences in ocean water density?
   A surface currents
   B deep currents
   C waves
   D Coriolis effect

2. ___ When a vast sheet of warm water moves east toward the coast of South America, which of the following occurs?
   A La Niña
   B El Niño
   C climate changes
   D seasons change

3. ___ What is the Gulf Stream?
   A a surface current
   B a deep current
   C a river
   D a climate event

4. ___ In the northern hemisphere, the Coriolis effect causes currents to do which of the following?
   A curve counterclockwise
   B curve clockwise
   C reverse direction
   D sink

If the statement is true, write _true_. If the statement is false, change the underlined word or words to make the statement true.

5. _____ Unlike waves, currents <u>do not</u> move water from one place to another.

6. _____ Earth's rotation causes the <u>Coriolis effect</u>.

7. _____ The Gulf Stream <u>cools</u> nearby land areas.

8. _____ The thermohaline circulation is a pattern of ocean currents driven by <u>density</u> differences.

9. _____ A surface current effects the <u>climate</u> of nearby land.

10. _____ <u>Deep</u> currents affect water down to a depth of several meters.

Currents and Climate

Answer Key

After the Inquiry Warm-Up

1. The boiling water would stay on top of the warm water.

2. The colder water would sink to the bottom, forming a third layer.

3. The warmer, less dense water stays near the surface of the ocean and the colder, more dense water sinks to the bottom.

4. As the two water samples approach each temperature of the other, they will also reach similar densities and will mix with each other.

Key Concept Summaries

Surface currents are streams of ocean water that affect water to a depth of several hundred meters and are caused mainly by winds. Deep currents are streams of water deep below the ocean surface caused by differences in the density of ocean water.

Review and Reinforce

1. Surface

2. Density differences

3. by moving warm or cold water around the globe, warming or cooling the air above

4. Deep currents move and mix water around the world. They carry cold water from the poles toward the equator.

5. La Niña   6. El Niño

7. Currents   8. Coriolis effect

9. Climate

Enrich

1. Early navigators tried to avoid the Sargasso Sea because of legends that ships could get trapped in its blanket of seaweed. Its usually weak winds also made it difficult for sailing ships to cross.

2. The waters of the Sargasso Sea are clearer, calmer, warmer, and saltier than the waters of the rest of the North Atlantic.

3. The Sargasso Sea is surrounded by fast-moving currents that keep its waters from mixing with the rest of the Atlantic Ocean.

4. The Sargasso Sea is so salty because it lies in a region where precipitation is low and the sun is hot, leading to high evaporation.

Lesson Quiz

1. B   2. B
3. A   4. B
5. do   6. true
7. warms   8. true
9. true   10. Surface

Place the outside corner, the corner away from the dotted line, in the corner of your copy machine to copy onto letter-size paper.

Study Guide

Review the Big Q UbD

Have students complete the statement at the top of the page. These Key Concepts support their understanding of the chapter's Big Question. Have them return to the chapter opener pages. What is different about how students view the image of the kayaker now that they have completed the chapter? Thinking about this will help them prepare for the *Apply the Big Q* activity in the Review and Assessment.

Partner Review

Have students review definitions of vocabulary terms by using the Study Guide to quiz each other. Students can read the Key Concept statements and leave out words for their partner to fill in, or change a statement so that it is false and then ask their partner to correct it.

Class Activity: Concept Map

Help students develop a display that shows how information in this chapter is related. Suggest students make a series of connected posters that form a giant concept map. The class can break into groups and each group can make a concept poster. Groups can select a concept for their poster using several of the chapter's big questions as topic guides:

- Where is water found?
- What is the water cycle?
- What is a river system?
- How can lakes change?
- How do conditions vary in Earth's oceans?
- What are some features of the ocean floor?
- How do waves affect the shore?
- What causes surface currents?
- What causes deep currents?

Have each group use illustration and labeling to graphically depict the answer to one of these big questions. The completed posters could be displayed with paper strips connecting the related concepts. Students can add labels to the connecting strips to explain the relationships.

My Science Coach allows students to complete the *Practice Test* online.

The Big Question allows students to complete the *Apply the Big Q* activity about how fresh water cycles on Earth.

Vocab Flash Cards offer a way to review the chapter vocabulary words.

MY SCIENCE online.com ▸ Water

REVIEW THE BIG Q Fresh water on Earth cycles between __surface water__, __groundwater__, and the atmosphere.

LESSON 1 Water on Earth

🔑 All living things need water in order to carry out their body processes.

🔑 Most of Earth's surface water—roughly 97 percent—is salt water found in oceans. Only 3 percent is fresh water.

🔑 In the water cycle, water moves between land, living things, bodies of water on Earth's surface, and the atmosphere.

Vocabulary
- habitat • groundwater • water cycle
- evaporation • transpiration • precipitation

LESSON 2 Surface Water

🔑 A river and all the streams and smaller rivers that flow into it together make up a river system.

🔑 Ponds and lakes form when water collects in hollows and low-lying areas of land.

🔑 Natural processes and human activities can cause lakes to disappear.

Vocabulary
- tributary • watershed • divide
- reservoir • eutrophication

LESSON 3 Water Underground

🔑 Water underground trickles down between particles of soil and through cracks and spaces in layers of rock.

🔑 People can obtain groundwater from an aquifer by drilling a well below the water table.

Vocabulary
- permeable • impermeable
- unsaturated zone • saturated zone
- water table • aquifer • artesian well

LESSON 4 Exploring the Ocean

🔑 The water in Earth's oceans varies in salinity, temperature, and depth.

🔑 Ocean surface temperatures vary with location and the seasons. The water temperature decreases with increasing depth.

🔑 In the ocean, pressure increases with depth.

🔑 Major ocean floor features include trenches, the continental shelf, the continental slope, the abyssal plain, and the mid-ocean ridge.

Vocabulary
- salinity • sonar • seamount • trench
- continental slope • continental shelf
- abyssal plain • mid-ocean ridge

LESSON 5 Wave Action

🔑 Most waves form when winds blowing across the water's surface transmit energy to the water.

🔑 Near shore, wave height increases and wavelength decreases.

🔑 Waves shape a beach by eroding the shore in some places and building it up in others.

Vocabulary
- wave • wavelength • frequency • wave height
- tsunami • longshore drift • rip current • groin

LESSON 6 Currents and Climate

🔑 Surface currents are driven mainly by winds. A surface current warms or cools the air above it, affecting the climate of the land near the coast.

🔑 Deep currents are caused by differences in the density of ocean water. They move and mix water around the world and carry cold water from the poles toward the equator.

Vocabulary
- current • Coriolis effect • climate
- El Niño • La Niña

ELL Support

4 Language Production

Use the key concept statements on this page to create Cloze sentences for students to complete. You can create additional Cloze sentences using the vocabulary terms for the chapter.

Beginning

LOW/HIGH Permit students to refer to their books or notes when completing the sentences.

Intermediate

LOW/HIGH Allow students extra time to complete the sentences.

Advanced

LOW/HIGH When students have completed the sentences, have them paraphrase each key concept in their own words.

Review and Assessment

LESSON 1 Water on Earth

1. Where is most of Earth's total water supply found?

  a. atmosphere   **b.** groundwater

  c. ice sheets   **(d.)** oceans

2. Apply Concepts Why is so little of Earth's water available for human use?

Most of Earth's water is salt water. Most of Earth's fresh water is frozen.

3. math! About 3 percent of Earth's water is fresh water. Of that 3 percent, about 69 percent is ice. About what percent of Earth's total water supply is ice?

About 2.07%

See TE note.

LESSON 2 Surface Water

4. What is the area that supplies water to a river system called?

  a. reservoir   **b.** tributary

  (c.) watershed   **d.** wetland

5. Two watersheds are separated by a(n)

divide.

6. Classify How can a large river also be a tributary?

If the large river flows into an even larger river, it becomes a tributary of the larger river.

LESSON 3 Water Underground

7. The top of the saturated zone forms the

  a. artesian well.   **b.** impermeable rock.

  c. unsaturated zone.   **(d.)** water table.

8. Water can flow through pores or cracks in a *permeable* material.

Use the diagram to answer Questions 9–11.

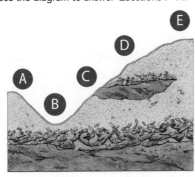

9. Make Judgments Would location D or E be a better place to dig a well? Explain.

Sample: Location D would be better, because it would require less digging.

10. Infer At which location could you obtain water without using a pump? What is this called?

Location C; a spring

11. Predict What changes would you expect to see in this area during a very rainy season?

The water table would rise and the saturated zone would be thicker. A pond or river might form at location B.

Review and Assessment

Assess Understanding

Have students complete the answers to the Review and Assessment questions. Have a class discussion about what students find confusing. Write Key Concepts on the board to reinforce knowledge.

RTI Response to Intervention

4. If students cannot categorize types of surface water, **then** remind them that river and all its tributaries together make up a river system. Help them recall that a watershed is the area that supplies water to a river system.

8. If students have trouble distinguishing permeable from impermeable material, **then** help them scan and read the text for the vocabulary terms.

Do the Math!

About 2.07% of Earth total water supply is ice. To find the answer, students should carry out the following multiplication problem: 69% of 3% or $0.69 \times 0.03 = .0207$ or 2.07%.

Alternate Assessment

L1 WATER CYCLE SKIT Have students write and stage a short skit that illustrates the water cycle. The various processes of the water cycle (evaporation, transpiration, condensation, precipitation) can be characters in the skit. Other plants, clouds, and the ocean can be other characters. One student can narrate the performance. In writing their script, encourage students to be humorous, as well as scientifically accurate. Students can perform their skit for their classmates or as part of an assembly.

Review and Assessment, Cont.

RTI Response to Intervention

13. If students cannot relate causes and effects of ocean conditions, **then** have them reread the boldface Key Concept statements and review **Figure 2**.

Apply the Big Q ❓ UbD

TRANSFER Students should be able to demonstrate understanding of Earth's fresh water cycle by answering this question. See the scoring rubric below.

Connect to the Big Idea ❓ UbD

BIG IDEA Earth's air, water, land, and life form a system.

Send students back to the Big Ideas of Science at the beginning of their student edition. Have them read what they wrote about Earth's fresh water and salty oceans before they started the chapter. Lead a class discussion about how their thoughts have changed. If all chapters have been completed, have students fill in the bottom section for the Big Idea.

L3 WRITING IN SCIENCE Ask students to write a blog entry that explains the water cycle to readers.

LESSON 4 Exploring the Ocean

12. Why is ocean water more dense than fresh water at the same temperature?

   a. circular winds   **b.** less pressure

   c. deep currents   **(d.)** higher salinity

13. Relate Cause and Effect Name two properties of ocean water affected by depth. How does depth affect each?

Temperature decreases with depth, and pressure increases with depth.

14. **Write About It** In what ways is the ocean at 1,000 meters deep different from the ocean at the surface in the same location?
 See TE rubric.

LESSON 5 Wave Action

15. Which describes rolling waves with a large horizontal distance between crests?

   (a.) long wavelength   **b.** deep trough

   c. great wave height   **d.** high frequency

16. Interpret Diagrams Where will sand pile up against the groins shown in the diagram? Explain.

Since the direction of the longshore drift is north, the sand will pile up on the south side of the groins.

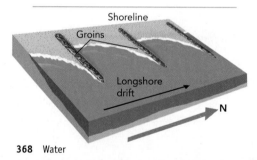

Shoreline

Groins

Longshore drift

N

LESSON 6 Currents and Climate

17. What makes winds and currents move in curved paths?

   (a.) Coriolis effect   **b.** wave height

   c. longshore drift   **d.** ocean trenches

18. Flooding is common during an El Niño, which is _a wind pattern that brings warm water toward the South American coast._

19. Compare and Contrast What causes surface currents? Deep currents?

Surface currents are caused by wind, deep currents by differences in density.

APPLY ❓ How does fresh water cycle on Earth?

20. In a process called cloud seeding, small particles of chemicals such as dry ice are spread into clouds from airplanes. The goal is to provide a place for condensation, causing raindrops to form and fall as precipitation. How would increased condensation affect the other processes of the water cycle?

Sample: The increased precipitation would lead to more run-off. The rates of evaporation and transpiration would probably increase somewhat, since there would be more water available for those processes. See TE rubric.

Write About It Assess student's writing using this rubric.

SCORING RUBRIC	SCORE 4	SCORE 3	SCORE 2	SCORE 1
Contrast ocean surface and depth	Student correctly contrasts both the temperature and pressure conditions of the two ocean areas.	Student correctly contrasts either the temperature or pressure conditions of the two ocean areas, but not both.	Student incorrectly contrasts both the temperature and pressure conditions of the two ocean areas.	Student does not contrast the temperature or pressure conditions of the two ocean areas.

❓ How does fresh water cycle on Earth?
Assess student's response using this rubric.

SCORING RUBRIC	SCORE 4	SCORE 3	SCORE 2	SCORE 1
Effect of cloud seeding on water cycle processes	Student fully explains the effects of cloud seeding.	Student adequately explains the effects of cloud seeding.	Student partially explains the effects of cloud seeding.	Student does not explain the effects of cloud seeding.

Standardized Test Prep

Multiple Choice

Circle the letter of the best answer.

1. Use the diagram to answer the question.

Which of the following is a process that occurs in the water cycle?

A condensation   B evaporation

C precipitation   Ⓓ all of the above

2. How do waves shape beaches?

A by preventing beach erosion

B by counteracting longshore drift

C by compacting the sand into permanent position

Ⓓ by eroding the shore in some places and building it up in others

3. For a science project, you must build a model of an aquifer. What material would be **best** to use for the layer where the water will accumulate?

A clay

B granite

Ⓒ gravel

D bedrock

4. What is a watershed?

Ⓐ the land area that supplies a river system

B the amount of oxygen in a lake

C the total water supply within a lake

D sediment from streams that fills up lakes

5. A major warm ocean surface current flows along a coastal area. What type of climate would you most likely find in the area influenced by the current?

A cool and dry

B very cool and wet

Ⓒ mild and wet

D very hot and dry

Constructed Response

Use the graph and your knowledge of science to answer Question 6. Write your answer on a separate sheet of paper.

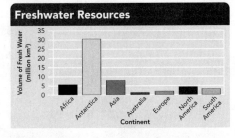

6. The graph shows the total amount of fresh water in all forms found on each continent. Why is so much of Earth's fresh water located in Antarctica? Is that water usable by humans? Explain your answer.
See TE note.

Standardized Test Prep

Test-Taking Skills

FORMULATING YOUR OWN ANSWER Before reading the answer choices provided in a multiple-choice question, students should try to answer the question. This can help them quickly find the correct answer among the alternatives. Also, they will be less likely to be thrown off by a tricky distracter.

Constructed Response

6. Sample: Much of Antarctica is covered by ice, which explains the large amount of fresh water. This water is not easily usable by humans because it is in the form of ice instead of liquid water.

Additional Assessment Resources

Chapter Test
EXAMVIEW® Assessment Suite
Performance Assessment
Progress Monitoring Assessments
SuccessTracker™

ⒺⓁⓁ Support

5 Assess Understanding

Have ELLs complete the Alternate Assessment. Provide guidelines on the information it must cover, and a rubric for assessment. You may wish to have them complete the activity in small groups of varying language proficiencies.

Beginning

LOW/HIGH Allow students to work on a diagram that shows the water cycle.

Intermediate

LOW/HIGH Allow students to refer to their books or notes when completing their scripts.

Advanced

LOW/HIGH Challenge students use vocabulary terms from the lesson in their scripts.

Remediate If students have trouble with...

QUESTION	SEE LESSON	STANDARDS
1	1	
2	5	
3	3	
4	2	
5	6	
6	1	

CHAPTER 10

Science and Society

Have students read *A Pearl of a Solution*. Point out that in the past when oysters in the Chesapeake Bay were thriving, the population could filter the entire volume of water in one day. In warm months, a large oyster can filter about two gallons (7.57 liters) of water in an hour. The bay covers about 4.5 million acres, so there were a lot of oysters to filter all that water. Today, the bay's oyster population is too small to filter all the bay's water. With attention from people in the fishing industry, sciences, and government, oysters are making a comeback. However, restoring the numbers of oysters takes time. Oyster hatcheries need many years to farm and supply programs for repopulating the bay.

Ask: **About how many gallons of water can one large oyster filter in one day?** *(Sample: about 50 gallons)* **Convert this answer into liters.** *(189.3 liters)* **What limitations are there today to using oysters to filter and clean all the water in the bay?** *(Sample: the current oyster population is too small to filter all the water in the bay and it takes many years for oyster farms and hatcheries to increase the population)* **By restoring the numbers of oysters to the bay, what are the Chesapeake Bay Foundation and scientists hoping to do?** *(Sample: They hope that the oysters can be part of the effort to help filter, clean up, and improve the quality of the water so that the bay can support other marine life and maintain a sustainable habitat.)*

SCIENCE MATTERS

Science and Society

A Pearl of a Solution

▲ Oysters filter nutrients and pollutants from the water in which they feed.

It's hard to say who are the bigger heroes in the Chesapeake Bay—the scientists or the oysters.

The Chesapeake Bay is the world's third-largest estuary. More than 17 million people live within the Chesapeake watershed. For many years, fishing has been an important industry for people in the area. People depend on the bay for food and work. Pollution and habitat loss in the watershed have dramatically reduced marine life in the bay, and people who live and work there have found it more difficult to find food or earn a living.

Now, scientists and volunteers are using oysters to help clean the bay's waters. Oysters get their food by filtering plankton and other nutrients from the water. In this way, oysters help remove pollutants from the water. The oyster population has fallen sharply in recent years, and there are not enough oysters to keep up with the pollution. The Chesapeake Bay Foundation is hoping to restock the bay with 31 million oysters in the next 10 years. If they succeed, other marine life may also return to the bay.

Research It Make a map that shows the Chesapeake Bay watershed and the major rivers that drain into it. On the map, indicate how freshwater pollutants, such as excess fertilizer, enter the bay. Write a paragraph explaining the impact on society if the pollution is allowed to continue.

Quick Facts

The original native oyster found in the Chesapeake Bay waters is the eastern oyster, or *Crassostrea virginica*. It is also known as the American or Virginia oyster. This bivalve mollusk has a rough outer shell in variations from white to gray. It habitats shallow water areas of the bay and its tributaries. The eastern oysters clean the bay by sucking in water, filtering out and swallowing plankton and pollutants, then spitting the clean water back out. Many organizations, such as the National Oceanic and Atmospheric Administration (NOAA) are educating people, and taking action to help repopulate the Chesapeake Bay waters with eastern oysters. Have students find out about a local wildlife recovery or rescue program in your area. Have them write an article for your school newspaper, wiki, or Web site that describes what the program is doing to help wildlife in your area.

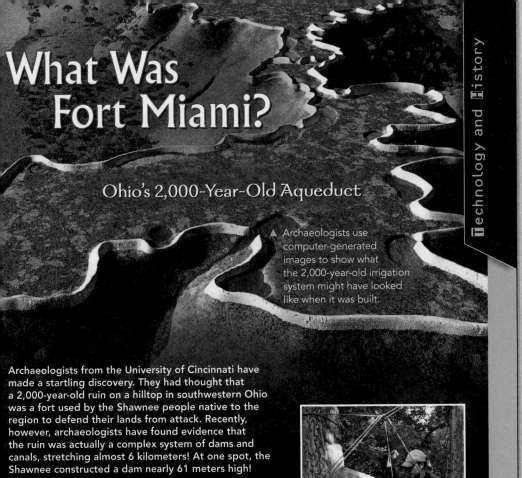

What Was Fort Miami?

Ohio's 2,000-Year-Old Aqueduct

▲ Archaeologists use computer-generated images to show what the 2,000-year-old irrigation system might have looked like when it was built.

Archaeologists from the University of Cincinnati have made a startling discovery. They had thought that a 2,000-year-old ruin on a hilltop in southwestern Ohio was a fort used by the Shawnee people native to the region to defend their lands from attack. Recently, however, archaeologists have found evidence that the ruin was actually a complex system of dams and canals, stretching almost 6 kilometers! At one spot, the Shawnee constructed a dam nearly 61 meters high!

The Shawnee built the system to collect water from a series of springs and to transport it to farmland, so that they could grow enough food to support their society. Climate records suggest that 2,000 years ago, when the Shawnee built the system, the region was colder and drier than it is now. So moving water from its source to where it was needed for farming would have helped the Shawnee survive.

Design It Find out more about water management systems used by ancient civilizations such as the Maya. Make a presentation that compares how two different civilizations used natural resources. Explain how the climate each group faced may have affected its water management systems.

▲ Archaeologists sift carefully through dirt removed from the site of the Fort Miami water works.

371

Technology and History

Have students read *What Was Fort Miami?* Point out that when archaeologists and students from the University of Cincinnati found new evidence, they had to reinterpret the structure on the hills in Ohio Valley and its uses. What they thought was an overgrown fortress was actually an irrigation system. The archaeologists found holes in the ground that they originally thought were left because the earth had been used as building material. Have students look at the computer-generated image of what the irrigation system might have look like. When looking at the evidence, what do students think the holes could be? The image shows reservoirs pits used for holding spring water. What do students think about the civilization who built these aqueducts?

Ask: **Why was Fort Miami originally thought to be a fortress?** (Sample: Because it was thought that the Shawnee used the structure as a fort for military purposes.) **What evidence did archaeologists use to support the idea that the structure at the Ohio Valley site was an aqueduct and not a fortress?** (Sample: Upon doing more investigating, archaeologists found that the fortress walls were a system of dams and canals, and holes were reservoir pits used to hold spring water.)

The Atmosphere

Introduce the Big Q ❓ UbD

Have students look at the image and read the Engaging Question and description. Ask them to write a hypothesis about how the hang glider flies. Point out that the hang glider is moving through air and that something about the air helps keep the hang glider flying. Ask: **What is one example of how you are warmed by the sun?** *(Sample: If I am outdoors on a sunny, warm day and a cloud moves in front of the sun, the air temperature goes down and it feels cooler.)* **What is moving air called?** *(Wind)* **What causes air to move, or what causes wind?** *(The sun heats Earth, which heats the air. Some air is heated more and rises, causing wind.)*

Untamed Science Video

GLIDING THROUGH THE ATMOSPHERE Before viewing, invite students to discuss what they already know about the atmosphere. Then play the video. Lead a class discussion and make a list of questions that the video raises. You may wish to have students view the video again after they have completed the chapter to see if their questions have been answered.

To access the online resources for this chapter, search on or navigate to *The Atmosphere.*

Untamed Science Video shows hang gliders in action.

The Big Question allows students to answer the Engaging Question about the effect of the sun's energy on Earth's atmosphere.

my science online.com | **The Atmosphere**

WHAT KEEPS THIS HANG GLIDER FLYING?

THE BIG ❓

How does the sun's energy affect Earth's atmosphere?

Imagine yourself lazily soaring like a bird above Earth. The quiet, gentle winds and warm sun are so relaxing. No noisy engine, no flapping wings, but wait, what's keeping you aloft? Everyone knows that humans can't fly. **Develop Hypotheses** **How does this hang glider fly?**

Sample: The wind under the wing keeps the hang glider flying.

> **UNTAMED SCIENCE** Watch the **Untamed Science** video to learn more about Earth's atmosphere.

Professional Development Note | **From the Author**

There is no definite boundary between the atmosphere and space. Even at altitudes of hundreds of kilometers, the atmosphere is thick enough to produce a drag force on spacecraft such as the International Space Station (ISS) so that they require periodic boosts to keep them from falling back to Earth. The atmosphere is self-cleaning as pieces of space junk lose energy and eventually burn up in the lower layers of the atmosphere. Depending on the altitude, mass, and surface area of an object, it may fall from orbit in a few days or up to thousands of years. Until removed from their orbits, these objects remain a hazard for other spacecraft.

✎ *Kathryn Thornton*

The Atmosphere

CHAPTER
11

Chapter at a Glance

CHAPTER PACING: 9–15 periods or $4\frac{1}{2}$–$7\frac{1}{2}$ blocks

INTRODUCE THE CHAPTER Use the Engaging Question and the opening image to get students thinking about the atmosphere. Activate prior knowledge and preteach vocabulary using the Getting Started pages.

Lesson 1: The Air Around You

Lesson 2: Air Pressure

Lesson 3: Layers of the Atmosphere

Lesson 4: Energy in Earth's Atmosphere

Lesson 5: Heat Transfer

Lesson 6: Winds

ASSESSMENT OPTIONS: Chapter Test, **EXAM**VIEW® Assessment Suite, Performance Assessment, Progress Monitoring Assessments, SuccessTracker™

Preference Navigator, in the online Planning tools, allows you to customize *Interactive Science* to your own teaching style. You can also edit lesson plans by selecting the Lesson Planner option.

Digital Teacher's Edition allows you to access your Teacher's Edition and Resource materials online.

my science online.com

Differentiated Instruction

L1 Cause and Effect Help students recall that one of the effects that the sun has on Earth's atmosphere relates to the water cycle. Students should recall that the heating of surface water by the sun causes evaporation of water into the atmosphere. Remind students that eventually some water in the atmosphere returns to Earth as precipitation.

L3 Hang Gliding Invite interested students to research hang gliding. They should find out how the gliders get into the air and the atmospheric conditions that are best for this activity. Students can report their findings to the class.

Getting Started

Check Your Understanding

This activity assesses students' understanding of the relationship among weight, volume, and mass. After students have shared their answer, point out that an object's weight is not identical to its mass. Weight measures the force of gravity on the object (how heavy or light it is), while mass refers to the amount of matter in the object.

Preteach Vocabulary Skills

Draw students' attention to the vocabulary terms listed in the *Chapter Preview*. Have students look for and underline each word that contains the root word *sphere*. *(Atmosphere, troposphere, stratosphere, mesosphere, thermosphere, ionosphere, exosphere)* Then challenge students to name other words that end in sphere. *(Sample: hemisphere, photosphere)* Explain that, like *meter* and *thermo*, the root *sphere* also comes from a Greek word. That word means or "ball" or "sphere." Ask students to review the list and see which words look familiar. Have them discuss what they think these familiar words mean. Invite students to speculate how the meaning of sphere relates to all the words. *(All represent something round, ball-shaped, or spherical in nature.)*

Check Your Understanding

1. **Background** Read the paragraph below and then answer the question.

> Helen blows up a balloon. She adds it to a large garbage bag already full of balloons. Its low **weight** makes the bag easy to carry, but its large **volume** might be a problem fitting it in the car. Capturing air in a balloon makes it easier to understand that air has **mass**.

> **Weight** is a measure of the force of gravity on an object.
>
> **Volume** is the amount of space that matter occupies.
>
> **Mass** is the amount of matter in an object.

• How could the bag's volume make it difficult to fit in the car?

  The bag could take up more space
  than the space available in the car.

> **MY READING WEB** If you had trouble completing the question above, visit **My Reading Web** and type in *The Atmosphere*.

Vocabulary Skill

Word Origins Many words come to English from other languages. Learning a few common Greek word parts can help you understand new science words.

Greek Word Part	Meaning	Example
-meter	measure	barometer, *n.* an instrument that measures air pressure
thermo-	heat	thermosphere, *n.* the outer layer of Earth's atmosphere

2. **Quick Check** Use the Greek word parts above to write a definition of a thermometer.

  A thermometer is an instrument for measuring
  heat.

My Reading Web offers leveled readings related to chapter content.

Vocab Flash Cards offer extra practice with the chapter vocabulary words.

Digital Lesson

• Assign the *Check Your Understanding* activity online and have students submit their work to you.

• Assign the *Vocabulary Skill* activity online and have students submit their work to you.

my science online.com — **The Atmosphere**

atmosphere

aneroid barometer

troposphere

wind

Chapter Preview

LESSON 1
- weather • atmosphere
- water vapor
- ⟳ **Summarize**
- △ **Infer**

LESSON 2
- density • air pressure
- barometer • mercury barometer
- aneroid barometer • altitude
- ⟳ **Relate Cause and Effect**
- △ **Develop Hypotheses**

LESSON 3
- troposphere • stratosphere
- mesosphere • thermosphere
- ionosphere • exosphere
- ⟳ **Identify Supporting Evidence**
- △ **Interpret Data**

LESSON 4
- electromagnetic waves
- radiation • infrared radiation
- ultraviolet radiation • scattering
- greenhouse effect
- ⟳ **Ask Questions**
- △ **Graph**

LESSON 5
- temperature • thermal energy
- thermometer • heat
- convection • conduction
- convection currents
- ⟳ **Identify the Main Idea**
- △ **Infer**

LESSON 6
- wind • anemometer
- windchill factor • local winds
- sea breeze • land breeze
- global winds • Coriolis effect
- latitude
- ⟳ **Identify Supporting Evidence**
- △ **Draw Conclusions**

375

CHAPTER 11

Preview Vocabulary Terms

Divide the class into three groups. Each group should complete a Frayer Model diagram for the vocabulary terms in two lessons. The diagram should include the definition, characteristics, an example, and a non-example of the term. Have the groups present their diagrams to the class.

L1 Have students look at the images on this page as you pronounce the vocabulary word. Have students repeat the word after you. Then read the definition. Use the sample sentence in italics to clarify the meaning of the term.

atmosphere *(AT muh sfeer)* The envelope of gases that surrounds the planet. *Clouds and other weather occur in the lower part of Earth's atmosphere.*

aneroid barometer *(AN uh royd buh RAHM uh tur)* An instrument used to measure air pressure that has an airtight metal chamber sensitive to changes in air pressure. *The most common type of instrument used to measure air pressure in homes is an aneroid barometer.*

troposphere *(TROH puh sfeer)* The lowest layer of the atmosphere in which people live. *The troposphere is the layer of the atmosphere in which Earth's weather occurs.*

wind *(Wind)* The movement of air parallel to Earth's surface. *Differences in air pressure cause wind.*

(E)(L)(L) Support

Have students complete the diagrams for the Preview Vocabulary Terms activity.

Beginning
LOW Create a drawing or symbol to support the characteristics. If literate, develop a definition using the native language.

HIGH Write the word and introduce it to the group by pointing and saying it aloud.

Intermediate
LOW/HIGH Brainstorm and write examples and non-examples. Present them to the group.

Advanced
LOW Write the definition and present it.

HIGH Explain to the group how the examples represent the word.

The Air Around You

 How does the sun's energy affect Earth's atmosphere?

Lesson Pacing: 1–2 periods or $\frac{1}{2}$–1 block

🕐 **SHORT ON TIME?** To do this lesson in approximately half the time, do the Activate Prior Knowledge activity. A discussion of the Key Concepts will familiarize students with the lesson content. Have students do the Quick Labs. The rest of the lesson can be completed by students independently.

Preference Navigator, in the online Planning tools, allows you to customize *Interactive Science* to your own teaching style. You can also edit lesson plans by selecting the Lesson Planner option.

Digital Teacher's Edition allows you to access your Teacher's Edition and Resource materials online.

my science online.com

Lesson Vocabulary

- weather   - atmosphere   - water vapor

Content Refresher

Professional Development Note

Formation of the Ozone Scientists hypothesize that the ozone layer began to form when free oxygen started to accumulate in Earth's upper atmosphere. The formation of ozone occurs when oxygen molecules break apart after absorbing ultraviolet radiation from the sun. Free oxygen atoms then can combine with oxygen molecules to form ozone. Early life forms began to appear near the surface of oceans after the formation of the ozone layer because it filtered harmful ultraviolet rays. These life forms produced their own food with oxygen as a byproduct. Over millions of years, the atmosphere's oxygen content slowly increased, allowing life to eventually emerge onto dry land.

The Composition of Air In the 1600s, English scientist Robert Boyle discovered that air contains a substance needed for life when he observed that animals died when they were deprived of air. He called this substance "vital air." We now call it oxygen. Joseph Black, a Scottish medical student, found that limestone mixed with acid gives off a substance that puts out flames. He called the substance "fixed air." We now know it as carbon dioxide. About 15 years later, a student of Black's named Daniel Rutherford used a liquid to absorb vital air and fixed air. The substance that remained he called "noxious air" because it put out flames and killed living things. We now call this substance nitrogen.

LESSON OBJECTIVES

🔑 Describe the composition of the atmosphere.

🔑 State how the atmosphere is a system.

Blended Path
Active learning using Student Edition, Inquiry Path, and Digital Path

ENGAGE AND EXPLORE

Teach this lesson using a variety of resources. Begin by reading **My Planet Diary** as a class. Have students share ideas about oxygen. Then have students do the **Inquiry Warm-Up activity.** Students will burn candles in different size jars. Discuss how the size of the jar impacts the burning time. The **After the Inquiry Warm-Up worksheet** sets up a discussion about what candles need to continue burning inside a jar. Have volunteers share their answers to number 4 about their predictions.

EXPLAIN AND ELABORATE

Teach Key Concepts by explaining the composition of Earth's atmosphere. **Lead a Discussion** about the humidity in different areas. Then have students practice the inquiry skill in the **Apply It activity.**

Continue to **Teach Key Concepts** by asking students to identify the parts of the Earth's atmosphere and describe how they work together. Use the **Support the Big Q** to illustrate how the atmosphere system gets energy. Use **Figure 2** to help students understand what parts of Earth's atmosphere interact to form a hurricane. Hand out the **Key Concept Summaries** as a review of each part of the lesson. Students can also use the online **Vocab Flash Cards** to review key terms.

EVALUATE

Have students take the **Lesson Quiz.** For an alternate assessment, the **EXAM**VIEW® Assessment Suite, Progress Monitoring Assessments, or SuccessTracker™.

⒠ⓛⓛ Support

1 Content and Language

Write the words *weather* and *whether* on the board. Explain to students that *weather* and *whether* are spelled differently and have different meanings, but they are pronounced the same. These two words are called homophones. Define the two words and ask students to use them in sentences.

Lab zone Inquiry Path
Hands-on learning in the Lab zone

ENGAGE AND EXPLORE

To teach this lesson with an emphasis on inquiry, begin with the **Inquiry Warm-Up activity.** Students will observe candles burning in various jars. Discuss how the burning time varies in relation to the size of the jar. Have students do the **After the Inquiry Warm-Up worksheet.** Talk about why the burning time is longer with a larger jar and shorter with a smaller jar. Have volunteers share their answers to number 4 about their predictions for the jar with a chip in its rim.

EXPLAIN AND ELABORATE

Focus on the **Inquiry Skill** for the lesson. Point out that when you infer, you use observations to formulate a reasonable conclusion. What are students able to infer about the oxygen supply of the smallest jar in the **Inquiry Warm-Up activity?** *(The smallest jar has the least amount of oxygen.)* Review the substances that make up Earth's atmosphere before beginning the **Apply It activity.** Ask volunteers to share the evidence they used to make their inferences and to complete the sentence. Have students do the **Quick Lab** and then share their results about carbon dioxide.

Use the **Support the Big Q** to illustrate how Earth's atmospheric system gets energy from the sun. Have students do the **Quick Lab** to model atmospheric events driven by the sun's energy. Students can use the online **Vocab Flash Cards** to review key terms.

EVALUATE

Have students take the **Lesson Quiz.** For an alternate assessment, the **EXAM**VIEW® Assessment Suite, Progress Monitoring Assessments, or SuccessTracker™.

Digital Path
Online learning at **my science online**.com

ENGAGE AND EXPLORE

Teach this lesson using digital resources. Begin by having students explore real-world connections to Earth's atmosphere at **My Planet Diary** online. Have them access the Chapter Resources to find the **Unlock the Big Question activity.** There they can answer the questions and refine their responses as they continue through the lesson. You can re-assign the activity and have students submit their work so you can track their progress.

EXPLAIN AND ELABORATE

Students reading above, at, or below the lexile measure of this lesson can access basic content readings at their level at **My Reading Web.** Have students use the online **Vocab Flash Cards** to preview key terms. Review the composition of Earth's atmosphere before assigning the online **Apply It activity.** Ask volunteers to share their inferences. Have students submit their work to you. Assign the **Quick Lab** and then ask students to share their results.

Use the **Support the Big Q** to reinforce understanding of how energy from the sun is used by Earth's atmospheric system. Have students do the **Quick Lab.** The **Key Concept Summaries** online allow students to read a summary and see an image associated with each part of the lesson. Online remediation is available at **My Science Coach.**

EVALUATE

Have students take the **Lesson Quiz.** For an alternate assessment, the **EXAM**VIEW® Assessment Suite, Progress Monitoring Assessments, or SuccessTracker™.

2 Frontload the Lesson
Preview the lesson visuals, labels, and captions. Ask students what they know about the words *atmosphere* and *water vapor.* Explain the specific meanings these words have in science.

3 Comprehensible Input
Have students study the visuals and their captions in **Figure 1** and **Figure 2** to support the key concepts of the lesson.

4 Language Production
Pair or group students with varied language abilities to complete labs collaboratively for language practice. Have each student copy the completed written lab for personal reference.

5 Assess Understanding
Make true or false statements using lesson content and have students indicate if they agree or disagree with thumbs up or thumbs down gesture to check whole-class comprehension.

The Air Around You

Establish Learning Objectives

After this lesson, students will be able to:

🔑 Describe the composition of the atmosphere.

🔑 State how the atmosphere is a system.

Engage

Activate Prior Knowledge

MY PLANET DIARY Read *Antoine Lavoisier* with the class. Point out that when a material is burned, it combines with oxygen. Explain that when oxygen in air combines with material that is burning, the weight of the oxygen is added to the material. This fact demonstrates that oxygen, a gas in air, has weight. Ask: **How is the rusting of iron a similar reaction to burning?** *(When an iron object rusts, oxygen combines with the iron, increasing the weight of the object.)*

BIG IDEAS OF SCIENCE REFERENCE LIBRARY 📖
Have students look up the following topic: Atmosphere.

Explore

Lab Resource: Inquiry Warm-Up

L1 **HOW LONG WILL THE CANDLE BURN?** Students will observe how long a burning candle in a closed jar will burn before using up the oxygen supply in the jar.

LESSON

1 The Air Around You

UNLOCK THE BIG ?

🔑 What Is the Composition of Earth's Atmosphere?

🔑 How Is the Atmosphere a System?

MY PLANET DIARY   VOICES FROM HISTORY

Antoine Lavoisier

French chemist Antoine Lavoisier was determined to solve a puzzle: How could a metal burned to a powder weigh more than the original metal? In his 1772 lab notes he observed, "Sulphur, in burning . . . gains weight." So did mercury. Lavoisier thought a gas in the air was combining with the mercury as it burned, making it heavier. Then he heated the mercury powder to a higher temperature. It turned back to liquid mercury and a gas. Lavoisier observed that a mouse exposed to the gas could breathe it. He named the gas *principe oxygine*. Today we call it oxygen.

Discuss Lavoisier's experiment with a partner and answer the question below.

Why do you think Lavoisier exposed a mouse to the gas he collected from the mercury?

Sample: He wanted to see if the gas was breathable.

> PLANET DIARY   Go to **Planet Diary** to learn more about air.

Lab zone Do the Inquiry Warm-Up *How Long Will the Candle Burn?*

What Is the Composition of Earth's Atmosphere?

The sun disappears behind thick, dark clouds. In the distance you see a bright flash. Then you hear a crack of thunder. You make it home just as the downpour begins. The weather changed quickly—that was close!

Weather is the condition of Earth's atmosphere at a particular time and place. But what is the atmosphere? Earth's **atmosphere** (AT muh sfeer) is the envelope of gases that surrounds the planet. 🔑 **Earth's atmosphere consists of nitrogen, oxygen, carbon dioxide, water vapor, and other gases, as well as particles of liquids and solids.**

SUPPORT ALL READERS
Lexile Measure = 800L   Lexile Word Count = 861

Prior Exposure to Content: Most students have encountered this topic in earlier grades

Academic Vocabulary: *infer, summarize*

Science Vocabulary: *atmosphere*

Concept Level: Generally appropriate for most students in this grade

Preteach With: My Planet Diary "Antoine Lavoisier" and Figure 1 activity

Go to **My Reading Web** to access leveled readings that provide a foundation for the content.

my science online.com

Vocabulary
- weather • atmosphere
- water vapor

Skills
- Reading: Summarize
- Inquiry: Infer

Nitrogen The most abundant gas in the atmosphere is nitrogen. It makes up a little more than three fourths of the air we breathe. Nitrogen occurs in all living things and makes up about 3 percent of the weight of the human body.

Oxygen Although oxygen is the second most abundant gas in the atmosphere, it makes up only about 21 percent of the volume. Plants and animals take oxygen directly from the air and use it to release energy from their food.

Oxygen is also involved in many other processes. A fire uses oxygen rapidly as it burns. Without oxygen, a fire will go out. Some processes use oxygen more slowly. Steel in cars and other objects reacts slowly with oxygen to form iron oxide, or rust.

Carbon Dioxide Carbon dioxide makes up much less than 1 percent of the atmosphere, but it is essential to life. Plants must have carbon dioxide to produce food. The cells of animals break down food and give off carbon dioxide as a waste product.

When fuels like coal and gasoline are burned, they also release carbon dioxide. Burning these fuels increases the amount of carbon dioxide in the atmosphere.

Other Gases Oxygen and nitrogen together make up 99 percent of dry air. Argon makes up most of the other 1 percent. The remaining gases are called trace gases because only small amounts of them are present.

FIGURE 1
Gases in the Air
The atmosphere is a thin layer of gases.

 Graph Identify which circle graph shows the correct percentage of gases in the atmosphere. Shade in the key and the graph. Give your graph a title.

Key
- Nitrogen
- Oxygen
- Other gases

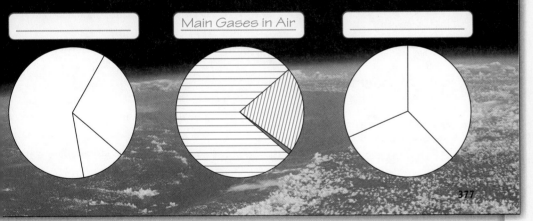

Main Gases in Air

377

Explain

Introduce Vocabulary

Students can probably give examples of weather but may not be able to define the term. Tell students that weather is the condition of Earth's atmosphere at a particular time and place.

Teach Key Concepts

Explain to students that Earth's atmosphere is a mixture of substances, not a pure substance. The mixture is made up mostly of nitrogen, plus oxygen, carbon dioxide, water vapor, and other gases, as well as particles of liquid and solids. Ask: **Which gas do living things use to release energy from food?** *(Oxygen)* **What substance exists as both a liquid and a gas in the atmosphere? Explain.** *(Water. It exists as both the gas water vapor and as tiny droplets that form clouds.)* **Why are some gases in the atmosphere called trace gases?** *(They are present in very small amounts.)*

My Planet Diary provides an opportunity for students to explore real-world connections to Earth's atmosphere.

my science *online* Earth's Atmosphere

LESSON 11.1

ELL Support

1 Content and Language
Students may be confused by the use of the word *envelope* in the definition of *atmosphere*. Put a piece of paper in an envelope noting that the paper is inside the envelope. Then show students a globe and help them see that the atmosphere envelops Earth.

2 Frontload the Lesson
Ask students to share what they know about air. Explain that what we call "air" is made up of gases and particles.

3 Comprehensible Input
Have the students write the word *atmosphere* in a circle. As they read, have them list the components of the atmosphere around the circle. Have volunteers suggest one sentence for each component that describes its importance.

Explain

Lead a Discussion

WATER VAPOR Students may know that the amount of water vapor in the air is called humidity. Ask students if they have lived in or visited a place that had very low or very high humidity. Invite them to describe the conditions. Ask: **How does an area with high humidity differ from conditions in our area? How does an area with very low humidity differ from conditions in our area?** *(Accept all reasonable responses.)*

Elaborate

Apply It!

L1 Review the composition of the atmosphere before beginning the activity.

▲ **Infer** Remind students that inferences are based on observations. Have students describe the differences in the two locations shown in the images.

Lab Resource: Quick Lab

L2 **BREATHE IN, BREATHE OUT** Students will detect carbon dioxide in their exhaled breath by blowing through a straw into limewater.

Evaluate

Assess Your Understanding

After students answer the questions, have them evaluate their understanding by completing the appropriate sentence.

RTI Response to Intervention

1a. If students have trouble defining the term *atmosphere*, **then** have them scan the section to locate the highlighted terms and read their definitions.

b, c. If students cannot identify components of air, **then** have them look at the red heads in this section to see what materials make up air. Students should reread the material under any head that is unfamiliar to them.

MY SCIENCE COACH Have students go online for help in understanding the composition of the atmosphere.

---

apply it!

The amount of water vapor in the air can differ from place to place.

❶ There is more water vapor in the (desert/rain forest) than in the (desert/rain forest).

❷ **Infer** What evidence do you see for your answer to Question 1?

The desert is brown. The forest is green.

❸ **CHALLENGE** What factors might affect the amount of water vapor in the air?

The weather; how much it rains

 Do the Quick Lab Breathe In, Breathe Out.

🔖 Assess Your Understanding

1a. Define The _atmosphere_ is the envelope of _gases_ that surrounds Earth.

b. List What are the four most common gases in dry air?
Nitrogen, oxygen, carbon dioxide, and argon

c. Compare and Contrast What is the difference between wet air and dry air?
Dry air contains no water vapor, while wet air does.

got it?

○ **I get it!** Now I know that the atmosphere is made up of *oxygen, nitrogen, carbon dioxide, argon, particles, water vapor, and trace gases.*

○ **I need extra help with** *See TE note.*

Go to **MY SCIENCE COACH** *online for help with this subject.*

Water Vapor

So far, we've discussed the composition of dry air. But in reality, air is not dry. Air contains **water vapor**—water in the form of a gas. Water vapor is invisible. It is not the same thing as steam, which is made up of tiny droplets of liquid water.

The amount of water vapor in the air varies greatly from place to place and from time to time. Water vapor plays an important role in Earth's weather. Clouds form when water vapor condenses out of the air to form tiny droplets of liquid water or crystals of ice. If these droplets or crystals become heavy enough, they fall as rain or snow.

Particles Pure air contains only gases. But pure air exists only in laboratories. In the real world, air contains tiny solid and liquid particles of dust, smoke, salt, and chemicals. You can see some of these particles in the air around you, but most of them are too small to see.

Digital Lesson: Assign the *Apply It* activity online and have students submit their work to you.

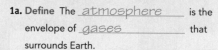
MY SCIENCE online.com | Earth's Atmosphere

How Is the Atmosphere a System?

The atmosphere is a system that interacts with other Earth systems, such as the ocean. The atmosphere has many different parts. Some of these parts you can actually see, such as clouds. But most parts of the atmosphere—like air, wind, and energy—you can't see. Instead, you might feel a wind when it blows on you. Or you might feel energy from the sun warming your face on a cool winter day.

At first, the wind that blows and the heat you feel may seem unrelated. But as you'll learn, the different parts of the atmosphere interact with one another. 🔑 **Events in one part of the atmosphere affect other parts of the atmosphere.**

Energy from the sun drives the motions in the atmosphere. A storm such as the hurricane in **Figure 2** involves a tremendous amount of energy. The spiraling shape of a hurricane is due in part to forces resulting from Earth's rotation. A hurricane also gains energy from warm ocean water. Since the ocean water is warmed by the sun, a hurricane's energy comes mostly from the sun.

✏️ **Summarize** Write a short summary of the third paragraph.

The sun's energy affects the atmosphere and can cause a hurricane.

FIGURE 2 ·······
Parts of the Atmosphere
✏️ **List** What parts of the atmosphere interact?

Sun, air, temperature, wind

Lab zone Do the Quick Lab *What Is the Source of Earth's Energy?*

🔑 **Assess Your Understanding**

got it? ·······

○ I get it! Now I know that events in one part of the atmosphere _affect other parts of the atmosphere._

○ I need extra help with _See TE note._

Go to my science ● coach *online for help with this subject.*

379

Differentiated Instruction

L1 Systems Students may have difficulty with the concept of the atmosphere as a dynamic system that continually changes. Point out that a system is made up of parts that work together. Students are probably familiar with body systems. Tell them that engineering systems include cars and computers. Communities are made up of social systems. Companies and schools are based on organizational systems.

L3 Composition of Air Ask students if they are familiar with the fire triangle often discussed in fire safety. Draw a triangle and ask students to identify the labels for the corners. *(Fuel, heat, air)* Elicit that these three components are needed to produce fire. Relate the triangle to the composition of air by asking which component of air is needed to produce fire. *(Oxygen)*

Explain

Teach Key Concepts 🔑

Explain that parts of the atmosphere interact with other parts as well as Earth's land and water. Ask: **What are some parts of the atmosphere that you can see?** *(Clouds, precipitation)* **What are some parts that you cannot see?** *(Air, wind energy)* **Are things that happen in the atmosphere connected? Explain.** *(Yes; events in one part of the atmosphere affect other parts of the atmosphere. For example, a hurricane gets energy from warm ocean waters, which were heated by the sun's energy.)*

🔄 **Summarize** Explain to students that when they summarize new information they should reduce it to the most important, or main ideas.

Support the Big Q ❓ UbD

ENERGY FROM THE SUN Explain to students that the atmosphere system gets its energy from the sun. Some energy is absorbed directly, and some is absorbed from Earth's land and water, which are warmed by the sun. Ask: **Where does a hurricane get its energy?** *(From warm ocean waters)* **Where does the ocean get its energy?** *(The oceans are warmed by the sun.)*

Teach With Visuals

Have students look at **Figure 2.** Explain that the photograph was taken from space. The large spiral of clouds is a hurricane off the coast of Florida. Help students locate Florida, the Gulf of Mexico, and the Atlantic Ocean. Ask: **Why do hurricanes happen during the summer?** *(The ocean is warm, so there is plenty of energy to create hurricanes.)*

Elaborate

Lab Resource: Quick Lab

L1 WHAT IS THE SOURCE OF EARTH'S ENERGY? Students will observe the sun's interaction with a model of Earth's atmosphere.

Evaluate

Assess Your Understanding

Have students evaluate their understanding by completing the appropriate sentence.

RTI Response to Intervention

If students have trouble understanding how the atmosphere is a system, **then** have them review the Key Concept on this page.

my science ⑤ coach Have students go online for help in understanding how the atmosphere is a system.

379

Name _____ Date _____ Class _____

LabZone After the Inquiry Warm-Up

The Air Around You

Inquiry Warm-Up, *How Long Will the Candle Burn?*

In the Inquiry Warm-Up, you investigated how long a candle will burn inside jars of different sizes. Using what you learned from that activity, answer the questions below.

1. **INFER** What is it about the size of the jar that affects how long the candle burns?

   _____

   _____

2. **PREDICT** If you repeated the experiment with a jar even smaller than the one you first used, how long do you think the candle would burn?

   _____

   _____

3. **PREDICT** If the first jar had a chipped rim, so that there was a small opening between the jar and the pie pan, how long do you think the candle would burn?

   _____

   _____

4. **EXPLAIN** Explain your answer to question 3.

   _____

   _____

   _____

379A

Assess Your Understanding

The Air Around You

What Is the Composition of Earth's Atmosphere?

1a. DEFINE The _____ is the envelope of

_____ that surrounds Earth.

b. LIST What are the four most common gases in dry air?

_____

c. COMPARE AND CONTRAST What is the difference between wet air
and dry air?

_____

_____

_____

got it? ....

○ **I get it!** Now I know that the atmosphere is made up of _____

_____

○ **I need extra help with** _____

_____

How Is the Atmosphere a System?

got it? ....

○ **I get it!** Now I know that events in one part of the atmosphere _____

_____

○ **I need extra help with** _____

_____

Key Concept Summaries

The Air Around You

What is the Composition of Earth's Atmosphere?

Weather is the condition of Earth's atmosphere at a particular time and place. Earth's **atmosphere** is the envelope of gases that surrounds the planet. **Earth's atmosphere consists of nitrogen, oxygen, carbon dioxide, water vapor, and other gases, as well as particles of liquids and solids.**

The most abundant gas in the atmosphere is nitrogen. It makes up a little more than three fourths of the air we breathe. Oxygen, the second most abundant gas, makes up about 21 percent of the volume. Plants and animals take oxygen from air and use it to release the energy in food. Oxygen is also necessary for fire to burn. Carbon dioxide makes up much less than 1 percent of the atmosphere, but it is essential to life. Plants must have carbon dioxide to produce food. Together, oxygen and nitrogen make up 99 percent of dry air. The other one percent is mostly argon, plus other gases in amounts so small that they are described as trace gases.

So far, we've discussed the composition of dry air. But in reality, air is not dry. Air contains **water vapor,** or water in the form of a gas. Water vapor is invisible. It is not the same thing as steam, which is made up of tiny droplets of liquid water. Clouds form when water vapor condenses out of the air to form tiny droplets of liquid water or crystals of ice. If these droplets become heavy enough, they fall as rain or snow. Air also contains tiny solid and liquid particles of dust, smoke, salt, and chemicals.

How Is the Atmosphere a System?

The atmosphere is a system that interacts with other Earth systems, such as the ocean. The atmosphere has many different parts, such as clouds, air, wind, and energy. **Events in one part of the atmosphere affect other parts of the atmosphere.** Energy from the sun drives the motions in the atmosphere. For example, a storm such as a hurricane involves a great deal of energy. A hurricane gets energy from warm ocean water, which gets its heat from the sun.

On a separate sheet of paper, describe the composition of Earth's atmosphere and give an example of how events in one part affect other parts of the atmosphere.

Review and Reinforce

The Air Around You

Understanding Main Ideas

If the statement is true, write *true*. If the statement is false, change the underlined word or words to make the statement true.

1. _____ More than three fourths of the air we breathe is <u>oxygen</u>.

2. _____ <u>Argon</u> is the second most abundant gas in air.

3. _____ Plants need <u>carbon dioxide</u> to produce food.

4. _____ Without <u>nitrogen</u> in the air, a fire will not burn.

5. _____ When fuels such as coal and gasoline are burned they release <u>nitrogen</u> into the air.

6. _____ Condensed water vapor in the atmosphere forms <u>clouds</u>.

7. _____ Energy from the <u>wind</u> drives the motions in the atmosphere.

Building Vocabulary

On a separate sheet of paper, write a definition for each of these terms.

8. atmosphere
9. water vapor
10. weather

Enrich

The Air Around You

> Earth's atmosphere once contained almost no oxygen, but as the planet changed, so did the atmosphere. Read the following passage. Then answer the questions that follow on a separate sheet of paper.

How Earth's Atmosphere Got Its Oxygen

When Earth's atmosphere first formed, it contained little, if any, oxygen. How, then, did our oxygen-rich atmosphere come about? The answer is life, which first appeared in the form of bacteria about 3.5 billion years ago.

By about 2.5 billion years ago, oxygen-producing organisms, called cyanobacteria, had evolved. Evolution is the process by which organisms change to give rise to new organisms over time. The cyanobacteria took in carbon dioxide and water and produced oxygen as a waste product. Over time, the oxygen they produced accumulated in the atmosphere. Some of this oxygen was converted to ozone by the sun's energy. This was important later for the development of life on land because as ozone increased, it protected Earth's surface from too much ultraviolet radiation.

By 700 million years ago, the oxygen concentration had reached about ten percent of the current level, and organisms made up of many cells had evolved. By 450 million years ago, the ozone level was getting close to its present value. Soon after that land plants evolved. Land animals followed about 380 million years ago. Both oxygen and ozone reached their current levels about 300 million years ago. By then there were many different kinds of complex land plants and animals living on Earth.

1. How did life influence the development of Earth's atmosphere?
2. What role did ozone play in the evolution of life on Earth?
3. What do you think Earth's atmosphere would be like today if life had not evolved on Earth?

Lesson Quiz

The Air Around You

Fill in the blank to complete each statement.

1. The amount of _____ in the air varies greatly from place to place and time to time.

2. Gases in air that are present in very small amounts are called _____ gases.

3. Earth is surrounded by an envelope of gases called the _____.

4. When gasoline is burned it releases the gas _____.

5. Clouds form when water vapor _____ out of the air.

6. The term used to describe the condition of Earth's atmosphere at a given place or time is _____.

Write the letter of the correct answer on the line at the left.

7. ___ What do dust, smoke, salt, and chemicals have in common?
   A They are gases in air.
   B They make up water vapor in air.
   C They are particles in air.
   D They are found only in pure air.

8. ___ Which of these does a fire need to burn?
   A argon
   B carbon dioxide
   C nitrogen
   D oxygen

9. ___ Which of these do plants need to make food?
   A argon
   B carbon dioxide
   C nitrogen
   D oxygen

10. ___ Which of these makes up about 21 percent of the atmosphere?
   A argon
   B carbon dioxide
   C nitrogen
   D oxygen

The Air Around You

Answer Key

After the Inquiry Warm-Up

1. The larger the jar, the more air it holds. The more air there is inside the jar, the longer the candle burns.

2. The candle would burn for an even shorter time than it did in the first, small jar.

3. The candle would burn until the wax was all burnt up.

4. If there were an opening between the jar and the pie pan, the candle would have an unlimited supply of air because air could enter the jar through the hole. With an unlimited air supply, the candle could burn until all the wax was gone.

Key Concept Summaries

Earth's atmosphere consists of nitrogen, oxygen, carbon dioxide, and small amounts of other gases. It also contains water vapor and tiny particles of liquids and solids. Nitrogen is the most abundant gas in the atmosphere. Oxygen, the second most abundant gas, makes up about 21 percent of the volume. Carbon dioxide makes up less than 1 percent, but is essential to life.

Evaporation brings water vapor into the atmosphere. Events in one part of the atmosphere affect other parts of the atmosphere. For example, energy from the sun heats ocean waters, causing evaporation. That air may then move over land, and, if it cools, the water vapor will condense into tiny droplets of liquid water or ice, which fall over that land as rain or snow.

Review and Reinforce

1. nitrogen
2. Oxygen
3. true
4. Oxygen
5. carbon dioxide
6. true

7. sun
8. the envelope of gases that surrounds Earth
9. water in the form of a gas
10. the condition of Earth's atmosphere at a particular time and place

Enrich

1. Before there was life on Earth, Earth's atmosphere contained little oxygen. Then cyanobacteria evolved in Earth's seas about 2.5 billion years ago. The cyanobacteria produced oxygen. Oxygen started to build up in the atmosphere, and some of it turned into ozone. By about 300 million years ago, oxygen and ozone reached their current levels in Earth's atmosphere.

2. Up until about 450 million years ago, all life on Earth lived in the water. There was no life on land, in part because of harmful ultraviolet radiation. As ozone increased in the atmosphere, it blocked much of the UV radiation. This allowed life to evolve on land. By about 380 million years ago, both land plants and land animals had evolved.

3. If life had not evolved on Earth, Earth's atmosphere would be very different. It would be much lower in oxygen and ozone. Levels of carbon dioxide and other gases might be higher or lower, too.

Lesson Quiz

1. water vapor
2. trace
3. atmosphere
4. carbon dioxide
5. condenses
6. weather
7. C
8. D
9. B
10. D

Place the outside corner, the corner away from the dotted line, in the corner of your copy machine to copy onto letter-size paper.

Air Pressure

2 How does the sun's energy affect Earth's atmosphere?

Lesson Pacing: 1–2 periods or $\frac{1}{2}$–1 block

🕐 **SHORT ON TIME?** To do this lesson in approximately half the time, do the Activate Prior Knowledge activity. A discussion of the Key Concepts will familiarize students with the lesson content. Have students do the Quick Labs. The rest of the lesson can be completed by students independently.

Preference Navigator, in the online Planning tools, allows you to customize *Interactive Science* to your own teaching style. You can also edit lesson plans by selecting the Lesson Planner option.

Digital Teacher's Edition allows you to access your Teacher's Edition and Resource materials online.

my science online.com

Lesson Vocabulary

- density • air pressure • barometer • mercury barometer
- aneroid barometer • altitude

Content Refresher

Professional Development Note

History of the Barometer The Italian physicist Evangelista Torricelli invented the first mercury barometer in 1643. Torricelli studied why liquids rise to only a certain height in a column. Because mercury is very dense, he thought it would rise to a lower height than water and be more convenient to study. He filled a long glass tube with mercury, blocked the open end with his finger, turned the tube upside down, and set it in a dish of mercury. The mercury went down to about 76 cm. He tested different-sized tubes, but the height of the mercury in the tube stayed the same. Torricelli concluded that the height of the mercury in the tube was directly related to the pressure of air on the mercury in the dish. Thus, he invented a way to measure air pressure.

LESSON OBJECTIVES

- 🔖 Identify some properties of air.
- 🔖 Describe how barometers can be used to measure air pressure.
- 🔖 Explain how altitude affects air pressure and density.

Blended Path
Active learning using Student Edition, Inquiry Path, and Digital Path

ENGAGE AND EXPLORE

Teach this lesson using a variety of resources. Begin by reading **My Planet Diary** as a class. Have students share ideas about some properties of air. Then have students do the **Inquiry Warm-Up activity.** Students will compare the mass of an object with and without air. Discuss why the mass of the balloon changes when it is inflated. The **After the Inquiry Warm-Up worksheet** sets up a discussion about the properties of air. Have volunteers share their answers to number 4 about how the mass of the balloon with water compares to the mass of the inflated balloon.

EXPLAIN AND ELABORATE

Teach Key Concepts by explaining the term *barometer* and have students answer questions about the properties of air.

Continue to **Teach Key Concepts** by identifying the two common types of barometers. Use **Figures 2** and **3** to illustrate how mercury barometers and aneroid barometers measure air pressure. **Lead a Discussion** about the different units of measurement used to indicate air pressure.

Teach Key Concepts to explain that the air pressure and density decrease as the altitude increases. Use the **Support the Big Q** to illustrate the effect that energy from the sun has on the density and pressure of the air. Then have students practice the inquiry skill in the **Apply It activity. Lead a Discussion** about how the number of molecules in the air decreases as the altitude increases—making it more difficult to breathe. Hand out the **Key Concept Summaries** as a review of each part of the lesson. Students can also use the online **Vocab Flash Cards** to review key terms.

EVALUATE

Have students take the **Lesson Quiz.** For an alternate assessment, the **EXAM**VIEW® Assessment Suite, Progress Monitoring Assessments, or SuccessTracker™.

(E)(L)(L) Support

1 Content and Language

Write the word *density* on the board. Circle the suffix *-ity*. Explain that *-ity* means "the state or condition of being." The root word *dense* means "compact or close together." So *density* means, "the condition of being close together." List other words with the suffix *-ity*.

Lab zone Inquiry Path
Hands-on learning in the Lab zone

Digital Path
Online learning at my science online.com

ENGAGE AND EXPLORE

To teach this lesson with an emphasis on inquiry, begin with the **Inquiry Warm-Up activity.** Students will investigate the mass of a balloon filled with air. Discuss how the mass of an object changes when inflated. Have students do the **After the Inquiry Warm-Up worksheet.** Talk about the properties of air. Have volunteers share their answers to number 4 about which has a greater mass: air or water.

EXPLAIN AND ELABORATE

Focus on the **Inquiry Skill** for the lesson. Point out that when you develop a hypothesis, you develop a possible explanation for why something occurred. What hypothesis could be developed based on the **Inquiry Warm-Up activity?** *(Water is denser than air.)* Do the **Teacher Demo** to reinforce understanding of density. Have students do the **Quick Lab** to explore the properties of air. Ask volunteers to share their results.

The next **Quick Lab** allows students to make a barometer. Use the **Support the Big Q** to explain how the density of air changes when Earth's atmosphere is warmed by the sun's energy. Review **Figure 4** before beginning the **Apply It activity.** In the last **Quick Lab** students will examine the effects of altitude on the atmosphere. Students can use the online **Vocab Flash Cards** to review key terms.

EVALUATE

Have students take the **Lesson Quiz.** For an alternate assessment, the **EXAM**VIEW® Assessment Suite, Progress Monitoring Assessments, or SuccessTracker™.

ENGAGE AND EXPLORE

Teach this lesson using digital resources. Begin by having students explore real-world connections to the properties of air at **My Planet Diary** online. Have them access the Chapter Resources to find the **Unlock the Big Question activity.** There they can answer the questions and refine their responses as they continue through the lesson. You can re-assign the activity and have students submit their work so you can track their progress.

EXPLAIN AND ELABORATE

Students reading above, at, or below the lexile measure of this lesson can access basic content readings at their level at **My Reading Web.** Have students use the online **Vocab Flash Cards** to preview key terms. Have students do the **Quick Lab** to investigate the properties of air.

Have students do the **Interactive Art activity** online to investigate how a mercury barometer works. Do the **Quick Lab** to demonstrate how a barometer works.

Support the Big Q by discussing how energy from the sun affects the density of the air. Review **Figure 4** before assigning the online **Apply It activity.** Ask volunteers to share their hypotheses. Have students submit their work to you. Do the **Quick Lab** to illustrate how altitude can affect the atmosphere. Have students do the online **Virtual Lab.** In this activity, students will explore how air pressure, volume, and temperature are connected. The **Key Concept Summaries** online allow students to read a summary and see an image associated with each part of the lesson. Online remediation is available at **My Science Coach.**

EVALUATE

Have students take the **Lesson Quiz.** For an alternate assessment, the **EXAM**VIEW® Assessment Suite, Progress Monitoring Assessments, or SuccessTracker™.

2 Frontload the Lesson
Preview the lesson visuals, labels, and captions. Ask students what they know about the words *density, barometer, pressure,* and *altitude.* Explain the specific meanings these words have in science.

3 Comprehensible Input
Have students use the lesson vocabulary words and content to write captions for the images in this lesson in their own words.

4 Language Production
Pair or group students with varied language abilities to complete labs collaboratively for language practice. Have each student copy the completed written lab for personal reference.

5 Assess Understanding
Have students keep a content area log. Use a two-column format with the headings "What I Understand" and "What I Don't Understand." Follow up so that students can move items from the "Don't Understand" to the "Understand" column.

Air Pressure

Establish Learning Objectives

After this lesson, students will be able to:

📖 Identify some properties of air.

📖 Describe how barometers can be used to measure air pressure.

📖 Explain how altitude affects air pressure and density.

Engage

Activate Prior Knowledge

MY PLANET DIARY Read *Flying High* with the class. Have students discuss what they know about space suits worn by astronauts. Help students understand that the suits provide the astronauts with an "atmosphere" like that on Earth. Ask: **What condition would cause a pilot's blood to boil?** *(The absence of air pressure)* **How does a high-altitude pilot overcome the lack of air pressure?** *(By wearing a pressure suit that keeps air pressure stable for the pilot)*

BIG IDEAS OF SCIENCE REFERENCE LIBRARY 📖 Have students look up the following topic: Altitude.

Explore

Lab Resource: Inquiry Warm-Up 🔬

 DOES AIR HAVE MASS? Students will weigh a balloon that is full of air.

Air Pressure

UNLOCK THE BIG ?

📖 **What Are Some Properties of Air?**

📖 **What Instruments Measure Air Pressure?**

📖 **How Does Altitude Affect Air Pressure and Density?**

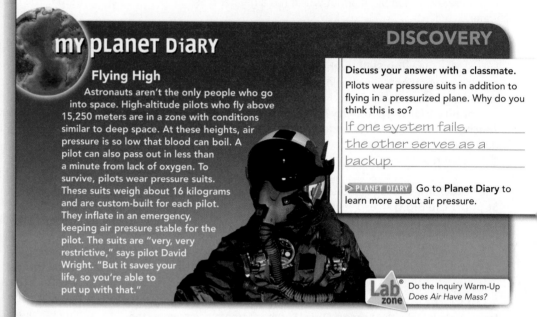

MY PLANET DIARY

DISCOVERY

Flying High

Astronauts aren't the only people who go into space. High-altitude pilots who fly above 15,250 meters are in a zone with conditions similar to deep space. At these heights, air pressure is so low that blood can boil. A pilot can also pass out in less than a minute from lack of oxygen. To survive, pilots wear pressure suits. These suits weigh about 16 kilograms and are custom-built for each pilot. They inflate in an emergency, keeping air pressure stable for the pilot. The suits are "very, very restrictive," says pilot David Wright. "But it saves your life, so you're able to put up with that."

Discuss your answer with a classmate. Pilots wear pressure suits in addition to flying in a pressurized plane. Why do you think this is so?

If one system fails, the other serves as a backup.

> **PLANET DIARY** Go to **Planet Diary** to learn more about air pressure.

🔬 **Lab zone** Do the Inquiry Warm-Up *Does Air Have Mass?*

What Are Some Properties of Air?

How do you know air exists? You can't see it. Instead, you have to understand what air does. It may seem to you that air has no mass. But the air in the atmosphere consists of atoms and molecules, which have mass. 📖 **Because air has mass, it also has other properties, including density and pressure.**

SUPPORT ALL READERS
Lexile Measure = 850L   Lexile Word Count = 1245

Prior Exposure to Content: Most students have encountered this topic in earlier grades

Academic Vocabulary: *cause, effect, hypothesis*

Science Vocabulary: *density, air pressure, altitude*

Concept Level: Generally appropriate for most students in this grade

Preteach With: My Planet Diary "Flying High" and Figure 1 activity

Go to **My Reading Web** to access leveled readings that provide a foundation for the content.

my science online

Vocabulary
- density • air pressure
- barometer • mercury barometer
- aneroid barometer • altitude

Skills
- Reading: Relate Cause and Effect
- Inquiry: Develop Hypotheses

Density The amount of mass in a given volume of air is its **density**. You calculate the density of a substance by dividing its mass by its volume. If there are more molecules in a given volume, the density is greater. If there are fewer molecules, the density is less.

Pressure The atmosphere is heavy. Its weight exerts a force on surfaces like you. The force pushing on an area or surface is called pressure. **Air pressure** is the result of the weight of a column of air pushing on an area.

As **Figure 1** shows, there is a column of air above you that extends all the way up through the entire atmosphere. In fact, the weight of the column of air above your desk is about the same as the weight of a large school bus. So why doesn't air pressure crush your desk? The reason is that the molecules in air push in all directions—down, up, and sideways. The air pushing down on top of your desk is balanced by the air pushing up on the bottom of your desk.

FIGURE 1 ....

Air Column
The weight of the column of air above you puts pressure on you.

✏ **Answer the questions below.**

1. **Describe** What's an air column?

   <u>The air above you going up</u>
   <u>through the atmosphere</u>

2. **Apply Concepts** Add arrows to the diagram below to indicate how the pressure from air molecules keeps you from being crushed.

AIR COLUMN

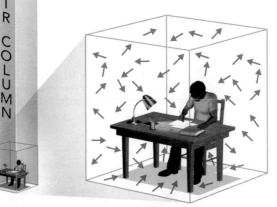

 Do the Quick Lab
Properties of Air.

🔑 Assess Your Understanding

got it? ....

○ I get it! Now I know that air has properties such as <u>density and pressure.</u>

○ I need extra help with <u>See TE note.</u>

Go to **my science** 🔵 **COACH** online for help with this subject.

381

ELL Support

1 Content and Language
Explain that *aneroid* contains the prefix *a-*, which means "without/not," and the root *neros*, which is Greek for "water."

2 Frontload the Lesson
Ask students if their ears have ever "popped." Explain that as you go higher, air pressure outside your body decreases while air pressure inside your body stays the same. Popping occurs because air

from inside the ears and throat escapes to even out the pressure.

3 Comprehensible Input
Squeeze the ends of two sink plungers together. Invite volunteers to pull the plungers apart. Ask: Why are the plungers hard to pull apart? (*Air pressing on the outside of the plungers holds them together.*)

Explain

Introduce Vocabulary
Students may have heard the term *barometric pressure* used on weather reports. Tell them that a barometer is a device used to measure air pressure.

Teach Key Concepts 🔑
Explain that air is made up of smaller particles—atoms and molecules. Because these particles have mass, air has mass, as well as other properties of matter. Ask: **How are mass and density related?** *(If there is more mass in a given volume of air, then the density is greater. If there is less mass in a given volume of air, then the density is less.)*

Elaborate

Teacher Demo 🔬

L1 DENSITY

Materials 16 meter sticks or masking tape

Time 5 minutes

Use meter sticks or, if permitted, masking tape to mark off two 2-meter by 2-meter square areas on the floor. Ask five volunteers to stand in one square. Have ten volunteers stand in the second square. Tell students that the individuals inside the squares represent gas molecules inside two containers.

Ask: **Which square is more crowded?** *(The one with more students)* **In which "container" is the "gas" denser?** *(The one with more "molecules").*

Lab Resource: Quick Lab 🔬

L1 PROPERTIES OF AIR Students will explore the properties of air.

Evaluate

Assess Your Understanding
Have students evaluate their understanding by completing the appropriate sentence.

RTI Response to Intervention
If students need help explaining the properties of air, **then** have them review the Key Concept statement.

my science 🔵 **COACH** Have students go online for help in understanding that the properties of air.

My Planet Diary provides an opportunity for students to explore real-world connections to the properties of air.

my science ▸ Properties of Air

Explain

Teach Key Concepts 🔑

Remind students that air pressure is the result of a column of air, which has mass, pushing down on an area. Explain to students that there are instruments that can measure air pressure. Ask: **What instrument is used to measure air pressure?** *(Barometer)* **What are the two common kinds of barometers?** *(Mercury barometer and aneroid barometer)*

Teach With Visuals

MERCURY BAROMETERS Direct students to look at the mercury barometer shown in **Figure 2.** Discuss the fact that the open end of the tube rests in a dish of mercury. Point out that the closed end is almost a vacuum. Help students understand that a space that is almost a vacuum is a space that contains almost no air. Ask: **How does a mercury barometer work?** *(Air pressing down on the surface of the mercury in the dish is equal to the pressure exerted by the column of mercury in the tube that is inverted in the dish. When the air pressure increases, it presses down more on the surface of the mercury in the dish).* **What does this increase in pressure do to the mercury?** *(The increased pressure forces the column of mercury higher in the tube. This rise of the mercury in the tube indicates what the air pressure is at that time.)*

What Instruments Measure Air Pressure?

Air pressure can change daily. A denser substance has more mass per unit volume than a less dense one. So denser air exerts more pressure than less dense air. A **barometer** (buh RAHM uh tur) is an instrument that is used to measure air pressure. 🔑 **The two common kinds of barometers are mercury barometers and aneroid barometers.**

Mercury Barometers Look at **Figure 2** to see a mercury barometer model. A **mercury barometer** consists of a long glass tube that is closed at one end and open at the other. The open end of the tube rests in a dish of mercury. The closed end of the tube is almost a vacuum—the space above the mercury contains very little air. The air pressing down on the surface of the mercury in the dish is equal to the pressure exerted by the weight of the column of mercury in the tube. When the air pressure increases, it presses down more on the surface of the mercury. Greater air pressure forces the column of mercury higher. So, the level of the mercury in the tube shows you the pressure of the air that day.

✏️ **Vocabulary** Greek Word Origins
The Greek word part *baro-* means "weight." How would it relate to the word part *-meter*?

It combines to mean something that measures weight.

FIGURE 2 ....

▶ **INTERACTIVE ART** Reading a Mercury Barometer
✏️ **Apply Concepts** Use the drawing of the barometer on the right to show what a low air pressure reading looks like.
1. Shade in the level of the mercury in the tube and in the dish.
2. Describe what is happening.

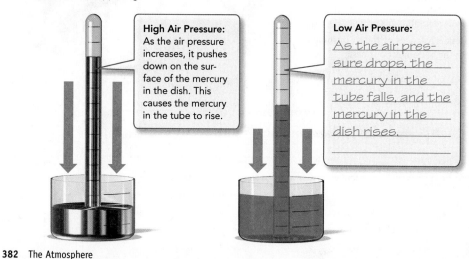

High Air Pressure: As the air pressure increases, it pushes down on the surface of the mercury in the dish. This causes the mercury in the tube to rise.

Low Air Pressure: *As the air pressure drops, the mercury in the tube falls, and the mercury in the dish rises.*

382 The Atmosphere

Interactive Art allows students to explore a mercury barometer in action.

my science online .com ▶ Measuring Air Pressure

Aneroid Barometers

If you have a barometer at home, it's probably an aneroid barometer. The word *aneroid* means "without liquid." An **aneroid barometer** (AN uh royd) has an airtight metal chamber, as shown in **Figure 3**. The metal chamber is sensitive to changes in air pressure. When air pressure increases, the thin walls of the chamber are pushed in. When the pressure drops, the walls bulge out. The chamber is connected to a dial by a series of springs and levers. As the shape of the chamber changes, the needle on the dial moves.

Units of Air Pressure

Weather reports use several different units for air pressure. Most weather reports for the general public use inches of mercury. For example, if the column of mercury in a mercury barometer is 30 inches high, the air pressure is "30 inches of mercury" or "30 inches."

National Weather Service maps indicate air pressure in millibars. The pressure of the atmosphere is equal to one bar. One inch of mercury is about 33.86 millibars, so 30 inches of mercury is equal to about 1,016 millibars.

FIGURE 3 ....

Inside an Aneroid Barometer
An aneroid barometer has an airtight metal chamber, shown in red, below.

✎ **Identify** Label the diagram that shows the aneroid barometer under high pressure and the diagram that shows it under low pressure.

 Low High

Lab zone ® Do the Quick Lab
Soda Bottle Barometer.

🔑 Assess Your Understanding

1a. Name What two instruments are commonly used to measure air pressure?

Mercury and aneroid barometers

b. Identify What units are used to measure air pressure?

Inches of mercury and millibars

c. CHALLENGE How many millibars are equal to 27.23 inches of mercury?

922 millibars

got it?

○ I get it! Now I know that air pressure can be measured *by using two kinds of barometers.*

○ I need extra help with *See TE note.*

Go to MY SCIENCE ⓢ COACH *online for help with this subject.*

383

Explain
Teach With Visuals

ANEROID BAROMETERS Tell students to look at **Figure 3**. Point out that the object shown in red is the metal container inside the barometer. Ask: **What does the word aneroid mean?** *(It means "without liquid.")* **How does the shape of the metal container shown in the two images change?** *(On the left, it is bulging. On the right, its walls are pushed in.)* **How does an aneroid barometer work?** *(The airtight metal chamber of an aneroid barometer is sensitive to changes in air pressure. When air pressure decreases, the thin chamber walls push in. When the pressure drops, the walls bulge out. The chamber wall is connected to a needle on a dial. As the shape of the chamber changes, the needle on the dial moves, indicating the air pressure.)*

Lead a Discussion

UNITS OF AIR PRESSURE Review the different units of air pressure students are likely to hear on weather reports. Students will most likely recognize inches of mercury as the unit of air pressure. If the column of mercury in a mercury barometer measures 30 inches high, then the air pressure is reported as 30 inches. Ask: **What unit does the National Weather Service use on weather maps to indicate air pressure?** *(Millibars)* **How many millibars does 1 inch of mercury equal?** *(33.86 millibars)* **How many does 30 inches of mercury equal?** *(1,016 millibars)*

Elaborate
Lab Resource: Quick Lab

L2 **SODA BOTTLE BAROMETER** Students will use a soda bottle to make a barometer.

Evaluate
Assess Your Understanding

After students answer the questions, have them evaluate their understanding by completing the appropriate sentence.

RTI Response to Intervention

1a. If students cannot name instruments to measure air pressure, **then** have them look at **Figures 2** and **3**.

b, c. If students need help identifying units of air pressure, **then** have them reread the paragraphs under the red head *Units of Air Pressure*.

MY SCIENCE ⓢ COACH Have students go online for help in understanding how air pressure is measured.

Differentiated Instruction

L1 **Pressure in All Directions** Help students understand that air pressure pushes in all directions. Fill a glass with water, place a piece of cardboard over the top, and invert the glass. Hold the cardboard in place until the glass is inverted, and then remove your hand. The cardboard will stay in place because of air exerting an upward pressure.

L3 **Calculate Air Pressure** Tell students that a quarter placed on a desk would exert a pressure of 0.0013 N per cm². Then explain that the pressure exerted by the atmosphere at sea level is 10.1 N per cm². Ask students how many stacked quarters would exert the same pressure as the air at sea level. *(10.1 N/cm² ÷ 0.0013 N/cm² = 7,769 quarters)* Explain that six stacked quarters are about 1 cm thick. Then have students calculate the height of 7,769 stacked quarters. *(7,769 ÷ 6 = 1,295 cm)*

Explain

Teach Key Concepts 🔑

Explain to students that as altitude increases, air pressure decreases. Point out that as air pressure decreases, air density also decreases. Ask: **Why is air pressure greater at sea level?** *(Air at sea level has the weight of the whole atmosphere that is above it pressing down on it.)* **Why might someone have to carry a supply of oxygen when climbing to the top of a very high mountain?** *(Because the air is less dense the higher you climb, there might not be enough oxygen to breathe at the top of the high mountain where the air is very thin.)*

Elaborate

Support the Big Q ❓ UbD

ENERGY AND DENSITY OF AIR Tell students that another factor affecting the density of air is heat. As energy from the sun warms the atmosphere, the air expands. Ask: **What happens to particles in air that is expanding?** *(They move farther apart.)* **How would this affect the density of the air?** *(It would decrease the density.)* **How would this affect air pressure?** *(Decreasing density would cause a decrease in air pressure.)*

Apply It!

L1 Review **Figure 4** before beginning the activity. Help students understand the meaning of the callouts showing dense air at the base of the mountain and less dense air at the top of the mountain.

🔺 **Develop Hypotheses** Help students articulate possible explanations for the observation that the bottle with the cap is crushed while the uncapped bottle is not. Explain that a hypothesis must be able to be tested. Elicit that the density of the air in the open bottle changed with the altitude of the climber.

How Does Altitude Affect Air Pressure and Density?

The higher you hike on a mountain, the more changes you'll notice. The temperature will drop, and the plants will get smaller. But you might not notice another change that is happening. At the top of the mountain, the air pressure is less than the air pressure at sea level—the average level of the oceans. **Altitude,** or elevation, is the distance above sea level. 🔑 **Air pressure decreases as altitude increases. As air pressure decreases, so does density.**

Altitude Affects Air Pressure Suppose you have a stack of books. Which book has more weight on it, the second book from the top or the book at the bottom? The second book from the top has the weight of only one book on top of it. The book at the bottom of the stack has the weight of all the books pressing on it.

Air at sea level is like the bottom book. Sea-level air has the weight of the whole atmosphere pressing on it. Air near the top of the atmosphere is like the second book from the top. There, the air has less weight pressing on it and thus has lower air pressure.

apply it!

You're back from a high-altitude hike. As you empty your bag, you notice that the two empty bottles you carried down from the mountain look different.

❶ Observe What observations can you make about the bottles?

The one with no cap is normal. The other with a cap is crushed.

❷ 🔺 Develop Hypotheses What's a possible explanation for your observations?

The pressure in and around the open bottle was the same. But the pressure on the outside of the closed bottle was greater than the pressure of the air inside it.

6 km

5 km

4 km

3 km

2 km

Which hiker has the least pressure on him/her?
The hiker at the top

1 km

Sea level

Professional Development Note — Teacher to Teacher

The Atmosphere To spark student interest in Earth's atmosphere, I like to point out to students that there are approximately 1×10^{16} breaths of air in Earth's atmosphere and the air in an average human's breath contains 1.4×10^{22} atoms and molecules. Since the atmosphere does a pretty good job of mixing thoroughly every 3 to 4 years, the odds are that each breath they take has atoms/molecules from every person alive on Earth 3–4 years ago. Just something to think about.

✏ *Joel Palmer, Ed.D.*
Mesquite ISD
Mesquite, Texas

Altitude Also Affects Density As you go up through the atmosphere, the density of the air decreases. This means the gas molecules that make up the atmosphere are farther apart at high altitudes than they are at sea level. If you were near the top of a tall mountain and tried to run, you would quickly get out of breath. Why? The air contains 21 percent oxygen, whether you are at sea level or on top of a mountain. However, since the air is less dense at a high altitude, each cubic meter of air you breathe has fewer oxygen molecules than at sea level. So you would become short of breath more quickly at a high altitude.

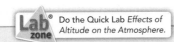
Relate Cause and Effect
Underline the sentence that explains how altitude can make you short of breath.

FIGURE 4 ....

 >VIRTUAL LAB **Effect of Altitude on Pressure and Density**
✎ Complete the activities below.

1. **Relate Evidence and Explanation** Draw the air column above each hiker on the mountain. Then answer the question below the hikers.

2. **Make Models** In the empty circles below, draw how densely packed you think the molecules would be at the altitudes shown.

Lab zone Do the Quick Lab *Effects of Altitude on the Atmosphere.*

🔑 **Assess Your Understanding**

2a. Define What is altitude?

Distance above sea level

b. Summarize How does air pressure change as altitude increases?

Air pressure decreases with increasing altitude.

c. Predict What changes in air pressure would you expect if you carried a barometer down a mine shaft?

Air pressure would increase because the amount of air above you increases.

got it? ....

○ **I get it!** Now I know the properties of air _change with altitude._

○ **I need extra help with** _See TE note._

Go to my science COACH *online for help with this subject.*

385

Explain

Lead a Discussion

ALTITUDE AND DENSITY Review the idea that the density of air depends on the number of molecules of gas in a given volume of space. Ask: **Are there more molecules in a sample of air at sea level or at great altitudes?** *(There are more molecules in air at sea level than at great altitudes.)* **Compare what breathing would be like for a person on a high mountain with what breathing would be like for a high-altitude pilot.** *(In both cases breathing would be difficult because of the small amount of oxygen present and an extra oxygen supply would likely be needed by both people.)*

 Relate Cause and Effect Tell students that relating cause and effect involves looking at two events to see if one caused the other. The effect is the result of the cause.

Elaborate

Lab Resource: Quick Lab **Lab zone**

L2 EFFECTS OF ALTITUDE ON THE ATMOSPHERE
Students will explore how altitude can affect the pressure and density of the atmosphere.

Evaluate

Assess Your Understanding

After students answer the questions, have them evaluate their understanding by completing the appropriate sentence.

RTI Response to Intervention

2a. If students have trouble defining *altitude*, **then** have them locate the highlighted term and read the definition.

b, c. If students need help describing changes in air pressure, **then** have them reread the paragraphs under the red head *Altitude Affects Air Pressure* and look at **Figure 4.**

my science COACH Have students go online for help in understanding altitude affects air pressure and density.

Digital Lesson: Assign the *Apply It* activity online and have students submit their work to you.

Virtual Lab allows students to investigate the connections among air pressure, volume, and tempaerature.

my science online | Altitude, Air Pressure, & Density

Differentiated Instruction

L1 Altitude Sketch an ocean and a mountain on the board. Ask students to describe the differences in air pressure and density for both locations as you point to them. Then, have students paraphrase the Key Concept statement by explaining it in their own words.

L3 High-Altitude Living Tell students that people who live at high altitudes have adjusted to the low air pressure and the low percentage of oxygen in the air around them. Ask students to hypothesize about the kinds of adjustments the body would need for survival at high altitudes. *(A larger chest and larger lungs would allow a person to take in more air.)*

Lab zone® **After the Inquiry Warm-Up**

Air Pressure

Inquiry Warm-Up, *Does Air Have Mass?*
In the Inquiry Warm-Up, you investigated how the mass of a deflated balloon compares to the mass of an inflated one. Using what you learned from that activity, answer the questions below.

1. **CALCULATE** Given the measurements of mass of the deflated balloon and the mass of the inflated balloon, what is the mass of the air in the inflated balloon?

   _____

2. **EXPLAIN** Explain how you calculated the answer to question 1.

   _____

   _____

   _____

3. **PREDICT** If you took the balloon and blew it up so that the inflated balloon was much smaller than it was when you found its mass during the experiment, how would you expect the partially inflated balloon's mass to compare to the deflated balloon and the fully inflated balloon?

   _____

   _____

   _____

4. **APPLY PRIOR KNOWLEDGE** If you filled the balloon with water, how would you expect its mass to compare to the mass of the air-filled balloon? Explain.

   _____

   _____

   _____

Assess Your Understanding

Air Pressure

What Are Some Properties of Air?

got it? ··

○ **I get it!** Now I know that air has properties such as _____

_____

○ **I need extra help with** _____

_____

What Instruments Measure Air Pressure?

1a. NAME What two instruments are commonly used to measure air
pressure?

_____

b. IDENTIFY What units are used to measure air pressure? _____

_____

c. CHALLENGE How many millibars are equal to 27.23 inches of mercury? _____

got it? ··

○ **I get it!** Now I know that air pressure can be measured _____

_____

○ **I need extra help with** _____

_____

Name _____ Date _____ Class _____

Air Pressure

How Does Altitude Affect Air Pressure and Density?

2a. DEFINE What is altitude? _____
_____

b. SUMMARIZE How does air pressure change as altitude increases?
_____

c. PREDICT What changes in air pressure would you
expect if you carried a barometer down a mine shaft? _____
_____

got it? ···

○ **I get it!** Now I know that the properties of air _____
_____

○ **I need extra help with** _____
_____

Air Pressure

What Are Some Properties of Air?

Air is made up of atoms and molecules, which have mass. **Because air has mass, it also has other properties, including density and pressure.** The amount of mass in a given volume of air is its **density.** You calculate the density of a substance by dividing its mass by its volume. The force pushing on an area or surface is called pressure. **Air pressure** is the result of the weight of a column of air pushing on an area. The reason air pressure does not crush you is because the molecules in air push in all directions. So the air pushing down is balanced by the air pushing up.

What Instruments Measure Air Pressure?

Air pressure can change daily. A **barometer** is an instrument that is used to measure air pressure. **The two common kinds of barometers are mercury barometers and aneroid barometers.**

A **mercury barometer** consists of a long glass tube that is closed at one end and open at the other. The open end rests in a dish of mercury. The closed end contains very little air. Increases in air pressure force the column of mercury higher in the tube. The level of the mercury in the tube shows the pressure of the air that day. An **aneroid barometer** has an airtight metal chamber. When air pressure increases, the thin walls of the chamber are pushed in. When air pressure drops, the walls bulge out. As the chamber's shape changes a needle on the dial moves. Weather reports air pressure in inches of mercury. National Weather Service maps indicate air pressure in millibars. One inch of mercury equals about 33.86 millibars.

How Does Altitude Affect Air Pressure and Density?

Altitude, or elevation, is distance above sea level. **Air pressure decreases as altitude increases. As air pressure decreases, so does density.** Because air is less dense at a high altitude, each cubic meter of air you breathe has fewer oxygen molecules than at sea level. So you would become short of breath more quickly at a high altitude.

On a separate sheet of paper, explain what air density and air pressure are, and how altitude affects these properties of air.

Review and Reinforce

Air Pressure

Understanding Main Ideas

Fill in the blank to complete each statement. Use the illustration to answer Questions 3–6.

1. When air pressure increases, the liquid in a mercury barometer

   _____.

2. An aneroid barometer does not use _____.

3. Air pressure is greater at point _____.

4. Altitude is greater at point _____.

5. Density of the air is greater at point _____.

Building Vocabulary

On a separate sheet of paper, write a definition for each of these terms.

6. air pressure
7. barometer
8. density
9. mercury barometer
10. aneroid barometer
11. altitude

Name _____ Date _____ Class _____

Air Pressure

Weather maps have special lines that show different areas of air pressure. Read the passage and examine the map. Refer to the map to complete the statements below.

Isobars and Air Pressure

Air pressure is an important factor affecting weather. Changes in air pressure help weather forecasters predict how the weather will change. Falling air pressure usually indicates stormy weather. Rising air pressure means that the weather is clearing. Air pressure readings from barometers are shown on weather maps, like the one below, with lines called isobars. Isobars are drawn to connect areas that have the same air pressure.

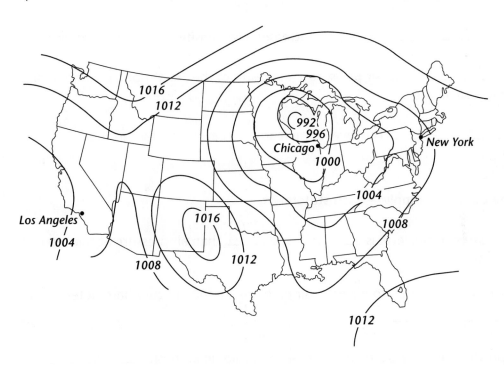

1. Each isobar differs from the next isobar by _____ miillibars.

2. The lowest air pressure reading shown is _____ millibars.

3. Where this low pressure occurs, the weather is likely to be _____.

4. The highest air pressure reading shown is _____ millibars.

5. This high-pressure area is likely to be experiencing _____ weather.

6. An area of _____ air pressure is centered northwest of Chicago.

Lesson Quiz

Air Pressure

If the statement is true, write *true*. If the statement is false, change the underlined word or words to make the statement true.

1. _____ To calculate the density of a substance divide its mass by its <u>weight</u>.

2. _____ The higher the altitude, the <u>lower</u> the air pressure.

3. _____ Most weather reports for the general public use <u>millibars</u> as units of air pressure.

4. _____ As altitude increases, the density of the air <u>increases</u>.

5. _____ Air pressure is the result of the <u>weight</u> of a column of air pushing on an area.

6. _____ The level of mercury in a barometer <u>falls</u> as the air pressure falls.

Fill in the blank to complete each statement.

7. Air pressure at sea level is _____ than air pressure at the top of a mountain.

8. Two instruments used to measure air pressure are the mercury barometer and the

_____.

9. Air pressure doesn't crush you because molecules in air push _____

_____.

10. The amount of mass in a given volume of air is its _____.

Air Pressure

Answer Key

After the Inquiry Warm-Up

1. Answers will vary. Accept answers that represent the difference between the mass of the inflated balloon and the mass of the deflated balloon.

2. Sample: I subtracted the mass of the deflated balloon from the mass of the inflated balloon to find the mass of the air inside the balloon minus the mass of the balloon itself.

3. The partially inflated balloon's mass would be greater than the mass of the deflated balloon but less than the mass of the fully inflated balloon.

4. The mass of the water-filled balloon would be much greater than the mass of the air-filled balloon. The mass of water is greater than the mass of an equal volume of air.

Key Concept Summaries

The amount of mass in a given volume of air is its density. The force pushing on an area or surface is pressure. Air pressure is the result of the weight of a column of air pushing on an area. As altitude increases, air pressure decreases. As air pressure decreases, so does density.

Review and Reinforce

1. rises
2. liquid
3. B
4. A
5. B
6. the result of the weight of a column of air pushing down on an area
7. any instrument that measures air pressure
8. the amount of mass in a given volume of air
9. an instrument that measures air pressure using liquid mercury
10. an instrument that measures air pressure without using a liquid
11. the distance above sea level, elevation

Enrich

1. 4
2. 992
3. stormy
4. 1016
5. fair
6. low

Lesson Quiz

1. volume
2. true
3. inches
4. decreases
5. true
6. true
7. greater
8. aneroid barometer
9. in all directions
10. density

Layers of the Atmosphere

LESSON

3

How does the sun's energy affect Earth's atmosphere?

Lesson Pacing: 1–2 periods or $\frac{1}{2}$–1 block

🕐 **SHORT ON TIME?** To do this lesson in approximately half the time, do the Activate Prior Knowledge activity. A discussion of the Key Concepts will familiarize students with the lesson content. Have students do the Quick Labs. The rest of the lesson can be completed by students independently.

Preference Navigator, in the online Planning tools, allows you to customize *Interactive Science* to your own teaching style. You can also edit lesson plans by selecting the Lesson Planner option.

Digital Teacher's Edition allows you to access your Teacher's Edition and Resource materials online.

my science online.com

Lesson Vocabulary

- troposphere
- stratosphere
- mesosphere
- thermosphere
- ionosphere
- exosphere

Professional Development Note **Content Refresher**

The Magnetosphere The magnetosphere is the region of Earth's magnetic field shaped by the solar wind, a stream of electrically charged particles from the sun. The magnetosphere is asymmetrical. On the side of Earth that faces the sun, the magnetosphere faces into the solar wind and is smaller. The side that faces away from the sun trails out into space for million of kilometers.

The magnetosphere contains electrically charged particles and is the site of magnetic storms and auroras. Magnetic storms are the result of bombardments of solar winds and may last for several days. Auroras are multicolored displays that are produced when charged particles from solar winds collide with the gas molecules in the magnetosphere.

Also located in the magnetosphere are the two Van Allen belts, concentric rings of charged particles that circle the Earth. The belts are named after their discoverer, James A. Van Allen. Discovered in 1958, the belts are found between 1,000 and 25,000 kilometers above Earth's surface.

LESSON OBJECTIVES

⚃ Identify the four main layers of the atmosphere and their characteristics.

⚃ Explain the characteristics of the atmosphere's layers.

Blended Path
Active learning using Student Edition, Inquiry Path, and Digital Path

ENGAGE AND EXPLORE

Teach this lesson using a variety of resources. Begin by reading **My Planet Diary** as a class. Have students share ideas about the thickness of Earth's atmosphere. Then have students do the **Inquiry Warm-Up activity.** Students will investigate the air in a sealed jar. Discuss the air pressure in a sealed jar. The **After the Inquiry Warm-Up worksheet** sets up a discussion about how the air pressure changes as the bag is moved in and out of the jar. Have volunteers share their answers to number 4 about the relationship between the air pressure in a sealed container and the volume of the container.

EXPLAIN AND ELABORATE

Teach Key Concepts by explaining that the atmosphere is divided into four layers based on changes in temperature.

Continue to **Teach Key Concepts** by discussing the characteristics of the troposphere and stratosphere. Use **Figure 1** to compare the depths of the first two atmospheric layers. Use the **Support the Big Q** to illustrate why the ozone layer is warm. **Teach Key Concepts** by identifying the characteristics of the mesosphere and thermosphere. **Lead a Discussion** about the temperature changes across the atmospheric layers. Hand out the **Key Concept Summaries** as a review of each part of the lesson. Students can also use the online **Vocab Flash Cards** to review key terms.

EVALUATE

Have students take the **Lesson Quiz.** For an alternate assessment, the **EXAM**VIEW® Assessment Suite, Progress Monitoring Assessments, or SuccessTracker™.

🄴 🄻 🄻 Support

1 Content and Language

Compare the words *troposphere, stratosphere, mesosphere,* and *thermosphere* featured in the lesson vocabulary. Explain what the word parts signal: *-sphere* ball; *tropo-* to change; *strato-* spread out; *meso-* middle; *thermo-* heat.

Lab zone Inquiry Path
Hands-on learning in the Lab zone

ENGAGE AND EXPLORE

To teach this lesson with an emphasis on inquiry, begin with the **Inquiry Warm-Up activity.** Students will explore pressure changes using a sealed jar and a plastic bag. Discuss the reason the pressure within the jar increases and decreases. Have students do the **After the Inquiry Warm-Up worksheet.** Talk about how the volume inside the sealed bag and jar changed during the investigation. Have volunteers share their answers to number 4 about how the volume of a jar and the air pressure are related.

EXPLAIN AND ELABORATE

Focus on the **Inquiry Skill** for the lesson. Point out that when you interpret data, you collect information during an experiment and analyze it. What data was interpreted during the **Inquiry Warm Up activity?** (The amount of air pressure and volume) Have students do the **Quick Lab** to explore the layers of the atmosphere and their characteristics.

Support the Big Q by discussing how the ozone layer is warmed. Do the **Quick Lab** to calculate the temperatures at different altitudes. Students can use the online **Vocab Flash Cards** to review key terms.

EVALUATE

Have students take the **Lesson Quiz.** For an alternate assessment, the **EXAM**VIEW® Assessment Suite, Progress Monitoring Assessments, or SuccessTracker™.

Digital Path
Online learning at my science online.com

ENGAGE AND EXPLORE

Teach this lesson using digital resources. Begin by having students explore real-world connections to the atmosphere at **My Planet Diary** online. Have them access the Chapter Resources to find the **Unlock the Big Question activity.** There they can answer the questions and refine their responses as they continue through the lesson. You can re-assign the activity and have students submit their work so you can track their progress.

EXPLAIN AND ELABORATE

Students reading above, at, or below the lexile measure of this lesson can access basic content readings at their level at **My Reading Web.** Have students use the online **Vocab Flash Cards** to preview key terms. Do the **Quick Lab** and then ask students to share their results about layers of the atmosphere and their characteristics.

Discuss how the ozone layer is warmed to **Support the Big Q.** Have students do the online **Do the Math activity** and submit their work to you. Have students calculate the temperatures at different altitudes by doing the last **Quick Lab.** The **Key Concept Summaries** online allow students to read a summary and see an image associated with each part of the lesson. Online remediation is available at **My Science Coach.**

EVALUATE

Have students take the **Lesson Quiz.** For an alternate assessment, the **EXAM**VIEW® Assessment Suite, Progress Monitoring Assessments, or SuccessTracker™.

2 Frontload the Lesson
Preview the lesson visuals, labels, and captions. Ask students what they know about the words that end in -sphere. Explain the specific meanings these words have in science.

3 Comprehensible Input
Have students draw a diagram of the atmospheric layers. Ask them to label the layers and write two defining characteristics of each layer in the appropriate section.

4 Language Production
Pair or group students with varied language abilities to complete labs collaboratively for language practice. Have each student copy the completed written lab for personal reference.

5 Assess Understanding
Have students create a portfolio of their notes and then do oral presentations of the lesson's content.

Lexile Measure = 870L

LESSON 11.3

Layers of the Atmosphere

Establish Learning Objectives

After this lesson, students will be able to:

- Identify the four main layers of the atmosphere and their characteristics.
- Explain the characteristics of the atmosphere's layers.

Engage

Activate Prior Knowledge

MY PLANET DIARY Read *Earth's Atmosphere* with the class. Review with students what they know about the thickness of Earth's atmosphere. Elicit that although the atmosphere extends thousands of miles into space, it becomes extremely thin just a short distance from sea level. Emphasize that most of the gas in the atmosphere is found close to the surface of Earth. Ask: **How much of the gas in the atmosphere is found in the bottom 5.5 kilometers?** *(Half)*

BIG IDEAS OF SCIENCE REFERENCE LIBRARY DK Have students look up the following topics: Atmosphere, Aurora Borealis.

Explore

Lab Resource: Inquiry Warm-Up

L1 **IS AIR THERE?** Students will investigate air pressure in a sealed jar.

LESSON 3

Layers of the Atmosphere

UNLOCK THE BIG ?

- What Are the Four Main Layers of the Atmosphere?
- What Are the Characteristics of the Atmosphere's Layers?

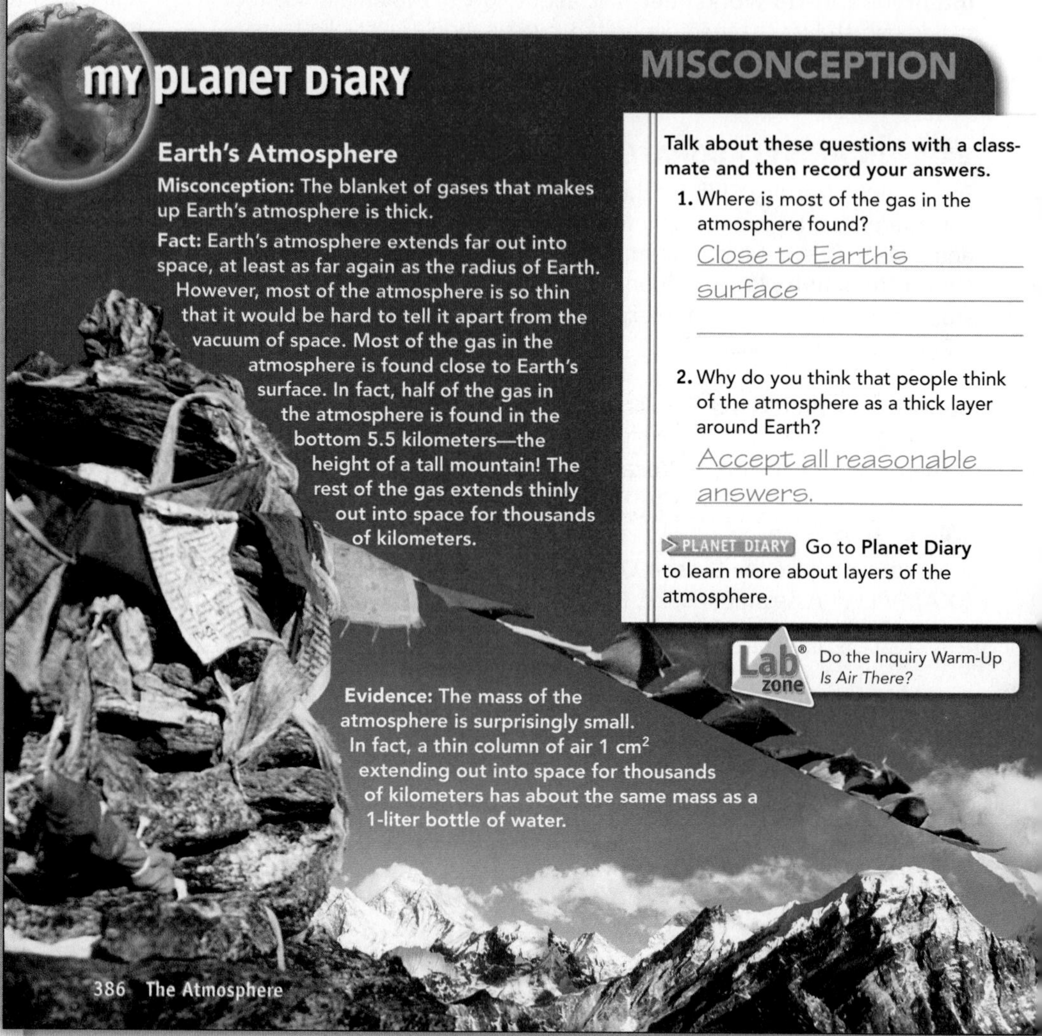

my planet Diary

MISCONCEPTION

Earth's Atmosphere

Misconception: The blanket of gases that makes up Earth's atmosphere is thick.

Fact: Earth's atmosphere extends far out into space, at least as far again as the radius of Earth. However, most of the atmosphere is so thin that it would be hard to tell it apart from the vacuum of space. Most of the gas in the atmosphere is found close to Earth's surface. In fact, half of the gas in the atmosphere is found in the bottom 5.5 kilometers—the height of a tall mountain! The rest of the gas extends thinly out into space for thousands of kilometers.

Evidence: The mass of the atmosphere is surprisingly small. In fact, a thin column of air 1 cm^2 extending out into space for thousands of kilometers has about the same mass as a 1-liter bottle of water.

Talk about these questions with a classmate and then record your answers.

1. Where is most of the gas in the atmosphere found?
   Close to Earth's surface
2. Why do you think that people think of the atmosphere as a thick layer around Earth?
   Accept all reasonable answers.

PLANET DIARY Go to **Planet Diary** to learn more about layers of the atmosphere.

Lab zone Do the Inquiry Warm-Up *Is Air There?*

386 The Atmosphere

SUPPORT ALL READERS

Lexile Measure = 870L Lexile Word Count = 994

Prior Exposure to Content: Many students may have misconceptions on this topic

Academic Vocabulary: *evidence, interpret*

Science Vocabulary: *troposphere, stratosphere, mesosphere, thermosphere*

Concept Level: May be difficult for students that struggle with math

Preteach With: My Planet Diary "Earth's Atmosphere" and Figure 1 activity

Go to **My Reading Web** to access leveled readings that provide a foundation for the content.

my science online .com

Vocabulary
- troposphere
- stratosphere
- mesosphere
- thermosphere
- ionosphere
- exosphere

Skills
- ⟳ Reading: Identify Supporting Evidence
- △ Inquiry: Interpret Data

What Are the Four Main Layers of the Atmosphere?

Imagine taking a trip upward into the atmosphere in a hot-air balloon. You begin on a warm beach near the ocean, at an altitude of 0 kilometers above sea level.

You hear a roar as the balloon's pilot turns up the burner to heat the air in the balloon. The balloon begins to rise, and Earth's surface gets farther away. As the balloon reaches an altitude of 3 kilometers, you realize the air is getting colder. At 6 kilometers you begin to have trouble breathing. The air is becoming less dense. It's time to go back down.

Six kilometers is pretty high. In fact, it's higher than all but the very tallest mountains. But there are still hundreds of kilometers of atmosphere above you. It may seem as though air is the same from the ground to the edge of space. But air pressure and temperature change with altitude. ☞ **Scientists divide Earth's atmosphere into four main layers classified according to changes in temperature. These layers are the troposphere, the stratosphere, the mesosphere, and the thermosphere.**

✏️ ⟳ **Identify Supporting Evidence**
Underline the evidence in the text above that explains how the atmosphere changes as you go up in a hot-air balloon.

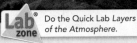
Lab zone ® Do the Quick Lab *Layers of the Atmosphere.*

☞ **Assess Your Understanding**

got it? ....

○ I get it! Now I know that the atmosphere has four main layers: *the troposphere, stratosphere, mesosphere, and thermosphere.*

○ I need extra help with *See TE note.*

Go to **my science** **coach** *online for help with this subject.*

387

 ELL Support

1 Content and Language
Have students pronounce the layers of the atmosphere in **Figure 1.** Pair students with those who are proficient in English, and ask each pair to search through the rest of the lesson to find the meanings of the prefixes for each layer.

2 Frontload the Lesson
Have students survey the diagrams and captions in this lesson. Then have them write questions they have about

the lesson based on their surveys. After students read the lesson, have them answer the questions they wrote at the start of the lesson.

3 Comprehensible Input
Pronounce and define the vocabulary terms for this lesson, pointing to the corresponding layer of atmosphere in **Figure 1.** Have students write the descriptions of each layer in a personal science glossary.

Explain ————

Introduce Vocabulary
Point out that the vocabulary terms for this lesson all end in –*sphere*. Remind students that the atmosphere completely encloses Earth, forming spherical layers around Earth. Tell students that the layer closest to Earth's surface is the troposphere.

Teach Key Concepts ⌐
Explain to students that Earth's atmosphere is not the same at all altitudes. Scientists divide Earth's atmosphere into four main layers according to changes in temperature. Ask: **What are the four main layers of Earth's atmosphere?** *(Troposphere, stratosphere, mesosphere, thermosphere)*

⟳ **Identify Supporting Evidence** Explain that identifying the supporting evidence for a hypothesis can help students understand the hypothesis. Evidence consists of facts—information about which accuracy can be confirmed by testing or by observation.

Elaborate ————

Lab Resource: Quick Lab 🧪
L2 **LAYERS OF THE ATMOSPHERE** Students will explore the different layers of the atmosphere and their characteristics.

Evaluate ————

Assess Your Understanding
Have students evaluate their understanding by completing the appropriate sentence.

R T I Response to Intervention
If students have trouble listing the layers of the atmosphere, **then** have them locate and reread the Key Concept statement for this section.

my science coach Have students go online for help in understanding the four main layers of the atmosphere.

My Planet Diary provides an opportunity for students to explore real-world connections to the atmosphere.

my science online .com ▸ **Mapping the Atmosphere**

Explain

Teach Key Concepts 🔑

Explain to students that the troposphere is the layer of the atmosphere with which they are most familiar. It is the layer in which they live. Ask: **Why is this layer called the troposphere?** (Tropo- means "changing" and conditions change more in this layer than in any other layer.) **What happens to the temperature of the troposphere as altitude increases?** (It decreases.) **Why are clouds that form at the top of the troposphere made up of ice?** (Water droplets that make up clouds would freeze at the top of the troposphere because the temperature there tends to stay at about –60°C.) **Why is the troposphere the densest layer of the atmosphere?** (Because it is the lowest layer, and air density decreases with altitude, the troposphere has the greatest number of molecules that make up air. For this reason it is the densest layer, containing almost all the mass of the atmosphere.)

Teach Key Concepts 🔑

Explain to students that the stratosphere is the layer of the atmosphere above the troposphere. The stratosphere contains the ozone layer.
Ask: **Would you expect the air pressure in the stratosphere to be greater or less than the pressure in the troposphere? Explain your answer.** (Less; air pressure decreases as altitude increases.) **Why is the upper layer of the stratosphere warmer than the lower layer?** (It is warmer because of the presence of the ozone layer in the middle part of the stratosphere. The ozone layer absorbs the sun's energy and warms the air above it in the upper stratosphere.)

Teach With Visuals

Tell students to look at **Figure 1.** Call attention to the orange band that represents the 12 km depth of the troposphere. Then have them compare this layer with the one above it. Ask: **About how many times deeper is the layer above the troposphere than the troposphere?** (It is about 3 times deeper.) **How do you know?** (The troposphere is 12 km deep and the next layer is 38 km deep (50 km – 12 km); 12 is about one-third of 38.)

What Are the Characteristics of the Atmosphere's Layers?

Unless you become an astronaut, you won't make a trip to the upper atmosphere. But if you could make that journey, what would you see? Read on to learn more about the conditions you would experience in each layer of the atmosphere.

The Troposphere You live in the inner, or lowest, layer of Earth's atmosphere, the **troposphere** (TROH puh sfeer). *Tropo-* means "turning" or "changing." Conditions in the troposphere are more variable than in the other layers. 🔑 **The troposphere is the layer of the atmosphere in which Earth's weather occurs.** The troposphere is about 12 kilometers thick, as you can see in **Figure 1.** However, it varies from 16 kilometers thick above the equator to less than 9 kilometers thick above the North and South poles. Although it's the shallowest layer, the troposphere is the most dense. It contains almost all the mass of the atmosphere.

As altitude increases in the troposphere, the temperature decreases. On average, for every 1-kilometer increase in altitude, the air gets about 6.5°C cooler. At the top of the troposphere, the temperature stops decreasing and stays at about –60°C. Water here forms thin, feathery clouds of ice.

FIGURE 1
The Atmosphere Layers
✏ Observe Use the journal pages in this lesson to record your observations of the layers of the atmosphere.

Altitude _About 0–12 km_
Temperature _6.5°C drop each 1-km increase in altitude_
Observations _Rain, snow, and most clouds occur in the troposphere. The weather varies throughout the troposphere._

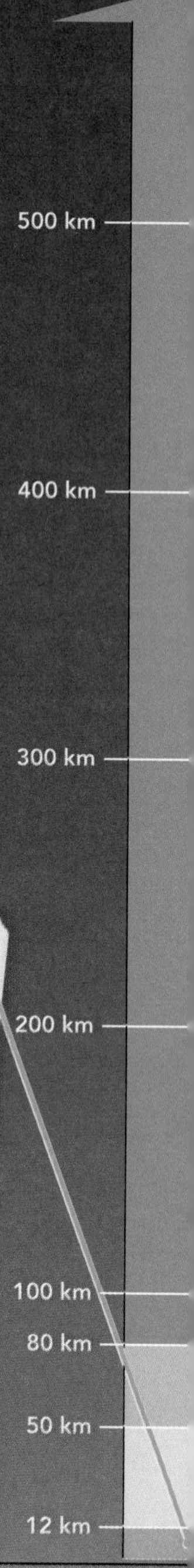

500 km — 400 km — 300 km — 200 km — 100 km — 80 km — 50 km — 12 km

388 The Atmosphere

Digital Lesson: Assign the *Do the Math* activity online and have students submit their work to you.

my science online | Layers of the Atmosphere

The Stratosphere The stratosphere extends from the top of the troposphere to about 50 kilometers above Earth's surface. *Strato-* means "layer" or "spread out." **The stratosphere is the second layer of the atmosphere and contains the ozone layer.**

The lower stratosphere is cold, about −60°C. Surprisingly, the upper stratosphere is warmer than the lower stratosphere. Why is this? The middle portion of the stratosphere has a layer of air where there is much more ozone than in the rest of the atmosphere. Ozone is a form of oxygen that has three atoms in each molecule instead of the usual two. When ozone absorbs energy from the sun, the energy is converted into heat, warming the air. The ozone layer protects living things from ultraviolet radiation from the sun.

- 500 km
- 400 km
- 300 km
- 200 km
- 100 km
- 80 km
- 50 km
- 12 km

Altitude __About 12–50 km__

Temperature __−60°C (lower portion)__

Observations __Middle portion has ozone layer; filters out UV light; warmer than lower stratosphere__

do the math!

Changing Temperatures

The graph shows how temperatures in the atmosphere change with altitude. Use it to answer the questions below.

1 Read Graphs What is the temperature at the bottom of the stratosphere?

__About −55°C__

2 ⚠ Interpret Data What layer of the atmosphere has the lowest temperature?

__Thermosphere__

Temperature in the Atmosphere

Troposphere | Stratosphere | Mesosphere | Thermosphere

(graph: Temperature (°C) vs Altitude (km), y-axis from −80 to 80, x-axis from 0 to 120)

3 CHALLENGE How does temperature change with altitude in the troposphere?

__Temperature decreases as altitude increases.__

389

Differentiated Instruction

L1 Layers of the Atmosphere
Encourage students to label the large arrow on these pages and the next two pages with the names of the layers. Seeing the names in order will help them remember the names.

L3 Investigating the Atmosphere
Discuss some ways that people who have studied Earth's atmosphere have

made scientific observations at high altitudes. Explain that a variety of both low and high technology has been employed including ascending in balloons and attaching instruments to balloons and satellites. Invite interested students to research weather balloons and weather satellites, and the information they have provided.

Explain

21st Century Learning

CRITICAL THINKING Help students compare and contrast the troposphere and the stratosphere. Ask: **Which layer is closer to Earth's surface?** *(Troposphere)* **Which layer is thicker?** *(Stratosphere)* **Which layer is warmer at the top than it is at the bottom?** *(Stratosphere)*

Address Misconceptions

L1 THE ROLE OF OZONE Students may think that ozone is always harmful because they have heard that ozone is an air pollutant. Point out that ozone occurs naturally. Explain that in the troposphere, the layer in which people live, ozone typically forms from gases produced by the combustion of fuels, forming smog. Some scientists use the phrase "good up high—bad nearby" to describe the helpful effects of ozone in the stratosphere and the harmful effects it can have in the troposphere. Ask: **How does the ozone layer in the stratosphere benefit living things on Earth?** *(It protects living things from harmful ultraviolet radiation from the sun.)*

Support the Big Q ❓ UbD

OZONE AND ENERGY Remind students that most of the energy absorbed by ozone is from ultraviolet radiation. Ask: **Why is the ozone layer warm?** *(It absorbs energy from the sun.)* **Why is the ozone layer important?** *(It absorbs harmful ultraviolet radiation.)*

Elaborate

Do the Math!

L1 Remind students that on the graph, altitude increases from left to right along the *x*-axis. If students are confused by the fact that the temperature scale on the *y*-axis does not begin at zero, remind them that the Celsius scale includes temperatures lower than zero.

See *Math Skill and Problem-Solving Activities* for support.

⚠ **Interpret Data** Help students understand that interpreting data involves analyzing the data collected during experiments. Point out that a line graph makes it easier to see trends in data. The red line on the graph represents data collected at different altitudes.

Explain

Teach Key Concepts 🔑

Explain to students that the mesosphere is the layer of the atmosphere above the stratosphere. This is the layer that protects Earth's surface from being hit by most meteoroids. Ask: **What are meteoroids?** *(They are chunks of stone and metal from space.)* Point out that despite the cold temperatures in the mesosphere, meteoroids burn up because of friction with gas molecules in the mesosphere.

Teach Key Concepts 🔑

Explain to students that the thermosphere is the outermost layer of Earth's atmosphere. Ask: **Where does the thermosphere begin and how far does it extend?** *(It begins at 80 kilometers above Earth's surface and extends outward into space. There is no definite outer limit of the thermosphere.)* **What are the two layers of the thermosphere?** *(The lower layer is the ionosphere and the outer layer is the exosphere.)*

21st Century Learning

CRITICAL THINKING Remind students that the upper level of the stratosphere is 50 km above sea level. Ask: **What characteristics make the mesosphere different from the stratosphere?** *(In the mesosphere, the temperature drops as the altitude increases. In the stratosphere, temperature generally increases with altitude.)* **Why is the mesosphere colder than the stratosphere?** *(It contains few ozone molecules to absorb energy from the sun.)* **How does ozone affect the temperature of the stratosphere?** *(Ozone absorbs energy from the sun, which warms the air).*

21st Century Learning 📖

COMMUNICATION Have students read *Aurora Borealis* in the **Big Ideas of Science Reference Library** and record themselves reporting on what they learned. Students could pretend to be a scientist or other person interested in or affected by this phenomenon.

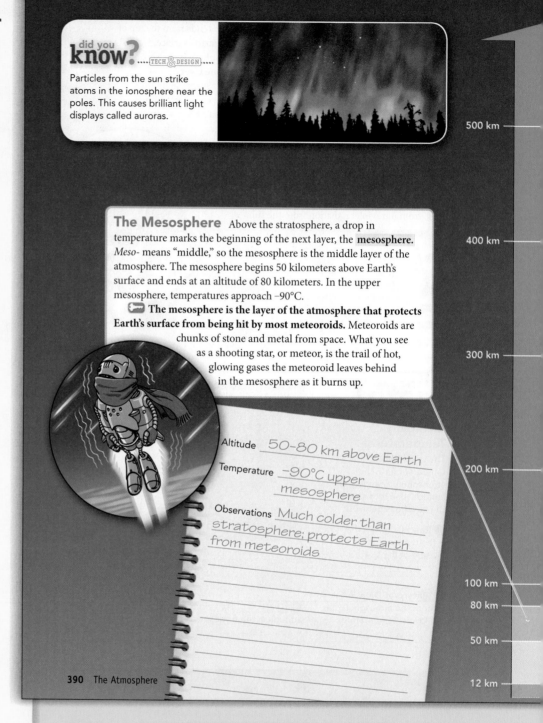

did you know? ····· TECH & DESIGN ·····

Particles from the sun strike atoms in the ionosphere near the poles. This causes brilliant light displays called auroras.

The Mesosphere Above the stratosphere, a drop in temperature marks the beginning of the next layer, the **mesosphere.** *Meso-* means "middle," so the mesosphere is the middle layer of the atmosphere. The mesosphere begins 50 kilometers above Earth's surface and ends at an altitude of 80 kilometers. In the upper mesosphere, temperatures approach −90°C.

🔑 **The mesosphere is the layer of the atmosphere that protects Earth's surface from being hit by most meteoroids.** Meteoroids are chunks of stone and metal from space. What you see as a shooting star, or meteor, is the trail of hot, glowing gases the meteoroid leaves behind in the mesosphere as it burns up.

Altitude _50–80 km above Earth_

Temperature _−90°C upper mesosphere_

Observations _Much colder than stratosphere; protects Earth from meteoroids_

500 km

400 km

300 km

200 km

100 km

80 km

50 km

12 km

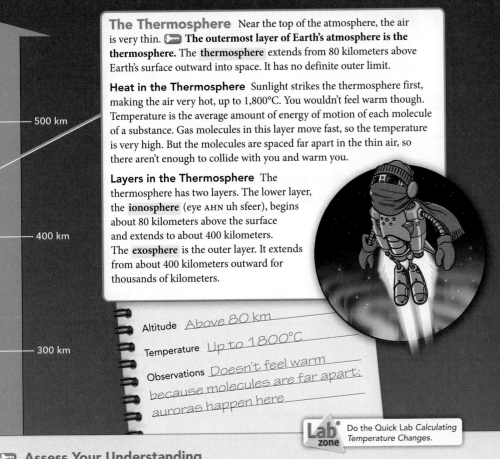

The Thermosphere Near the top of the atmosphere, the air is very thin. 🔑 **The outermost layer of Earth's atmosphere is the thermosphere.** The thermosphere extends from 80 kilometers above Earth's surface outward into space. It has no definite outer limit.

Heat in the Thermosphere Sunlight strikes the thermosphere first, making the air very hot, up to 1,800°C. You wouldn't feel warm though. Temperature is the average amount of energy of motion of each molecule of a substance. Gas molecules in this layer move fast, so the temperature is very high. But the molecules are spaced far apart in the thin air, so there aren't enough to collide with you and warm you.

Layers in the Thermosphere The thermosphere has two layers. The lower layer, the **ionosphere** (eye AHN uh sfeer), begins about 80 kilometers above the surface and extends to about 400 kilometers. The **exosphere** is the outer layer. It extends from about 400 kilometers outward for thousands of kilometers.

Altitude *Above 80 km*

Temperature *Up to 1800°C*

Observations *Doesn't feel warm because molecules are far apart; auroras happen here*

Lab zone Do the Quick Lab *Calculating Temperature Changes.*

🔑 **Assess Your Understanding**

1a. List Name the four main layers of the atmosphere.

The four main layers are the troposphere, stratosphere, mesosphere, and thermosphere.

b. Apply Concepts Why would you feel cold in the thermosphere?

The gas molecules there are so far apart they would rarely collide with you to warm you.

got it?

O **I get it!** Now I know there are four main layers in the atmosphere that vary in *temperature and altitude.*

O **I need extra help with** *See TE note.*

Go to **my science COACH** *online for help with this subject.*

391

Explain

Lead a Discussion

THE THERMOSPHERE Tell students to look back at the graph in the *Do the Math* activity. Ask: **What happens to temperature from the mesosphere to the thermosphere?** *(The temperature decreases in the mesosphere and then rises in the thermosphere.)* **Why is the thermosphere warmer than the stratosphere?** *(Energy from the sun strikes gas molecules in the thermosphere first, making this layer very hot.)*

Lab Resource: Quick Lab [Lab zone]

L2 CALCULATING TEMPERATURE CHANGES Students will calculate temperatures at different altitudes.

Evaluate

Assess Your Understanding

After students answer the questions, have them evaluate their understanding by completing the appropriate sentence.

R T I Response to Intervention

1. If students cannot identify the layers of the atmosphere, **then** have them skim the section to locate the Key Concept statements. Students should also review the notes they made in their books as they read about the layers of the atmosphere.

MY SCIENCE COACH Have students go online for help in understanding the characteristics of the layers of the atmosphere.

Differentiated Instruction

L1 Compare Layers Have students use a graphic organizer to compare and contrast the characteristics of the four layers of the atmosphere. Allow students to choose a graphic organizer that they think is the most suitable to visually display the information.

L3 Signals in the Thermosphere Tell students that when they make a long-distance phone call or watch television, the signal that carries the information most likely travels to and from a satellite that is orbiting Earth in the exosphere. Ask if any students know why the lower layer of the thermosphere is named the ionosphere. *(A distinguishing characteristic of the ionosphere is that ions form in this layer; radio waves bounce off the ions and back to Earth's surface)*

Lab zone® **After the Inquiry Warm-Up**

Layers of the Atmosphere

Inquiry Warm-Up, *Is Air There?*
In the Inquiry Warm-Up, you investigated differences in air pressure by using a jar and a plastic bag. Using what you learned from that activity, answer the questions below.

1. **OBSERVE** When the bag was outside of the jar and you tried to push it in, how did you change the volume inside the sealed bag and jar?

    _____

    _____

2. **OBSERVE** When the bag was inside of the jar and you tried to pull it out, how did you change the volume inside the sealed bag and jar?

    _____

    _____

3. **OBSERVE** When the bag was outside of the jar and you tried to gradually push it in, did the bag push back at a constant force, or did the force increase or decrease the more you pushed?

    _____

    _____

4. **DEVELOP HYPOTHESES** Based on your observations in questions 1 and 2, how are the air pressure inside a sealed container and the volume of the container related?

    _____

    _____

    _____

Layers of the Atmosphere

What Are the Four Main Layers of the Atmosphere?

got it? ....

○ **I get it!** Now I know that the atmosphere has four main layers: _____

_____

○ **I need extra help with** _____

_____

What Are the Characteristics of the Atmosphere's Layers?

1a. LIST Name the four main layers of the atmosphere.

_____

_____

b. APPLY CONCEPTS Why would you feel cold in the thermosphere?

_____

got it? ....

○ **I get it!** Now I know that there are four layers in the atmosphere that vary in _____

_____

○ **I need extra help with** _____

_____

Layers of the Atmosphere

What Are the Four Main Layers of the Atmosphere?

Scientists divide Earth's atmosphere into four main layers classified according to changes in temperature.

These layers are the troposphere, the stratosphere, the mesosphere, and the thermosphere.

What Are the Characteristics of the Atmosphere's Layers?

The **troposphere** is the lowest layer of Earth's atmosphere. *Tropo-* means "turning" or "changing." Conditions in the troposphere are more variable than in the other layers. **The troposphere is the layer of the atmosphere in which Earth's weather occurs.** At about 12 kilometers thick, it is the thinnest and most dense layer. It contains almost all the mass of the atmosphere. On average, for every 1-kilometer increase in altitude, the air gets about 6.5°C cooler.

The **stratosphere** extends from the top of the troposphere to about 50 kilometers above Earth's surface. *Strato-* means "layer" or "spread out." **The stratosphere is the second layer of the atmosphere and contains the ozone layer.** The lower stratosphere is cold, about –60°C. The upper stratosphere is warmer because the ozone layer absorbs energy from the sun.

Above the stratosphere a drop in temperature marks the beginning of the next layer, the **mesosphere.** *Meso-* means "middle." The mesosphere extends from about 50 kilometers to 80 kilometers above Earth's surface. In the upper mesosphere, temperatures approach –90°C. **The mesosphere is the layer of the atmosphere that protects Earth's surface from being hit by most meteoroids.**

The outermost layer of Earth's atmosphere is the thermosphere. The **thermosphere** extends from 80 kilometers above Earth's surface outward into space. It has no definite outer limit. Gas molecules in the thermosphere move fast, so the temperature is very high. But the molecules are spaced far apart. The thermosphere has two layers. The lower layer, the **ionosphere.** extends from about 80 kilometers to 400 kilometers above Earth's surface. The outer layer, the **exosphere,** extends from about 400 kilometers outward for thousands of kilometers.

On a separate sheet of paper, describe the characteristics of the four main layers of the atmosphere.

Name _____ Date _____ Class _____

Layers of the Atmosphere

Understanding Main Ideas
Fill in the blank to complete each statement.

1. The middle layer of Earth's atmosphere is the _____.

2. The upper region of the stratosphere is warm because energy from the sun is absorbed by the _____ _____.

3. The exosphere is the outer layer of the _____.

4. The _____ contains almost all the mass of the atmosphere.

5. The _____ is thicker over the equator than over the poles.

6. The lower layer of the thermosphere is the _____.

Building Vocabulary
On a separate sheet of paper, write a definition for each of these terms.

7. stratosphere
8. thermosphere
9. troposphere
10. mesosphere

Name ______________________ Date ____________ Class ____________

Enrich

Layers of the Atmosphere

Earth's weather occurs in the troposphere, and air pressure is an important factor in weather. Use the data on air pressure in the table to make a graph showing how air pressure changes as you move upward in the troposphere. Then answer the questions below on a separate sheet of paper.

Air Pressure in the Troposphere

Altitude (m above sea level)	Average Air Pressure
0 (sea level)	1013.2
500	954.6
1,000	898.8
1,500	845.6
2,000	795.0
2,500	746.9
3,000	701.2
3,500	657.8
4,000	616.6
4,500	577.5
5,000	540.5

Altitude (m above sea level)	Average Air Pressure
5,500	505.4
6,000	472.2
6,500	440.8
7,000	411.0
7,500	383.0
8,000	356.5
8,500	331.5
9,000	308.0
9,500	285.8
10,000	265.0

1. Describe the relationship between altitude and air pressure shown in the graph.
2. Estimate the average air pressure in a hole 500 meters below sea level.
3. If you were flying in a plane at an altitude of 1,500 meters, what would the air pressure outside the plane be? When you fly that high, why might your ears "pop"?

Place the outside corner, the corner away from the dotted line, in the corner of your copy machine to copy onto letter-size paper.

Name _____ Date _____ Class _____

Layers of the Atmosphere

If the statement is true, write *true*. If the statement is false, change the underlined word or words to make the statement true.

1. _____ The troposphere is thickest over the <u>equator</u>.

2. _____ Water forms thin, feathery clouds of ice at the top of the <u>exosphere</u>.

3. _____ The upper stratosphere is <u>cooler</u> than the lower stratosphere.

4. _____ The <u>mesosphere</u> contains the ozone layer.

5. _____ The <u>ionosphere</u> is the lower layer of the thermosphere.

6. _____ Most meteoroids burn up in the <u>ionosphere</u>.

Write the letter of the correct answer on the line at the left.

7. ___ Which layer of the atmosphere has no definite outer limit?

   A thermosphere

   B stratosphere

   C mesosphere

   D troposphere

8. ___ In which layer does Earth's weather occur?

   A mesosphere

   B stratosphere

   C thermosphere

   D troposphere

9. ___ Which layer is just above the stratosphere?

   A troposphere

   B exosphere

   C mesosphere

   D thermosphere

10. ___ In which layer can air temperatures reach 1,800°C?

   A mesosphere

   B thermosphere

   C exosphere

   D stratosphere

391F

Layers of the Atmosphere

Answer Key

After the Inquiry Warm-Up

1. The volume was reduced.

2. The volume was increased.

3. Sample: As I pushed further, the force of the bag pushing back increased.

4. As the volume of the sealed container increases, the air pressure inside it also increases. As the volume of the sealed container decreases, the air pressure inside it also decreases.

Key Concept Summaries

The lowest layer of the atmosphere, the troposphere, extends to about 12 kilometers above Earth's surface. It contains almost all the mass of the atmosphere and is the layer in which weather occurs. The second layer, the stratosphere, extends from the top of the troposphere to about 50 kilometers above Earth. It contains the ozone layer. Because the ozone layer absorbs energy from the sun, the upper stratosphere is warmer than the lower stratosphere. The cooler mesosphere extends from about 50 kilometers to 80 kilometers above Earth's surface. It is the layer that protects Earth from being hit by most meteoroids. The outermost layer of atmosphere, the thermosphere, begins about 80 kilometers above Earth and has no definite outer limit. Gas molecules here move fast, so the temperature is very high. But the molecules are spaced far apart. The lower layer of the thermosphere is the ionosphere and the outer layer is the exosphere.

Review and Reinforce

1. mesosphere
2. ozone layer
3. thermosphere
4. troposphere
5. troposphere
6. ionosphere

7. The stratosphere is the second layer of the atmosphere and extends from the top of the troposphere to about 50 kilometers above Earth's surface.

8. The thermosphere is the outermost layer of Earth's atmosphere that extends from 80 kilometers above Earth's surface outward into space.

9. The troposphere is the inner or lowest layer of Earth's atmosphere and extends to about 12 miles above Earth's surface.

10. The mesosphere is the middle layer of the atmosphere and extends from about 50 kilometers to 80 kilometers above Earth's surface.

Enrich

Students should graph average air pressure (in millibars) against altitude above sea level (in meters), using the data in the table. Their graphs should slope downward to the right, showing an inverse relationship between the two variables, altitude and air pressure.

1. As altitude increases, air pressure decreases.

2. about 1,070 millibars

3. Outside the plane, the air pressure would be 845.6 millibars. Your ears might "pop" as air escaped to equalize the air pressure inside and outside your ears.

Lesson Quiz

1. true
2. troposphere
3. warmer
4. stratosphere
5. true
6. mesosphere
7. A
8. D
9. C
10. B

Place the outside corner, the corner away from the dotted line, in the corner of your copy machine to copy onto letter-size paper.

Energy in Earth's Atmosphere

 How does the sun's energy affect Earth's atmosphere?

Lesson Pacing: 2–3 periods or 1–1½ blocks

🕐 **SHORT ON TIME?** To do this lesson in approximately half the time, do the Activate Prior Knowledge activity. A discussion of the Key Concepts will familiarize students with the lesson content. Have students do the Quick Lab. The rest of the lesson can be completed by students independently.

> **Preference Navigator,** in the online Planning tools, allows you to customize *Interactive Science* to your own teaching style. You can also edit lesson plans by selecting the Lesson Planner option.
>
> **Digital Teacher's Edition** allows you to access your Teacher's Edition and Resource materials online.

my science online.com

Lesson Vocabulary

- electromagnetic waves
- radiation
- infrared radiation
- ultraviolet radiation
- scattering
- greenhouse effect

Content Refresher

Professional Development Note

Remote-Sensing Imagery Infrared radiation has practical applications for scientists studying Earth's surface and its atmosphere. Scientists are able to produce satellite images by using special equipment to absorb specific wavelengths of electromagnetic radiation, including infrared. This technology is known as remote-sensing imagery. Information about features on Earth's surface is gathered by sensor systems on satellites. Sensors record as digital data the amount of electromagnetic radiation emitted from Earth's surface. The data are transmitted to ground stations and are used to produce an image of Earth's surface that is similar to an aerial photograph. The data can cover a large area of Earth's surface.

Remote-sensing imagery can be used in a variety of applications, including monitoring plant growth, detecting diseased crops, measuring heat generated by certain industries, surveying soil, making maps, and assessing damage caused by natural disasters. It is also used by archaeologists to detect artifacts.

LESSON OBJECTIVES

🔑 State in what form energy travels from the sun to Earth.

🔑 Explain what happens to the sun's energy in the atmosphere and at Earth's surface.

Blended Path
Active learning using Student Edition, Inquiry Path, and Digital Path

ENGAGE AND EXPLORE

Teach this lesson using a variety of resources. Begin by reading **My Planet Diary** as a class. Have students share ideas about how the sun affects their outdoor activities. Then have students do the **Inquiry Warm-Up activity.** Students will investigate if an air-filled bag traps heat from light. Discuss the temperature measurements students observe. The **After the Inquiry Warm-Up worksheet** sets up a discussion about why they think the temperatures in and out of the light differs. Have volunteers share their answers to number 4 about their own experiences with how sunlight can become trapped heat.

EXPLAIN AND ELABORATE

Teach Key Concepts by explaining the terms *radiation* and *electromagnetic waves.* Ask students to identify forms of visible light and nonvisible radiation.

Continue to **Teach Key Concepts** by discussing which of the sun's rays reach Earth's surface and which are absorbed or reflected before reaching the surface. Use **Figure 2** to identify and discuss the characteristics of the layers of the atmosphere. **Lead a Discussion** about how gas molecules scatter short wavelengths of visible light. In addition, discuss what happens to the energy that reaches Earth's surface. Then have students practice the inquiry skill in the **Apply It activity. Teach Key Concepts** by asking students to use **Figure 3** to explain what happens to the energy in the lower atmosphere and at Earth's surface. Use the **Support the Big Q activity** to discuss how energy from the sun warms Earth and the atmosphere. Hand out the **Key Concept Summaries** as a review of each part of the lesson. Students can also use the online **Vocab Flash Cards** to review key terms.

EVALUATE

Have students take the **Lesson Quiz.** For an alternate assessment, the **EXAM**VIEW® Assessment Suite, Progress Monitoring Assessments, or SuccessTracker™.

ELL Support

1 Content and Language

Identify the prefix *ultra-* in *ultraviolet.* Explain that *ultra-* means "beyond or extremely." When this prefix is combined with *violet* the word *ultraviolet* is formed meaning "extremely short wavelengths or beyond the violet light." List other words that use the prefix *ultra-*.

Lab zone Inquiry Path
Hands-on learning in the Lab zone

Digital Path
Online learning at MY SCIENCE ONLINE.com

ENGAGE AND EXPLORE

To teach this lesson with an emphasis on inquiry, begin with the **Inquiry Warm-Up activity.** Students will measure the temperature of air in a sealed bag. Discuss the temperature differences they notice. Have students do the **After the Inquiry Warm-Up worksheet.** Talk about what factors impact the temperature of the air. Have volunteers share their answers to number 4 about a real-world connection to how sunlight can trap heat.

EXPLAIN AND ELABORATE

Focus on the **Inquiry Skill** for the lesson. Point out that when you graph, you display data to make comparisons. Ask students what type of data they might have displayed in a graph about the **Inquiry Warm-up activity.** (*The temperatures of the air in the sunlight and in the shade*) Have students do the **Quick Lab** to explore how the sun's energy reaches Earth in the form of electromagnetic radiation.

Review the concept that land and water absorb energy from the sun before beginning the **Apply It activity.** Ask volunteers to share their graphs. **Support the Big Q** by discussing how the atmosphere and Earth are warmed. Then do the **Teacher Demo** to model that energy from the sun is not equally absorbed by Earth's surface. Have students do the **Lab Investigation** to compare how different materials are affected by heat. Students can use the online **Vocab Flash Cards** to review key terms.

EVALUATE

Have students take the **Lesson Quiz.** For an alternate assessment, the **EXAM**VIEW® Assessment Suite, Progress Monitoring Assessments, or SuccessTracker™.

ENGAGE AND EXPLORE

Teach this lesson using digital resources. Begin by having students explore real-world connections to radiation from the sun at **My Planet Diary** online. Have them access the Chapter Resources to find the **Unlock the Big Question activity.** There they can answer the questions and refine their responses as they continue through the lesson. You can re-assign the activity and have students submit their work so you can track their progress.

EXPLAIN AND ELABORATE

Students reading above, at, or below the lexile measure of this lesson can access basic content readings at their level at **My Reading Web.** Have students use the online **Vocab Flash Cards** to preview key terms. Do the **Quick Lab** on how electromagnetic waves warm objects and then ask students to share their results.

Review the concept that energy from the sun that is absorbed by land and water changes to heat before assigning the online **Apply It activity.** Ask volunteers to share their graphs. Have students submit their work to you. **Support the Big Q** by discussing how energy from the sun warms the atmosphere. Have students do the online **Art in Motion activity.** The **Key Concept Summaries** online allow students to read a summary and see an image associated with each part of the lesson. Online remediation is available at **My Science Coach.**

EVALUATE

Have students take the **Lesson Quiz.** For an alternate assessment, the **EXAM**VIEW® Assessment Suite, Progress Monitoring Assessments, or SuccessTracker™.

2 Frontload the Lesson
Preview the lesson visuals, labels, and captions. Ask students what they know about the terms *radiation* and *greenhouse effect.* Explain the specific meanings these words have in science.

3 Comprehensible Input
Have students study the visuals and their captions in **Figures 1, 2, 3,** and **4** to support the key concepts of the lesson.

4 Language Production
Pair or group students with varied language abilities to complete labs collaboratively for language practice. Have each student copy the completed written lab for personal reference.

5 Assess Understanding
Make true or false statements using lesson content and have students indicate if they agree or disagree with thumbs up or thumbs down gesture to check whole-class comprehension.

Energy in Earth's Atmosphere

Establish Learning Objectives

After this lesson, students will be able to:

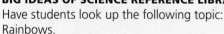 State in what form energy travels from the sun to Earth.

 Explain what happens to the sun's energy in the atmosphere and at Earth's surface.

Engage

Activate Prior Knowledge

MY PLANET DIARY Read *Amanda's Blog* with the class. Elicit from students that the first time Amanda left the water it was sunny out and she dried quickly; the second time it was cloudy and it took longer for her to dry. Ask: **What would cause such a difference in drying time?** (*When it was sunny, more of the sun's energy could warm Amanda and cause water to evaporate from her skin and swimsuit more rapidly than when the sun was behind clouds.*)

BIG IDEAS OF SCIENCE REFERENCE LIBRARY
Have students look up the following topic: Rainbows.

Explore

Lab Resource: Inquiry Warm-Up

L1 **DOES A PLASTIC BAG TRAP HEAT?** Students will measure the temperature of air in a plastic bag in sunlight.

Energy in Earth's Atmosphere

  How Does Energy From the Sun Travel to Earth?

 What Happens to the Sun's Energy When It Reaches Earth?

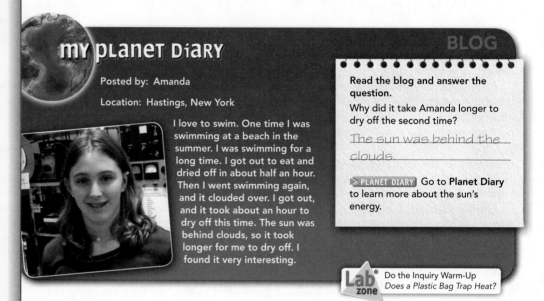

MY PLANET DIARY

BLOG

Posted by: Amanda

Location: Hastings, New York

I love to swim. One time I was swimming at a beach in the summer. I was swimming for a long time. I got out to eat and dried off in about half an hour. Then I went swimming again, and it clouded over. I got out, and it took about an hour to dry off this time. The sun was behind clouds, so it took longer for me to dry off. I found it very interesting.

Read the blog and answer the question.

Why did it take Amanda longer to dry off the second time?

The sun was behind the clouds.

> **PLANET DIARY** Go to **Planet Diary** to learn more about the sun's energy.

Lab zone Do the Inquiry Warm-Up *Does a Plastic Bag Trap Heat?*

How Does Energy From the Sun Travel to Earth?

Nearly all the energy in Earth's atmosphere comes from the sun. This energy travels to Earth as **electromagnetic waves,** a form of energy that can move through the vacuum of space. Electromagnetic waves are classified according to wavelength, or distance between wave peaks. **Most of the energy from the sun travels to Earth in the form of visible light and infrared radiation. A smaller amount arrives as ultraviolet radiation.**

SUPPORT ALL READERS

Lexile Measure = 890L   Lexile Word Count = 846

Prior Exposure to Content: Most students have encountered this topic in earlier grades

Academic Vocabulary: *graph*

Science Vocabulary: *radiation, greenhouse effect*

Concept Level: Generally appropriate for most students in this grade

Preteach With: My Planet Diary "Amanda's Blog" and Figure 1 activity

Go to **My Reading Web** to access leveled readings that provide a foundation for the content.

my science online.com

Vocabulary
- electromagnetic waves
- radiation
- infrared radiation
- ultraviolet radiation
- scattering
- greenhouse effect

Skills
- Reading: Ask Questions
- Inquiry: Graph

Visible Light Visible light includes all of the colors that you see in a rainbow: red, orange, yellow, green, blue, and violet. The different colors are the result of different wavelengths. Red and orange light have the longest wavelengths, while blue and violet light have the shortest wavelengths, as shown in **Figure 1**.

Nonvisible Radiation The direct transfer of energy by electromagnetic waves is called **radiation.** One form of electromagnetic energy, **infrared radiation,** has wavelengths that are longer than wavelengths for red light. Infrared radiation is not visible by humans, but can be felt as heat. The sun also gives off **ultraviolet radiation,** which is an invisible form of energy with wavelengths that are shorter than wavelengths for violet light. Ultraviolet radiation can cause sunburns.

FIGURE 1 ....
Radiation From the Sun
Energy travels to Earth as electromagnetic waves.
✎ **Identify** Label the types of electromagnetic radiation in the diagram.

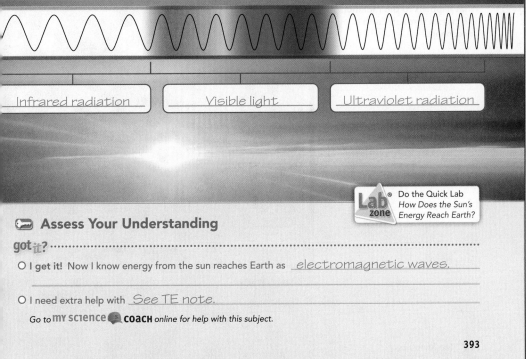

Infrared radiation   Visible light   Ultraviolet radiation

Lab zone ® Do the Quick Lab *How Does the Sun's Energy Reach Earth?*

Assess Your Understanding

got it? ....

○ **I get it!** Now I know energy from the sun reaches Earth as *electromagnetic waves.*

○ **I need extra help with** *See TE note.*

Go to my science **COACH** *online for help with this subject.*

393

Explain

Introduce Vocabulary
Tell students that radiation is a way that energy is transferred. Infrared radiation and ultraviolet radiation are two specific examples of radiation.

Teach Key Concepts 🔑
Explain to students that energy from the sun travels to Earth as electromagnetic waves. Most of this energy is in the form of visible light and infrared radiation. Ask: **What are electromagnetic waves?** *(A form of energy that can move through the vacuum of space)* **In addition to visible light and infrared radiation, what other form of energy travels to Earth from the sun?** *(Ultraviolet radiation)*

Elaborate

Lab Resource: Quick Lab 🔬
L1 **HOW DOES THE SUN'S ENERGY REACH EARTH?**
Students will explore how the sun's energy reaches Earth in the form of electromagnetic radiation.

Evaluate

Assess Your Understanding
Have students evaluate their understanding by completing the appropriate sentence.

RTI Response to Intervention
If students need help explaining how energy from the sun reaches Earth, **then** help them make a graphic organizer to show that visible light, infrared radiation, and ultraviolet radiation are all types of electromagnetic radiation.

my science 🔎 COACH Have students go online for help in understanding radiation from the sun.

My Planet Diary provides an opportunity for students to explore real-world connections to radiation from the sun.

my science online | Radiation From the Sun

Explain

Teach Key Concepts 🗯

Explain to students that not all sunlight reaches Earth's surface. Some sunlight is absorbed or reflected by the atmosphere before it can reach the surface. Ask: **Almost all of which type of radiation from the sun reaches the troposphere?** *(Almost all visible light passes through to the troposphere.)*

🗯 **Ask Questions** Explain to students that asking themselves questions is an excellent way to focus on and remember new information they encounter as they read.

Teach With Visuals

Have students to look at **Figure 2** to review with students the layers of the atmosphere. Ask: **What happens to ultraviolet radiation when it reaches the atmosphere?** *(Some is absorbed by the ozone layer in the upper layer of the stratosphere.)* **What happens to infrared radiation?** *(It penetrates farther before some of it is absorbed by water vapor and carbon dioxide.)*

What Happens to the Sun's Energy When It Reaches Earth?

Sunlight must pass through the atmosphere before it reaches Earth's surface. The path of the sun's rays is shown in **Figure 2.** 🗯 **Some sunlight is absorbed or reflected by the atmosphere before it can reach the surface. The rest passes through the atmosphere to the surface.**

Upper Atmosphere Different wavelengths of radiation are absorbed by different layers in the atmosphere. For example, some ultraviolet radiation is absorbed by the ozone layer in the stratosphere. Infrared radiation penetrates farther into the atmosphere before some of it is absorbed by water vapor and carbon dioxide.

FIGURE 2 ·······································
Energy in the Atmosphere
Some wavelengths reach Earth's surface. Other wavelengths are completely or partially absorbed in the atmosphere.

✎ **Compare and Contrast**
What happens to the radiation as it passes through Earth's atmosphere?

<u>Most ultraviolet radiation penetrates the thermosphere and is absorbed in the mesosphere. But almost all visible light makes it to the troposphere. More infrared radiation than ultraviolet radiation makes it to the stratosphere and troposphere.</u>

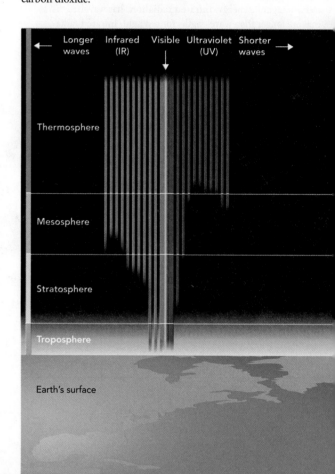

Digital Lesson: Assign the *Apply It* activity online and have students submit their work to you.

my science
online .com ⟩ | **Energy Reaching Earth** |

Troposphere Clouds act as mirrors, reflecting sunlight back into space. Dust-size particles and gases in the atmosphere disperse light in all directions, a process called **scattering.** When you look at the sky, the light you see has been scattered by gas molecules in the atmosphere. Gas molecules scatter short wavelengths of visible light (blue and violet) more than long wavelengths (red and orange). Scattered light looks bluer than ordinary sunlight. That's why the clear daytime sky looks blue.

Earth's Surface It may seem like a lot of the sun's energy is absorbed by gases in the atmosphere or reflected by clouds and particles. However, about 50 percent of the energy that reaches Earth's surface is absorbed by land and water and changed into heat. Look at **Figure 3** to see what happens to incoming sunlight at Earth's surface.

⟳ **Ask Questions** Before you read, preview the headings on these two pages. Ask a question you'd like to have answered. After you read, answer your question.

<u>Sample: What hap-</u>
<u>pens to the sun's</u>
<u>energy at Earth's</u>
<u>surface? About half</u>
<u>of it is absorbed by</u>
<u>land or water.</u>

apply it!

The materials at Earth's surface shown below reflect different amounts of energy.

❶ **Graph** Use the higher percentages below to draw a bar graph. Give it a title.

❷ Based on your graph, which material reflects the most sunlight? Which absorbs the most?

<u>Fresh snow; asphalt</u>

❸ **CHALLENGE** Predict what might happen if a forested area was replaced with an asphalt parking lot.

<u>The area would get hotter.</u>
<u>Asphalt holds more heat</u>
<u>than a forest.</u>

Amount of Energy Reflected

(Bar graph — Percent Reflected vs. Material: Asphalt ~10, Fresh snow ~90, Deciduous forest ~20, Dry soil ~25)

Asphalt
5–10% reflected

Fresh snow
80–90% reflected

Deciduous forest
15–20% reflected

Dry soil
20–25% reflected

395

Lead a Discussion

SCATTERING Point out to students that some incoming sunlight is reflected back into space by clouds. Ask: **What is scattering?** (*It is a process by which dust-size particles and gases in the atmosphere disperse light in all directions.*) **Explain why the clear daytime sky looks blue.** (*Gas molecules scatter short wavelengths of visible light, which are blue and violet, more than they scatter long wavelengths, which are red and orange. Scattered light looks bluer than ordinary sunlight.*)

Lead a Discussion

EARTH'S SURFACE Explain that although much of the sun's energy is absorbed or reflected by gases, dust, and clouds in the atmosphere, about 50 percent of the energy that reaches the surface is absorbed by Earth's land and water. Ask: **What happens to the energy that is absorbed by Earth's land and water?** (*The absorbed energy changes to heat.*)

Elaborate

21st Century Learning

CREATIVITY Remind students that the moon has no atmosphere. Have them imagine standing on the surface of the moon during the day. Ask them what color the sky would appear to be? (*Black*) Have students explain why it would not be blue. (*Without an atmosphere, there are no gas molecules to scatter the light and make the sky appear blue.*)

Apply It!

🔲 Before students begin the activity, review the concept that energy from the sun that is absorbed by land and water changes to heat.

△ **Graph** Help students understand that making a graph allows them to display and compare collected data. Suggest that they first look at the range of data before they create a scale for the percent of energy reflected by the different materials.

Differentiated Instruction

🔲 **Heat From the Sun** Encourage students to think about the way the sun heats Earth's surface. Explain, for example, that grass absorbs less heat than pavement, even when both surfaces receive the same amount of sunlight. As a result, the grass does not get as hot as the pavement.

🔲 **Heating Your Home** Have students explore the role that radiation from the sun plays in heating their homes. Students should consider whether the sun's radiation makes some rooms warmer in the morning or in the afternoon, and how opening and closing curtains or blinds affects the room's temperature. Have students present their observations to the class.

Explain

Teach Key Concepts 🔑

Explain that some of the energy that reaches Earth's surface is returned to the atmosphere as infrared radiation. Ask: **What effect does infrared radiation from Earth's surface have on the atmosphere?** *(Some of it is absorbed by the gases in air, heating the air.)* **What is the greenhouse effect?** *(The process by which the gases in air hold heat in Earth's atmosphere.)* **How does the greenhouse effect affect life on Earth?** *(The heat that is held in the atmosphere by the greenhouse effect keeps Earth at a temperature that is comfortable for most living things.)*

Teach With Visuals

Tell students to look at **Figure 3.** Use the image to review with students what happens to energy in the lower atmosphere and at Earth's surface. Ask: **About what percent of incoming sunlight is reflected by clouds?** *(About 25 percent)* **About what percent of sunlight is absorbed by Earth's surface?** *(About 50 percent)* **What happens to this absorbed sunlight?** *(It changes to heat and warms the land and water.)* **Does all absorbed sunlight warm the land and water? Explain.** *(No, some absorbed energy is radiated back into the atmosphere.)* **About what percent of sunlight is reflected by Earth's surface back into the atmosphere?** *(About 5 percent)* **Gases and particles of dust in the atmosphere absorb about what percent of incoming sunlight?** *(About 25 percent)*

Support the Big Q ❓ UbD

GREENHOUSE EFFECT Remind students that the greenhouse effect is a natural process, which keeps Earth warm enough to sustain life. Ask: **Where does the energy that warms Earth and the atmosphere come from?** *(The sun)* **In what two ways does energy from the sun warm the atmosphere?** *(Some energy is absorbed directly. Some energy is reflected or reradiated by Earth's surface into the atmosphere.)*

FIGURE 3 ··

Energy at Earth's Surface

✏️ **Identify** What's happening to energy in the lower atmosphere and at Earth's surface? Find out by using the words in the word bank below to complete each sentence.

> **Word Bank**
>
> reflected   absorbed   radiated
>
> *Words may be used more than once.*

✏️ **Draw Conclusions** Using the diagram below, draw a conclusion about energy at Earth's surface.

Sample: More energy is absorbed at Earth's surface than is reflected.

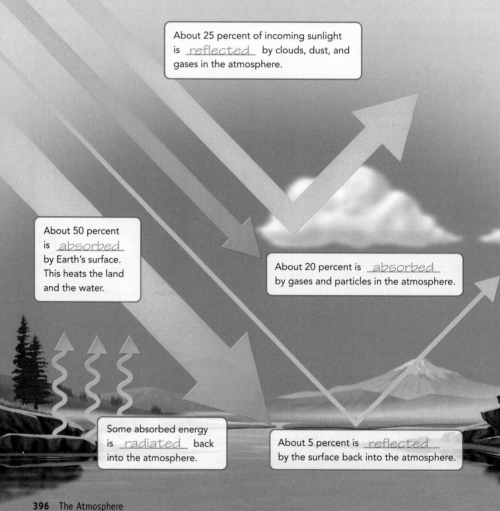

About 25 percent of incoming sunlight is __reflected__ by clouds, dust, and gases in the atmosphere.

About 50 percent is __absorbed__ by Earth's surface. This heats the land and the water.

About 20 percent is __absorbed__ by gases and particles in the atmosphere.

Some absorbed energy is __radiated__ back into the atmosphere.

About 5 percent is __reflected__ by the surface back into the atmosphere.

396 The Atmosphere

Art in Motion allows students to explore the essential factors that are involved in the greenhouse effect.

my science online.com ▶ | **Energy Reaching Earth**

Earth's Energy Budget What happens to the energy that heats the land and water? 🔲 **Earth's surface radiates some energy back into the atmosphere as infrared radiation.** Much of this infrared radiation doesn't immediately travel all the way back into space. Instead, it's absorbed by water vapor, carbon dioxide, methane, and other gases in the air. The energy from the absorbed radiation heats the gases in the air. These gases in turn hold heat in Earth's atmosphere in a process called the **greenhouse effect.**

The greenhouse effect, shown in **Figure 4,** is a natural process. It keeps Earth's atmosphere at a temperature that is comfortable for most living things. Over time, the amount of energy absorbed by the atmosphere and Earth's surface is in balance with the amount of energy radiated into space. In this way, Earth's average temperatures remain fairly constant. But scientists have evidence that human activities may be altering this process.

FIGURE 4 ....
▶ **ART IN MOTION** **Greenhouse Effect**
The greenhouse effect is a natural heat-trapping process.

✎ **Sequence** Number each step in the diagram to show how the greenhouse effect takes place. Discuss the diagram with a partner.

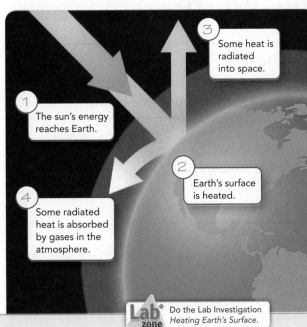

1. The sun's energy reaches Earth.
2. Earth's surface is heated.
3. Some heat is radiated into space.
4. Some radiated heat is absorbed by gases in the atmosphere.

Lab zone Do the Lab Investigation *Heating Earth's Surface.*

🔲 **Assess Your Understanding**

1a. Summarize What happens to most of the sunlight that reaches Earth?

<u>It's absorbed by land and water.</u>

b. Interpret Diagrams In **Figure 3,** what percentage of incoming sunlight is reflected by clouds, dust, and gases in the atmosphere?

<u>About 25 percent</u>

c. Predict How might conditions on Earth be different without the greenhouse effect?

<u>If energy wasn't held in the atmosphere, it might get too cold. Certain plants and animals might not survive.</u>

got it? ....

○ I get it! Now I know some energy <u>is absorbed and reflected in the atmosphere before it reaches Earth's surface.</u>

○ I need extra help with <u>See TE note.</u>

Go to **MY SCIENCE** 🔲 **COACH** *online for help with this subject.*

Differentiated Instruction

L1 **What Happens to Sunlight?** Have each student make a circle graph that shows what happens to sunlight that reaches Earth. Students should also list the percent of light for each entry in the chart.

L3 **The Greenhouse Effect** Encourage students to research the greenhouse effect and the gases in the atmosphere that increase this phenomenon. Students can present their findings to the class.

Elaborate

Teacher Demo **Lab** zone

L1 **ABSORPTION OF HEAT**

Materials construction paper (white, black, and other light and dark colors), bandannas or other materials for blindfolds

Time 10 minutes

Explain that not all parts of Earth's surface absorb energy from the sun equally. Place the sheets of construction paper in direct sunlight. After five minutes, ask student volunteers to put on blindfolds. Then rearrange the order of the papers. Have blindfolded students tell which papers are light and which are dark, according to how warm or cool the papers feel.

Ask: **How did you decide which papers were dark?** *(The dark papers felt warmer than the light ones.)*

Lab Resource: Lab Investigation **Lab** zone

L2 **HEATING EARTH'S SURFACE** Students will compare the effects that heating has on different materials.

Evaluate

Assess Your Understanding

After students answer the questions, have them evaluate their understanding by completing the appropriate sentence.

R T I **Response to Intervention**

1a, b. If students have trouble summarizing what happens to sunlight, **then** have them review **Figure 3.**

c. If students cannot predict how Earth might be different without the greenhouse effect, **then** have them reread the last paragraph under the red head *Earth's Energy Budget.*

MY SCIENCE 🔲 **COACH** Have students go online for help in understanding what happens to the sun's energy in the atmosphere and at Earth's surface.

Lab zone® **After the Inquiry Warm-Up**

Energy in Earth's Atmosphere

> **Inquiry Warm-Up,** *Does a Plastic Bag Trap Heat?*
> In the Inquiry Warm-Up, you investigated whether an air-filled plastic bag traps heat from light. Using what you learned from that activity, answer the questions below.

1. **PREDICT** If you left the bag with the thermometer in it in the light for an additional five minutes, how would you expect the temperature to change?

   _____

2. **PREDICT** Think of what you've learned about whether a plastic bag traps heat. Imagine that at the end of the experiment, you move both thermometers out of the light. After five minutes you record their temperatures. How do you expect the temperatures of the two thermometers to compare to their temperatures after five minutes in the light?

   _____

3. **APPLY CONCEPTS** Consider your response to question 2. How do you think the temperatures of the thermometers after five minutes out of the light will compare to their temperatures at the start of the experiment?

   _____
   _____
   _____

4. **USE PRIOR KNOWLEDGE** Give an example from your own experience of how sealed containers exposed to strong sunlight can trap heat.

   _____
   _____

Name _____ Date _____ Class _____

Energy in Earth's Atmosphere

How Does Energy From the Sun Travel to Earth?

got it? ···

○ **I get it!** Now I know energy from the sun reaches Earth as _____
_____

○ **I need extra help with** _____
_____

What Happens to the Sun's Energy When It Reaches Earth?

1a. **SUMMARIZE** What happens to most of the sunlight that reaches Earth?
_____

b. **INTERPRET DIAGRAMS** In Figure 3, what percentage of incoming
sunlight is reflected by clouds, dust, and gases in the atmosphere? _____

c. **PREDICT** How might conditions on Earth be different without the
greenhouse effect? _____
_____
_____

got it? ···

○ **I get it!** Now I know some energy _____
_____

○ **I need extra help with** _____
_____

Energy in Earth's Atmosphere

How Does Energy From the Sun Travel to Earth?

Nearly all the energy in Earth's atmosphere comes from the sun. This energy travels to Earth as **electromagnetic waves,** a form of energy that can move through the vacuum of space. Electromagnetic waves can be classified according to wavelength, or distance between waves. **Most of the energy from the sun travels to Earth in the form of visible light and infrared radiation. A smaller amount arrives as ultraviolet radiation.**

Visible light includes all the colors of the rainbow. The different colors you see are the result of different wavelengths. The direct transfer of energy by electromagnetic waves is called **radiation.** One form, **infrared radiation,** has wavelengths longer than red light. It is invisible to humans but can be felts as heat. The sun also gives off **ultraviolet radiation,** which is an invisible form of energy with wavelengths shorter than violet light.

What Happens to the Sun's Energy When It Reaches Earth?

Some sunlight is absorbed or reflected by the atmosphere before it can reach the surface. The rest passes through the atmosphere to the surface. Different wavelengths of radiation are absorbed by different layers in the atmosphere. Some ultraviolet radiation is absorbed by the ozone layer. Infrared radiation passes farther before some is absorbed by water vapor and carbon dioxide. In the troposphere, clouds reflect some sunlight back into space. Dust-sized particles and gases in the atmosphere disperse light in all directions in a process called **scattering.**

About 50 percent of the sun's energy that reaches Earth's surface is absorbed. It heats land and water. **Earth's surface radiates some energy back into the atmosphere as infrared radiation.** Some travels all the way back into space, but much is absorbed by water vapor, carbon dioxide and other gases in the atmosphere, heating them. These gases hold heat in the atmosphere in a process called the **greenhouse effect.** The greenhouse effect keeps Earth's atmosphere at a comfortable temperature. But scientists have evidence that human activities may be altering this process.

On a separate sheet of paper, briefly explain how energy from the sun travels to Earth and describe what happens to this energy as it passes through the atmosphere.

Name _____ Date _____ Class _____

Energy in Earth's Atmosphere

Understanding Main Ideas

If the statement is true, write *true*. If the statement is false, change the underlined word or words to make the statement true.

1. _____ Electromagnetic waves are classified according to <u>wavelength</u>.

2. _____ Visible light with the <u>shortest</u> wavelengths are red and orange light.

3. _____ Infrared radiation is <u>visible</u> to humans.

4. _____ During the day, the sky appears blue because of <u>scattering</u>.

5. _____ As it passes through the atmosphere, some <u>infrared</u> radiation is absorbed by the ozone layer.

Building Vocabulary

Match each term with its definition by writing the letter of the correct definition in the right column on the line beside the term in the left column.

6. _____ electromagnetic waves

7. _____ radiation

8. _____ infrared radiation

9. _____ ultraviolet radiation

10. _____ scattering

11. _____ greenhouse effect

a. a form of energy with wavelengths that are longer than those of red light

b. the direct transfer of energy by electromagnetic waves

c. reflection of light in all directions

d. a form of energy that can travel through space

e. the process by which gases in the atmosphere hold heat

f. a form of energy with wavelengths that are shorter than those of violet light

Enrich

Energy in Earth's Atmosphere

Read the following passage and examine the figure. Then use the figure to answer the questions below on a separate sheet of paper.

Reflection of Solar Radiation

On average, about half of the sunlight that strikes Earth's atmosphere reaches the surface of the planet to be absorbed and converted to heat. This absorbed light is a key factor in determining Earth's temperature and weather. Also it is crucial for the normal functioning of Earth's greenhouse effect.

The other half of the sunlight that strikes the Earth's atmosphere is either absorbed by the atmosphere or reflected back into space by clouds or by Earth's surface itself. The amount of sunlight that is reflected back into space in a particular place depends mainly on how thick the clouds are and whether Earth's surface is dark or light. The figure below shows how much energy is reflected back into space with different thicknesses of cloud cover and different types of surface on Earth.

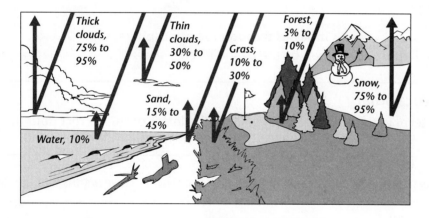

1. Which two types of surface on Earth are most important for absorbing solar energy and keeping the planet warm? Explain your answer.

2. Why do skiers often get sunburned even in the winter, when the sun's rays are not very strong?

3. What effect would thick cloud cover have on the temperature of Earth's surface? Explain.

4. Why might a major volcanic eruption lead to cooler temperatures over a large area around a volcano?

5. Which do you think would be warmer on a winter day when there is no wind, a thick forest or a grassy field? Explain your answer.

Lesson Quiz

Energy in Earth's Atmosphere

Fill in the blank to complete each statement.

1. Sunburn can result from exposure to _____ radiation.

2. Red light has a _____ wavelength than violet light.

3. A natural process called _____ holds heat in Earth's atmosphere.

4. _____ occurs when particles and gases in the atmosphere disperse light in all directions.

5. Energy from the sun travels to Earth in the form of _____ _____.

6. About 50 percent of the sun's energy that reaches Earth is _____ by land and water, which becomes heated.

If the statement is true, write *true*. If the statement is false, change the underlined word or words to make the statement true.

7. _____ Some ultraviolet radiation is absorbed by <u>clouds</u> in the upper stratosphere.

8. _____ The direct transfer of energy by electromagnetic waves is called <u>radiation</u>.

9. _____ Electromagnetic waves are classified by <u>distance between waves</u>.

10. _____ Scattered light looks <u>yellower</u> than ordinary sunlight.

Energy in Earth's Atmosphere

Answer Key

After the Inquiry Warm-Up

1. Sample: I think the temperature would increase further.

2. The temperatures of both thermometers probably will have decreased.

3. Answers will vary. Sample: The temperature of the thermometer outside the bag will probably be at or near its temperature at the start of the experiment. The temperature of the thermometer inside the bag will probably remain higher than it was at the start of the experiment.

4. Answers will vary. Samples: a closed car or room or house with summer sun streaming in the windows, a sealed transparent bottle of water or another liquid left in the sun

Key Concept Summaries

Energy from the sun travels to Earth as electromagnetic waves, a form of energy that can travel through the vacuum of space. Most energy from the sun travels to Earth in the form of visible light and infrared radiation. A smaller amount is ultraviolet radiation.

Some sunlight is absorbed or reflected by the atmosphere before it can reach Earth's surface. Some ultraviolet radiation is absorbed by the ozone layer. Some infrared radiation is absorbed by water vapor and carbon dioxide. In the troposphere, clouds reflect some sunlight back into space. About 50 percent of the energy that reaches Earth is absorbed by land and water, which it heats. Some of that energy radiates back into the atmosphere as infrared radiation. But much of it is absorbed by gases in air, heating them, in what is known as the greenhouse effect.

Review and Reinforce

1. true
2. longest
3. invisible
4. true
5. ultraviolet
6. d
7. b
8. a
9. f
10. c
11. e

Enrich

1. Forests and oceans are most important for absorbing solar energy and keeping the planet warm because they reflect the least amount of sunlight and occupy most of Earth's surface area.

2. Skiers often get sunburned because most of the sunlight that strikes snow, reflects back upward.

3. Thick cloud cover lowers the temperature of Earth's surface because it reflects a high percentage of sunlight back into space.

4. A major volcanic eruption might lead to cooler temperatures because it would add gases and particles to the atmosphere that would absorb or reflect sunlight before it could strike Earth's surface.

5. A thick forest would be warmer because it would absorb more sunlight and radiate it as heat.

Lesson Quiz

1. ultraviolet
2. longer
3. the greenhouse effect
4. Scattering
5. electromagnetic waves
6. absorbed
7. the ozone layer
8. true
9. true
10. bluer

Place the outside corner, the corner away from the dotted line, in the corner of your copy machine to copy onto letter-size paper.

Heat Transfer

LESSON 5

 How does the sun's energy affect Earth's atmosphere?

Lesson Pacing: 1–2 periods or $\frac{1}{2}$–1 block

🕐 **SHORT ON TIME?** To do this lesson in approximately half the time, do the Activate Prior Knowledge activity. A discussion of the Key Concepts will familiarize students with the lesson content. Have students do the Quick Labs. The rest of the lesson can be completed by students independently.

Preference Navigator, in the online Planning tools, allows you to customize *Interactive Science* to your own teaching style. You can also edit lesson plans by selecting the Lesson Planner option.

Digital Teacher's Edition allows you to access your Teacher's Edition and Resource materials online.

my science online.com

Lesson Vocabulary

* temperature • thermal energy • thermometer • heat
* convection • conduction • convection currents

 ## Content Refresher

The Thermometer Galileo is generally credited with the invention of the thermometer in 1592. He showed that temperature changes inside an inverted glass cause the level of the liquid in the container to rise and fall. This liquid-in-glass thermometer is made up of a small bulb and a capillary tube. By 1720, Daniel Gabriel Fahrenheit introduced the first mercury thermometer calibrated to a scale that ranged from the freezing point of water (32°F) to normal body temperature (originally 90°F, now 98.6°F). In 1742, Swedish astronomer Anders Celsius devised the Centigrade (Celsius) scale. Celsius originally used 0°C for the boiling point of water and 100°C for the freezing point, but this was later reversed.

Energy Transfer in the Troposphere Solar radiation heats Earth's surface, which, in turn, transfers energy to the troposphere. Energy is released by Earth's surface in the form of infrared radiation. Atmospheric gases—such as water vapor, carbon dioxide, and methane—absorb infrared radiation. (These greenhouse gases also reradiate some of that energy back to Earth's surface.) This transfer of energy by radiation is the primary mechanism by which the troposphere is heated. Convection is a less effective way of transferring heat to the troposphere. Because air is not a good heat conductor, conduction is the least significant way in which heat is transferred in the troposphere.

LESSON OBJECTIVES

🔑 Describe how temperature is measured.
🔑 Describe how heat is transferred.

Blended Path
Active learning using Student Edition, Inquiry Path, and Digital Path

ENGAGE AND EXPLORE

Teach this lesson using a variety of resources. Begin by reading **My Planet Diary** as a class. Have students share ideas about what other foods are heated in a similar manner. Then have students do the **Inquiry Warm-Up activity.** Students will observe how air moves when it is heated. Discuss how students knew in which direction the heated air was moving. The **After the Inquiry Warm-Up worksheet** sets up a discussion about the movement of air that is heated and cooled. Have volunteers share their answers to number 4, where a diagram shows the movement of the air.

EXPLAIN AND ELABORATE

Teach Key Concepts by discussing what students know about thermometers and measuring temperature. Explain that *thermo-* means "heat."

Continue to **Teach Key Concepts** by explaining the three ways heat is transferred. Ask students to explain how heat is transferred by convection. Use **Figure 2** to identify the different ways heat is transferred. Use the **Support the Big Q** to illustrate how conduction and radiation are also used to warm the troposphere. Then have students practice the inquiry skill in the **Apply It activity.** Hand out the **Key Concept Summaries** as a review of each part of the lesson. Students can also use the online **Vocab Flash Cards** to review key terms.

EVALUATE

Have students take the **Lesson Quiz.** For an alternate assessment, the **EXAM**VIEW® Assessment Suite, Progress Monitoring Assessments, or SuccessTracker™.

ⒺⓁⓁ Support

1 Content and Language

Distinguish between the word *meter* and the word part *-meter*. Explain to students that the word *meter* is a noun meaning "one unit of length in the metric system." The word part *-meter* means "measure." For example, the word *thermometer* includes *-meter* and means "a device that measures heat." Have students identify other words that include the word part *-meter*.

DIFFERENTIATED INSTRUCTION KEY
L1 Struggling Students or Special Needs
L2 On-Level Students **L3** Advanced Students

LESSON PLANNER 11.5

Lab zone Inquiry Path
Hands-on learning in the Lab zone

ENGAGE AND EXPLORE

To teach this lesson with an emphasis on inquiry, begin with the **Inquiry Warm-Up activity.** Students will use a metal spiral to explore how air moves when heated. Discuss in which direction the air moves as it is warmed. Have students do the **After the Inquiry Warm-Up worksheet.** Talk about what causes the air to move upward and downward. Have volunteers share their answers to number 4 and show the movement of air on their diagrams.

EXPLAIN AND ELABORATE

Focus on the **Inquiry Skill** for the lesson. Point out that when you infer, you interpret information to draw a reasonable conclusion. What can be inferred about warm air based on the **Inquiry Warm-up activity?** *(Warm air rises.)* Have students do the **Quick Lab** to measure temperatures using different thermometers.

Use **Support the Big Q** to illustrate how radiation and conduction are also used to warm the troposphere. Review *convection, conduction,* and *radiation* before beginning the **Apply It activity.** Ask volunteers to share their inferences. Do the **Quick Lab** to compare temperatures at different heights. Students can use the online **Vocab Flash Cards** to review key terms.

EVALUATE

Have students take the **Lesson Quiz.** For an alternate assessment, the **EXAM**VIEW® Assessment Suite, Progress Monitoring Assessments, or SuccessTracker™.

Digital Path
Online learning at my science online.com

ENGAGE AND EXPLORE

Teach this lesson using digital resources. Begin by having students explore real-world connections to measuring temperature at **My Planet Diary** online. Have them access the Chapter Resources to find the **Unlock the Big Question activity.** There they can answer the questions and refine their responses as they continue through the lesson. You can re-assign the activity and have students submit their work so you can track their progress.

EXPLAIN AND ELABORATE

Students reading above, at, or below the lexile measure of this lesson can access basic content readings at their level at **My Reading Web.** Have students use the online **Vocab Flash Cards** to preview key terms. Do the **Quick Lab** and then ask students to share their temperature measurements.

Support the Big Q by discussing how the troposphere is warmed. Review the three forms of heat transfer before assigning the online **Apply It activity.** Ask volunteers to share their inferences. Have students submit their work to you. Have students do the **Quick Lab** to reinforce their understanding of how temperatures differ at various heights above ground. The **Key Concept Summaries** online allow students to read a summary and see an image associated with each part of the lesson. Online remediation is available at **My Science Coach.**

EVALUATE

Have students take the **Lesson Quiz.** For an alternate assessment, the **EXAM**VIEW® Assessment Suite, Progress Monitoring Assessments, or SuccessTracker™.

2 Frontload the Lesson
Preview the lesson visuals, labels, and captions. Ask students what they know about the words *convection, conduction,* and *thermal energy.* Explain the specific meanings these words have in science.

3 Comprehensible Input
Have students draw and write captions for three diagrams that show how heat is transferred.

4 Language Production
Pair or group students with varied language abilities to complete labs collaboratively for language practice. Have each student copy the completed written lab for personal reference.

5 Assess Understanding
Divide the class into small groups. Have each student identify a key concept from the lesson to discuss in his or her group. After the discussions, have students talk about the key concepts as a group.

Heat Transfer

Establish Learning Objectives

After this lesson, students will be able to:

- Describe how temperature is measured.
- Describe how heat is transferred.

Engage

Activate Prior Knowledge

MY PLANET DIARY Read *From the Freezer to the Table* with the class. Point out that when the potatoes are placed in the hot oil, heat from the oil moves into the potatoes, cooking them. Ask: **How does the oil become hot?** *(Heat is applied to the container, such as a pot or deep fryer, that the oil is in. The container becomes hot and some of that heat is transferred to the oil. This heats the oil, which then heats the potatoes.)*

BIG IDEAS OF SCIENCE REFERENCE LIBRARY Have students look up the following topic: Gliding.

Explore

Lab Resource: Inquiry Warm-Up

L1 **WHAT HAPPENS WHEN AIR IS HEATED?**
Students will use a metal spiral to model convection in the atmosphere.

 LESSON 5 Heat Transfer

 UNLOCK THE BIG Q?

- How Is Temperature Measured?
- How Is Heat Transferred?

MY PLANET DIARY — SCIENCE IN THE KITCHEN

From the Freezer to the Table

French fries are on many restaurant menus. But have you ever wondered how they get from the freezer to the table? It takes a little science in the kitchen to make it happen.

First, you heat oil in a fryer until it's around 340°F. Then, the frozen potato slices are dropped in. Hot oil moves from the bottom of the fryer and begins to heat the potatoes. Exposure to so much heat causes the water in the potatoes to boil. This is indicated by bubbles rising to the surface of the oil. As the outside of the potato heats up, it transfers heat to the inside of the potato slice. In a matter of minutes it's crunchy on the outside and soft on the inside.

Answer the following question and discuss it with a partner.

Explain in your own words what happens when the potatoes are exposed to heat.

The outside gets warm first and heat moves inside.

> **PLANET DIARY** Go to **Planet Diary** to learn more about heat transfer.

 Lab zone Do the Inquiry Warm-Up *What Happens When Air Is Heated?*

How Is Temperature Measured?

All substances are made up of tiny particles (atoms and molecules) that are constantly moving. The faster the particles are moving, the more energy they have. **Temperature** is the *average* amount of energy of motion of each particle of a substance. In **Figure 1**, the hot tea in the teapot is the same temperature as the hot tea in the teacup. But do they have the same thermal energy?

SUPPORT ALL READERS
Lexile Measure = 860L   Lexile Word Count = 821

Prior Exposure to Content: Most students have encountered this topic in earlier grades

Academic Vocabulary: *infer*

Science Vocabulary: *thermal energy, convection, conduction*

Concept Level: Generally appropriate for most students in this grade

Preteach With: My Planet Diary "From Freezer Table" and Figure 1 activity

Go to **My Reading Web** to access leveled readings that provide a foundation for the content.

my science online.com

Vocabulary

- temperature • thermal energy
- thermometer • heat • convection
- conduction • convection currents

Skills

- Reading: Identify the Main Idea
- Inquiry: Infer

Thermal energy measures the *total* energy of motion in the particles of a substance. This means that the tea in the pot has more thermal energy than the tea in the cup because it has more mass.

Measuring Temperature Temperature is an important factor affecting weather. 🔑 **Air temperature is usually measured with a thermometer.** A **thermometer** is a device that measures temperature. Some thermometers have a thin glass tube with a bulb on one end that holds liquid mercury or colored alcohol. When the air temperature increases, the temperature of the liquid in the bulb increases. This causes the liquid to expand and rise up the column.

Temperature Scales Temperature is measured in units called degrees. Two temperature scales are the Celsius scale and the Fahrenheit scale. On the Celsius scale at sea level, the freezing point of water is 0°C, while the boiling point is 100°C. On the Fahrenheit scale at sea level, the freezing point of water is 32°F and the boiling point is 212°F. To convert from Farenheit to Celsius, you would use the following formula:

$$\frac{Fahrenheit - 32}{1.8} = Celsius$$

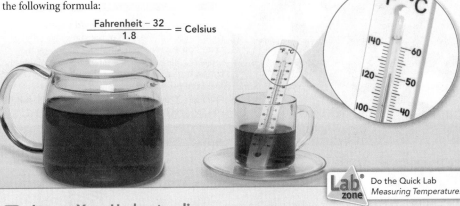

FIGURE 1 ·······

Measuring Temperature
✏️ Read and then answer the questions.

1. **Review** Circle the correct word in this sentence: The tea in the cup has (the same/less/more) thermal energy than the tea in the pot.

2. **Calculate** If the tea in the cup cooled to 70°F, what would a Celsius thermometer read?

About 21°C

Lab zone Do the Quick Lab *Measuring Temperature.*

🔑 Assess Your Understanding

got it? ·······

- ○ I get it! Now I know that temperature and thermal energy are different because temperature measures average energy and thermal energy measures total energy.
- ○ I need extra help with See TE note.

Go to MY SCIENCE COACH *online for help with this subject.*

399

ELL Support

1 Content and Language
Explain that *temperature* is a measurement of the average amount of energy of motion of the particles in a substance, while *heat* is thermal energy that moves.

2 Frontload the Lesson
Ask students if they have ever seen objects shimmer or waver on a hot, sunny day. Explain that the sun heats up the ground more quickly than it

heats the air, especially if the ground is a dark color. The heated air rises and bends light waves as it passes through them, making objects on the other side shimmer.

3 Comprehensible Input
Have students use a graphic organizer to distinguish among convection, conduction, and radiation. Tell students to provide examples of each type.

Explain

Introduce Vocabulary

To help students understand the terms *thermometer* and *thermal energy*, explain that *thermo-* means "heat." A thermometer is a device that measures heat. Thermal energy is heat energy.

Teach Key Concepts 🔑

Explain to students that a thermometer is a tool for measuring temperature. Ask: **What liquids are used in some thermometers?** (Mercury or alcohol) **How do these liquids indicate temperature?** (As their temperature increases, they expand and rise in the tube.) **What are two temperature scales?** (Celsius and Fahrenheit)

21st Century Learning

COMMUNICATION Have groups of students develop posters showing temperature in Fahrenheit and Celsius units on either side. Ask them to provide familiar examples of temperatures for each scale. Examples could include normal body temperature, temperatures at which water freezes and at which it boils. Some groups may wish to illustrate clothing or activities appropriate for various temperatures.

Elaborate

Lab Resource: Quick Lab

L1 MEASURING TEMPERATURE Students will compare temperature measurements of various types of thermometers.

Evaluate

Assess Your Understanding

Have students evaluate their understanding by completing the appropriate sentence.

RTI Response to Intervention

If students need help distinguishing between temperature and thermal energy, **then** have them reread the first two paragraphs of the section.

MY SCIENCE COACH Have students go online for help in measuring temperature.

My Planet Diary provides an opportunity for students to explore real-world connections to measuring temperature.

LESSON 11.5

Explain

Teach Key Concepts 🔑

Explain to students that there are three ways in which heat is transferred, but heat is always transferred from a warmer object to a cooler one. Ask: **What are three ways that heat is transferred?** *(Convection, conduction, and radiation)* **What is convection?** *(The transfer of heat by movement of a fluid)* **What is conduction?** *(The transfer of heat by substances that are in direct contact)* **What is radiation?** *(The transfer of energy by electromagnetic waves)*

Teach Key Concepts 🔑

Point out to students that within the troposphere, heat is transferred mostly by convection. Ask: **What causes a convection current?** *(The movement of cooler, denser air sinking toward the surface, forcing warmer air near the surface to rise)* **What are convection currents?** *(Currents that form from the resulting upward movement of warm air and downward movement of cool air)*

Teach With Visuals

Refer students to **Figure 2** as you discuss heat transfer. Ask: **Describe how heat is transferred by convection.** *(Atoms and molecules in fluids can move about freely from place to place. As they move, their energy moves along with them.)* **What affects how well molecules transfer heat by conduction?** *(How close together the molecules are)* **In which state does conduction work best?** *(Solids)* **What is an example of heat transfer by radiation?** *(Being warmed by a campfire or feeling the heat of the sun's rays on skin)*

21st Century Learning 📖

CREATIVITY Have students read *Gliding* in the **Big Ideas of Science Reference Library.** Ask students to make a drawing or painting of a scene showing a glider. Students should include arrows to indicate the direction of the thermals.

How Is Heat Transferred?

Heat is thermal energy that is transferred from a hotter object to a cooler one. 🔑 **Heat is transferred in three ways: convection, conduction, and radiation.**

1 **Convection** In fluids (liquids and gases), atoms and molecules can move easily from one place to another. As they move, their energy moves along with them. The transfer of heat by the movement of a fluid is called **convection.**

2 **Conduction** The transfer of heat between two substances that are in direct contact is called **conduction.** In **Figure 2,** heat is being conducted between the pot and the grate and between the pot and the liquid. When a fast-moving molecule bumps into a slower-moving molecule, the faster molecule transfers some of its energy to the slower one. The closer together the molecules are in a substance, the better they conduct heat. Conduction works well in some solids, such as metals, but not as well in liquids and gases. Air and water do not conduct heat well.

3 **Radiation** Have you ever warmed yourself by a campfire or felt the heat of the sun's rays on your face? You are feeling the transfer of energy by radiation. Radiation is the direct transfer of energy by electromagnetic waves. Most of the heat you feel from the sun travels to you as infrared radiation. You cannot see infrared radiation, but you can feel it as heat.

FIGURE 2 ···
Heat Transfer
✏️ **Identify** Use the numbers provided in the text to identify each type of heat transfer in the photo.

apply it!

Heat transfer occurs when a warm radiator heats a room.

Infer What type of heat transfer could keep the paper in the air? Draw arrows on the image to indicate your answer and explain below.

Convection currents; the paper floats on the rising convection current from the warm radiator.

Digital Lesson: Assign the *Apply It* activity online and have students submit their work to you.

my science online.com ▸ | **Heat Transfer**

Heating the Troposphere Radiation, conduction, and convection work together to heat the troposphere. Notice in **Figure 3** how the sun's radiation heats Earth's surface during the day. The land gets warmer than the air. Air doesn't conduct heat well. So only the first few meters of the troposphere are heated by conduction. When ground-level air warms up, its molecules move more rapidly. As they bump into each other they move farther apart, making the air less dense. Cooler, denser air sinks toward the surface, forcing the warmer air to rise. The upward movement of warm air and the downward movement of cool air form convection currents. ⚷ Heat is transferred mostly by convection within the troposphere.

> ✎ **Identify the Main Idea**
> Underline the main idea in the paragraph at the left.

FIGURE 3 ·····················

Heating the Troposphere
✎ **Summarize** Describe the process of heat transfer taking place in the diagram at the left.

<u>The sun heats the surface. The surface radiates heat. There is conduction between land and air. In convection, heat transfer occurs through the movement of air particles.</u>

 Do the Quick Lab
Temperature and Height.

⚷ **Assess Your Understanding**

1a. Explain Why is convection more important than conduction in the troposphere?

<u>Convection transfers heat in fluids like air. Conduction doesn't heat air well.</u>

b. Apply Concepts Explain how a convection current can enable a hawk or eagle to soar upward without flapping its wings.

<u>Warm air rises, so a bird can rise on warm air flowing upward.</u>

got it? ··

○ **I get it!** Now I know that heat transfer happens in three ways in the atmosphere: <u>convection, conduction, and radiation.</u>

○ **I need extra help with** <u>See TE note.</u>

Go to my science ⬤ coach *online for help with this subject.*

401

Differentiated Instruction

L1 Model Heat Transfer To help students distinguish between convection and conduction, write the word *HEAT* on a piece of paper and hand it to a student at the front of the room. Ask students to pass the paper to a student at the back of the room. Point out that this is like conduction, in which heat is passed from one particle to the next. Then ask the student at the back of the room to bring the paper to you. Point out that this is like convection, in which particles move and carry heat from one place to another.

L3 Heating Systems Invite students to find out how their own homes are heated. Students can share with the class information on hot water, hot air, or steam heating systems. Make sure that students show how heat is transferred by each system.

Explain
Support the Big Q ❓ UbD

ENERGY IN THE TROPOSPHERE Students have seen that heat is transferred in the troposphere mainly by convection. However, conduction and radiation also contribute to warming the troposphere. Ask: **During the day, how does the sun heat Earth's surface?** *(By radiation)* **How are the first few meters of the troposphere, just above Earth's surface, heated?** *(By conduction of heat from Earth's surface to the air)*

🔁 **Identify the Main Idea** Explain that when students read science material it is important for them to understand the ideas and concepts in a passage. Point out that good readers try to identify the most important—or biggest—idea in every paragraph or section.

Elaborate
Apply It!

L1 Review all three methods of heat transfer before beginning the activity.

△ **Infer** Help students understand that when they interpret an observation they are making an inference. Students will need to study the illustration carefully before they make their inferences. Make sure that students understand that the paper is being held up by heated air.

Lab Resource: Quick Lab

L2 TEMPERATURE AND HEIGHT Students will measure outdoor temperatures at different heights above ground.

Evaluate
Assess Your Understanding

After students answer the questions, have them evaluate their understanding by completing the appropriate sentence.

R T I Response to Intervention

1a. If students need help evaluating conduction and convection in the troposphere, **then** explain to them the atmosphere is made up of gases. Most heat movement throughout the troposphere is by convection currents and not by conduction.

b. If students cannot explain convection currents, **then** have them review their answers to the *Apply It!* activity.

my science ⬤ coach Have students go online for help in understanding heat transfer.

Lab zone® **After the Inquiry Warm-Up**

Heat Transfer

Inquiry Warm-Up, *What Happens When Air Is Heated?*

In the Inquiry Warm-Up, you investigated how air moves when it is heated. Using what you learned from that activity, answer the questions below.

1. **USE PRIOR KNOWLEDGE** Give an example from your own experience that, like this experiment, demonstrates how air moves when it is heated.

   _____

   _____

2. **COMMUNICATE** Draw a diagram of the experiment showing the movement of air as it is heated by the flame.

3. **PREDICT** What do you think will happen to the heated air as it continues to rise beyond the tin spiral and starts to cool?

   _____

   _____

4. **COMMUNICATE** Add lines, arrows, and labels to your diagram in question 2 to indicate how the heated air moves as it begins to cool, as well as how cool air flows toward the flame to replace the heated air that is rising.

Assess Your Understanding

Heat Transfer

How Is Temperature Measured?

got it? ···

○ **I get it!** Now I know that temperature and thermal energy are different because _____

_____

_____

○ **I need extra help with** _____

_____

How Is Heat Transferred?

1a. EXPLAIN Why is convection more important than conduction in the troposphere?

_____

_____

b. APPLY CONCEPTS Explain how a convection current can enable a hawk or eagle to soar upward without flapping its wings?

_____

_____

got it? ···

○ **I get it!** Now I know that heat transfer happens in three ways in the atmosphere: _____

_____

○ **I need extra help with** _____

_____

Name _____ Date _____ Class _____

Heat Transfer

How Is Temperature Measured?

All substances are made up of tiny particles (atoms and molecules) that are constantly moving. The faster the particles move, the more energy they have. **Thermal energy** measures the *total* energy of motion in the particles of a substance. **Temperature** is the *average* amount of energy of motion of each particle of a substance. **Air temperature is usually measured with a thermometer.** A thermometer is a device that measures temperature. Temperature is measured in units called degrees. Two temperature scales are the Celsius scale and the Fahrenheit scale.

How Is Heat Transferred?

Heat is thermal energy that is transferred from a hotter object to a cooler one. **Heat is transferred in three ways: convection, conduction, and radiation.** Atoms and molecules in fluids (liquids and gases) can move easily. As they move, their energy moves with them. The transfer of heat by the movement of a fluid is called **convection.** The transfer of heat between two substances that are in direct contact is called **conduction.** When a fast moving molecule bumps into a slower moving molecule, the faster one transfers some of its energy to the slower one. The closer together the molecules are in a substance, the better they conduct heat. Conduction works best in some solids, such as metals, but not as well in liquids and gases. Radiation is the direct transfer of energy by electromagnetic waves. Most of the heat that you feel from the sun travels to you as infrared radiation, which you cannot see but can feel.

Radiation, conduction, and convection work together to heat the troposphere. During a sunny day the land gets warmer than the air. But because air doesn't conduct heat well, only the first few meters of the troposphere are heated by conduction. When air at ground level warms, its molecules spread out, making it less dense. Cooler denser air sinks toward the surface, forcing the warmer air to rise. The upward movement of warm air and the downward movement of cool air form **convection currents. Heat is transferred mostly by convection within the troposphere.**

On a separate sheet of paper, explain how energy from the sun becomes thermal energy on Earth and how that energy raises the temperature of the troposphere.

Name _____ Date _____ Class _____

Heat Transfer

Understanding Main Ideas

If the statement is true, write *true*. If the statement is false, change the underlined word or words to make the statement true.

1. _____ In the troposphere, heat is transferred mostly by <u>conduction</u>.

2. _____ Conduction works best in some <u>solids</u>.

3. _____ Air temperature is usually measured with a <u>barometer</u>.

4. _____ The upward movement of warm air and the downward movement of cool air form a <u>convection current</u>.

5. _____ The <u>farther apart</u> the molecules in a substance are, the better they conduct heat.

6. _____ In the <u>Fahrenheit</u> temperature scale, water freezes at 0° and boils at 100°.

Building Vocabulary

On a separate sheet of paper, write a definition for each of these terms.

7. heat

8. conduction

9. thermal energy

10. convection

Enrich

Heat Transfer

Read the following passage and examine the figure. Then answer the questions below on a separate sheet of paper.

Heat and Human Health

Extremely hot weather can be dangerous to human health. During a heat wave, the body struggles to maintain a healthy temperature of about 37°C. Heat stress may set in before the air temperature exceeds this mark, however, because the body also produces heat when it does work. The figure shows how the brain and body respond to excessive heat.

The additional stress this response places on the heart and blood vessels can trigger heart and other medical problems, especially in the elderly. Because of this, death rates often rise when a heat wave strikes.

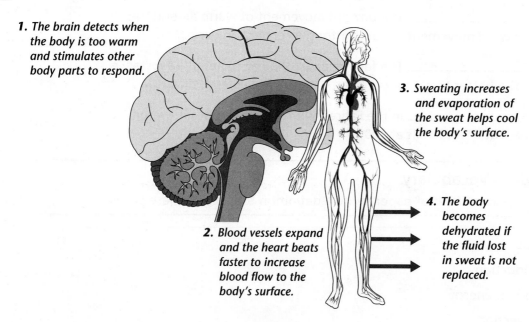

1. The brain detects when the body is too warm and stimulates other body parts to respond.

2. Blood vessels expand and the heart beats faster to increase blood flow to the body's surface.

3. Sweating increases and evaporation of the sweat helps cool the body's surface.

4. The body becomes dehydrated if the fluid lost in sweat is not replaced.

1. Heat can be lost from the body in the same ways that heat is lost from Earth's surface. Based on what you know about heat transfer from Earth's surface to the atmosphere, describe how the body can lose heat in each of these ways.

2. The body also loses heat by the evaporation of sweat. How is a tea kettle boiling similar to the evaporation of sweat from the body?

3. Why are you more likely to become dehydrated in hot weather?

Name _____ Date _____ Class _____

Lesson Quiz

Heat Transfer

Write the letter of the correct answer on the line at the left.

1. ___ In which substance would heat transfer by conduction work best?

   A   oxygen

   B   iron

   C   water

   D   alcohol

2. ___ Which is true of a pot and a penny with equal temperatures?

   A   they have the same thermal energy

   B   they are both gaining thermal energy

   C   the penny has more thermal energy

   D   the pot has more thermal energy

3. ___ How is heat transferred from the sun to Earth?

   A   by convection currents

   B   by conduction

   C   by radiation

   D   by thermal energy

4. ___ Which temperature is the freezing point of water in the Celsius scale?

   A   100°

   B   32°

   C   10°

   D   0°

Fill in the blank to complete each statement.

5. The transfer of heat between two substances that are in direct contact is called
   _____.

6. _____ measures the total energy of the particles in a substance.

7. The transfer of heat by the movement of a fluid is called _____.

8. The average amount of energy of motion of each particle of a substance is called
   _____.

9. Radiation is the direct transfer of energy by _____
   _____.

10. Only the first few meters of the troposphere are heated by _____.

Heat Transfer

Answer Key

After the Inquiry Warm-Up

1. Answers will vary. Samples: smoke rising from a chimney, the upstairs or attic in a house being warmer than its basement

2. Students should show the candle and tin spiral, and use arrows and labels to show that the heated air rises up and hits the spiral.

3. The air will start to drift downward as it cools.

4. Students should add arrows and labels to their diagrams indicating that the heated air above the candle starts to move downward again as it cools and that cool air rushes in toward the base of the candle and rises toward the flame.

Key Concept Summaries

Energy from the sun travels to earth as electromagnetic waves. During a sunny day, these waves strike the ground. They make the atoms and molecules in the ground speed up, increasing their thermal energy, and the temperature of the ground. Heat passes by conduction from the ground to the air just above it. But because air is not a very good conductor of thermal energy, only the first few meters of the troposphere are heated this way. As the air at ground level warms, its molecules move farther apart making the air less dense. Cooler, denser air sinks toward the surface, forcing the warmer air to rise. The upward movement of warm air and the downward movement of cool air form convection currents. Convection heats most of the troposphere.

Review and Reinforce

1. convection
2. true
3. thermometer
4. true
5. closer together
6. Celsius

7. Heat is the thermal energy that is transferred from a hotter object to a cooler one.

8. Conduction is the transfer of heat between two substances that are in direct contact.

9. Thermal energy is the total energy of motion in the particles of a substance.

10. Convection is the transfer of heat by the movement of a fluid.

Enrich

1. When the body surface is hotter than the surrounding air, heat radiates from the surface and can be carried away in convections currents. The body can also lose heat by conduction if the body surface comes into contact with a cooler surface.

2. To evaporate water in a tea kettle by boiling requires heat from the stove. To evaporate sweat from the skin requires heat from the body.

3. You are more likely to become dehydrated in hot weather because the body responds to excessive heat by increasing the output of sweat.

Lesson Quiz

1. B
2. D
3. C
4. D
5. conduction
6. thermal energy
7. convection
8. temperature
9. electromagnetic waves
10. conduction

Place the outside corner, the corner away from the dotted line, in the corner of your copy machine to copy onto letter-size paper.

401H

Winds

LESSON
6

How does the sun's energy affect Earth's atmosphere?

Lesson Pacing: 2–3 periods or 1–1$\frac{1}{2}$ blocks

SHORT ON TIME? To do this lesson in approximately half the time, do the Activate Prior Knowledge activity. A discussion of the Key Concepts will familiarize students with the lesson content. Use the Explore the Big Q to help students understand how the sun's energy affects the atmosphere. Do the Quick Labs and have students complete the Interactive Art online. The rest of the lesson can be completed by students independently.

Preference Navigator, in the online Planning tools, allows you to customize *Interactive Science* to your own teaching style. You can also edit lesson plans by selecting the Lesson Planner option.

Digital Teacher's Edition allows you to access your Teacher's Edition and Resource materials online.

my science online.com

Lesson Vocabulary

- wind
- anemometer
- windchill factor
- local winds
- sea breeze
- land breeze
- global winds
- Coriolis effect
- latitude

Content Refresher
Professional Development Note

The Jet Stream The jet stream reaches speeds of 200 to 400 km per hour. It is a large-scale wind system is composed of several horizontal, narrow, high-speed air currents that flow eastward in the stratosphere or upper troposphere. Two jet streams flow over the contiguous United States—the polar jet stream and the subtropical jet stream. Both shift positions during winter and summer seasons, affecting surface weather patterns. The polar jet stream along the polar front, wanders between 30° and 70° north latitude. This jet stream can meander as far south as Texas during winter. When it does, it causes an increase in the number of cold air masses in North America and changes surface storm paths that travel eastward.

The polar jet stream has less of an effect on summer weather because it stays far to the north. The subtropical jet stream generally migrates between 20° and 50° north latitude and may exist of North America at the same time as the polar jet stream. Although the subtropical jet stream is a weaker wind system than the polar jet stream, it can reach greater speeds.

LESSON OBJECTIVES

➡ Explain how scientists describe and explain winds.

➡ Distinguish between local winds and global winds and identify major global wind belts.

Blended Path
Active learning using Student Edition, Inquiry Path, and Digital Path

ENGAGE AND EXPLORE

Teach this lesson using a variety of resources. Begin by reading **My Planet Diary** as a class. Have students share ideas about how the wind moves objects. Then have students do the **Inquiry Warm-Up activity.** Students will explore how the Earth's rotation affects wind direction. Discuss the movement of the air in relation to the ball. The **After the Inquiry Warm-Up worksheet** sets up a discussion about how cold air moves from the North and South Poles and across the Americas. Have volunteers share their answers to number 4 about the direction weather systems move across North America.

EXPLAIN AND ELABORATE

Teach Key Concepts by explaining that air moves because of differences in air pressure, which causes winds. **Lead a Discussion** about how wind is measured and characterized.

Continue to **Teach Key Concepts** by describing local winds and what causes local winds. Use **Figure 3** to model the cause of sea breezes and land breezes. **Teach Key Concepts** by discussing the similarities and differences between local and global winds. **Lead a Discussion** about how the temperature differences between the equator and the poles create giant convection currents. Continue to **Lead a Discussion** by explaining why global winds curve rather than blow in a straight line. Then have students practice the inquiry skill in the **Apply It activity.** Use **Figure 5** to illustrate the pattern of wind belts and calm areas around Earth. **Lead a Discussion** about what causes the areas of calm. Use the diagragm in the **Explore the Big Q** activity to show how different parts of Earth's atmosphere are related. Discuss student's responses to the **Answer the Big Q.** Hand out the **Key Concept Summaries** as a review of each part of the lesson. Students can also use the online **Vocab Flash Cards** to review key terms.

EVALUATE

Have students take the **Lesson Quiz.** For an alternate assessment, the **EXAM**VIEW® Assessment Suite, Progress Monitoring Assessments, or SuccessTracker™.

ELL Support

1 Content and Language
Tell students the word *latitude* comes from the Latin word "latitudo" meaning "breadth." Show students how lines of latitude span the breadth of a map.

Inquiry Path
Hands-on learning in the Lab zone

ENGAGE AND EXPLORE

To teach this lesson with an emphasis on inquiry, begin with the **Inquiry Warm-Up activity.** Students will model the Coriolis effect. Discuss how the Earth's rotation affects wind direction. Have students do the **After the Inquiry Warm-Up worksheet.** Talk about how cold air moves from the Poles and across the Americas. Have volunteers share their answers to number 4 about what direction weather systems typically move across the United States.

EXPLAIN AND ELABORATE

Focus on the **Inquiry Skill** for the lesson. Point out that when you draw conclusions, you summarize what you have learned. What conclusion can be drawn from the **Inquiry Warm-up activity?** (*The winds from the Poles turn and blow west across North and South America.*) Have students do the **Quick Lab** to investigate wind direction.

Review the *Coriolis effect* before beginning the **Apply It activity.** Ask volunteers to share their conclusions. **Explore the Big Q** by completing the diagram and discussing how Earth's atmosphere is a system of parts. Do the **Quick Lab** to model global wind belts. **Answer the Big Q** to understand how the sun's energy affects Earth's atmosphere. Students can use the online **Vocab Flash Cards** to review key terms.

EVALUATE

Have students take the **Lesson Quiz.** For an alternate assessment, the **EXAM**VIEW® Assessment Suite, Progress Monitoring Assessments, or SuccessTracker™.

Digital Path
Online learning at **MY SCIENCE ONLINE**.com

ENGAGE AND EXPLORE

Teach this lesson using digital resources. Begin by having students explore real-world connections to winds at **My Planet Diary** online. Have them access the Chapter Resources to find the **Unlock the Big Question activity.** There they can answer the questions and refine their responses as they continue through the lesson. You can re-assign the activity and have students submit their work so you can track their progress.

EXPLAIN AND ELABORATE

Students reading above, at, or below the lexile measure of this lesson can access basic content readings at their level at **My Reading Web.** Have students use the online **Vocab Flash Cards** to preview key terms. Do the **Quick Lab** and then ask students to model how their devices work.

Review the *Coriolis effect* before assigning the online **Apply It activity.** Ask volunteers to share their conclusions. Have students submit their work to you. Have students do the online **Interactive Art.** Use the **Explore the Big Q** to outline the different parts of Earth's atmospheric system. Have students do the **Quick Lab** to reinforce understanding of global wind belts. Discuss students' responses to the **Answer the Big Q activity.** The **Key Concept Summaries** online allow students to read a summary and see an image associated with each part of the lesson. Online remediation is available at **My Science Coach.**

EVALUATE

Have students take the **Lesson Quiz.** For an alternate assessment, the **EXAM**VIEW® Assessment Suite, Progress Monitoring Assessments, or SuccessTracker™.

2 Frontload the Lesson
Preview the lesson questions. Ask students if there are any terms they do not understand. Explain the specific meanings these terms have in science.

3 Comprehensible Input
Have students study the visuals and their captions in **Figure 3, 4,** and **5** to support the key concepts of the lesson.

4 Language Production
Pair or group students with varied language abilities to complete labs collaboratively for language practice. Have each student copy the completed written lab for personal reference.

5 Assess Understanding
Have students keep a content area log. Use a two-column format with the headings "What I Understand" and "What I Don't Understand." Follow up so that students can move items from the "Don't Understand" to the "Understand" column.

LESSON 11.6

Winds

Establish Learning Objectives

After this lesson, students will be able to:

🔑 Explain how scientists describe and explain winds.

🔑 Distinguish between local winds and global winds and identify major global wind belts.

Engage

Activate Prior Knowledge

MY PLANET DIARY Read *Windsurfing* with the class. Ask students who have flown kites to describe the experience. Remind students of how difficult it can be to hold on to a kite against the force of a strong wind. Then have students imagine that the kite is on the water and they are attached to it. Suggest that trying to control a kite might feel something like windsurfing in a strong wind. Ask: **What moves the windsurfer along the water?** (*Wind*)

BIG IDEAS OF SCIENCE REFERENCE LIBRARY 📖
Have students look up the following topics: Dust Storms, Sailing.

Explore

Lab Resource: Inquiry Warm-Up

L1 DOES THE WIND TURN? Students will use a spinning balloon to model the Coriolis effect.

LESSON

6 Winds

🔑 **What Causes Winds?**

🔑 **How Do Local Winds and Global Winds Differ?**

MY PLANET DIARY

EXTREME SPORTS

Windsurfing

Imagine being able to ride a wave at almost 81 km/h—not in a boat powered by a motor but on a board powered only by the wind. That's what windsurfing is all about.

Windsurfers stand on a sailboard, which is similar to a surfboard. But the sailboard has a mast and a sail that the surfer can control with his or her hands. It uses a sail to capture wind and move the surfer along the surface of the water. Jim Drake, one of the first inventors of windsurfing, points out:

"It's the simplicity of standing up so you can adjust your weight and move quickly, as well as actively participate in transmitting the sail's forces to the board."

Discuss these questions with a classmate. Write your answers below.

1. How does wind move the sail?
   The wind pushes against the sail, moving the wind-surfer across the water.

2. How have you experienced the effects of wind?
   Accept all reasonable answers.

> PLANET DIARY Go to **Planet Diary** to learn more about winds.

 Do the Inquiry Warm-Up
Does the Wind Turn?

402 The Atmosphere

SUPPORT ALL READERS

Lexile Measure = 880L   Lexile Word Count = 1440

Prior Exposure to Content: Most students have encountered this topic in earlier grades

Academic Vocabulary: *draw conclusions, evidence*

Science Vocabulary: *anemometer, Coriolis effect, latitude*

Concept Level: May be difficult for students who struggle with abstract ideas

Preteach With: My Planet Diary "Windsurfing" and Figure 1 activity

Go to **My Reading Web** to access leveled readings that provide a foundation for the content.

 my science ONLINE.com

Vocabulary

- wind • anemometer • windchill factor
- local winds • sea breeze • land breeze
- global winds • Coriolis effect • latitude

Skills

🔄 Reading: Identify Supporting Evidence

△ Inquiry: Draw Conclusions

What Causes Winds?

Air is a fluid, so it can move easily from place to place. But how does it do that? 🔑 **Differences in air pressure cause the air to move.** Wind is the movement of air parallel to Earth's surface. Winds move from areas of high pressure to areas of lower pressure.

🔑 **Most differences in air pressure are caused by the unequal heating of the atmosphere.** Recall that convection currents form when an area of Earth's surface is heated by the sun's rays. Air over the heated surface expands and becomes less dense. As the air becomes less dense, its air pressure decreases. If a nearby area is not heated as much, the air above the less-heated area will be cooler and denser. The cool, dense air with a higher pressure flows underneath the warm, less dense air. This forces the warm air to rise.

FIGURE 1 ·····························

Moving Air

Windsurfers need wind in order to move across the water. ✏️ **Explain** How do differences in air pressure cause wind?

Cooler air is less dense and has
higher pressure than warm air.
When cool air comes in contact
with warmer air, the cool air
flows beneath the warm air.

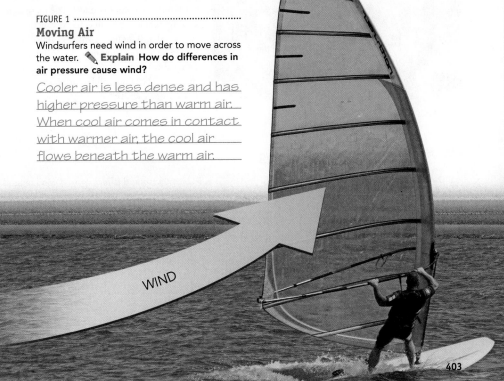

WIND

403

Explain

Introduce Vocabulary

To help students understand the term *anemometer*, explain that *anemo* comes from a Greek word meaning "wind," and *meter* means "measure." An anemometer is a device that measures wind speed.

Teach Key Concepts 🔑

Explain to students that moving air, or wind, is caused by differences in air pressure. Help students understand that differences in air pressure are caused by the unequal heating of the atmosphere. Ask: **What is a wind?** *(The movement of air parallel to Earth's surface)* **In terms of air pressure, how do winds move?** *(From areas of high pressure to areas of low pressure)* **What happens to the density of air when it is heated?** *(It decreases.)* Explain to students that unequal heating of the troposphere leads to differences in air pressure and causes wind.

My Planet Diary provides an opportunity for students to explore real-world connections to winds.

my science online | Winds

ELL Support

1 Content and Language

Have students work in small groups to compare and contrast local winds and global winds, giving examples of each and how they are formed. Have students record the information in a graphic organizer.

2 Frontload the Lesson

Use the section headings to help set the purpose for reading. Preview the vocabulary by saying aloud each term as students point to the visuals.

3 Comprehensible Input

Have students outline the lesson by using the headings and subheadings. As they read, students can list the main points under each heading. Pair students with more proficient readers if needed.

403

Explain

Lead a Discussion

WIND MEASUREMENTS Have students relate experiences listening to weather reports. Ask: **What characteristics of wind does a weather report contain?** *(Weather reports usually give the direction and speed of the wind.)* **How is wind direction determined?** *(By using a weather vane)* **How are winds named?** *(They are named for the direction from which the wind is coming.)* **Give an example.** *(A west wind blows from the west to the east.)* **How is wind speed measured?** *(With an anemometer)* Explain to students the windchill factor is a measure of how cold people feel when they are outside in cold temperatures and the wind is blowing. Ask: **What happens to the body when wind blows over the skin?** *(Body heat is removed.)* **What is the windchill factor?** *(It is the increased cooling that a wind can cause a person to feel.)*

Elaborate

Lab Resource: Quick Lab

L1 **BUILD A WIND VANE** Students will build a simple device to show wind direction.

Evaluate

Assess Your Understanding

After students answer the questions, have them evaluate their understanding by completing the appropriate sentence.

RTI Response to Intervention

1a. If students have trouble defining *wind*, **then** have them locate the highlighted term and reread the definition.

b. If students cannot relate wind to air pressure and temperature, **then** have them reread the first two paragraphs of this section.

MY SCIENCE COACH Have students go online for help in understanding what causes wind.

FIGURE 2 ·······························

Wind Direction and Speed

 Identify Based on the direction of the wind vane, which direction would your kite be flying? Indicate your answer by shading in your kite.

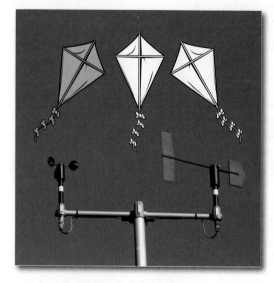

Measuring Wind Winds are described by their direction and speed. Winds can blow from all directions: north, south, east, and west. Wind direction is determined with a wind vane. The wind swings the wind vane so that one end points into the wind. The name of a wind tells you where the wind is coming from. For example, a south wind blows from the south toward the north. A north wind blows to the south.

Wind speed can be measured with an **anemometer** (an uh MAHM uh tur). An anemometer has three or four cups mounted at the ends of spokes that spin on an axle. The force of the wind against the cups turns the axle. A meter connected to the axle shows the wind speed. **Figure 2** shows a wind vane and an anemometer.

Windchill Factor On a warm day, a cool breeze can be refreshing. But during the winter, the same breeze can make you feel uncomfortably cold. The wind blowing over your skin removes body heat. The stronger the wind, the colder you feel. The increased cooling that a wind can cause is called the **windchill factor.** A weather report may say, "The temperature outside is 20 degrees Fahrenheit. But with a wind speed of 30 miles per hour, the windchill factor makes it feel like 1 degree above zero."

Lab zone Do the Quick Lab Build a Wind Vane.

Assess Your Understanding

1a. Define What is wind?
The movement of air between areas of different pressure

b. Relate Cause and Effect How is wind related to air pressure and temperature?
Differences in temperature cause differences in air pressure.

got it?

O I get it! Now I know that wind is *caused by differences in air pressure.*

O I need extra help with *See TE note.*

Go to **MY SCIENCE COACH** *online for help with this subject.*

How Do Local Winds and Global Winds Differ?

Have you ever noticed a breeze at the beach on a hot summer day? Even if there is no wind inland, there may be a cool breeze blowing in from the water. This breeze is an example of a local wind.

Local Winds Winds that blow over short distances are called **local winds**. The unequal heating of Earth's surface within a small area causes local winds. These winds form only when large-scale winds are weak. Two types of local winds are sea breezes and land breezes, as shown in **Figure 3**.

FIGURE 3

Local Winds

✎ **Relate Text and Visuals** Read about sea breezes. Add arrows to the bottom diagram to indicate how a land breeze develops. Then summarize the process.

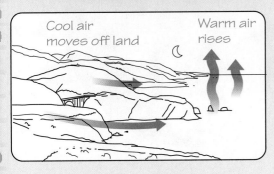

Sea Breeze During the day, the land warms up faster than the water. The air over the land gets warmer than the air over the water. This warm air is less dense. It expands and rises, creating a low-pressure area. Cool air blows inland from over the water and moves underneath the warm air, causing a sea breeze. A **sea breeze** or a lake breeze is a local wind that blows from an ocean or lake.

Land Breeze At night, the process is reversed. The flow of air from land to a body of water forms a **land breeze**. _The land cools off faster than the water. So cool air from the land moves under the warm air rising off the water._

405

Explain

Teach Key Concepts 🔑

Explain to students that local winds are caused by the unequal heating of Earth's surface within a small area. Ask: **What are local winds?** (Winds that blow over short distances) **What causes local winds to form?** (The unequal heating of Earth's surface within a small area) **When do local winds form?** (When large-scale winds are weak) **What are two types of local winds?** (Sea breezes and land breezes.) **What is a sea breeze?** (A local wind that blows from an ocean or lake to the land) **What is a land breeze?** (A flow of air from land to a body of water)

Teach With Visuals

Tell students to look at **Figure 3**. Direct students to look at the top diagram of a sea breeze. Ask: **During the day, does land or water heat up more?** (Land) **How does this uneven heating cause a sea breeze?** (The area over the land is warmer and less dense than the air over the water. This warm air expands and rises, creating a low-pressure area. Cooler denser air blows inland from the water and moves under the warm air, causing a sea breeze) Direct students to look at the lower diagram of a land breeze and describe where they placed the arrows. Ask: **What causes a land breeze?** (At night, the process is reversed. The land cools faster than the water. So the air over the land is cooler than the air over the water. The cooler, denser air from the land moves under the warm air rising off the water, causing a land breeze.)

21st Century Learning

L3 **CRITICAL THINKING** Tell students that a wind is moving from land toward the ocean and that the clock shows 2 o'clock. Ask students whether it is likely to be 2 P.M. or 2 A.M. Have them explain their thinking. (It is likely to be 2 A.M, or nighttime. At night the air above the ocean is warmer and less dense than air above the land. The warm ocean air rises and the cool, denser air from the land moves towards the ocean.)

Differentiated Instruction

L3 **Wind Vanes** Some homes have a decorative wind vane on the roof. Have students research how a wind vane works and what constraints there are on designs so that they are attractive and function correctly.

L1 **Compare and Contrast Local Winds** Have students summarize the differences between a land breeze and a sea breeze by making a compare-and-contrast chart.

405

Explain

Teach Key Concepts 🔑

Explain to students that global winds are caused by the same factors that cause local winds, but global winds occur over a large area. Ask: **What are global winds?** *(Winds that blow steadily from specific directions over long distances.)* Help students understand that global winds are similar to local winds in that they form from unequal heating of Earth's surface. Ask: **What causes Earth's surface to be heated unevenly?** *(During the day, direct rays from the sun heat the surface near the equator intensely. Near the poles the sun's energy is spread out over a large area so the surface is heated less. The result is that temperatures at the poles are much lower than near the equator.)*

Lead a Discussion

GLOBAL CONVECTION CURRENTS Explain that there are global convection currents from the poles to the equator and the equator to the poles. Ask: **How do global winds develop?** *(The temperature difference between the equator and poles produces giant convection currents in the atmosphere. Warm air at the equator rises. Cold air sinks at the poles. Pressure differences cause surface winds to blow from the poles toward the equator. Air flows away from the equator and toward the poles higher in the atmosphere. These air movements produce global winds.)* **How is the formation of global convection currents similar to the way that land and sea breezes are formed?** *(Both are caused by warm air rising and cooler air sinking.)*

Global Winds |Global winds| Global winds are winds that blow steadily from specific directions over long distances. 🔑 **Like local winds, global winds are created by the unequal heating of Earth's surface. But unlike local winds, global winds occur over a large area.** In **Figure 4**, you can see how the sun's radiation strikes Earth. In the middle of the day near the equator, the sun is almost directly overhead. The direct rays from the sun heat Earth's surface intensely. Near the poles, the sun's rays strike Earth's surface at a lower angle. The sun's energy is spread out over a larger area, so it heats the surface less. As a result, temperatures near the poles are much lower than they are near the equator.

Global Convection Currents How do global winds develop? Temperature differences between the equator and the poles produce giant convection currents in the atmosphere. Warm air rises at the equator, and cold air sinks at the poles. Therefore air pressure tends to be lower near the equator and greater near the poles. This difference in pressure causes winds at Earth's surface to blow from the poles toward the equator. Higher in the atmosphere, however, air flows away from the equator toward the poles. Those air movements produce global winds.

FIGURE 4 ·······································
Heating of Earth's Surface
✏️ **Interpret Diagrams** The angle of the sun's rays causes temperature differences at Earth's surface.
1. Label the areas where the sun hits Earth most directly (M) and least directly (L).
2. CHALLENGE Draw a convection current in the atmosphere north of the equator.

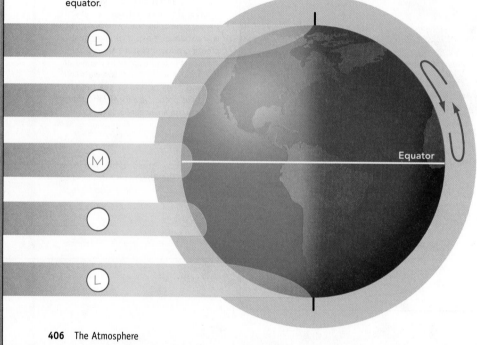

Digital Lesson: Assign the *Apply It* activity online and have students submit their work to you.

MY SCIENCE online.com ▷ | Local and Global Winds

The Coriolis Effect If Earth did not rotate, global winds would blow in a straight line from the poles toward the equator. Because Earth is rotating, however, global winds do not follow a straight path. As the winds blow, Earth rotates from west to east underneath them, making it seem as if the winds have curved. The way Earth's rotation makes winds curve is called the **Coriolis effect** (kawr ee OH lis). Because of the Coriolis effect, global winds in the Northern Hemisphere gradually turn toward the right. A wind blowing toward the south gradually turns toward the southwest. In the Southern Hemisphere, winds curve toward the left.

Identify Supporting Evidence Underline the text that describes how winds blow due to the Coriolis effect.

apply it!

The Coriolis effect determines the direction of global winds.

1 Look at the globe on the left. Shade in the arrows that show the direction the global winds would blow without the Coriolis effect.

2 Look at the globe on the right. Shade in the arrows that show the direction the global winds blow as a result of the Coriolis effect.

3 Draw Conclusions Based on your last answer, what direction do global winds blow in the Northern Hemisphere? In the Southern Hemisphere?

In the Northern Hemisphere, winds that blow south turn to the west.
In the Southern Hemisphere, winds that blow north turn to the west.

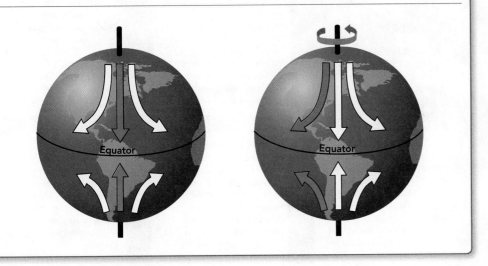

Explain

Lead a Discussion

THE CORIOLIS EFFECT Point out to students that if Earth did not rotate, global winds would blow in a straight line from the poles toward the equator. But because Earth rotates, global winds curve. Ask: **In which direction does Earth rotate?** (Earth rotates from west to east.) **What is the Coriolis effect?** (The way Earth's rotation makes winds curve) **Which way do winds curve in the Northern Hemisphere?** (They turn gradually toward the right.) **Which way do winds in the Southern Hemisphere curve?** (They turn gradually toward the left.)

Identify Supporting Evidence Explain that once they have identified the main idea in a passage, students should look for other information in the passage or related passages. They should evaluate this information to see how it supports or further explains the main idea.

Elaborate

Apply It!

L1 Review the Coriolis effect before beginning the activity. Remind students that if Earth did not rotate, global winds would tend to blow in a straight line from the higher-pressure regions at the poles toward the lower-pressure regions at the equator.

Draw Conclusions Help students understand that a conclusion is a statement that sums up what they have learned.

Differentiated Instruction

L1 Outline the Section Suggest that students outline the section by using its headings and subheadings. As they read, students should list the main points under each heading. If necessary, pair students with more proficient readers.

L3 Winds and Airplanes Ask students why airline companies would have a special interest in knowing about global winds. (The speed and direction of global winds can affect the speed of planes and the course that they follow.) Invite interested students to do research on flight times on long-distance flights so see if East-to-West flights have different times than West-to-East flights.

Explain

Teach With Visuals

Tell students to look at **Figure 5**. Ask: **What does each letter on the diagram represent?** *(The name of a global wind belt or a calm area on Earth)* **What are the calm areas called?** *(Doldrums and horse latitudes)* **What are the names of the global winds?** *(Trade winds, prevailing westerlies, polar easterlies)* **What do the small blue arrows pointing north and south represent?** *(Convection currents in the atmosphere)* **What do the large red arrows represent?** *(Global winds)* **What causes the trade winds that blow toward the equator to turn west?** *(The Coriolis effect)* **In what direction does the Coriolis effect cause the prevailing westerlies to turn in the mid-latitudes, between 30° and 60° north and south?** *(Toward the east)* **In what direction does the Coriolis effect cause air near the poles, the prevailing easterlies, to turn?** *(Toward the west)*

Lead a Discussion

GLOBAL WIND BELTS Remind students that winds, including global winds, are caused by differences in air pressure. Ask: **Where are the areas of calm and what causes them?** *(Doldrums: Air is heated strongly at the equator. Warm air rises steadily creating a low-pressure area. The cool air moving into take its place is warmed rapidly and rises before it moves very far, so there is little wind. Horse latitudes: At these latitudes, about 30° north and south, the air stops moving toward the poles, and sinks.)*

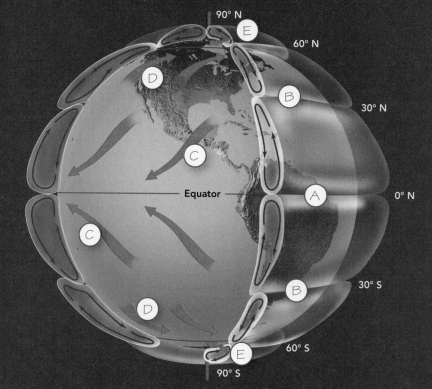

FIGURE 5 ·······························

▶ **INTERACTIVE ART**

Global Wind Belts

The Coriolis effect and other factors combine to produce a pattern of wind belts and calm areas around Earth.

✎ **Relate Text and Visuals**
Match the descriptions of the global winds with their location on the globe.

A **Doldrums** are a calm area where warm air rises. They occur at the equator where the sun heats the surface strongly. Warm air rises steadily, creating an area of low pressure. Cool air moves into the area, but is warmed rapidly and rises before it moves very far.

B **Horse Latitudes** are two calm areas of sinking air. **Latitude** is the distance from the equator, measured in degrees. At about 30° north and south latitudes, the air stops moving toward the poles and sinks.

C **Trade Winds** blow from the horse latitudes toward the equator. As cold air over the horse latitudes sinks, it forms a region of high pressure. This causes surface winds to blow. The winds that blow toward the equator are turned west by the Coriolis effect.

D **Prevailing Westerlies** blow from west to east, away from the horse latitudes. In the mid-latitudes, between 30° and 60° north and south, winds that blow toward the poles are turned toward the east by the Coriolis effect.

E **Polar Easterlies** blow cold air away from the poles. Air near the poles sinks and flows back toward lower latitudes. The Coriolis effect shifts these polar winds to the west, producing the polar easterlies.

408 The Atmosphere

Interactive Art allows students to explore global wind belts.

my science online.com | **Local and Global Winds**

Parts of the Atmosphere

How does the sun's energy affect Earth's atmosphere?

FIGURE 6 ·······················

Earth's atmosphere is a system made up of many different parts.

✏ **Communicate** In the space below, draw a picture or a diagram that helps you understand the relationship between the concepts in the word bank. Explain your diagram to a classmate.

Word Bank	
atmosphere	air pressure
convection	radiation
global winds	

Sample:

Sun's radiation → Warms Earth's surface/atmosphere → Unequal heating causes differences in air pressure. → Forms convection currents → Causes global winds

Do the Quick Lab
Modeling Global Wind Belts.

Assess Your Understanding

2a. Summarize What causes local winds?

Unequal heating of Earth's surface in a small area

b. Identify What is a global wind?

A wind blowing over a large area

c. ANSWER How does the sun's energy affect Earth's atmosphere?

The sun heats the Earth unevenly. This causes differences in temperature, which cause differences in air pressure. Winds then form.

got it? ·······················

○ **I get it!** Now I know that winds blow locally and globally due to uneven heating in the atmosphere.

○ **I need extra help with** See TE note.

Go to MY SCIENCE 🔲 COACH *online for help with this subject.*

409

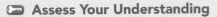

Differentiated Instruction

L1 Model Wind Have students observe as you alternately hold a pinwheel over an unlit incandescent light bulb and then over the same bulb lit. The pinwheel will remain stationary when the bulb is off and will spin when the bulb is lit. Have students explain what causes the pinwheel to spin. *(The hot bulb heats the air around the* pinwheel. *The heated air rises and cooler air moves in. This moving air causes the pinwheel to turn.)*

L3 Names of Global Winds Have students with an interest in history research the names of global winds, such as trade winds, horse latitudes, and doldrums.

Explain

Explore the Big Q ? UbD

Direct students' attention to the terms in the word bank and review the meaning of each term. Ask: **Where does radiation that enters Earth's atmosphere come from?** *(The sun)* **How does the sun's radiation affect Earth's surface and atmosphere?** *(It warms them.)* **Why are there differences in air pressure?** *(Unequal heating of the atmosphere causes some areas to heat up more, expand, and become less dense resulting in lower air pressure; other areas heat up less, are denser, and so have higher air pressure.)* **What happens when there are differences in air pressure?** *(Convection currents form as air moves from areas of high pressure to areas of low pressure.)* **What causes global winds to form?** *(Unequal heating of Earth's surface over a large area)*

Elaborate

Lab Resource: Quick Lab

L3 MODELING GLOBAL WIND BELTS Students will explore global distribution of solar energy and major wind belts.

Evaluate

Assess Your Understanding

After students answer the questions, have them evaluate their understanding by completing the appropriate sentence.

Answer the Big Q ? UbD

To help students focus on the Big Question, lead a class discussion about how the sun's energy affects Earth's atmosphere.

RTI Response to Intervention

2a, b. If students need help describing local winds and global winds, **then** have them review **Figure 3** and **Figure 5** and read the captions.

c. If students cannot explain how the sun's energy affects Earth's atmosphere, **then** have them review the effects of the uneven heating of Earth's surface and its atmosphere, including the resulting differences in air pressure and the winds that form.

MY SCIENCE 🔲 COACH Have students go online for help in understanding how the sun's energy affects Earth's atmosphere.

Name _____ Date _____ Class _____

Lab zone® **After the Inquiry Warm-Up**

Winds

> **Inquiry Warm-Up, *Does the Wind Turn?***
> In the Inquiry Warm-Up, you investigated how Earth's rotation affects wind direction.
> Using what you learned from that activity, answer the questions below.

1. **COMMUNICATE** Using what you observed during the experiment, make a diagram of the Western Hemisphere showing how cold air from the North Pole moves down through Canada and the United States.

2. **INFER** Given what you've learned about how Earth's rotation affects the direction of cold air from the North Pole as it moves south, how would cold air from the South Pole move as it heads north across South America?

   _____

   _____

3. **COMMUNICATE** To the diagram you made in question 1, add lines, arrows, and labels showing how cold air from the South Pole moves up through South America.

4. **USE PRIOR KNOWLEDGE** At some point, on television news or a weather Web site, you have probably seen either an animated weather map or weather radar images. In which general direction do weather systems, such as rainstorms, move across the United States?

   _____

   _____

Name _____ Date _____ Class _____

Winds

What Causes Winds?

1a. DEFINE What is wind? _____

_____

b. RELATE CAUSE AND EFFECT How is wind related to air pressure and temperature? _____

_____

got it? ....

○ **I get it!** Now I know that wind is _____

_____

○ **I need extra help with** _____

_____

How Do Local Winds and Global Winds Differ?

2a. SUMMARIZE What causes local winds? _____

_____

b. IDENTIFY What is a global wind? _____

_____

c. ANSWER How does the sun's energy affect Earth's atmosphere? _____

_____

_____

_____

got it? ....

○ **I get it!** Now I know that winds blow locally and globally due to _____

_____

○ **I need extra help with** _____

_____

409B

Key Concept Summaries

Winds

What Causes Winds?

Differences in air pressure cause the air to move. A **wind** is the movement of air parallel to Earth's surface. Winds move from areas of high pressure to areas of lower pressure. **Most differences in air pressure are caused by the unequal heating of the atmosphere.** As air over heated surfaces expands and becomes less dense, its air pressure decreases. If nearby air is cooler, it will flow under the warmer, less dense air. Winds are described by their direction, determined with a wind vane, and speed, measured with an **anemometer.** A wind is named for the direction it blows from.

How Do Local Winds and Global Winds Differ?

Winds that blow over short distances are called **local winds. They are caused by the unequal heating of Earth's surface within a *small* area.** Local winds form only when large-scale winds are weak. Two types of local winds are sea breezes and land breezes. A **sea breeze** is a local wind that blows from an ocean. During the day land warms faster than water. The air above the land heats and rises, and cool air from the ocean flows in to take its place. At night the process is reversed, land cools faster than the ocean. The flow of air from land to a body of water forms a **land breeze.**

Global winds are winds that blow steadily from specific directions over long distances. **Global winds are created by the unequal heating of Earth's surface over a *large* area.** Because of Earth's spherical shape, rays from the sun strike directly at the equator but hit the poles at an angle. As a result, temperatures near the poles are much lower than near the equator. The difference produces giant convection currents in the atmosphere. Surface winds blow from the poles toward the equator. Higher in the atmosphere, winds flow from equator to poles. The way Earth's rotations make winds curve is called the **Coriolis effect.** Because of the Coriolis effect, global winds in the Northern Hemisphere gradually turn toward the right. The Coriolis effect and other factors combine to produce a pattern of wind belts and calm areas around Earth. These include doldrums, horse latitudes, trade winds, prevailing westerlies, and polar easterlies.

On a separate sheet of paper, describe what causes winds to form and explain how local winds and global winds differ.

Name _____ Date _____ Class _____

Winds

> ## Understanding Main Ideas
> Answer the following questions in the spaces provided.

1. How does heating air affect its density and pressure?

   _____

2. What are two types of local winds?

   _____

3. Describe the movement of air over two nearby land areas, one of which is heated more than the other.

   _____

   _____

4. What causes local winds to form?

   _____

   _____

5. Identify where the sun's rays strike Earth most directly and least directly.

   _____

   _____

> ## Building Vocabulary
> On a separate sheet of paper, write a definition for each of these terms.

6. wind
7. anemometer
8. windchill factor
9. sea breeze
10. Coriolis effect

Enrich

Winds

In cities, large buildings and other obstacles can change the direction of the wind and make it difficult to tell from which direction the wind is blowing. To get the true direction of the wind over a city, it is better to observe how the clouds are moving. You can make a simple device, called a nephoscope, to track cloud movement. Follow the directions given. Then answer the questions below on a separate sheet of paper.

Using Clouds to Measure the Wind

With a large mirror and a grease pencil or marker that will write on glass, go outside in an open area on a day with some wind and clouds. Place the mirror face up on the ground. (**CAUTION:** *Handle the mirror carefully so it does not break*.) Use a compass to determine the four directions and mark them on the four sides of the mirror. Now your nephoscope is ready to use.

To measure cloud direction, watch the mirror for cloud reflections to appear. Put an X in the reflection of a cloud as it appears on the edge of the mirror. As the reflection of the cloud moves across the mirror, plot its course by putting more Xs along its path. After the cloud's reflection has passed across the mirror, join the Xs with a line and use the line to determine the overall direction of the cloud.

1. What wind direction did your nephoscope indicate? How does that direction compare with the direction based on on-the-ground indicators, such as wind vanes, flags flying, or smoke drifting? If the directions are different, what do you think is the reason?

2. Why is a nephoscope a more accurate indicator of wind direction over a city than a wind vane on the ground?

3. Can you think of any disadvantage in depending on a nephoscope to measure wind direction?

Lesson Quiz

Winds

Write the letter of the correct answer on the line at the left.

1. ___ What is the movement of air parallel to Earth's surface called?
   A   the Coriolis effect
   B   windchill
   C   wind
   D   air pressure

2. ___ Which of the following is a calm area on Earth's surface where warm air rises?
   A   polar easterlies
   B   doldrums
   C   trade winds
   D   prevailing westerlies

3. ___ Which of the following occurs over a small area?
   A   polar easterlies
   B   the Coriolis effect
   C   horse latitudes
   D   sea breezes

4. ___ What is an anemometer used to measure?
   A   wind speed
   B   windchill
   C   air pressure
   D   wind direction

Fill in the blanks to complete each statement.

5. If the Earth did not rotate, global winds would follow a(n) _____ path.

6. Trade winds blow from the horse latitudes toward the _____.

7. The two qualities used to describe winds are _____ and speed.

8. A local wind that blows during the day from an ocean toward land is a(n)

   _____.

9. The increase in cooling that wind can cause is called the _____

   _____.

10. Temperature differences between the equator and poles produce

   _____ currents.

Winds

Answer Key

After the Inquiry Warm-Up

1. Students should show the Western Hemisphere with lines, arrows, and labels indicating cold air from the North Pole turns west as it moves south through Canada and the United States.

2. Cold air from the South Pole would also turn westward as it moves north across South America.

3. Students should add lines, arrows, and labels indicating cold air from the South Pole turns west as it moves north through South America.

4. from west to east

Key Concept Summaries

Winds are caused by differences in air pressure. They move from areas of high pressure to areas of lower pressure. Most differences in air pressure are caused by the unequal heating of the atmosphere. As air over heated surfaces expands and becomes less dense, its air pressure decreases. If nearby air is cooler, it will flow under the warmer, less dense air. This forces the warmer air to rise.

Local winds, such as land breezes and sea breezes, blow over short distances. Global winds blow steadily from specific directions over long distances. Both local winds and global winds are caused by the unequal heating of Earth's surface. But local winds occur within a small area while global winds occur over a large area. Local winds form only when large-scale winds are weak.

Review and Reinforce

1. Both density and air pressure decrease.

2. sea breezes and land breezes

3. The air above the less-heated area will be cooler, and denser and will flow underneath the warmer, less dense air, forcing it to rise.

4. the unequal heating of Earth's surface within a small area

5. the sun's rays strike most directly at the equator and least directly at the poles.

6. a movement of air parallel to Earth's surface

7. an instrument used to measure wind speed

8. the increased cooling that a wind can cause

9. a flow of air from an ocean to the land

10. the way Earth's rotation makes winds curve

Enrich

1. Wind direction indicated by the nephoscope will vary, depending on local weather conditions. The direction indicated by the nephoscope may or may not agree with the direction based on on-the-ground indicators such as wind vanes, because of obstacles on the ground, such as buildings, that change the direction of the wind close to the surface.

2. A nephoscope is more accurate because the movement of clouds reflects the direction of the wind above obstacles that may change the direction of the wind close to the ground.

3. A potential disadvantage is that it requires the presence of individual clouds in the sky. It cannot be used on a clear day or when the sky is completely overcast.

Lesson Quiz

1. C
2. B
3. D
4. A
5. straight
6. equator
7. direction
8. sea breeze
9. windchill factor
10. convection

Place the outside corner, the corner away from the dotted line, in the corner of your copy machine to copy onto letter-size paper.

CHAPTER 11

Study Guide

Review the Big Q ? UbD

Have students complete the statement at the top of the page. These Key Concepts support their understanding of the chapter's Big Question. Have them return to the chapter opener pages. What is different about how students view the image of the hang glider now that they have completed the chapter? Thinking about this will help them prepare for the *Apply the Big Q* activity in the Review and Assessment.

Partner Review

Have partners review definitions of vocabulary terms by using the Study Guide to quiz each other. Students could read the Key Concept statements and leave out words for their partner to fill in, or change a statement so that it is false and then ask their partner to correct it.

Class Activity: The Atmosphere

Have students work in three groups. Assign students to Group A, B, or C. Have each group make concept maps and/or labeled illustrations that answer the big topic questions assigned to it. Group A: *What are some properties of air? What instruments measure air pressure? How does altitude affect air pressure and density?* Group B: *How does energy from the sun travel to Earth? What happens to the sun's energy when it reaches Earth?* Group C: *How is temperature measured? How is heat transferred? What causes winds? How do local winds and global winds differ?* Have each group present their products to the class.

My Science Coach allows students to complete the *Practice Test* online.

The Big Question allows students to complete the *Apply the Big Q* activity about the effect of the sun's energy on Earth's atmosphere.

Vocab Flash Cards offer a way to review the chapter vocabulary words.

---

my science online.com ▸ **The Atmosphere**

CHAPTER
11 Study Guide

The sun's energy affects Earth's atmosphere by <u>heating</u> Earth's surface, causing differences in <u>air pressure</u> that result in <u>winds</u>.

LESSON 1 The Air Around You

🔑 Earth's atmosphere consists of nitrogen, oxygen, carbon dioxide, water vapor, and other gases, as well as particles of liquids and solids.

🔑 Events in one part of the atmosphere affect other parts of the atmosphere.

Vocabulary
• weather
• atmosphere
• water vapor

LESSON 2 Air Pressure

🔑 Because air has mass, it also has other properties, including density and pressure.

🔑 Two common kinds of barometers are mercury barometers and aneroid barometers.

🔑 Air pressure decreases as altitude increases. As air pressure decreases, so does density.

Vocabulary
• density • air pressure • barometer
• mercury barometer • aneroid barometer
• altitude

LESSON 3 Layers of the Atmosphere

🔑 Scientists divide Earth's atmosphere into four main layers according to changes in temperature.

🔑 Earth's weather occurs in the troposphere. The stratosphere contains the ozone layer.

🔑 The mesosphere protects Earth from meteoroids. The thermosphere is the outermost layer of Earth's atmosphere.

Vocabulary
• troposphere • stratosphere • mesosphere
• thermosphere • ionosphere • exosphere

LESSON 4 Energy in Earth's Atmosphere

🔑 The sun's energy travels to Earth as visible light, infrared radiation, and ultraviolet radiation.

🔑 Some sunlight is absorbed or reflected by the atmosphere. Some of the energy Earth absorbs is radiated back out as infrared radiation.

Vocabulary
• electromagnetic waves • radiation
• infrared radiation • ultraviolet radiation
• scattering • greenhouse effect

LESSON 5 Heat Transfer

🔑 Air temperature is usually measured with a thermometer.

🔑 Heat is transferred in three ways: convection, conduction, and radiation.

🔑 Heat is transferred mostly by convection within the troposphere.

Vocabulary
• temperature • thermal energy • thermometer
• heat • convection • conduction
• convection currents

LESSON 6 Winds

🔑 Winds are caused by differences in air pressure.

🔑 The unequal heating of Earth's surface within a small area causes local winds.

🔑 Global winds are caused by the unequal heating of Earth's surface over a large area.

Vocabulary
• wind • anemometer • windchill factor
• local winds • sea breeze • land breeze
• global winds • Coriolis effect • latitude

---

410 The Atmosphere

(E L L) Support

4 Language Production

Divide students into teams of three for a game show. You may want to have teams of students with varying language proficiencies. Using the essential questions from the chapter, create questions that the teams must answer. Teams get one point for every question answered correctly. The team with the most points at the end of the game wins.

Beginning
LOW/HIGH Allow students extra time to share their answers.

Intermediate
LOW/HIGH Allow students to answer with words or short phrases.

Advanced
LOW/HIGH Challenge students to incorporate vocabulary terms when answering questions.

410 The Atmosphere

Review and Assessment

LESSON 1 The Air Around You

1. Which gas forms less than one percent of the atmosphere, but is essential to life?

a. carbon dioxide **b.** oxygen
c. hydrogen **d.** nitrogen

(a. circled)

2. Weather occurs in Earth's troposphere, which is <u>the layer of the atmosphere closest to Earth's surface.</u>

3. **Draw Conclusions** Why is it difficult to include water vapor in a graph of the percentages of various gases in the atmosphere? How could you solve the problem?

<u>The amount of water vapor in the atmosphere varies by both place and time; by adding time or place as variables</u>

LESSON 2 Air Pressure

4. When density increases, the number of molecules in a volume

a. increases. **b.** decreases.
c. stays the same. **d.** varies.

(a. circled)

5. One force affecting an object is air pressure, which is <u>the force pushing on an area or surface.</u>

6. **Apply Concepts** Why can an aneroid barometer measure elevation as well as air pressure?

<u>Air pressure decreases with altitude.</u>

7. **Write About It** Suppose you're on a hot-air balloon flight. Describe how air pressure and the amount of oxygen would change during your trip. What would the changes feel like? *See TE rubric.*

LESSON 3 Layers of the Atmosphere

8. The layers of the atmosphere are classified according to changes in

a. altitude. **b.** air pressure.
c. distance. **d.** temperature.

(d. circled)

9. **Sequence** List the layers of the atmosphere in order, moving up from Earth's surface.

<u>Troposphere, stratosphere, mesosphere, thermosphere</u>

10. The ozone layer is important because

<u>it protects Earth from ultraviolet radiation.</u>

11. **Infer** Why are clouds at the top of the troposphere made of ice crystals rather than drops of water?

<u>Temperatures are very cold, around −60°C.</u>

12. **Compare and Contrast** How are the upper and lower parts of the stratosphere different?

<u>The upper part is warmer than the lower part. A layer of ozone is between the two. This layer absorbs ultraviolet radiation.</u>

13. **Calculate** The table shows the temperature at various altitudes above Omaha, Nebraska, on a January day. Suppose an airplane was 6.8 kilometers above Omaha. What is the approximate temperature at this height?
<u>−36°C</u>

Altitude (kilometers)	0	1.6	3.2	4.8	6.4	7.2
Temperature (°C)	0	−4	−9	−21	−32	−40

411

Review and Assessment

Assess Understanding

Have students complete the answers to the Review and Assessment questions. Have a class discussion about what students find confusing. Write Key Concepts on the board to reinforce knowledge.

RTI Response to Intervention

5. If students cannot define *air pressure,* **then** have them scan the text for the highlighted term and reread the definition.

9. If students cannot identify the four main layers of the atmosphere, **then** review the layers—troposphere, stratosphere, mesosphere and thermosphere—with the students.

Alternate Assessment

L3 **PRESENTATION** Have students work in two groups. Each group will prepare an informative presentation. One presentation should be about a trip from Earth's surface to the top of the exosphere and should address these ideas: *how temperature, density and pressure change as altitude increases; in what form energy travels from the sun to Earth; what happens to the sun's energy in different parts of the atmosphere.* The second presentation should be about the winds a sailing ship encounters as it sails around the globe and should address these ideas: *the difference between local winds and global winds; identify global wind belts.*

Write About It Assess student's writing using this rubric.

SCORING RUBRIC	SCORE 4	SCORE 3	SCORE 2	SCORE 1
Describe changes in temperature and pressure	Describes in detail changes in temperature & pressure	Describes changes in temperature & pressure	Describes changes in one factor, but not the other	Does not describe changes
Describe effects of changes in temperature and pressure	Describes in detail effects of changes in temperature & pressure	Describes effects of changes in temperature & pressure	Partially describes effects of changes in temperature & pressure	Does not describe effects of changes

Review and Assessment, Cont.

RTI Response to Intervention

15. If students need help identifying the three forms of radiation, **then** remind them that most of the energy from the sun travels to Earth as visible light and infrared radiation, and that a smaller amount travels as ultraviolet radiation.

18. If students cannot compare and contrast the thermal energy of the pail and the lake, **then** have them review the information under the head *How Is Heat Transferred?*

22. If students have trouble explaining what causes global wind patterns, **then** elicit that differences in air pressure due to the unequal heating of the atmosphere are what causes these wind patterns.

Apply the Big Q ? UbD

TRANSFER Students should be able to demonstrate understanding of how the sun's energy affects Earth's atmosphere. See the scoring rubric below.

Connect to the Big Idea ? UbD

BIG IDEA Earth's land, water, air, and life form a system.

Send students back to the Big Ideas of Science at the beginning of their student edition. Have them read what they wrote about how changes in one part of Earth can affect another part before they started the chapter. Lead a class discussion about how their thoughts have changed. If all chapters have been completed, have students fill in the bottom section for the Big Idea.

L3 WRITING IN SCIENCE Ask students to write a summary of the information in this chapter.

LESSON 4 Energy in Earth's Atmosphere

14. How does most of the energy from the sun travel to Earth's surface?

- **a.** convection
- **b.** conduction
- **c.** radiation
- **d.** scattering

15. What are three forms of radiation that come from the sun?

Ultraviolet, infrared, visible

16. Relate Cause and Effect Why do people need to wear sunscreen at the beach?

People need to use sunscreen to protect themselves from ultraviolet radiation, which can cause sunburn.

LESSON 5 Heat Transfer

17. What is the main way heat is transferred in the troposphere?

- **a.** radiation currents
- **b.** reflection currents
- **c.** conduction currents
- **d.** convection currents

18. Compare and Contrast A pail of lake water is the same temperature as a lake. Compare the thermal energy of the pail of water with the thermal energy of the lake.

The water in the lake has much more thermal energy because it has many more particles than the water in the pail.

19. Write About It Describe an example of heat transfer in your daily life.
See TE rubric.

LESSON 6 Winds

20. The calm areas near the equator where warm air rises are

- **a.** horse latitudes.
- **b.** trade winds.
- **c.** doldrums.
- **d.** polar easterlies.

21. Nights often feature land breezes, which blow
cool air out to sea.

22. Relate Cause and Effect How does the movement of hot air at the equator and cold air at the poles produce global wind patterns?

Warm air rises at the equator and flows toward the poles. Cold air sinks at the poles and spreads toward the equator. These movements create global winds.

APPLY THE BIG ? How does the sun's energy affect Earth's atmosphere?

23. Imagine you are sailing around the world. What winds would you expect to find on different parts of your route? Explain the role of the sun's energy in creating those winds.

Sample: Answers will vary by the route chosen but should correctly identify global wind belts and the role of the sun's energy in creating each.
See TE rubric.

Write About It   Assess student's writing using this rubric.

SCORING RUBRIC	SCORE 4	SCORE 3	SCORE 2	SCORE 1
Describe an example of heat transfer in daily life	Student describes an example of heat transfer in daily life and correctly identifies the type(s) of heat transfer involved.	Student describes an example of heat transfer but misidentifies one type of heat transfer involved.	Student describes an example of heat transfer but does not identify any type of heat transfer.	Student does not describe an example of heat transfer.

? How does the sun's energy affect Earth's
Assess student's response using this rubric.

SCORING RUBRIC	SCORE 4	SCORE 3	SCORE 2	SCORE 1
Identify winds	Student identifies all global wind belts.	Student identifies most global wind belts.	Student identifies at least one global wind belt.	Student fails to identify any global wind belt.
Explain role of sun in creating global winds	Explains sun unevenly heats Earth's surface resulting in global winds	Explains sun unevenly heats Earth's surface, but not global winds	Explains sun heats Earth's surface but not uneven heating or global winds	Explains only that the atmosphere is heated by sun

Standardized Test Prep

Multiple Choice

Circle the letter of the best answer.

1. Which of the following determines the movement of global winds?

   A humidity and temperature

   B infrared and ultraviolet radiation

   C prevailing winds and upper air currents

   Ⓓ convection currents in the atmosphere and the Coriolis effect

2. What is the most abundant gas in the atmosphere?

   A ozone

   B water vapor

   C oxygen

   Ⓓ nitrogen

3. What happens to air with increased altitude?

   A temperature increases

   Ⓑ pressure decreases

   C pressure increases

   D wind speed decreases

4. Which layer of the atmosphere protects Earth from meteoroids?

   Ⓐ mesosphere

   B troposphere

   C ionosphere

   D stratosphere

5. Uneven heating of Earth's atmosphere causes which of the following?

   A global temperature increase

   B infrared radiation

   C the greenhouse effect

   Ⓓ local and global winds

Constructed Response

Use the diagram and your knowledge of science to answer Question 6. Write your answer on another sheet of paper.

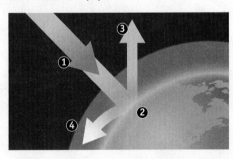

6. Describe the process that results in the greenhouse effect. How does it affect Earth's atmosphere?

   See TE note.

Test-Taking Skills

ANSWERING THE QUESTION Tell students that after they read a multiple-choice question, they should try to answer it in their head before reading the choices provided. This way they can identify the information they need to answer the question without being confused or tricked by the choices.

Constructed Response

6. Energy from the sun travels to Earth. Much of that energy is radiated back into the atmosphere as infrared radiation. A lot of that radiated energy is absorbed by gases in the air, thus heating them. These gases then hold heat in Earth's atmosphere, warming it like the air in a greenhouse.

Additional Assessment Resources

Chapter Test

EXAMVIEW® Assessment Suite

Performance Assessment

Progress Monitoring Assessments

SuccessTracker™

ⒺⓁⓁ Support

5 Assess Understanding

Have ELLs complete the Alternate Assessment. Provide guidelines on the information it must cover, and a rubric for assessment. You may wish to have them complete the activity in small groups of varying language proficiencies.

Beginning

LOW/HIGH Allow students to work on visuals for the presentation.

Intermediate

LOW/HIGH Allow students to share in presenting the information to the class.

Advanced

LOW/HIGH Allow students to act as recorders for their group.

Remediate If students have trouble with...

QUESTION	SEE LESSON	STANDARDS
1	6	
2	1	
3	2	
4	3	
5	6	
6	5	

Science Matters

Everyday Science

Have students read *The Aura Mission.* Point out that NASA's Earth Observing System (EOS) program delivers more than two terabytes (2 times 1012 bytes) of raw data each day. EOS satellites transmit atmospheric, ocean, and land surface data at regular intervals to ground stations where a computer network processes, stores and distributes the data. Computers programs translate the raw instrument data into scientific parameters, such as ocean surface temperature and cloud classification, which are useful to researchers.

Teams of scientists around the world analyze the long-term observations on global climate changes. By measuring and monitoring the components in Earth's atmosphere over time, scientists can put together more accurate computer models. They can use the models to forecast likely causes and potential effects of changes in the planet's atmosphere.

The Aura mission focuses on monitoring gases in Earth's atmosphere, while other satellites monitor ocean and land conditions. Help students organize the information they find on NASA's EOS program.

Ask: **Why do scientists measure and monitor Earth's atmosphere?** (Sample: to put together forecasts of causes and effects of changes in Earth's atmosphere) **What are three questions the EOS missions that monitor the ocean might seek to answer?** (Sample: How does ocean precipitation compare to land precipitation? Are the ocean temperatures getting warmer? Are the ocean levels changing? How do changes in the ocean affect Earth's climate?)

SCIENCE MATTERS

Everyday Science

THE AURA MISSION

When someone mentions the National Aeronautics and Space Administration (NASA), you might think of missions to Mars or Pluto. However, many of NASA's missions help us understand our own planet. In 2004, NASA launched *Aura*, the third satellite in its Earth Observing System (EOS) program. *Aura* helps scientists study the chemistry of the atmosphere.

The *Aura* mission seeks to answer three questions about our atmosphere.

1. Is the ozone layer recovering? *Aura* helps scientists monitor atmospheric gases, such as chlorofluorocarbons (CFCs), that affect the ozone layer. If the ozone layer does not recover, scientists predict that we will need to learn to better protect ourselves from the sun. In the next 10 years, will we need SPF 100 sunscreen?

2. How do pollutants affect air quality? *Aura* monitors levels of ozone, particulate matter, carbon monoxide, nitrogen dioxide, and sulfur dioxide. The data help scientists understand—and predict—the movement of air pollutants. Are attempts to reduce air pollution working?

3. How is Earth's climate changing? *Aura* checks levels of greenhouse gases in the atmosphere to help scientists build more accurate models of climate change. This way, we will have a better idea of how to plan for long-term climate change. Will you need to invest in a really good raincoat?

Research It Research NASA's EOS program. What are the major satellites in this program? Which Earth systems are they designed to monitor? What discoveries has the EOS program made? Make a display with information and pictures to show what you find out.

414 The Atmosphere

Quick Facts

The Columbia Scientific Balloon Facility, located in Texas, provides full-service balloon operations and engineering support to the National Aeronautics and Space Administration (NASA) and the scientific community. The facility's services cover launches, tracking, managing, and recoveries of scientific, high altitude balloons.

Have students search the Web site of the Columbia Scientific Balloon Facility or another NASA facility for a current balloon campaign. Have students track and record real time information from either a weather observation chart or a position map twice a week for a month. Review the results with the class at the end of the month.

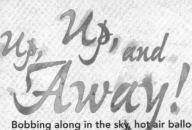

Up, Up, and Away!

Bobbing along in the sky, hot air balloons look like a fun way to spend a day. Before the invention of satellites or airplanes, though, scientists used hot air balloons to study the atmosphere. Riding in their balloons, scientists recorded air temperatures and humidity, and even gathered information about cosmic rays. For more than 150 years, balloons were cutting-edge atmospheric observatories.

Research It Find out more about the history of ballooning. How did scientific research using balloons contribute to early space missions? Make a timeline showing balloonists' discoveries.

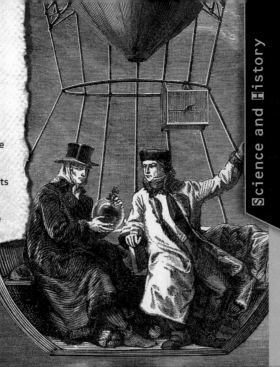

Science and History

PLUGGING INTO THE JET STREAM

Hot Science

It's windy up there! About 10 kilometers above Earth's surface, the jet stream winds blow constantly. The winds average 80 to 160 km/h, and they can reach 400 km/h. If we could harness just a small fraction of the wind's energy, we could meet the electricity needs of everyone on Earth!

Scientists are testing designs for high-altitude wind farms. They propose that kite-like wind generators flying above Earth could generate electricity. Cables could then transfer the electricity to Earth.

Design It Research the proposed designs for wind farms in the sky. Make a graphic organizer to show the proposed designs, the risks, and the ways scientists are addressing these risks.

415

Science and History

Have students read *Up, Up, and Away*. Point out that scientific balloons today can accomplish a broader range of experimentation than research hot air balloons in the past. While today's science balloons are unoccupied, they carry observational instruments, cameras, and GPS to transmit data for various investigations. Helium fills these research balloons rather than hot air. Super pressure balloons made of high-tech materials, have longer inflation durations and can rise to higher altitudes.

Ask: **What are some differences between research hot air balloons used in the past and scientific balloons used today?** (Sample: *People occupied the hot air balloons of the past to collect data. Today's balloons are unoccupied, but carry instruments to transmit data. Super pressure balloons filled with helium maintain longer inflation durations and rise to higher altitudes.*)

Hot Science

Have students read *Plugging into the Jet Stream*. Point out that a typical ground-base wind turbine produces about 5 megawatts of wind power, while a high-altitude wind turbine is expected to produce about 20 megawatts. How is this information important to scientists? Remind students that megawatts are a standard measure of electric power. One megawatt equals one thousand kilowatts or 1 million watts. When students do research, remind them to use consistent measuring units to avoid confusing and misleading information.

Ask: **Why are scientists testing designs that plug into the jet stream?** (Sample: *Faster winds at higher altitudes in the jet stream have potential to generate more electricity than ground-based wind turbines.*) **Why do you think the proposed designs for wind farms in the sky look like kites?** (Sample: *Accept all reasonable answers.*)

this is your book

you can write in it

416

this is your book

you can write in it

418

this is your book

you can write in it